W9-ADN-372

EXPERIMENTS IN PHYSICAL CHEMISTRY

EXPERIMENTS IN PHYSICAL CHEMISTRY

SECOND EDITION

DAVID P. SHOEMAKER
Professor of Chemistry
Massachusetts Institute of Technology

CARL W. GARLAND
Associate Professor of Chemistry
Massachusetts Institute of Technology

McGRAW-HILL BOOK COMPANY
New York
St. Louis
San Francisco
Toronto
London
Sydney

EXPERIMENTS IN PHYSICAL CHEMISTRY

Library of Congress Catalog Card Number 67-11880
57002

2 3 4 5 6 7 8 9 0 BABA 7 4 3 2 1 0 6 9 8 7

PREFACE

This book is intended as a textbook for a junior- or senior-level laboratory course in physical chemistry. It is assumed that the student will be taking concurrently (or has previously taken) a lecture course in the principles of physical chemistry taught with a modern point of view but containing a good basic coverage of traditional topics. The book contains forty-seven selected experiments which have been tested by extensive use in a course given at the Massachusetts Institute of Technology. This second edition contains all of the experiments that were in the first edition, with corrections of minor errors and numerous small descriptive changes. In addition there are three new experiments of a contemporary flavor, two concerned with chemical kinetics and one with the helix-coil transition in a polypeptide.

The experiments in this book are not concerned with "methods" or "techniques" per se or with the analytical applications of physical chemistry. We believe that an experimental physical chemistry course should serve a dual purpose: (1) to illustrate and test established theoretical principles and (2) to develop a research orientation by providing basic experience with physical measurements that yield quantitative results of important chemical interest.

Each experiment is accompanied by a theoretical development in sufficient detail to provide a clear understanding of the method to be used, the calculations required, and the significance of the final results. The level of this coverage is approximately that of a good undergraduate course in physical chemistry, but the depth of coverage is frequently greater than that which is available in introductory physical chemistry textbooks. Experimental procedures are described in considerable detail as an aid to the efficient use of laboratory time and teaching staff. Emphasis is given to the reasons behind the design and procedure for each experiment so that the student can learn the general principles of a variety of experimental techniques.

In addition to a coverage of traditional material, there are many original experiments, most of which are based on modern topics. A few of the experiments are quite easy to perform and involve only an elementary theoretical background; some of them are very challenging either in the experimental work or in the theoretical interpretation. Although there is a certain logic to the order in which the experiments are presented, they are written in such a way that they can be performed in almost any desired order.

About half of the experiments in this book require only the traditional physical chemistry laboratory apparatus which is available commercially. About a quarter of them require simple apparatus, not available commercially, which can be constructed without difficulty from the drawings given in this book. The remaining experiments, dealing with high-vacuum, electrical and magnetic dipole moments, high-resolution spectroscopy, and X-ray diffraction, require more elaborate apparatus than is normally available in an undergraduate laboratory. These experiments have been included because of the importance of these topics in present-day physical chemistry, and we feel strongly that a modern physical chemistry laboratory course should include at least some experiments of this kind. If the necessary apparatus cannot be acquired for the principal use of the laboratory, arrangements can often be made to obtain it on short-term loan from a research project.

In addition to the experiments themselves there are several chapters containing material of a more general nature, dealing with apparatus and techniques in physical chemistry. It is our hope that this part will be useful for special experiments, senior thesis work, graduate research, and general research. Considerable attention is given in the second chapter to the assessment of experimental uncertainties.

In the teaching of the laboratory course at MIT, increasing emphasis is being placed on stimulation of individual resourcefulness and research creativity through the use of special projects and of variations or extensions of the experiments given in this book. A brief description of our special projects with a representative list of subjects may be found in the first chapter. The response of the students to work of this kind has been good. Several special projects have been successful enough to take their place in our repertoire of regular experiments; these include the new experiments which appear in this edition. We strongly urge the users of this book to look beyond the detailed directions given for the experiments presented here and use them frequently as points of departure for work of a more independent nature.

The development of new experiments and the adaptation of older ones to form a selection of significant laboratory experiments in physical chemistry have proved to be a task that could not have been successfully completed without the aid of alert students, excellent graduate teaching assistants, and a congenial group of faculty colleagues. We gratefully acknowledge all of these contributions and would like especially to acknowledge the assistance given by Professor I. Amdur, J. A. Beattie, and W. H. Stockmayer in suggesting new experiments, contributing helpful advice on experimental techniques, and making valuable comments during the preparation of the first edition. For the development of the new experiments in this second edition and for many helpful discussions, we are indebted to Professors G. G. Hammes and J. L. Kinsey. We wish to thank Miss Mary Filoso and Miss Frances Doherty for the typing.

We dedicate this book to our wives, Clara Shoemaker and Joan Garland, who in more ways than we can mention have contributed to the completion of this undertaking.

David P. Shoemaker
Carl W. Garland

CONTENTS

I

INTRODUCTION

Physical chemistry deals with the physical principles underlying the properties of chemical substances. Like other branches of physical science, it contains a body of theory which has stood the test of experiment and which is continually growing as a result of new experiments. In order to learn physical chemistry, one must become familiar with the experimental foundations on which the theoretical principles are based. Indeed, in many cases, the ability to apply the principles usefully requires an intimate knowledge of those methods and practical arts that are called "experimental technique."

For this reason, a lecture course in physical chemistry should be accompanied by a program of laboratory work. Such experimental work not only should demonstrate established principles but should also develop research aptitudes by providing experience with the kind of measurements that yield important new results. This book attempts to achieve that goal. Its aim is to provide a clear understanding of the principles of important experimental methods, the design of basic apparatus, the planning of experimental procedures, and the significance of the final results. In short, the aim is to train not laboratory technicians but future research scientists.

Severe limitations of time and equipment must be faced in presenting a set of experiments as the basis of a laboratory course that will provide a reasonably broad coverage of the wide and varied field of physical chemistry. Although high-precision research measurements would occasionally require refinements in the methods described here and would often require more sophisticated and more elaborate equipment, each experiment in this book is designed so that meaningful results of reasonable accuracy can be obtained. Unfortunately, there is seldom sufficient time to permit the student to plan each experimental procedure entirely by himself and to learn good technique by trial and error. To encourage the efficient use of available time, both the apparatus and the procedure for these experiments are described in considerable detail. The student should keep in mind the importance of understanding why the experiment is done in the way described. This understanding is a vital part of the experience necessary for planning special or advanced experiments of a research character.

In addition to a general knowledge of laboratory techniques, creative research work requires the ability to apply two different kinds of theory. Many an experimental method is based on a special phenomenological theory of its own; this must be well understood in order to design the experiment properly and in order to calculate the desired physical property from the observed raw data. Once the desired result has been obtained, it is necessary to understand its significance and its interrelationship with other known facts. This requires a sound knowledge of the fundamental theories of physical chemistry (e.g., thermodynamics, statistical mechanics, and quantum theory). Considerable emphasis has been placed on both kinds of theory in this book.

In the final analysis, however, research ability cannot be learned merely by performing experiments described in a textbook; it has to be acquired through contact with inspired teachers and through the accumulation of considerable experience. The most this book can attempt to do is to provide a solid frame of reference for future growth.

PREPARATION FOR AN EXPERIMENT

Although most of the experiments in this book can be performed by a single person, they have been written with the assumption that a pair of students will work together as a team. Such teamwork is advantageous, since it provides an opportunity for valuable discussion of the experiment between partners. The amount of experimental work to be assigned will be based on the amount of laboratory time available for each experiment. Many of the experiments can be completed in full during a single four-hour laboratory period. Many others are designed for six to eight hours of laboratory work but may be abridged so that meaningful results can be obtained in a single four-hour period.

Some of the experiments require at least six hours and should not be attempted in a shorter time (in particular, Exps. 8, 16, 28, 33, 34, 36, 38, 44, 47).

Before the student arrives in the laboratory to perform a given experiment, it is essential that he study the experiment carefully with special emphasis on the method, the apparatus design, and the procedure. It will usually be necessary to make changes in the procedure whenever the apparatus to be used or the system to be studied differs from that described in this book. Planning such changes or even carrying out successfully the experiment exactly as described requires a clear understanding of the experimental method.

APPARATUS

A complete and very detailed list of equipment and chemicals is given at the end of each experiment. The list is divided into two sections: Those items listed in the first paragraph are required for the exclusive use of a single team; those in the second paragraph are available for the common use of several teams performing the same experiment simultaneously. It is assumed that standardized stock solutions will be made up in advance and will be available for the student's use. The quantities indicated in parentheses† are for the use of the instructor and do *not* indicate the amounts of each chemical to be taken by a single team. In addition to

† On the basis of the authors' experience with the laboratory course at MIT, it is necessary to make available these amounts per team who will do the experiment. They are scaled up from the amounts stated in the experiment to provide for possible wastage and to give a generous safety factor. It is hoped that they will be useful as a rough guide the first time an experiment is given.

the items included in these apparatus lists, it is assumed that the laboratory is equipped with analytical balances, a distilled-water supply, and a barometer as well as gas, water, and 110-v ac power lines. Also desirable, but not absolutely necessary, are dc power lines, gas-handling lines, and a rough vacuum line.

Experimental work in physical chemistry requires many complex and expensive pieces of apparatus; many of these have been constructed especially for the student's use and cannot be readily replaced. Each team should accept complete responsibility for its equipment and should *check it over carefully before starting an experiment.*

SAFETY

Experimental work is subject to hazards of many kinds, of which every person working in a laboratory should be aware. Once one is aware of the particular hazards involved in an experimental procedure, one's instinct for self-preservation usually provides a sufficient motivation for finding ways of avoiding them. The principal danger lies in ignorance of specific hazards and in forgetfulness.

A detailed analysis of all laboratory hazards and procedures for dealing with them would be beyond the scope of this book. Certain specific hazards are pointed out in connection with individual experiments. Some general remarks on the kinds of safety hazards which should be kept in mind are given in Appendix E. It is assumed that the instructing staff will provide specific warnings and reminders where needed.

RECORDING OF EXPERIMENTAL DATA

It is standard practice in experimental research work to record *everything relevant* (data, calculations, notes and comments, literature surveys, and even some graphs) directly in a bound notebook with numbered pages. Such notebooks are available with pages which are ruled vertically as well as horizontally to give a ¼-in. grid; this facilitates tabulation of columns of figures and permits rough plots of the data to be made directly on the notebook pages during the experiment. In an undergraduate laboratory course it is often convenient to make a carbon copy of the recorded data to include with the written report. (Notebooks with duplicate sets of numbered pages, in which alternate pages are perforated for removal, may be used; however, ordinary carbon paper and bond paper can be used with any style of research notebook.) In any case, the *original* is a part of a permanent notebook. Whatever style of notebook is used, the principle is the same: *Record all data directly in your notebook.* Data may be copied into the notebook from a partner's notebook in those cases where it is clearly impossible for both partners to record data at the same time. (Even then an extra carbon copy of a single original page is often better, since it avoids copy errors and saves time when a large number of figures are involved.) In particular, do *not* record on odd scraps of paper such incidental data as weights, barometer readings, and temperatures with the idea of copying them into the notebook at a later time. If anything must be copied from another source (calibration chart, reference book, etc.) identify it with an appropriate reference.

A ball-point pen is best for recording data, especially if carbon copies are required; otherwise a fountain pen with permanent ink is also satisfactory. Pencils are usually considered unsuitable for recording primary data. If a correction is necessary, draw a single line through the incorrect figure so as to leave it legible and then write the correct figure directly above or beside the old one. Every data page for an experiment should have a clear heading which includes the name of the student and of his partner, the name of the experiment, the date, and a page number. Neatness and good organization are desirable, but legibility, proper labeling, and completeness are absolute necessities.

LITERATURE WORK

Every attempt has been made to write each experiment in sufficient detail so that it can be intelligently performed without the necessity of extensive outside reading. However, it is assumed that the student will refer frequently to a standard textbook in physical chemistry for any necessary review of elementary theory. Literature sources are explicitly cited for those topics of an advanced or special nature which are beyond the scope of a typical undergraduate textbook, and these numbered references are listed together at the end of each experiment. In addition, a selected list of reading pertinent to the general topic of each experiment is given under the heading "General Reading." It is hoped that the interested student will do as much reading in these books and journal articles as his time allows, since such reading is an important aspect of broadening and deepening his scientific background.

As a matter of policy, very few of the experiments contain a direct reference to published values of the final result which is to be reported by the student. Any student who wishes to compare his result with the accepted literature value is expected to do the necessary library work. As a general principle it is best to refer directly to an original journal article rather than to some secondary source; the starting point for such a literature search is *Chemical Abstracts.* Another valuable but unfortunately rather old source of data is the "International Critical Tables," published for the National Research Council by McGraw-Hill, New York (1926). This seven-volume work contains selected values of many properties based on the best work available prior to 1926 and gives very complete references to the original articles. More recently, the National Bureau of Standards has issued several quite comprehensive tables, such as the following:

Tables of Thermal Properties of Gases, *Natl. Bur. Standards Circ.* 564, Washington, D.C. (1955).

Selected Values of Chemical Thermodynamic Properties, *Natl. Bur. Standards Circ.* 500, Washington, D.C. (1952).

Tables of Chemical Kinetics: Homogeneous Reactions, *Natl. Bur. Standards Circ.* 510, Washington, D.C. (1951).

Most students are familiar with and very likely own a personal copy of one of the two general handbooks:

N. A. Lange (ed.), "Handbook of Chemistry," 10th ed., McGraw-Hill, New York (1961).

"Handbook of Chemistry and Physics," 42 ed., Chemical Rubber Publishing Co., Cleveland, Ohio (1960).†

† Although a new edition is issued every year, changes are introduced very slowly. Any recent copy is as suitable as the newest one for almost all purposes.

These handbooks are very convenient but are distinctly secondary as sources of data. It is often difficult to judge the quality of the data listed, since references to original sources are frequently inadequate; many of the tables are taken directly from other compilations which may now be out of date.

It is commonly assumed that recent measurements are more precise than older ones; this assumption is based on the fact that methods and equipment are constantly being improved. But this does not mean that there is valid reason to reject or suspect a published result merely because it is old. The quality of research data depends strongly on the integrity, conscientious care, and patience of the research worker; much fine work done many years ago in certain areas of physical chemistry has never been improved upon. In evaluating results based on old but high-quality research data, one must, however, be alert to the possible need for corrections necessitated by more recent theoretical developments or by improved values of physical constants.

REPORTS

The final evaluation of any experimental work is based primarily on the examination of a written report. This report should be well organized and readable, so that anyone unfamiliar with the experiment can easily follow the presentation (with the aid of explicit references where necessary) and thereby obtain a clear idea as to what was actually done and what result was obtained.

An attempt should be made to use a scientific style comparable in quality to the literary style expected in an essay. Correct spelling and grammar should not be disregarded just because the report is to be read by a scientist instead of the editor of a literary magazine. The report should be as concise and factual as possible without sacrificing clarity. In particular, mathematical equations should be accompanied by enough verbal material to make their meaning clear.

Most important of all, the report must be an original piece of writing. Copying or even paraphrasing of material from textbooks, printed notes, or other reports is clearly dishonest and must be carefully avoided. Brief quotations, enclosed in quotation marks and accompanied by a complete reference, are permissible where a real advantage is to be gained. Certainly there is no point in giving more than a brief summary of the theory or the details of experimental procedure if these are adequately described in some readily available reference. In part, a report is likely to be judged on how clearly it states the essential points without oscillating between minute detail on one topic and vague generalities on another.

Except for general physical and numerical constants or well-known theoretical equations, any data or material taken from an outside source must be accompanied by a complete reference to that source.

The content and length of any given report will depend on the subject matter of the experiment and on the standards established by the instructor. It is our belief that at least in some cases the report should be quite complete and should include a quantitative analysis of the experimental uncertainties and a detailed discussion of the significance of the results; see the sample report given below. For many experiments a brief report (with only a qualitative treatment of errors and a short discussion) may be considered as adequate. In either case, a clear presentation of the data, calculations, and results is essential to every experiment in physical chemistry.

Format. Unless otherwise instructed, all reports should be prepared on 8½- by 11-in. paper with reasonable margins on all sides. The pages should be stapled together or bound in a folder with paper fasteners. Legibility is absolutely essential. Double-spaced typewritten reports are a pleasure to read, but they are time consuming to prepare unless one is a facile typist. Hand-written reports submitted in ink on wide-line ruled paper are perfectly satisfactory unless you are cursed with illegible handwriting. Crossing out and the insertion of corrections are permissible, but try to keep the report as a whole reasonably neat.

Presentation of Graphs. A general discussion of the graphical treatment of experimental data is given in Chap. II. As part of that discussion, the proper technique for plotting data points and drawing lines or curves is fully described. We shall be concerned here only with the final steps necessary for the presentation of such graphs as part of a report.

Vertical and horizontal axes should be drawn in, and the main divisions along each axis must be clearly marked and numbered. Each axis is then labeled with the appropriate symbol or words with the units indicated in parentheses [for example: t(sec), A(cm^2), density (g cm^{-3})]. The data points and the symbols surrounding them (usually small circles) are inked in so that the data will stand out prominently.

All light lines are "heavied up" with a sharp pencil, but the final line should not actually be drawn through symbols surrounding the data points. If several lines or curves lie close together, distinguish them from one another by using dashed lines as well as solid lines. When necessary, one can achieve further differentiation by varying the lengths of the dashes or alternating long and short dashes. If a curve is drawn to represent an equation, the points should not be inked or encircled and the curve should be drawn so as to conceal the points. The equation itself or the number by which it is designated in the text should be written beside the curve. It is good practice to indicate clearly on the graph the numerical values of any slopes, intercepts, areas, maxima, or other features that are important in the calculations.

Each figure must have a figure number and a short legend prominently displayed, and it should be referred to by number in the body of the report.

Sample Report. Given on pages 7 to 14 is a sample report on a very simple experiment. Its purpose is to illustrate how a report should be organized and to indicate the kind of material it should contain. This example is not meant to provide a rigid outline; the content of any given report will necessarily depend upon the judgment of the individual student. General comments on the various sections of this sample report are given in a series of footnotes.

DETERMINATION OF THE DENSITY OF CRYSTALLINE GERMANIUM[a]

John A. Doe | Thurs. section: Sept. 29, 1960
Partner: Richard Roe | Date of report: Oct. 6, 1960

I. Introduction[b]

The purpose of this experiment is to measure the density of crystals of germanium. Since the density ρ is defined by

$$\rho = W_S/V_S \qquad (1)$$

it is desired to measure the volume, V_S, occupied by a known weight, W_S, of the metal.

The method involves the use of a pycnometer of known volume which is first weighed empty, then weighed containing the solid sample to be studied. The difference gives the weight of the solid, W_S. Finally the pycnometer (containing the solid sample) is filled with a liquid of known density and reweighed; the weight, and therefore the volume, of the liquid can be found by difference. Since the total volume of the pycnometer is known, one can then calculate the volume V_S which is occupied by the solid.

[a] In addition to the title of the report, the heading should include your name, your partner's name, the laboratory section, the date on which the experiment was performed, and the date on which the report was submitted. For a long report, this information should be displayed on a separate title page.

[b] The introduction should state the purpose of the experiment and give a *very brief* outline of the necessary theory, which is often accomplished by citing pertinent equations. (In this sample report, the theory is trivially simple.) A very short description of the experimental method, including mention of any special apparatus, should also be included. The introduction should cover the above topics as concisely as possible; this sample contains about 135 words. More complicated experiments will require longer introductions, but the normal length should be between 100 and 300 words.

II. Experimental[c]

The experimental method was similar to that described in the textbook (Aardvark and Zebra, 2nd ed., Exp. 13). The design of the pycnometer used, which differs from that described in the textbook, is shown in the following sketch:

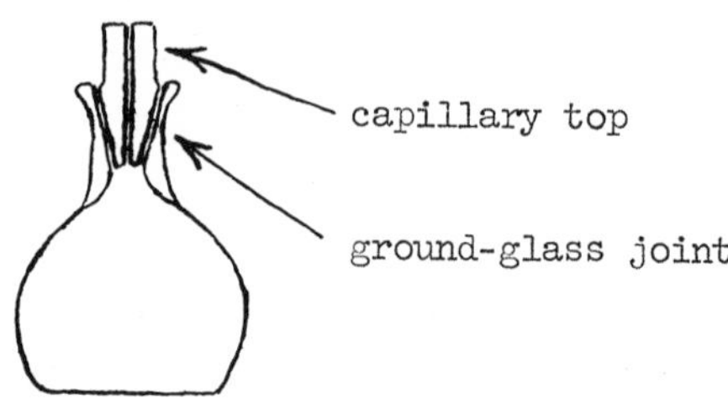

The procedure was modified as follows: After distilled water had been added to the pycnometer containing the sample, the pycnometer (with capillary top removed) was completely immersed in a flask of distilled water and boiled under low pressure for 15 minutes to remove air trapped by the solid or dissolved by the water.[1] After this boiling the pycnometer was equilibrated for 15 minutes in a 25°C thermostat bath before the top was inserted.

Two duplicate runs, carried out using the same procedure, were made on each of two different germanium samples. Sample I consisted of larger and somewhat more irregular pieces than did Sample II.

[c] This section is usually *extremely brief* and merely cites the appropriate references which describe the details of the experimental procedure. If reference is made to the textbook and/or laboratory notes assigned for the course, an abbreviated title may be cited in lieu of a complete bibliographic entry. Any references to other books or material should be assigned footnote numbers and should be properly listed at the end of the experiment in the form illustrated by the references in this book. Description of experimental procedures should be given *only* for those features not described in or differing from the reference. A simple sketch of apparatus is appropriate only when it differs from that described in the reference. NOTE: A statement of the number of runs made and the conditions under which they were carried out (concentration, temperature, etc.) should always be included at the end of this section.

III. Calculations[d]

The weight of the solid sample is given by

$$W_S = W_2 - W_1 \tag{2}$$

where W_1 is the weight of the empty pycnometer and W_2 is that of the pycnometer plus the solid sample. The weight of water contained in the pycnometer, W_L, is

$$W_L = W_3 - W_2 \tag{3}$$

where W_3 is the weight of pycnometer plus sample plus water. If the density of the liquid (water) is denoted by ρ_L, it follows from Eq.(3) that the volume of the solid sample is given by

$$V_S = V - V_L = \frac{\rho_L V + W_2 - W_3}{\rho_L} \tag{4}$$

where V is the total volume of the pycnometer. From Eqs. (1), (2) and (4), we obtain

$$\rho = \frac{W_S}{V_S} = \frac{\rho_L(W_2 - W_1)}{\rho_L V + W_2 - W_3} \tag{5}$$

Since the values of V and ρ_L are known, it is only necessary to determine W_1, W_2 and W_3 in order to calculate the density of the solid. The average values of these weights are listed below together with the values of V and ρ_L.

[d] A condensed derivation of the equations to be used may be given here. Each equation should be part of a complete sentence; number all equations consecutively throughout the entire report and refer to them by number. All symbols should be defined at the point where they first appear. A condensed tabulation of essential raw data to be used in the calculations is often useful. For a long calculation, it is very desirable to tabulate all important intermediate results. It is unnecessary and undesirable to present all computations in the report; however, a typical sample computation should be given to illustrate how the calculations were performed. A general discussion of the proper methods for handling calculations is given in Chap. II. Many reports will require graphical presentation of the data or the calculated results. Each graph should be given a figure number and a title; it should be referred to in the text by number.

ρ_L = 0.997044 g cm^{-3} at 25°C (taken from the Handbook of Chemistry and Physics[2])

V = 12.410 ± 0.004 cm^{-3} (given by instructor)

W_1 = 8.6309 g

Sample I: W_2 = 42.0301 g
W_3 = 48.1732 g

Sample II: W_2 = 45.8479 g
W_3 = 51.2944 g

The density of germanium can now be calculated by substitution of the above data into Eq. (5). The computation will be shown in detail for Sample I:

$$\rho_I = \frac{(.99704)(42.0301 - 8.6309)}{(.99704)(12.410) + 42.0301 - 48.1732}$$

$$= \frac{(.99704)(33.3992)}{12.3733 - 6.1431} = \frac{33.3003}{6.2302} = 5.345 \text{ g cm}^{-3}$$

The result for Sample II is 5.357 g cm^{-3}. The weights used in these calculations have not been corrected for the effect of air buoyancy on the weighings. Rather than correct each weight to vacuum, we may use a simple formula given by Bauer[1] for correcting the final calculated result. This formula gives for the corrected density ρ^*,

$$\rho^* = \rho + 0.0012\,(1 - \rho/\rho_L) \qquad (6)$$

When Eq. (6) is applied to our results we obtain for ρ^* the following values:

Sample I: 5.340 g cm^{-3}
Sample II: 5.352 g cm^{-3}
Average: 5.346 g cm^{-3}

IV. Uncertainties in Results[e]

According to Eq. (5) the uncertainty in ρ will depend on the uncertainty in each of five variables; however, the value of ρ_L is known to six significant figures and its uncertainty may be neglected in comparison to those of the other variables. With this in mind we can develop a propagation-of-errors treatment by taking the differential of both sides of Eq. (5) to obtain

$$d\rho = \frac{\rho}{W_2 - W_1}(dW_2 - dW_1) - \frac{\rho}{W_2 - W_3 + \rho_L V}(dW_2 - dW_3 + \rho_L dV) \qquad (7)$$

We note that $(dW_2 - dW_1)$ is less than $(dW_2 - dW_3 + \rho_L dV)$ (on substituting error values for differentials) and that $(W_2 - W_1)$ is about five times as large as $(W_2 - W_3 + \rho_L V)$. It is therefore possible to neglect the first term on the right-hand side of Eq. (7) in obtaining an approximate uncertainty figure. Thus the limit of error in ρ, $\lambda(\rho)$, is approximately given by

$$\lambda(\rho) = \frac{\rho}{W_2 - W_3 + \rho_L V}[\lambda(W_2) + \lambda(W_3) + \rho_L \lambda(V)] \qquad (8)$$

where $\lambda(W_2)$, $\lambda(W_3)$ and $\lambda(V)$ are the limits of error in the respective quantities W_2, W_3, and V. We may take as reasonable limits of error $\lambda(W_2) = 0.001\text{g}$ and $\lambda(W_3) = 0.002\text{g}$. The higher value for $\lambda(W_3)$ includes the effect of failure to attain an exact filling of the pycnometer with water. For $\lambda(V)$ we take 0.004 cm^3, the value given by

[e] The type of treatment of uncertainties will depend a great deal on the nature of the experiment; see Chap. II for a detailed discussion of error analysis. The material given above is typical of a straightforward propagation-of-errors treatment. It is important to combine and simplify all expressions as much as possible in order to avoid obtaining unwieldy error equations. Since uncertainty figures need not be calculated to better than about 10 or 20 per cent accuracy, one should always try to find laborsaving approximations. Where the number of runs is so small that reliable limits of error cannot be deduced from statistical considerations, limits of error must be assigned largely on the basis of experience and judgment. Make them large enough to be safe, but not ridiculously large. For a long and detailed report, a quantitative analysis of uncertainties should always be derived and a numerical value of the limit of error (or some other appropriate measure of uncertainty) should be presented. For a brief report, a qualitative discussion of the sources of error may suffice. In such a case, this section may be omitted and the error discussion included as part of the general discussion.

the instructor. Thus for Sample I,

$$\lambda(\rho_I) = \frac{5.340}{6.230}\ (0.001 + 0.002 + 0.004)$$

$$= 0.86 \times (0.007) = 0.006\ g\ cm^{-3}$$

Similarly, we obtain $\lambda(\rho_{II}) = 0.006\ g\ cm^{-3}$

V. Discussion[f]

The values and limits of error obtained for the density of germanium at 25°C are

Sample I: $5.340 \pm 0.006\ g\ cm^{-3}$
Sample II: $5.352 \pm 0.006\ g\ cm^{-3}$

The average value is $5.346\ g\ cm^{-3}$. The value given in the Handbook of Chemistry and Physics[3] is $5.35\ g\ cm^{-3}$ at 20°C; the value calculated from the volume of the crystallographic unit cell[4] and the atomic weight is $5.355\ g\ cm^{-3}$. Only the higher of our two results (that for Sample II) is in agreement with the literature value to within our limits of error.

The values obtained for the two samples deviate from the average by just the assigned limit of error. However, the difference is much larger than it should be considering the fact that the contribution of any error in V is the same in both runs. This suggests

[f] This is the most flexible section of the entire report, and the student must depend heavily on his own judgment for the choice of topics for discussion. The final results of the experiment should be clearly presented, often in a tabular or graphical form. A comparison between these results and theoretical values or experimental values from the literature is usually appropriate. A comment should be made on any discrepancies with the accepted or expected values. In this sample discussion, comment is also made on "internal discrepancies," possible systematic errors, and the relative importance of various sources of random error; and a brief suggestion is made for an improvement in the experimental method. Other possible topics include suitability of the method used compared with other methods, other applications of the method, mention of any special circumstances or difficulties which might have influenced the results, discussion of any approximations made or which could have been made, suggestions for changes or improvements in the calculations, mention of the theoretical significance of the result. At the end of several of the experiments in this book there are questions which provide topics for discussion; however, the student should usually go beyond these topics and include whatever other discussion he feels to be pertinent.

that the material examined may be somewhat inhomogeneous, so as to yield two samples of slightly different density. We suggest the possibility that cracks or fissures inaccessible to the liquid are present in Sample I, or even in both samples to different degrees. On this assumption, the greater confidence would be placed in the higher value, namely that for Sample II, although on the basis of results for only two samples there is no internal evidence that Sample II is completely free of defects. The agreement of the result for Sample II with the literature values is gratifying, but in general the best indication of reliability would be good agreement among the results for several samples.

Equations (8) and (9) show that the largest contribution to the overall error comes from the uncertainty in the pycnometer volume V. Our experimental precision indicates that by measuring the weight of the pycnometer filled with water alone, a better value of V could have been obtained. This would have reduced the uncertainty in the density but would not have improved the agreement between the two samples.

References[g]

1. N. Bauer, "Determination of Density", Chap. VI in A. Weissberger (ed.), "Technique of Organic Chemistry", 2nd ed., Vol. I, Part I, esp. pp 288 - 290, Interscience, New York (1949).
2. "Handbook of Chemistry and Physics", 41st ed., p 2129 Chemical Rubber Publishing Co., Cleveland (1959).
3. Ibid, p 579.
4. R. W. G. Wyckoff, "Crystal Structures", Vol. I. p II - 10 and Table II, 6, Interscience, New York (1951).

[g] An appropriate style for referring to a book is illustrated by entry 4 above. If the publisher's name is not well known, it should be given in full (see entry 2); if the city of publication is not well known, the state or country should also be given (e.g., "Reading, Mass."). The citation style for referring to a book containing chapters by several different authors is illustrated by entry 1. The proper citation style for journal articles is shown by the many references given elsewhere in this book. For typewritten reports, it is common practice to underline only the journal volume number.

Sample Notebook Page[h]

24

John Doe 9/29/'60
Partner: Dick Roe Exp: Density of Ge

Balance #3 Pycnometer #7
($V = 12.410 \pm .004$ cm³)

Sample I - Run I

W_1 5 + 3 + 0.6 + 0.0307 = 8.6307 g
corr +.25 + .00 + .25 + .10 mg +.0006 g = W_1 = 8.6313 g

W_2 30 + 10 + 2 + .0323 = 42.0323 g
corr −1.60 + .00 − .15 + .10 mg −.0016 g = W_2 = 42.0307 g

W_3 30 + 10 + 5 + 3 + 0.1 + .0758 = 48.1758 g
corr −1.60 + .00 +.25 +.00 +.20 +.25 mg −.0009 g = W_3 = 48.1749 g

Sample I - Run II

W_1 5 + 3 + 0.6 + .0302 = 8.6302 g
corr +.25 +.00 +.25 +.10 mg +.0006 g = W_1 = 8.6308 g

W_2 30 + 10 + 2 + .0311 = 42.0311 g
corr −1.60 +.00 −.15 +.10 mg −.0016 g = W_2 = ~~42.0327 g~~ 42.0295 g

W_3 30 + 10 + 5 + 3 + 0.1 + .0724 = 48.1724 g
corr −1.60 +.00 +.25 +.00 +.20 +.25 mg −.0009 g = W_3 = 48.1715 g

Sample II - Run I

W_1 5 + 3 + 0.6 + .0310 = 8.6310 g
corr +.25 +.00 +.25 +.10 mg +.0006 g = W_1 = 8.6316 g

[h] All data must be recorded directly in a notebook or on special data sheets. Be sure to record any identifying numbers on special apparatus and all necessary apparatus calibration data. If separate data sheets were used or if carbon copies were made of the pages in a bound research notebook, the complete data should be arranged in order at the end of the report. If a bound notebook was used, make a table of contents on the first page and list for each experiment the location of the data pages. The first page of data should have a clear and complete heading; all pages should carry the name of the student and his partner. (The instructor may also require that data sheets be checked over and initialed by a teaching assistant at the end of the experiment.)

SPECIAL PROJECTS

In order to become a creative and independent research scientist, one must acquire a complex set of abilities. It is often necessary to invent new experimental methods or at least to adapt old ones to new needs. New apparatus must be designed, constructed, and fully tested. Most important of all, an intelligent procedure must be established for the use of this apparatus in making precise measurements. Performing assigned experiments which are described in detail is merely the first step in developing such research ability. Later on, individually supervised experimental work on an original thesis problem will often be undertaken in order to develop independence and experience with advanced research techniques. In preparation for thesis work in physical chemistry we have found it profitable to encourage interested students to perform a "special project" in lieu of two or three regular experiments.

These special projects are intended to provide experience in choosing an interesting topic, in designing an experiment with the aid of literature references, in building apparatus, and in planning an appropriate experimental procedure. At least 15 hours of laboratory time should be available for carrying out such an experiment. Although there are certain limitations which are imposed by the available time and equipment, challenging and feasible topics with a research flavor can be found in most branches of physical chemistry. Indeed, it is sometimes possible to make a significant start on an original research problem that will eventually lead to publishable results. The primary emphasis should, however, be placed on independent planning of the experimental work rather than on original proposals for new research.

The two (or possibly three) partners working on a given special project should plan the experiment together, starting three or four weeks in advance, and should discuss their ideas frequently with an instructor or a graduate teaching assistant. All work done in the laboratory should be supervised by an experienced research worker in order to prevent any serious safety hazards.

Some of the projects done over the past ten years in the laboratory course at MIT are listed below as examples of the kind of problems which might be attempted.

Heat of fusion of mercury
Transition temperatures in ammonium halides
Spectrophotometric study of the relative stability of metal ion—EDTA complexes
Determination of the solubility of $Fe(OH)_3$ using radioactive iron
Dimerization of dye molecules in solution
Kinetics of the $H_2 + I_2 = 2HI$ reaction in the gas phase
Weak-acid catalysis of BH_4^- decomposition
Photochemistry of the cis-trans azobenzene interconversion
Isotope effect on reaction-rate constants
Susceptibility of a paramagnetic solid as a function of temperature
Dielectric constant of polypropylene glycol
X-ray study of short range order in liquid mercury
Fluorescence and phosphorescence of complex ions in solution
Infrared study of hydrogen bonding of CH_3OD with various solvents
Raman spectra of toluene, chlorinated methanes
Light scattering near the critical point in ethane
Franck-Hertz experiment

Polanyi dilute flame reaction, e.g., K + Br_2
Flash photolysis and recombination of I atoms
Single-crystal X-ray diffraction (precession camera)
EPR study of gas-phase hydrogen and deuterium atoms
EPR spectra of methyl semiquinones
Photodissociation of NO_2
Fluorescence quenching of excited K atoms
Shock-tube kinetics: recombination of I atoms
Dielectric dispersion in high-polymer solutions

Many of these projects were quite ambitious and required hard work and enthusiasm on the part of both students and staff. Not all were completely successful in terms of precise numerical results, but each one was instructive and enjoyable. Frequently they resulted in an excellent scientific rapport between the students and the instructing staff.

Chapters I, II, and XV to XIX contain general information about experimental work in physical chemistry, while Chaps. III to XIV contain the experiments which are numbered 1 to 47 consecutively throughout the book. In addition, Chaps. IV and V each contain some separate introductory material. Each figure, equation, and table is identified by a single number, and the numbers in each category run consecutively within single experiments. Outside the experiments, numbering is consecutive within single chapters. Within the experiment or chapter concerned, reference is made with the appropriate single number: e.g., Fig. 1, Eq. (8), Table 1. For cross references, double numbering is used: e.g., Fig. 38-1 refers to Fig. 1 in Exp. 38, and Eq. (V-8) refers to Eq. (8) in the introductory part of Chap. V.

II

TREATMENT OF EXPERIMENTAL DATA

The ultimate object of performing an experiment in physical chemistry is usually to obtain one or more numerical results. Between the recording of measured values and the reporting of numerical results there are processes of arithmetical calculation, some of which may involve averaging or smoothing the measured values but most of which involve the application of formulas derived from physics or physical chemistry. Part of this chapter is devoted to a discussion of general techniques for carrying out such calculations.

However, our concern with the treatment of experimental data is not ended when we have obtained the desired numerical result. An important part of the job is the determination of the degree of uncertainty to which the numerical result is subject. Every physical quantity whose *a priori* range of possible numerical values constitutes a continuum is subject to error in its determination. It is not possible to determine exactly what this error is: this would be equivalent to measuring the quantity without error, since correction can be made for any *known* error. But it is important to specify the highest amount by which the quantity *might* be in error or to specify the value of some other parameter (standard error, probable error, etc.) from which the probability of the existence of an error of any given magnitude can be predicted.

The reported value of a physical quantity, when not accompanied by a statement of its uncertainty, can be of small value. For example, suppose that the experimental value of a physical quantity is being compared with a value predicted for that quantity by a theoretical equation. If the agreement is very good, is it possibly to some degree fortuitous? If the agreement is very bad, is it outside the limits of experimental error? The significance of the degree of agreement (upon which may rest the validity of the theory) depends upon the answers to questions of this kind, and these answers require knowledge of the experimental uncertainty.

Assessment of the uncertainty involves some knowledge of the accuracy and precision of the instruments used, analysis of the experimental method and technique, determination of the degree of internal consistency in the experimental data, and, finally, a study of how errors or uncertainties in experimental data affect the final calculated result.

ERRORS IN OBSERVATIONAL DATA

Systematic and Random Errors. The measurement of a physical quantity with a continuous-reading instrument is generally subject to error owing to inability of the observer to discriminate between readings differing by less than some small amount or to his inability to make the instrumental adjustments required for each reading to higher than a certain precision or to unpredictable fluctuations in the environmental conditions. Independent readings made with this instrument will generally differ by small, random amounts, and we say that the measurements are subject to *random error.* Random error may, in principle, be reduced by any arbitrary factor by taking and averaging a sufficiently large number of independent measurements. However, as the precision of the arithmetic mean of a number of measured values increases only in proportion to the square root of the number of individual values, the ultimate precision obtainable in practice is only a few times that of an individual measurement.

Even if random errors could be completely eliminated (as by taking an infinite number of measurements), the measured value may still be in error, owing to characteristics of the instrument or of the technique of using it that are the same for all measurements. Error of this kind is called *systematic error.* Examples of systematic error are calibration error in the instrument, uncompensated instrumental drift, leakage of material (e.g., gas in a pressure or vacuum system) or of electricity (as in electrometer measurements in a high-resistance circuit), incomplete fulfillment of assumed conditions for the measurement (e.g., incomplete reaction in a calorimeter, incomplete dehydration of a weighed precipitate), or some consistent operational error (parallax, uncompensated human reaction times, even personal bias). Systematic errors have been termed "corrigable errors," implying that (in principle, at least) they can be eliminated or else estimated and corrected for by sufficient attention to calibration, controls and blanks, and other experimental conditions. Sad experience hath shown, however, that more often than not systematic errors are undetected and uncorrected for, and not infrequently they are larger than the much more easily estimated random errors. The experimenter, therefore, should be eternally vigilant in respect to the possibility of systematic errors and conservatively objective in their estimation, but he cannot be infallible. Many are the published results that have been later shown to be in error by amounts far beyond the claimed limits of error.

Accuracy and Precision. The *precision* of a numerical result is concerned with its reproducibility when measured again with the same instrument and is therefore an expression of the uncertainty due to random error; the *accuracy* of the result is an expression of its total uncertainty including that due to systematic error. The terms accuracy and precision are also applied to instruments and methods to characterize the numerical results that can be obtained with them.

Error Frequency Distribution.[1,†] Let it be supposed that a large number of measurements x_i ($i = 1, 2, \ldots, N$) are made of a physical quantity x and that

† Superior numbers refer to references given at the end of chapters or experiments.

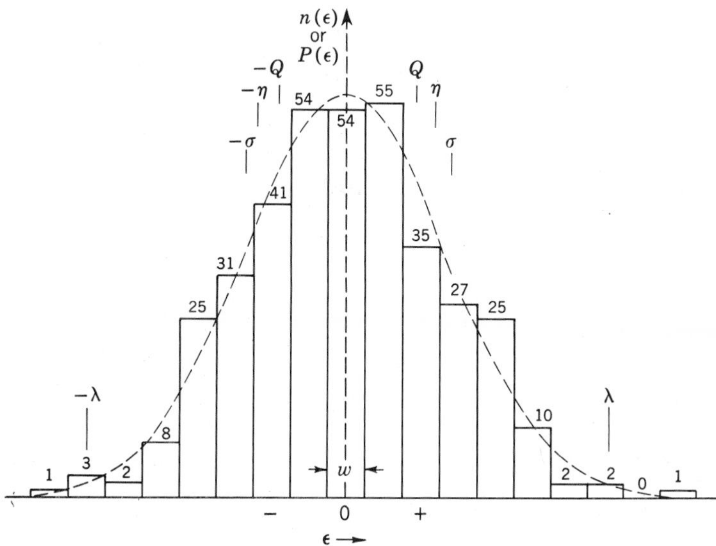

FIG. 1. A typical distribution of errors. The bar graph represents the actual error frequency distribution $n(\epsilon)$ for 376 measurements; the estimated normal error probability function $P(\epsilon)$ is given by the dashed curve. Estimated values of standard error σ, probable error Q, mean deviation η, and limit of error (1 per cent) λ are indicated in relation to the normal error curve.

these are subject to random errors ϵ_i. For simplicity we shall assume that the true value x_0 of this quantity is known and therefore that the errors are known. We are here concerned with the frequency $n(\epsilon)$ of occurrence of errors of size ϵ. This can be shown by means of a bar graph, like that of Fig. 1, in which the error scale is divided into ranges of equal width and the height of each bar represents the number of measurements yielding errors that fall within the respective range. The width w is chosen as a compromise between the desirability of having the numbers in each bar as large as possible and the desirability of having the number of bars as large as possible.

It is seen that even with as many as 376 measurements the graph shows irregularities, owing to the fact that the number of measurements represented by each bar is subject to statistical fluctuations that are not small in comparison with the number itself. From this graph we can make rough predictions concerning the probability that a measurement will yield an error of a given size. If we greatly increase the number of measurements represented, while perhaps decreasing the width w of the range in inverse proportion to the total number of measurements, the statistical fluctuations will become smaller in relation to the heights of the bars and our probability predictions are improved; we may even draw a smooth curve through the tops of the bars and assume it to represent an *error probability function* $P(\epsilon)$. The vertical scale of this function should be adjusted by multiplication with an appropriate factor so that the function is normalized, i.e., so that

$$\int_{-\infty}^{\infty} P(\epsilon)\, d\epsilon = 1 \tag{1}$$

Its significance is that the probability that a single measurement will be in error by an amount lying in the range between ϵ and $\epsilon + d\epsilon$ is equal to $P(\epsilon)\, d\epsilon$.

A probability function derived in this way is approximate; the true probability function cannot be inferred from any finite number of measurements. However, it can often be assumed that the probability function is represented by the *normal error probability function,*

$$P(\epsilon) = \frac{1}{\sqrt{2\pi}\sigma} e^{-\epsilon^2/2\sigma^2} \tag{2}$$

where σ is a parameter variously called the *standard error* or estimated standard deviation. It is the root-mean-square error expected with this probability function:

$$(\overline{\epsilon^2})^{1/2} = \left(\frac{1}{\sqrt{2\pi}\sigma} \int_{-\infty}^{\infty} \epsilon^2 e^{-\epsilon^2/2\sigma^2} d\epsilon \right)^{1/2} \equiv \sigma \tag{3}$$

Its value can be estimated from the errors ϵ_i themselves if known:

$$\sigma = \left(\frac{1}{N} \sum_{i=1}^{N} \epsilon_i^2 \right)^{1/2} \tag{4}$$

The dashed curve in Fig. 1 represents a normal error probability function, with a value of σ calculated with Eq. (4) from the 376 errors ϵ_i.

The usual assumptions leading to the normal error probability function are that an error in a measurement is compounded of a large number of unpredictably variable contributions (which are limited in magnitude but need not conform to any particular probability function), that these contributions are mutually independent, and that on the average all of them are small in comparison with the error itself. The derivation of the normal error probability function from these assumptions is approximate unless the number of contributions is infinite and the contributions themselves are infinitesimal. The assumptions are sufficient but not altogether necessary; the normal error probability function may arise at least in part from different circumstances. The factors which, in fact, determine the distribution are seldom known in detail. Thus it is common practice to assume that the normal error probability function is applicable even in the absence of valid *a priori* reasons, and indeed the distributions obtained frequently conform to the normal error probability function to within ordinary statistical error, as in the case of the distribution of Fig. 1. However, even with 376 measurements the normal error probability function is not proved to be valid in all respects; with a much larger number of measurements it may become apparent that the true probability function is somewhat skewed or flat-topped or double-peaked, etc.

The above discussion has been based on random errors, as these are best suited to an investigation of frequency distribution. Where all the N measurements are subject to a systematic error ϵ_s, the distribution is shifted by that amount; in the event that random errors are normally distributed, the probability function becomes

$$P(\epsilon) = \frac{1}{\sqrt{2\pi}\sigma} e^{-(\epsilon-\epsilon_s)^2/2\sigma^2} \tag{5}$$

So far the discussion has dealt with the errors themselves, as if we knew their magnitudes. In actual circumstances we cannot know the errors ϵ_i by which the measurements x_i deviate from the true value x_0, but only the deviations δ_i from the mean x_m of the given set of measurements. The predicted error probability function, as deduced from these deviations, will then be centered about the mean x_m rather than the true value x_0. The distribution of the deviations δ_i is closely related to that of the errors ϵ_i but is on the average slightly narrower. The "best" value of σ for the normal error probability function can be obtained from the observed deviations δ_i with the equation

$$\sigma = \left(\frac{1}{N-1}\sum_{i=1}^{N} \delta_i{}^2\right)^{1/2} \tag{6}$$

which resembles Eq. (4) but has $(N - 1)$ replacing N in the denominator.

We are now ready to discuss the parameters which are commonly used to specify the uncertainty due to random error. The magnitudes of these parameters in relation to the normal error curve are illustrated in Fig. 1. In what follows we shall refer to a distribution which follows or is expected to follow a normal error probability function as a *normal error distribution.* The assumption of the normal error distribution is often mathematically convenient in that it permits the use of many useful formulas derived from normal error theory. These formulas often retain some measure of validity when the distributions are not normal but should be used with care in such cases.

Standard Error. This quantity σ has already appeared as a parameter in the normal error probability function. When the error distribution is indeed normal, the probability that a measurement will be in error by an amount no larger than σ is found by integrating the function, Eq. (2), between the limits $\pm\sigma$; it is 68.26 per cent, or about two-thirds.

The standard error may also be given the meaning, *applicable to any frequency distribution,* of the expected root-mean-square deviation of a measurement from the true value, as indicated by Eq. (4). As in the case of a normal distribution, the best value for σ can be calculated from the observed deviations with Eq. (6).

The standard error estimated in this way is itself uncertain; it is subject to a standard error of

$$\sigma_\sigma = \sqrt{\frac{2}{N}}\,\sigma \tag{7}$$

It is therefore apparent that several observations (certainly at least four) are required if the value for the standard error, as obtained by application of Eq. (6), is to have much significance.

Probable Error. This is a very popular parameter for expressing uncertainty. It is a quantity Q with such a value that the probability that an error will be less than Q in magnitude is equal to the probability that it will exceed Q in magnitude:

$$\int_{-Q}^{Q} P(\epsilon)\, d\epsilon = \frac{1}{2} \tag{8}$$

The relation of the probable error to the standard error depends upon the nature of the frequency distribution. For a normal distribution the former is about two-thirds of the latter:

$$Q = 0.6745\sigma \tag{9}$$

Mean Error and Mean Deviation. The mean deviation

$$|\overline{\delta}| = \frac{1}{N}\sum_{i=1}^{N} |\delta_i| \tag{10}$$

is commonly quoted, on account of its ease of calculation. A quantity with more significance is the expected mean error $|\overline{\epsilon}|$ or η. If the errors themselves were known, we could use the equation

$$\eta = \frac{1}{N} \sum_{i=1}^{N} |\epsilon_i| \tag{11}$$

but since they are not, we must estimate η with the equation

$$\eta = \left(\frac{N}{N-1}\right)^{1/2} |\overline{\delta}| \tag{12}$$

which assumes (but does not sensitively depend upon) a normal frequency distribution. For such a distribution we can also write

$$\sigma = 1.253\eta \tag{13}$$

and

$$Q = 0.845\eta \tag{14}$$

As means of calculating σ and Q, Eqs. (10) to (14) are less precise than the equations given earlier.

Limit of Error. A limit of error λ is a quantity chosen sufficiently large that the probability that an error will exceed it is for most practical purposes negligible. The definition is somewhat arbitrary. "One per cent confidence limits," meaning that an error is expected to lie outside the limits $(-\lambda, \lambda)$ only 1 per cent of the time, are commonly accepted. For λ defined in this way,

$$\lambda \cong 2.6\sigma \cong 3.8Q \cong 3.2\eta \tag{15}$$

for a normal frequency distribution.

In practice the number of independent measurements of a given experimental quantity is often small (usually no more than three or four) owing to limited time available, and it is often unrealistic to estimate uncertainties from the deviations from the mean. In this case, and also in cases where systematic errors must be estimated as well, limits of error must be assigned on the basis of the individual judgment and experience of the experimeter. The ability to assign realistic limits of error, taken large enough to be safe but not so large as to detract unnecessarily from the value of the measurement, is one of the marks of a good experimentalist. It would be very difficult to formulate a set of rules that would be applicable in all cases; the limit of error assigned in any given case will depend on the characteristics and capabilities of the instrument, the reproducibility of its reading, the quality of its calibration, and the user's experience and familiarity with it. A reasonable limit of error in weighing a small solid object on an ordinary Chainomatic analytical balance with weights calibrated to 0.05 mg might be 0.3 mg; in reading a 50-ml burette it might be 0.03 ml; in determining a short time interval with a stopwatch it might be 0.4 sec; in measuring a temperature difference with a Beckmann thermometer it might be 0.01°C; etc. Estimation of standard errors or probable errors in this way is much more difficult.

The Arithmetic Mean and Its Uncertainty. The arithmetic mean x_m of several independent measurements of equal weight

$$x_m = \frac{1}{N} \sum_{i=1}^{N} x_i \tag{16}$$

has a higher precision than a single measurement. The standard error of the mean is given by

$$\sigma_m = \frac{1}{\sqrt{N}}\sigma = \left[\frac{1}{N(N-1)}\sum_{i=1}^{N}\delta_i{}^2\right]^{1/2} \tag{17}$$

independent of the frequency distribution; analogous formulas valid for normal distributions

$$Q_m = \frac{1}{\sqrt{N}}Q \qquad \lambda_m = \frac{1}{\sqrt{N}}\lambda \tag{18}$$

are also roughly applicable in most cases to non-normal distributions.

CALCULATIONS

Each directly measured experimental quantity that is to be used in the calculation of the desired final result should be measured in the laboratory to the utmost usable sensitivity of the instrument involved. This is usually greater than that corresponding to the smallest indicated scale graduation, and it is therefore usually desirable to obtain an additional digit by interpolation between scale divisions. The figure recorded for the measurement should ordinarily be one in which the last one or two digits are somewhat uncertain.

Rejection of Discordant Data. It occasionally happens in making multiple measurements that one value differs from the rest considerably more than they differ from one another. Should the discordant value be rejected before an average is taken? This question provides one of the most severe tests to which the scientific objectivity of the experimenter is exposed, for he may (indeed, he should) reject any measurement, whether concordant or discordant, if he has valid reason to believe that it is defective. In the absence of such a known reason, how large a discrepancy may be taken as evidence of a defect that has escaped notice? The answer depends upon a balance between the estimated *a priori* probability of such an event and the estimated probability of a normal random deviation as large as that observed. If we accept that the *a priori* probability of a defective measurement is of the order of 1 or 2 per cent, we are probably justified in rejecting one of five or more measurements if it differs from the mean of the others by more than four times their average deviation.

Arithmetical Calculations. The calculations may be performed by any method that does not introduce round-off errors that are significant in comparison with the experimental errors. A 10-in. slide rule is precise to only three or perhaps four significant figures. Five-place logarithms will always provide enough precision for the computations required by the experiments in this book. A desk calculator, if available, is, of course, a great convenience and provides as much precision as is needed. Finally, longhand arithmetic should not be regarded as a lost art.

The calculations should be organized so as to prevent inadvertent loss of precision, such as frequently occurs in dealing with small differences between large quantities. Experiment 12 provides a good example of a situation of this kind. Any calculation worth doing is worth checking for possible arithmetical mistakes. Even calculations performed on a desk calculator may suffer from errors in entering or reading numbers and occasionally from machine errors.

The best way to check a calculation is to repeat it, preferably in a different way, to the same precision. When an experiment has been performed by two persons as partners, the calculations can be done by each person independently, with cross-checking of intermediate and final numerical results. A less desirable but often adequate method of checking is to perform the calculation quickly at lower precision; calculations performed with logarithms can be checked for gross errors with a slide rule.

Longhand arithmetical calculations can be checked routinely by the method known as "casting out nines." In this method, every element of the calculations (multiplicand, multiplier, product, etc.) is reduced modulo nine; that is, the remainder on division by 9 is found. This remainder is found by casting out 9's and combinations of digits adding to 9, adding the remaining digits, and continuing the process until a single digit less than 9 is obtained. The calculation is then checked to see whether it is valid (modulo 9) for these single digits:

```
                                                     35      8
 213     6          3485   11    2            62 | 2175   8 | 6
 -95    -5          × 97        × 7                186         1
 ---    --          -----       ---                ---        --
 118     1          24395        14   5            315         5
                   31365                           310
                   ------                          ---
                   338045   14    5                  5
```

This procedure is not infallible, since two errors may compensate and fail to be detected. The procedure is therefore most valuable when the probability of any one error is small.

Numerical Methods. This term is commonly used in contradistinction to analytic methods for carrying out such mathematical procedures as differentiation, integration, solution of algebraic equations, etc. Analytic methods are exact, or at least capable of being carried to any arbitrary precision; numerical methods as applied to experimental data are necessarily approximate, being limited by the finite number of data employed and by their precision.

In what follows we shall suppose that a function $y = f(x)$ is represented by a number of experimental values y_i at a series of x_i *which for convenience we shall take to be evenly spaced.* If there is reason to believe that this function should conform to some analytic form, depending on a few parameters, these parameters can be estimated by the method of least squares as described later. In this case the analytic expression can be differentiated, integrated, etc., by analytic methods, and there is no further need for numerical work.

If no clear-cut analytic form exists, these manipulations must be done numerically (or graphically as described later). For certain purposes, especially differentiation and the solving of equations, it may be necessary to "smooth" the data so that differences from point to point do not show random fluctuations. A number of methods for performing this smoothing operation are described elsewhere.[2] We shall here give one method, based on fitting a third-degree polynominal to $2n + 1$ adjacent points. For $n = 2$, the "smoothed" value of y_i is

$$y_i' = \tfrac{1}{35}\left[17y_i + 12(y_{i+1} + y_{i-1}) - 3(y_{i+2} + y_{i-2})\right] \tag{19}$$

For $n = 3$,

$$y_i' = \tfrac{1}{21}\left[7y_i + 6(y_{i+1} + y_{i-1}) + 3(y_{i+2} + y_{i-2}) - 2(y_{i+3} + y_{i-3})\right] \tag{20}$$

For $n = 4$,

$$y_i' = \tfrac{1}{231}[59y_i + 54(y_{i+1} + y_{i-1}) + 39(y_{i+2} + y_{i-2}) + 14(y_{i+3} + y_{i-3}) - 21(y_{i+4} + y_{i-4})] \quad (21)$$

For purposes of differentiation[3] it is useful to compute a table of successive differences as follows:

$$\begin{array}{l|llllll}
x_0 = x_0 & y_0 & & & & & \\
 & & \Delta y_0 & & & & \\
x_1 = x_0 + w & y_1 & & \Delta^2 y_0 & & & \\
 & & \Delta y_1 & & \Delta^3 y_0 & & \\
x_2 = x_0 + 2w & y_2 & & \Delta^2 y_1 & & \Delta^4 y_0 & \\
 & & \Delta y_2 & & \Delta^3 y_1 & & \Delta^5 y_0 \\
x_3 = x_0 + 3w & y_3 & & \Delta^2 y_2 & & \Delta^4 y_1 & \vdots \\
 & & \Delta y_3 & & \Delta^3 y_2 & \vdots & \\
x_4 = x_0 + 4w & y_4 & & \Delta^2 y_3 & \vdots & & \\
 & & \Delta y_4 & \vdots & & & \\
x_5 = x_0 + 5w & y_5 & \vdots & & & & \\
\vdots & \vdots & & & & &
\end{array} \quad (22)$$

where $\Delta y_0 = y_1 - y_0$, $\Delta y_1 = y_2 - y_1$, $\Delta^2 y_0 = \Delta y_1 - \Delta y_0$, etc. The degree of smoothness of the date can be seen by inspection of the differences; there is no point in continuing the table beyond the point where the differences cease to vary in a reasonably smooth and regular manner. An expression for y as a function of x in the neighborhood of x_0 is given by the Gregory-Newton interpolation expression

$$y = y_0 + r\,\Delta y_0 + \frac{r(r-1)}{2!}\Delta^2 y_0 + \frac{r(r-1)(r-2)}{3!}\Delta^3 y_0 + \cdots \quad (23)$$

where

$$r \equiv \frac{x - x_0}{w} \quad (24)$$

By differentiation we obtain

$$\frac{dy}{dx} = \frac{1}{w}\left(\Delta y_0 + \frac{2r-1}{2!}\Delta^2 y_0 + \frac{3r^2 - 6r + 2}{3!}\Delta^3 y_0 + \frac{4r^3 - 18r^2 + 22r - 6}{4!}\Delta^4 y_0 + \frac{5r^4 - 40r^3 + 105r^2 - 100r + 24}{5!}\Delta^5 y_0 + \cdots\right) \quad (25)$$

$$\frac{d^2y}{dx^2} = \frac{1}{w^2}\left[\Delta^2 y_0 + (r-1)\,\Delta^3 y_0 + \frac{6r^2 - 18r + 11}{12}\Delta^4 y_0 + \frac{2r^3 - 12r^2 + 21r - 10}{12}\Delta^5 y_0 + \cdots\right] \tag{26}$$

On referring to Eq. (22) we see that the successive differences entering into Eqs. (23), (25), and (26) lie on a downward-slanting line. With as much justification an upward-slanting line may be used and, indeed, must be used if x_0 is at or very near the end of the table. No changes in the above expressions other than a replacement of $\Delta y_0, \Delta^2 y_0, \Delta^3 y_0, \ldots$ by $\Delta y_{-1}, \Delta^2 y_{-2}, \Delta^3 y_{-3}$ and a change of all signs in Eqs. (23), (25), and (26) to plus are required if we continue to define r with Eq. (24). Indeed a good procedure is to employ both downward-slanting and upward-slanting Δ's, and to restrict r to the range $-\frac{1}{2} \leqslant r \leqslant \frac{1}{2}$.

For evaluation of the definite integral

$$Y(a,b) = \int_a^b y\,dx \tag{27}$$

it is often possible to utilize procedures that do not require smoothing of the data.[4] The simplest procedure, based on the "trapezoidal rule," makes use of the expression

$$Y(x_0,x_n) = \frac{w}{2}(y_0 + 2y_1 + 2y_2 + \cdots + 2y_{n-1} + y_n) \tag{28}$$

This is equivalent to approximating the function by linear segments between the tabular entries (data points). A better procedure makes use of "Simpson's one-third rule":

$$Y(x_0,x_n) = \frac{w}{3}(y_0 + 4y_1 + 2y_2 + 4y_3 + 2y_4 + \cdots + 4y_{n-1} + y_n) \tag{29}$$

This rule requires that n be even, i.e., that the number of values of y be odd. This procedure is exact if y is strictly a quadratic function of x. Its use in other cases is equivalent to fitting quadratic forms (parabolas) to three points at a time, joining them at the even-numbered points. Still another rule, "Simpson's three-eighth rule,"

$$Y(x_0,x_n) = \frac{3w}{8}[y_0 + 3(y_1 + y_2) + 2y_3 + 3(y_4 + y_5) + 2y_6 + \cdots + 3(y_{n-2} + y_{n-1}) + y_n] \tag{30}$$

requires that n be divisible by 3 and is equivalent to fitting third-degree functions to four points at a time. More refined procedures are available, such as Weddel's rule, but their slight superiority seldom justifies the added complications.

In cases where n is divisible neither by 2 nor by 3, the range of integration may be split into two parts, one for Simpson's one-third rule, the other for Simpson's three-eighth rule. Alternatively, if the curve is approximately linear in one or two intervals, the trapezoidal rule may be used in these intervals.

Least Squares.[5] Let it be supposed that the experimental values y_i are expected to conform to some analytic functional form

$$y = f(\alpha_1, \ldots, \alpha_n, x) \tag{31}$$

where $\alpha_1, \ldots, \alpha_n$ are parameters the values of which are unknown. The number n of parameters should be considerably smaller than the number m of experimental values. It is not required that the x_i be equally spaced. It is desired to determine the "best" values of the parameters α_i and thereby to specify as completely as possible the functional dependence of y on x. According to the theory of least squares, which is based on normal error distributions, the most probable values of the parameters α_i are those for which (in the case that all y_i are weighted equally)

$$R = \sum_i [y_i - f(\alpha_1, \ldots, \alpha_n, x_i)]^2$$

is at a minimum. If the function is well behaved, this requires that

$$\frac{\partial R}{\partial \alpha_1} = \frac{\partial R}{\partial \alpha_2} = \cdots = \frac{\partial R}{\partial \alpha_n} = 0$$

For the derivative with respect to α_1 we obtain

$$-2 \sum_i [y_i - f(\alpha_1, \ldots, \alpha_n, x_i)] \frac{\partial f}{\partial \alpha_1} = 0 \tag{32}$$

If we expand f in a Taylor series around the values

$$y_i^0 \equiv f(\alpha_1^0, \ldots, \alpha_n^0, x_i)$$

calculated with trial values α_j^0 of the parameters, *keeping only terms to first order,* we obtain on rearranging Eq. (32)

$$\sum_i \left(\frac{\partial f_i}{\partial \alpha_1}\right)^2 \Delta\alpha_1 + \sum_i \frac{\partial f_i}{\partial \alpha_1}\frac{\partial f_i}{\partial \alpha_2} \Delta\alpha_2 + \cdots + \sum_i \frac{\partial f_i}{\partial \alpha_1}\frac{\partial f_i}{\partial \alpha_n} \Delta\alpha_n = \sum_i \frac{\partial f_i}{\partial \alpha_1}(y_i - y_i^0) \tag{33a}$$

where by $(\partial f_i/\partial \alpha_1)$ we mean $(\partial f/\partial \alpha_1)$ evaluated at $\alpha_1 = \alpha_1^0, \ldots, \alpha_n = \alpha_n^0, x = x_i$; etc. Similarly, from the other derivatives we obtain

$$\begin{gathered} \sum_i \frac{\partial f_i}{\partial \alpha_2}\frac{\partial f_i}{\partial \alpha_1} \Delta\alpha_1 + \sum_i \left(\frac{\partial f_i}{\partial \alpha_2}\right)^2 \Delta\alpha_2 + \cdots + \sum_i \frac{\partial f_i}{\partial \alpha_2}\frac{\partial f_i}{\partial \alpha_n} \Delta\alpha_n = \sum_i \frac{\partial f_i}{\partial \alpha_2}(y_i - y_i^0) \\ \vdots \\ \sum_i \frac{\partial f_i}{\partial \alpha_n}\frac{\partial f_i}{\partial \alpha_1} \Delta\alpha_1 + \sum_i \frac{\partial f_i}{\partial \alpha_n}\frac{\partial f_i}{\partial \alpha_2} \Delta\alpha_2 + \cdots + \sum_i \left(\frac{\partial f_i}{\partial \alpha_n}\right)^2 \Delta\alpha_n = \sum_i \frac{\partial f_i}{\partial \alpha_n}(y_i - y_i^0) \end{gathered} \tag{33b}$$

These n equations in the n unknowns $\Delta\alpha_1 \ldots \Delta\alpha_n$ are called the *normal equations.* If the determinant of the coefficients of the $\Delta\alpha_j$ does not vanish, these equations can be solved to obtain the $\Delta\alpha_j$, and a new and improved set of α's can be obtained:

$$\begin{aligned} \alpha_1' &= \alpha_1^0 + \Delta\alpha_1 \\ \alpha_2' &= \alpha_2^0 + \Delta\alpha_2 \\ &\vdots \\ \alpha_n' &= \alpha_n^0 + \Delta\alpha_n \end{aligned} \tag{34}$$

Except when the function f is linear, it is necessary to start with trial parameters α_j^0 reasonably close to the correct values to minimize error resulting from the omission of second- and perhaps higher-order terms from the Taylor expansion. Additional improvement in the parameters can be obtained by another cycle of least squares where the derivatives are evaluated at α_j' rather than at α_j^0. This process can be repeated as many times as necessary.

The normal equations (33) can be derived in another way. Let us write as an *equation of condition* or *observational equation* for the experimental value y_i

$$y_i = f(\alpha_1, \ldots, \alpha_n, x_i) = y_i^0 + \frac{\partial f_i}{\partial \alpha_1}\Delta\alpha_1 + \frac{\partial f_i}{\partial \alpha_2}\Delta\alpha_2 + \cdots + \frac{\partial f_i}{\partial \alpha_n}\Delta\alpha_n$$

making use of the Taylor expansion to first order as before. Rearranging, we obtain

$$\frac{\partial f_i}{\partial \alpha_1}\Delta\alpha_1 + \frac{\partial f_i}{\partial \alpha_2}\Delta\alpha_2 + \cdots + \frac{\partial f_i}{\partial \alpha_n}\Delta\alpha_n = (y_i - y_i^0) \tag{35}$$

There is one of these equations for each of the m experimental values y_i. There are many more equations than there are unknowns, and owing to experimental errors in the y_i (and possibly approximations in the function), the equations are mutually incompatible and incapable of possessing a set of solutions $\Delta\alpha_j$ that satisfy them exactly. To obtain solutions, the equations must be reduced to as many as there are unknowns. This could be done simply by choosing n equations of condition at random to solve exactly. The parameters obtained would be subject to error owing to the experimental errors in the y_i. Different errors would result from a different choice of n equations. The errors in the α_j can be made much smaller by a procedure which makes use of *all* the observational equations. Such a procedure is as follows: Multiply each equation of condition (35) by $(\partial f_i/\partial\alpha_1)$ and add all equations. This yields a single equation which can be seen to be identical with the first normal equation (33*a*). The other normal equations (33*b*) are obtained in a similar manner by multiplying by $\partial f_i/\partial\alpha_2, \ldots, \partial f_i/\partial\alpha_n$.

A trivial example of a least-squares calculation is the calculation of the arithmetic mean. In this case the independent variable x does not appear and there is only one parameter α which is the desired average value. The observational equations are of the form

$$\Delta\alpha = \alpha = y_i - 0$$

since we may take $\alpha^0 = 0$. The single normal equation is

$$\sum_i (1)^2\alpha = \sum_i (1)y_i$$

whence

$$\alpha = \frac{1}{m}\sum_{i=1}^{m} y_i$$

A more significant example is that of a linear relationship

$$y = f(x) = \alpha_1 x + \alpha_2 \tag{36}$$

(Here again, because of linearity, we may take $\alpha_1^0 = \alpha_2^0 = 0, y^0 = 0$.) The m observational equations are

$$\alpha_1 x_i + \alpha_2 = y_i \tag{37}$$

and the two normal equations are

$$\begin{aligned}\sum_i x_i^2 \alpha_1 + \sum_i x_i(1)\alpha_2 &= \sum_i x_i y_i \\ \sum_i (1)x_i\alpha_1 + \sum_i (1)^2\alpha_2 &= \sum_i (1)y_i\end{aligned} \tag{38}$$

Solving, we obtain

$$\begin{aligned}\alpha_1 &= \frac{1}{D}\left(m\sum_{i=1}^{m} x_i y_i - \sum_{i=1}^{m} x_i \sum_{i=1}^{m} y_i\right) \\ \alpha_2 &= \frac{1}{D}\left(\sum_{i=1}^{m} x_i^2 \sum_{i=1}^{m} y_i - \sum_{i=1}^{m} x_i \sum_{i=1}^{m} x_i y_i\right)\end{aligned} \tag{39}$$

where

$$D = m\sum_{i=1}^{m} x_i^2 - \left(\sum_{i=1}^{m} x_i\right)^2 \tag{40}$$

In the foregoing we have dealt with only one independent variable. However, the method is no different with any number of independent variables.

Graphical Methods. These are inherently more limited in precision than numerical methods but are frequently easier and convey more of a feel for the nature of the manipulations involved. They reveal, much more clearly than a table of numbers does, such features as linearity or nonlinearity, maxima and minima, points of inflection, etc. Also, graphical methods of differentiation and integration are often easier than numerical methods. Graphical methods suffer, of course, from the fact that a plotted point has only two degrees of freedom; these we shall here assume to be represented by one independent variable x and one dependent variable y.

Use a sheet of good-quality graph paper which has a reasonable margin on all sides and which is accurately printed with thin, lightweight lines. Choose your scales of abscissas (x) and ordinates (y) so as to make best use of the area available. The type of graph paper (millimeter, inch, etc.) should be selected with a view to the use of a rational scale; the smallest divisions should preferably represent multiples of the digit 1 or 2 or perhaps 5. The axes should be clearly drawn and labeled. Plot experimental points as small dots with a sharp, hard pencil, and draw small circles (or squares, etc.) around them for better visibility. For a straight line, use a good straightedge such as a draftsman's transparent triangle, and do not hesitate to erase the line and try again until you are satisfied that the best fit has been obtained. A curve may be drawn either freehand or with ships curves or other devices with as much trial and error and erasing as is required. Any needed smoothing is done in accordance with the experimenter's judgment.

The first derivative of the plotted function is given by the slope of the tangent to the curve at the point concerned. A good way to draw the tangent is to hold a small rectangular mirror with its reflecting surface perpendicular to the paper, adjust it so that the reflection of the curve is tangent to and symmetrical with the curve itself, and then use the mirror as a straightedge to draw the tangent line. Another method is to use a compass to strike off arcs intersecting the curve on both sides and then draw a chord through the intersection points. The tangent can be drawn parallel to the chord if the curvature is uniform. If it is not, construct a second chord at a different distance in the same way and extend both lines to an

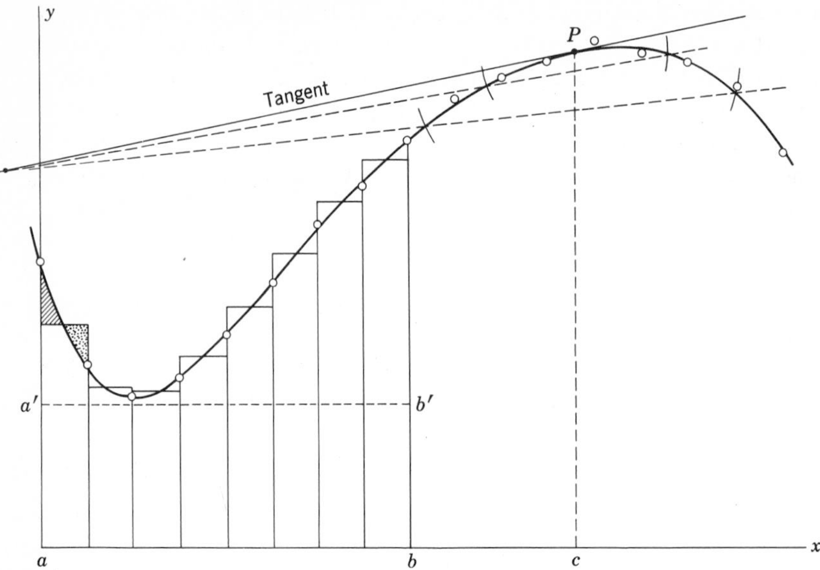

FIG. 2. An illustration of the construction of a tangent by the method of chords and of the evaluation of a definite integral by approximating the curve by a bar graph. The top of each bar is drawn so that the two small areas thereby defined (e.g., the shaded and stippled areas on first bar) appear equal.

intersection. Draw the (approximate) tangent line through this intersection point (see Fig. 2).

A definite integral, such as Eq. (29), can be determined by measuring the area under the curve between the desired limits (see Fig. 2). The area can be measured by use of an instrument known as a planimeter, by cutting out the area concerned with a pair of scissors and weighing it, by approximating it as well as possible by a bar graph, or by "counting squares." In the last method a count is made of the smallest squares of the graph-paper grid that lie wholly or *more than half* inside the area concerned. Whatever the method used, the area to be measured should be minimized as much as possible; there is no need to run the planimeter around the rectangular area below $a'b'$ in Fig. 2, for instance.

Whenever possible the data plotted should be made to correspond to a linear function, not only because a straight line is the easiest kind of line to draw through the points but also because deviations from a linear function are easier to detect than those from a function of any other kind. Good examples are the log p vs. $1/T$ plot for the vapor pressure of a liquid (Exp. 17) and the log r vs. t curve in first-order kinetics (Exp. 27). Optimum use of the graphical method is often obtained by making a *deviation plot,* in which the deviations of the experimental data from a predicted function are plotted instead of the data themselves. This is especially advantageous in certain cases where an extrapolation is to be made (Exps. 15 and 24).

PROPAGATION OF ERRORS

Once we have calculated the final result for an experiment, we are faced with the task of determining the uncertainty to which it is subject. At this point it is assumed that the limits of error in the experimental data have been estimated.† Let the desired result, for which the experiment was carried out, be designated by F, and let the directly measured quantities (e.g., weights, volumes, barometer readings, temperatures, measured emf's) be designated by x_i. The x_i are assumed to be mutually independent. The value of F is to be determined by substituting the experimentally determined values of the quantities x_i into a formula, which will be schematically written as

$$F = f(x_1, x_2, \ldots, x_n) \tag{41}$$

Infinitesimal changes dx_i in the experimentally determined values of x_i will produce in F the infinitesimal change

$$dF = \frac{\partial F}{\partial x_1} dx_1 + \frac{\partial F}{\partial x_2} dx_2 + \cdots + \frac{\partial F}{\partial x_n} dx_n \tag{42}$$

If the changes are finite rather than infinitesimal but are small enough that the values of the partial derivatives are not appreciably affected by the changes, we have approximately

$$\Delta F = \frac{\partial F}{\partial x_1} \Delta x_1 + \frac{\partial F}{\partial x_2} \Delta x_2 + \cdots + \frac{\partial F}{\partial x_n} \Delta x_n \tag{43}$$

(This is equivalent to a Taylor expansion in which only the first-power terms have been retained.) Now suppose that the Δx_i represent experimental errors $\epsilon(x_i)$ in the quantities x_i:

$$\Delta x_i = \epsilon(x_i) \equiv x_i \text{ (measured)} - x_i \text{ (true)} \tag{44}$$

These errors will produce an error in F,

$$\Delta F = \epsilon(F) \equiv F \text{ (calc'd from measured } x_i) - F \text{ (true)} \tag{45}$$

the value of which is given by

$$\epsilon(F) = \frac{\partial F}{\partial x_1} \epsilon(x_1) + \frac{\partial F}{\partial x_2} \epsilon(x_2) + \cdots + \frac{\partial F}{\partial x_n} \epsilon(x_n) \tag{46}$$

Since we do not know the actual values of the $\epsilon(x_i)$, we cannot know the actual value of $\epsilon(F)$. The most we can know is something about the magnitudes that the errors *may* assume; we have already assigned to each x_i a limit of error $\lambda(x_i)$ so defined that

$$-\lambda(x_i) \leqq \epsilon(x_i) \leqq \lambda(x_i) \tag{47}$$

We now undertake to deduce a corresponding limit of error $\lambda(F)$ in our final result F:

$$-\lambda(F) \leqq \epsilon(F) \leqq \lambda(F) \tag{48}$$

To do this, we calculate the largest $\epsilon(F)$ within the limits of error assigned to the x_i by setting the $\epsilon(x_i)$ in Eq. (46) equal numerically to the respective limits $\lambda(x_i)$ and assigning algebraic signs to the $\epsilon(x_i)$ in such a way as to give every term in Eq.

† If more than four independent measurements were made of the same experimental quantity, Eqs. (6), (15), and (18) can be used to deduce a limit of error in the mean value. If less than four were made (or if systematic errors must be taken into account), a limit of error should be estimated on the basis of personal experience.

(46) the same algebraic sign. This is equivalent to replacing $\epsilon(x_i)$ by $\lambda(x_i)$ and replacing each partial derivative by its absolute magnitude. The final result is

$$\lambda(F) = \left|\frac{\partial F}{\partial x_1}\right|\lambda(x_1) + \left|\frac{\partial F}{\partial x_2}\right|\lambda(x_2) + \cdots + \left|\frac{\partial F}{\partial x_n}\right|\lambda(x_n) \tag{49}$$

The expression for F can now be differentiated with respect to each of the variables $x_1, x_2, \ldots, x_n$ in turn, and the derivatives and assigned limits of error can be substituted into Eq. (49) for the purpose of calculating $\lambda(F)$.

However, it is frequently true that the expression for F is complicated enough or the functional form sufficiently awkward to justify a breakdown of the procedure into steps:

$$F = f_0(A,B, \ldots)$$

where $A = f_1(x_1,x_2, \ldots) \qquad B = f_2(y_1,y_2, \ldots)$, etc. (50)

We can then write

$$\lambda(F) = \left|\frac{\partial F}{\partial A}\right|\lambda(A) + \left|\frac{\partial F}{\partial B}\right|\lambda(B) + \cdots$$

$$\lambda(A) = \left|\frac{\partial A}{\partial x_1}\right|\lambda(x_1) + \left|\frac{\partial A}{\partial x_2}\right|\lambda(x_2) + \cdots \tag{51}$$

$$\lambda(B) = \left|\frac{\partial B}{\partial y_1}\right|\lambda(y_1) + \left|\frac{\partial B}{\partial y_2}\right|\lambda(y_2) + \cdots, \text{ etc.}$$

provided that $A, B, \ldots$ are *independent;* if they are not independent (that is, in the event that some of the x_i are identical with some of the y_i), the calculated limit of error may be too large. For example, if we let

$$F = a(e^{kx} - 1) + b(y - cx) = A + B$$

it would be improper to write

$$\lambda(F) = \lambda(A) + \lambda(B)$$
$$\lambda(A) = |ake^{kx}|\lambda(x) \qquad \lambda(B) = |b|\lambda(y) + |bc|\lambda(x)$$

Treatment of the function as a whole gives the correct result

$$\lambda(F) = |ake^{kx} - bc|\lambda(x) + |b|\lambda(y)$$

which will differ from the result first given if ak and bc have the same algebraic sign.

In certain cases the propagation-of-error treatment becomes very simple. Two examples are

$$F = x + y \quad (\text{or } x - y) \tag{52a}$$

for which

$$\lambda(F) = \lambda(x) + \lambda(y) \tag{52b}$$

and

$$F = Axyz \quad \left(\text{or } A\frac{xy}{z} \text{ or } A\frac{x}{yz} \text{ or } \frac{A}{xyz}\right) \tag{53a}$$

for which

$$\frac{\lambda(F)}{|F|} = \frac{\lambda(x)}{|x|} + \frac{\lambda(y)}{|y|} + \frac{\lambda(z)}{|z|} \tag{53b}$$

Equations (52) represent an important case applicable, for example, to differences between two readings of the same variable (e.g., the weight of the liquid plus container and the weight of the empty container, the initial and final readings of a burette or a thermometer). In many cases the limits of error in the initial and final readings may be taken as equal, in which case the limit of error in the difference between the two readings is equal to twice the limit of error in a single reading.

Equations (53) represent another important case, dealing *only* with situations in which F is directly proportional to the first power or inverse first power of each and every variable. In such a case, the relative (or percentage) limit of error in F is the sum of the relative (or percentage) limits of error in the x_i.

Most propagation-of-error treatments are not so simple as those illustrated by Eqs. (52) and (53). Where the expression for F is a complicated one, it is advisable to watch for opportunities for transforming the expression or parts of the expression so that single symbols representing known quantities can be substituted for groupings of several symbols. The most advantageous simplifications are usually obtained when the quantities substituted are the end results of the calculations, such as F itself, or at least quantities which represent the later stages of the calculation of F. This is advantageous not only because it results in the greatest economy of symbols but also because it presents the most frequent opportunities for cancellation and simplification. For example, the limit of error of

$$F = C\frac{x^2}{y}$$

can be written as

$$\lambda(F) = \left|\frac{2Cx}{y}\right| \lambda(x) + \left|\frac{Cx^2}{y^2}\right| \lambda(y)$$

but for computational purposes it will usually be more convenient to introduce F by substitution into the right-hand side, since the value of F will already have been calculated; we obtain

$$\lambda(F) = \left|\frac{2F}{x}\right| \lambda(x) + \left|\frac{F}{y}\right| \lambda(y) \qquad \text{or} \qquad \frac{\lambda(F)}{|F|} = \frac{2\lambda(x)}{|x|} + \frac{\lambda(y)}{|y|}$$

Before one begins an uncertainties treatment, it is well to examine the formula for F to determine whether any simplification can be made in it. For example, in the cryoscopic determination of the molecular weight of an unknown substance, the molecular weight is given by Eq. (13–21) as

$$M = \frac{1000gK_f}{G\,\Delta T_f}(1 - k_f\,\Delta T_f)$$

and since k_f is of the order of 0.01 deg^{-1} the term $k_f\,\Delta T_f$ is itself very small compared with unity and will contribute negligibly to the uncertainty in comparison to ΔT_f itself; therefore, the treatment of uncertainties may be based on the simpler, approximate expression

$$M = \frac{1000gK_f}{G\,\Delta T_f}$$

At various stages during the development of the derivation of the limit of error it is advisable to examine the various terms to see if any of them are negligible in comparison with other terms additive with them; if so, the negligible terms can be dropped if any material simplification of the treatment would result. A quantity can often be considered negligible for this purpose even when it could not be neglected in the calculation of F itself, for we are ordinarily interested only in obtaining a fairly rough figure for the limit of error. Thus, a term can ordinarily be dropped in the limit-of-error treatment if the effect produced in $\lambda(F)$ by dropping it is less than about 10 to 20 per cent. An overgenerous (overconservative) estimate of uncertainty is to be preferred to an insufficient (overoptimistic) estimate; if a term is to be dropped, it is better that dropping it make $\lambda(F)$ a little too large than a little too small.

The foregoing propagation-of-error treatment does not take into consideration the high probability that the errors in the several variables x_i will tend somewhat to cancel one another out. A treatment which takes this into account will now be given. Let us square both sides of Eq. (46):

$$[\epsilon(F)]^2 = \left(\frac{\partial F}{\partial x_1}\right)^2 [\epsilon(x_1)]^2 + \left(\frac{\partial F}{\partial x_2}\right)^2 [\epsilon(x_2)]^2 + \cdots + 2\left(\frac{\partial F}{\partial x_1}\right)\left(\frac{\partial F}{\partial x_2}\right)\epsilon(x_1)\epsilon(x_2) + \cdots$$

Now let us average this expression over all values expected for $\epsilon(x_1)$, $\epsilon(x_2)$, . . . , in accordance with the frequency distributions. Since the $\epsilon(x_i)$ independently have average value zero, we expect the cross terms to vanish. However, the squared terms are always positive and will not vanish. If we replace the average of each squared error by its equivalent, namely the square of the standard error, and then take the square root of both sides, we obtain

$$\sigma(F) = \left\{\left(\frac{\partial F}{\partial x_1}\right)^2 [\sigma(x_1)]^2 + \left(\frac{\partial F}{\partial x_2}\right)^2 [\sigma(x_2)]^2 + \cdots + \left(\frac{\partial F}{\partial x_n}\right)^2 [\sigma(x_n)]^2\right\}^{1/2} \tag{54}$$

If now we define the limit of error in accordance with Eq. (15), we have

$$\lambda(F) = \left\{\left(\frac{\partial F}{\partial x_1}\right)^2 [\lambda(x_1)]^2 + \left(\frac{\partial F}{\partial x_2}\right)^2 [\lambda(x_2)]^2 + \cdots + \left(\frac{\partial F}{\partial x_n}\right)^2 [\lambda(x_n)]^2\right\}^{1/2} \tag{55}$$

which, if all the terms in the braces are of roughly equal magnitude, gives a smaller result than is given by Eq. (49) by a factor approximately equal to the square root of the number of variables.

Uncertainties in Graphically Derived Quantities. It frequently happens that an intermediate or final result of the calculations in a given experiment is obtained from the slope or an intercept of a straight-line graph, say a plot of y against x. In such a case it is desirable to evaluate the uncertainty in the slope or in the position of the intercept. A rough procedure for doing this is based on drawing a rectangle with width $2\lambda(x_i)$ and height $2\lambda(y_i)$ around each experimental point (x_i,y_i), with the point at its center. The assignments of the limits of error $\lambda(x_i)$ and $\lambda(y_i)$ are made as described previously. The significance of the rectangle is that any point contained in it represents a possible position of the "true" point (x_i,y_i) and all points outside are ruled out as possible positions. Having already drawn the best straight line through the experimental points, and having derived from this line the slope or intercept, draw now two other (dashed) lines representing maximum and minimum values of the slope or intercept, consistent with the requirement that both lines pass through every rectangle, as shown in Fig. 3. (It should be borne in mind that the way in which the limiting lines are drawn will depend upon whether it is the slope or an interpolate intercept or an extrapolate

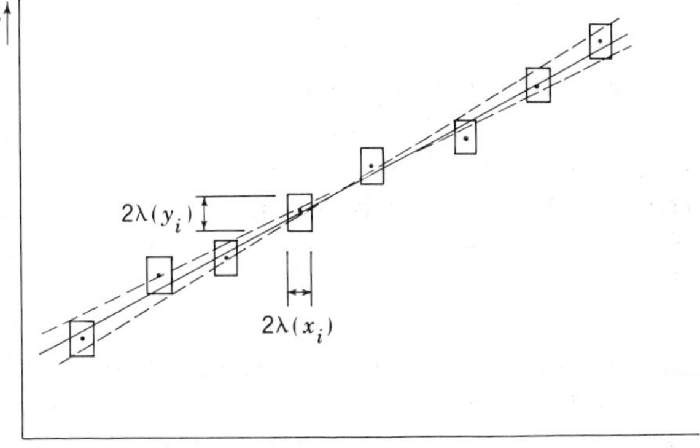

FIG. 3. A graphical method of determining the limit of error in a slope.

intercept that is the quantity of interest.) Where there are a half dozen or more experimental points, it may be justifiable to neglect partially or completely one or more obviously "bad" points in drawing the original straight line and the limiting lines, provided that good judgment is exercised. The difference between the two slopes or intercepts of the limiting lines can be taken as an estimate of twice the limit of error in the slope or intercept of the best straight line.

Where the number of points is sufficiently large, the limits of error of the position of plotted points can be inferred from their scatter. Thus, an upper bound and a lower bound can be drawn, and the lines of limiting slope drawn so as to lie within these bounds. Alternatively, the theory of least squares can be applied not only to yield the equation for the best straight line but also to estimate the uncertainties in the parameters entering into the equation;[3] this is beyond the scope of this book. In either case, the possibility of systematic error should be kept in mind.

Significant Figures. The final result should be reported with the estimated uncertainty and the proper units. The uncertainty may be a limit of error, standard error, or probable error; it is important to indicate which, in order to avoid possible confusion. A "$\pm$" sign without further explanation is generally understood to indicate a limit of error.

The number of "significant figures" to be retained in the reported result will depend upon the uncertainty. Normally, enough digits should be given so that the last one to the right is largely uncertain (by 3 or more) and the next to the last may be slightly uncertain (by as much as 3); that is, the number of digits given should be such that the limit of error is in the range 3 to 30 in the last two digits. The uncertainty figure should be expressed in the same units as the result to which it applies, and the last digit of the uncertainty figure should correspond to that of the digit to which it applies. Examples:

$$8.412 \pm 0.008 \text{ cal deg}^{-1} \text{ mole}^{-1}$$
$$(2.6101 \pm 0.0022) \times 10^4 \text{ cm}^{-1}$$
$$0.00522 \pm 0.00005 \text{ sec}^{-1}$$

FUNDAMENTAL LIMITATIONS ON INSTRUMENTAL PRECISION

In all experiments given in this book the precision of the measurements is governed by practical limitations of apparatus construction and operation; the precision is presumably capable of being increased by further refinement of the apparatus or of the technique for using it, and it might well be imagined that there is no limit to the possible improvement. However, there are certain definite limitations imposed by physics, and although these limitations are not likely to be encountered by the beginning laboratory student, it is well that he should be aware of them.[6]

Limitations Due to Thermal Agitation. The classical law of equipartition of energy states that every degree of freedom of a system has an average kinetic energy equal to $kT/2$, where k is Boltzmann's constant. The student is accustomed to thinking of this amount of energy (about 2×10^{-14} erg at room temperature) as being of significance only for individual atoms or molecules or at most for microscopic particles undergoing Brownian motion. However, Brownian motion may be observable in systems as large as laboratory galvanometers and may even result in a practical limit in their precision. It can be shown[6] that the rms fluctuation of scale reading in a *critically damped* galvanometer is

$$\begin{aligned} x_{\text{rms}} &= (\overline{x^2})^{1/2} = (\overline{V^2})^{1/2}\frac{1}{S_V} = (\overline{i^2})^{1/2}\frac{1}{S_i} \\ &= \left(\frac{\pi kTR}{\tau}\right)^{1/2}\frac{1}{S_V} = \left(\frac{\pi kT}{R\tau}\right)^{1/2}\frac{1}{S_i} \end{aligned} \tag{56}$$

where R is the total resistance of the circuit (system plus external critical damping), τ is the period of the *undamped* galvanometer, and S_V and S_i are, respectively, the voltage and current sensitivities of the galvanometer (expressed as voltage or current per unit deflection). If the units used are volts, amperes, ohms, and seconds, k must be given in joules per degree per molecule (1.38×10^{-23}). For the galvanometers listed in Table XV-1, as ordinarily used, the thermal fluctuations are too small to detect (being at most of the order of a few microns on the scale). For exceedingly sensitive galvanometers used with long light paths, these fluctuations are observable and must be dealt with.

This limitation applies to a single measurement and can be overcome to some degree by making many measurements and taking the mean or by observing the mean position of the galvanometer light beam over a long period of time, provided the conditions of measurement do not change during that time. However, as in cases discussed earlier, the improvement in precision varies as the square root of the number of measurements and is therefore severely limited in practice.

Analogous "thermal noise" exists in purely electrical circuits and becomes important when exceedingly weak signals (e.g., radio signals) must be amplified.

Limitations Due to Particulate Nature. An important limitation sometimes encountered is due to the particulate nature of electricity (electrons, ions) and radiation (photons, etc.). Certain noises in vacuum tube and transistor circuits result from the discrete nature of the current carrier. An example is "shot noise," which results from statistical fluctuations in the space charge around the cathode of a vacuum tube.

The measurement of radiation intensities (see Chap. XVIII) is in certain cases (e.g., X rays) performed by counting particles or photons one at a time. The number N counted in a time interval of given magnitude is subject to statistical fluctuations; a count of N is subject to a standard error given by

$$\sigma = \sqrt{N} \tag{57}$$

The only way of overcoming limitations imposed by the particulate nature of electricity and radiation is to scale up the experiment in physical size, time span, or intensity. Doubling the source intensity in an X-ray experiment or doubling the counting time will (on the average) result in the number of counts being doubled, while the standard error is increased by a factor of $\sqrt{2}$ and the relative error is decreased in the same proportion. To improve the relative precision by a factor of 10 requires a scale-up factor of 100; again the square-root relationship imposes a severe limitation to improvement of precision.

Limitations Due to the Uncertainty Principle of Quantum Mechanics. According to quantum mechanics one cannot simultaneously measure (or define) both of two conjugate variables (position and momentum, or energy and time) to infinite precision; the product of the two standard errors may not be less than $h/2\pi$, where h is Planck's constant (6.64×10^{-27} erg sec). For instance, the energy of an excited state of an atom relative to the ground state, as determined by the wavelength of an emitted photon, is somewhat uncertain because the lifetime of the excited state is limited by collisions or other perturbations, if not by the finite probability of spontaneous emission. The uncertainty principle applies to the results of any *one* experiment comprising a pair of simultaneous measurements, as if in the example cited a single photon were to enter a very high resolution spectrograph and expose a single grain in the emulsion, the position of which could be accurately measured with a microscope comparator to obtain the wavelength. As in the case of thermal fluctuations the precision can be improved by repeating the experiment if one can be sure that the repeated experiments are made with the same system or with identical systems under the same conditions. A spectral "line" on a photographic plate normally contains the results of an extremely large number of "experiments" of the kind described above—so large, in fact, that the square-root relation between precision and number of measurements seldom provides a severe limitation. Thus, although the uncertainty principle may largely determine the width of a spectral line, its center can often be found to a small fraction of that width.

Although real examples in which the precision of a physical measurement is materially and primarily limited by the uncertainty principle are somewhat hard to find, outside particle physics at any rate, this principle should be kept in mind as a potential limiting factor in future experiments.

REFERENCES

1. E. Whittaker and G. Robinson, "The Calculus of Observations," 4th ed., chap. VIII, pp. 164ff., Blackie, Glasgow (1949).
2. *Ibid.*, chap. XI, pp. 285ff.; pp. 92ff.
3. A. G. Worthing and J. Geffner, "Treatment of Experimental Data," p. 17, Wiley, New York (1943).
4. *Ibid.*, pp. 94ff.
5. E. Whittaker and G. Robinson, *op. cit.*
6. H. J. J. Braddick, "The Physics of the Experimental Method," chap. IX, Chapman and Hall, London (1956).

GENERAL READING

E. Whittaker and G. Robinson, *op. cit.*

A. G. Worthing and J. Geffner, *op. cit.*

W. M. Smart, "Combination of Observations," Cambridge Univ. Press, New York (1958).

III

GASES

EXPERIMENTS

1. Gas Thermometry
2. Vapor Density and Molecular Weight
3. Joule-Thomson Effect
4. Heat-capacity Ratios for Gases

Experiment 1. Gas Thermometry

A fundamental attribute of temperature is that for any body in a state of equilibrium the temperature may be expressed by a number on a *temperature scale,* defined without particular reference to that body. The applicability of a universal temperature scale to all physical bodies at equilibrium is a consequence of an empirical law (sometimes called the "zeroth law of thermodynamics"), which states that, if a body is in thermal equilibrium separately with each of two other bodies, these two will be also in thermal equilibrium with each other.

However, a temperature scale must be somehow defined, in order that each attainable temperature shall have a unique numerical value. A temperature scale may be defined over a certain range by the readings of a *thermometer*, which is a body possessing some easily measurable physical property that is for all practical purposes a sensitive function of the temperature alone. The specific volume of a fluid, the electrical resistivity of a metal, and the thermoelectric potential at the junction of a pair of different metals are examples of properties frequently used. Since these properties can be much more easily and precisely measured on a relative basis than on an absolute one, it is convenient to base a temperature scale, in large part, on certain reproducible "fixed points" defined by systems whose temperatures are fixed by nature. Examples of these are the triple point of water (the temperature at which ice, liquid water, and water vapor coexist in equilibrium) and the melting or boiling points of various pure substances under 1 atm pressure. Once the temperature has been fixed at one or more points, the temperatures at other points in the range of the thermometer can be defined in terms of the value of the physical property concerned. Thus, the thermometer may serve as a device for interpolating among two or more fixed points.

In the familiar centigrade scale of temperature the two fixed points were taken as the "ice point" (temperature at which ice and air-saturated water are in equilibrium under a total pressure of 1 atm), assigned a value of 0°C, and the "steam point" (temperature at which pure water and water vapor are in equilibrium under a pressure of 1 atm), assigned a value of 100°C. A mercury thermometer with a capillary of uniform bore could be marked at 0 and at 100° on the capillary stem by use of these fixed points, and the intervening range could then be marked off into 100 equal subdivisions. It is important to recognize that the scale thus defined is not identical with one similarly defined with alcohol (for example) as the thermometric fluid; in general, the two thermometers would give different readings at the same temperature.

Thus any one physical property of any arbitrarily specified substance would seem to define a temperature scale of a rather arbitrary kind. It would seem clearly preferable to define the temperature on the basis of some fundamental law. In the middle of the nineteenth century, Clausius and Kelvin stated the second law of thermodynamics and proposed the *thermodynamic temperature scale,* which is based on that law.[1] This scale is fixed at its lower end at the absolute zero of temperature. A scale factor, corresponding to the size of the degree, must be specified to complete the definition of the temperature scale; this can be accomplished by specifying the numerical value of the temperature of a reproducible fixed point or by specifying the numerical width of the interval between two fixed points. Kelvin adopted the latter procedure in order to make the degree coincide with the (mean) centigrade degree; accordingly, the interval between the ice point and the steam point was fixed as 100°, and the absolute (or Kelvin) temperature of the ice point has been found by experiment to be approximately 273.15°. However, by recent international agreement (1948, 1954) the former procedure was substituted: The triple point of pure water is now defined as exactly 273.16°K (degrees Kelvin) and as exactly 0.01°C (degrees Celsius). The relation of the Celsius (formerly centigrade) temperature t to the Kelvin (or absolute) temperature T is†

$$t \equiv T - 273.15 \tag{1}$$

Practical difficulties arise in making very precise determinations of temperature on the thermodynamic scale; the precision of the more refined thermometric techniques considerably exceeds the accuracy with which the experimental thermometer scale may be related to the thermodynamic scale. For this reason, a practical scale known as the *International Temperature Scale* has been devised, with several fixed points and with interpolation formulas based on practical thermometers (e.g., the platinum resistance thermometer between −182.97 and 630.5°C). This scale is intended to correspond as closely as possible to the thermodynamic scale but to permit more precision in the measurement of temperatures. Further details about this scale are given in Chap. XVI.

† The differences between the original and the new Kelvin scales and between the old centigrade and the new thermodynamic Celsius scales are small (on the order of 10^{-3} deg) and of importance only for refined measurements.

METHOD

The establishment of the International Temperature Scale has required that the thermodynamic temperatures of the fixed points be determined with as much accuracy as possible. For this purpose a device was needed that measures essentially the thermodynamic temperature and does not depend on any particular thermometric substance. On the other hand, since it was needed only for a few highly accurate measurements, it did not need to have the convenience of such instruments as resistance thermometers, mercury thermometers, and thermocouples. The device that has filled this need is the *gas thermometer*. It is based on the perfect gas law, expressed by

$$pV = NRT \tag{2}$$

where N is the number of moles, R a universal constant, and T the "perfect-gas" temperature. At ordinary gas densities there are deviations from the perfect-gas law, but it is exact in the limit of zero gas density, where it is applicable to all gases. The "perfect-gas temperature scale" defined by Eq. (2) can be shown by thermodynamics to be identical with a thermodynamic temperature scale,† defined in terms of the second law of thermodynamics.

Gas thermometry measurements must, of course, be made with a real gas at ordinary pressures. However, it is possible to estimate the deviations from perfect-gas behavior and to convert measured pV values to "perfect-gas" pV values. For this purpose a virial equation of state for a real gas is often used:

$$\frac{p\tilde{V}}{RT} = 1 + \frac{B}{\tilde{V}} + \frac{C}{\tilde{V}^2} + \cdots \tag{3}$$

where B, C, . . . are known as the second, third, . . . *virial coefficients* and $\tilde{V}$ is the molal volume of the gas at p and T. At ordinary pressures the series converges rapidly, and for many purposes terms beyond the one containing B can be neglected. Values of second (and in some cases, third and fourth) virial coefficients are known over a wide range of temperatures from gas compressibility measurements; these values of B are useful in correcting the readings of a gas thermometer.

The establishment of the International Temperature Scale has been accomplished largely with the aid of measurements made with the helium gas thermometer. Some of the most significant work was done by Beattie and coworkers.[2]

The most precise gas thermometry method is the constant-volume method, in which a definite quantity of the gas is confined in a bulb of constant volume V at the temperature T to be determined and the pressure p of the gas is measured. A problem is encountered, however, in measuring the pressure, which is usually done with a mercury manometer operating at room temperature; a way must be found to communicate between the bulb and the manometer. This is usually accomplished by connecting the bulb to the room-temperature part of the system by a slender tube and allowing a portion of the gas to occupy a relatively small, constant "dead-space" volume at room temperature. The pressure in the manometer system is then equalized to the gas pressure in this dead space by a null device, represented in the apparatus of the present experiment by the null manometer.

† The perfect-gas properties required for this identity are: (1) Boyle's law is obeyed: $p\tilde{V} = f(T)$; and (2) the internal energy per mole is a function of temperature only: $\tilde{E} = g(T)$.

THEORY

The number of moles of gas N in the bulb of volume V at temperature T and in the dead space of volume v at room temperature is constant. Assuming the perfect-gas law, we have

$$\frac{pV}{RT} + \frac{pv}{RT_r} = N \tag{4}$$

where T_r is room temperature. The small region of large temperature gradient actually existing between the bulb and the dead space is replaced, without appreciable error, by a sharp division between two uniform temperatures T and T_r. Since the second term is small in comparison with the first, we shall introduce only a very small error ($\sim$0.05 per cent with the present apparatus) by making the substitution

$$T_r = \frac{p_r}{p} T \tag{5}$$

where p_r is the pressure measured by the manometer when the bulb is at room temperature. We then obtain

$$\frac{pV}{RT}\left(1 + \frac{pv}{p_r V}\right) = N \tag{6}$$

Since only the pressure is being measured directly, the volume V must remain constant or else vary in a known way with the temperature (and pressure). If α is the coefficient of linear thermal expansion of the material from which the bulb is constructed, the coefficient of volume expansion is 3α. If this is assumed constant with temperature, we can write

$$\frac{pV_0}{RT}\left(1 + \frac{pv}{p_r V} + 3\alpha t\right) = N \tag{7}$$

where V_0 is the bulb volume at 0° Celsius and t is the Celsius temperature of the gas thermometer bulb. For very precise work other variables, including the dependence of the bulb volume on the difference between internal and external pressure, must be taken into account. To the precision of the present experiment, this effect of pressure is inconsequential.

Finally, if we allow for gas imperfections by including the second virial term, we can write

$$\frac{pV_0}{RT}\left(1 + \frac{pv}{p_r V} + 3\alpha t - \frac{B}{\tilde{V}}\right) = N \tag{8}$$

where

$$\frac{1}{\tilde{V}} = \frac{N}{V} \cong \frac{p_0}{RT_0} \tag{9}$$

and p_0 and T_0 are the values of p and T at (say) the ice point.

The above equations contain approximations that are acceptable for the present experiment. For precise work a much more detailed treatment is required.[2]

EXPERIMENTAL

The object of the experiment described below is to set up a gas thermometer, calibrate it at the ice point (in lieu of the experimentally more difficult triple point), and use it to determine the temperatures of one or more other fixed points. These may include the steam point, the boiling point of liquid nitrogen (in lieu of liquid oxygen, which is more difficult to obtain and more hazardous to use), the sublimation temperature of solid carbon dioxide (Dry Ice), the transition temperature of sodium sulfate decahydrate to the monohydrate and saturated solution, etc. The experiment will be performed with an apparatus which resembles in principle a research gas thermometer but is very much simpler and somewhat less precise. The apparatus is shown in Fig. 1.

Gas thermometer bulb *a*. This is a Pyrex bulb with a volume V of about 100 ml, with an attached glass capillary passing through a large rubber stopper. The upper end of this capillary tube is connected, by a length of flexible stainless-steel capillary tubing, to the null manometer.

Null manometer *b*. When the mercury surfaces in the two arms are at the same level, the pressure in the bulb is equal to that in the rest of the system, including the manometer *d*; moreover, the "dead-space" volume v then has a fixed value. This dead space is the volume of gas at temperature T_r between the top of the bulb and the mercury in the left arm. The upper part of each arm consists of a long capillary tube. This design prevents loss of mercury in the event of any accidentally large pressure difference across the null manometer. The two arms are connected at the top by a capillary stopcock, which can be opened to admit or remove

FIG. 1. Gas thermometry apparatus.

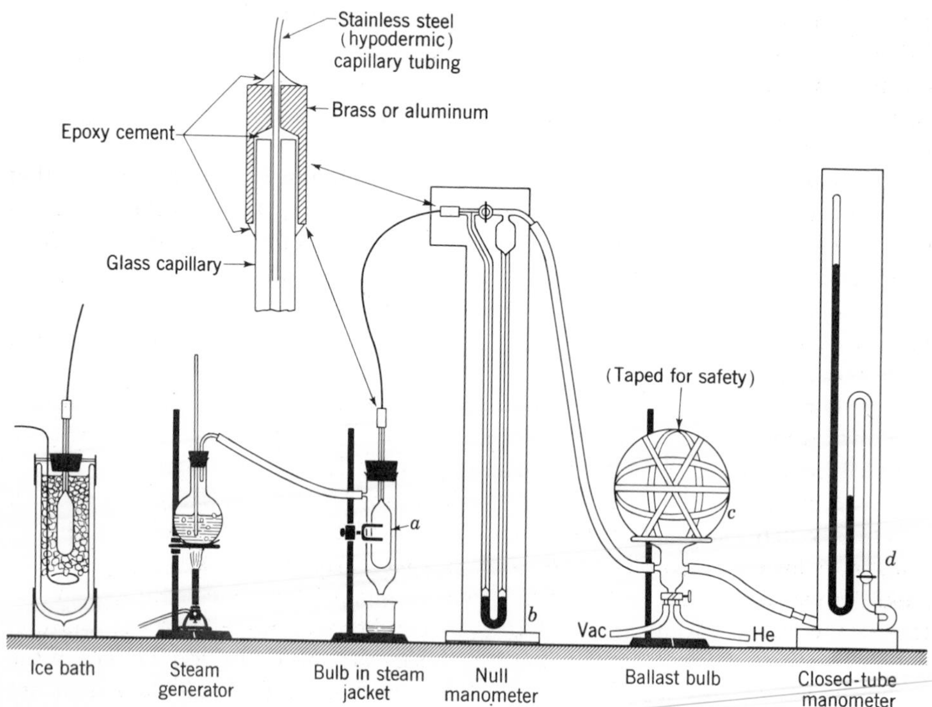

gas from the bulb. During measurements this stopcock is kept closed, and the quantity of gas in the bulb and dead space is thereby fixed.

Ballast bulb *c*. This is a bulb of large volume (at least 5 liters) which permits small adjustments in pressure to be made by the addition or removal of small quantities of gas or air through the three-way stopcock at the bottom. One of the two lower arms of this stopcock is connected to the source of gas to be used (or to room air); the other is connected to a laboratory vacuum line, an aspirator, or a vacuum pump.

Closed-tube mercury manometer *d*. This is the instrument used for the measurement of gas pressures in this experiment. The space in the closed arm is evacuated, so the difference between the two mercury levels is a direct measure of the pressure of the gas in the other arm. For precise work, the temperature of the manometer should be determined and the manometer readings corrected (to 0°C) for the differential expansion of the mercury and the scale; however, in this experiment, if the ambient temperature is reasonably constant, the corrections should ultimately cancel out and may be omitted.

The gas thermometer bulb is first filled with the gas to be used, preferably helium or nitrogen (free of water contamination). With the stopcock on the null manometer open, the entire system is evacuated and then filled to the desired pressure with the gas. If complete evacuation is not possible (as is the case when an aspirator or a laboratory vacuum line is used), the filling must be done several times, with a delay of 1 or 2 min between each repetition to allow for diffusive mixing. When the bulb has been filled with the gas to the desired pressure, the stopcock on the null manometer is closed. After this point any gas, including air, may be allowed in the ballast bulb and manometer.

When a temperature is being measured with the thermometer, gas or air is removed from or admitted to the ballast bulb until the null manometer is balanced. When it is evident that equilibrium has been attained and the null manometer is precisely balanced, the closed-tube manometer levels are read and recorded. It is suggested that four readings be taken, alternatively bringing the pressure to the null value from above and below.

Procedure. Assemble the apparatus as indicated in Fig. 1. Make sure that the stopcock on the null manometer is properly greased. Then fill the apparatus with the gas to be used, as described above. At the final filling, adjust the pressure to about 60 cm Hg, and after 1 or 2 min close the null-manometer stopcock. After drift has ceased, make a reading with the bulb at room temperature. The difference between the two manometer levels is then the pressure of gas in the bulb at room temperature, p_r.

To check for possible leaks, it is advisable to restore the ballast bulb to atmospheric pressure for 10 or 15 min and then reduce the pressure so as to rebalance the null manometer. If p_r has increased significantly, a leak should be suspected.

Ice point: In the Dewar flask, prepare a "slushy" mixture of finely shaved clean ice and distilled water. This should be fluid enough to permit the gas thermometer bulb to be lowered into place and to allow a metal ring stirrer to be operated but should have sufficient ice to maintain two-phase equilibrium over the entire surface of the bulb. Mount the bulb in place, and commence stirring the mixture, moving the stirrer slowly up and down from the very top to the very bottom of the Dewar flask. Do not force the stirrer, since the bulb and its capillary stem are fragile. After equilibrium is achieved, take the ice-point pressure readings and record p_0.

Steam point: While the ice-point readings are being made, the water in the steam generator should be heated to boiling. When ready, the gas thermometer bulb should be positioned in the steam jacket so that it does not touch the wall at any point. Steam should be passed through the jacket at a rate slow enough to avoid overpressure in the jacket; steam should emerge from the bottom at low velocity. The rubber tubing connecting the steam generator to the steam jacket should run downhill all the way to permit steady drainage of any water condensed in the tubing. When drift ceases, the steam-point readings may be taken.

Repeat the ice-point measurements. The results should agree with those obtained previously to within experimental error; if the differences are larger, a leak must be suspected.

Measure the other fixed points assigned. If liquid nitrogen is used, insert the bulb into the Dewar slowly to prevent violent boiling and excessive loss of liquid.

If time permits, refill the gas thermometer bulb with another gas or reduce p_r to 30 cm and repeat some or all of the above measurements. During the steam-point measurements, record the barometric pressure. (The barometer reading must be corrected for temperature. A discussion of the use of precision barometers is given in Chap. XVIII, and the necessary corrections are given in Appendix B.)

Also record the values of V and v for the apparatus used in the experiment.

CALCULATIONS

Equation (8) can be written in the form

$$T = Ap \tag{10}$$

where the proportionality factor

$$A = \frac{V_0}{NR}\left(1 + \frac{pv}{p_r V} + 3\alpha t - \frac{B}{\tilde{V}}\right) \tag{11}$$

is nearly constant with temperature; but for the precision attainable with this experiment, the proportionality factor should be evaluated at each temperature. Making use of the known thermodynamic temperature of the ice point, we can write

$$T = \frac{273.15}{p_0} \frac{A}{A_0} p \tag{12}$$

$$\frac{A}{A_0} = 1 + \frac{p - p_0}{p_r} \frac{v}{V} + 3\alpha t - \frac{1}{\tilde{V}}(B - B_0) \tag{13}$$

where p_0, A_0, and B_0 pertain to the ice point. Since the last two terms depend on the temperature, an approximate value of the temperature must be known before they can be evaluated; this can be obtained by setting A/A_0 equal to unity in Eq. (12). For Pyrex glass, $\alpha = 3.2 \times 10^{-6}$ deg^{-1}. Second virial coefficients for various gases are given in Table 1, and $\tilde{V}$ can be calculated from Eq. (9).

The student should report the temperature determined for each fixed point on both the Kelvin and Celsius scales. In cases where the temperature is a boiling point or sublimation point, calculate and report also the temperature on both scales corrected to a pressure of 1 atm. In the neighborhood of 1 atm, the boiling point

TABLE 1. Second Virial Coefficients
(in cm^3 $mole^{-1}$)

t, °C	He^a	A^a	$N_2^{b,c}$	CO_2^b
−250	~0			
−200	+10.4			
−150	11.4			
−100	11.7	−64.3	−51.9	
−50	11.9	−37.4	−26.4	
0	11.8	−21.5	−10.4	−154
50	11.6	−11.2	−0.4	−103
100	11.4	−4.2	+6.3	−73
150	11.0	+1.1	11.9	−51

[a] J. A. Beattie, private communication.
[b] W. Thomas, *Z. Physik,* **147,** 92 (1957).
[c] J. Otto, *Hand. d. Exp. Physik,* **8,** 2 (1929).

of water increases 0.037° per mm Hg increase in pressure. For liquid nitrogen, the increase is 0.013° per millimeter.

DISCUSSION

What property of helium makes it particularly suitable for gas thermometry over the temperature range covered by this experiment? Is the correction for gas imperfection in this experiment of significant magnitude in relation to the experimental uncertainty? If not, by how much must the precision of the pressure measurements be improved before gas imperfection corrections become significant? How does this depend on the choice of gas to be used?

APPARATUS

Closed-tube manometer; null manometer; properly taped and mounted ballast bulb; heavy-wall pressure tubing; Dewar flask; large ring stirrer; notched cover plate for Dewar with hole for mounting gas thermometer bulb; bunsen burner; steam generator with rubber connecting tubing; steam jacket; two ring stands; ring clamp and iron gauze; two clamp holders; one large and one medium clamp.

Cylinder of helium or dry nitrogen; pure ice (3 lb); ice grinder; liquid nitrogen (1 liter); boiling chips; stopcock grease; vacuum pump or water aspirator.

REFERENCES

1. W. J. Moore, "Physical Chemistry," 2d ed., pp. 51ff., Prentice-Hall, Englewood Cliffs, N.J. (1955).
2. J. A. Beattie and coworkers, *Proc. Am. Acad. Arts Sci.,* **74,** 327 (1941); **27,** 255 (1949).

GENERAL READING

C. O. Fairchild, "Thermometry," Encyclopaedia Britannica, vol. 22, p. 110 (1959).
"Temperature: Its Measurement and Control in Science and Industry," vol. 1, Reinhold, New York (1941); vol. 2 (1955).

Experiment 2. Vapor Density and Molecular Weight

Avogadro's hypothesis states that equal volumes of different gases at the same temperature and pressure contain the same number of molecules. It thus implies that R is a universal constant in the perfect-gas equation

$$pV = NRT \tag{1}$$

in which N is the number of moles. As mentioned in Exp. 1 on gas thermometry, Eq. (1) is obeyed only approximately by real gases and vapors at ordinary pressures and temperatures but is an exact description in the limit of zero gas pressure or density. Within this limitation, Avogadro's hypothesis has withstood experimental tests for a century and a half and has long since been accepted as an important natural law.

At ordinary pressures and temperatures, the gas law holds well enough to serve as a means of calculating an approximate molecular weight M of a gas or a vapor from its measured density:

$$pV = \frac{g}{M}RT \qquad M = \frac{g}{V}\frac{RT}{p} = \rho\frac{RT}{p} \tag{2}$$

where ρ is the vapor density. The precise molecular weight can then be deduced from the formula weight if the empirical formula of the gas is known from chemical analysis. The importance of this means of molecular-weight determination is chiefly historical, since volatile substances are now rarely encountered for which the molecular weights are not already known or else determinable by superior methods. However, the important position occupied by Avogadro's law in the development of the kinetic-molecular theory of gases perhaps recommends its laboratory demonstration by one of the methods described here.

A. Dumas Method

This is the most direct method of vapor-density determination, although a difficult one with which to achieve high precision. It consists of filling a glass bulb with the vapor, sealing it off at a known, convenient temperature and pressure, and weighing it. The volume of the bulb is determined by filling it with water and reweighing. The weight of the empty bulb is also required; if the bulb is weighed containing air rather than a vacuum, the air density must be known. The method described below is appropriate to the vapor of a volatile liquid; with modifications it can be applied to permanent gases.

EXPERIMENTAL

For each determination, one Dumas bulb of about 200 ml volume is required (Fig. 1). If such bulbs are not provided ready for use, make them from long-neck Florence flasks by thickening and drawing down the neck with a flame (a bunsen or Meker flame for soft glass or a gas-oxygen flame for Pyrex) to yield a long capillary neck with a diameter of about 1 mm. Then scratch lightly with a sharp file

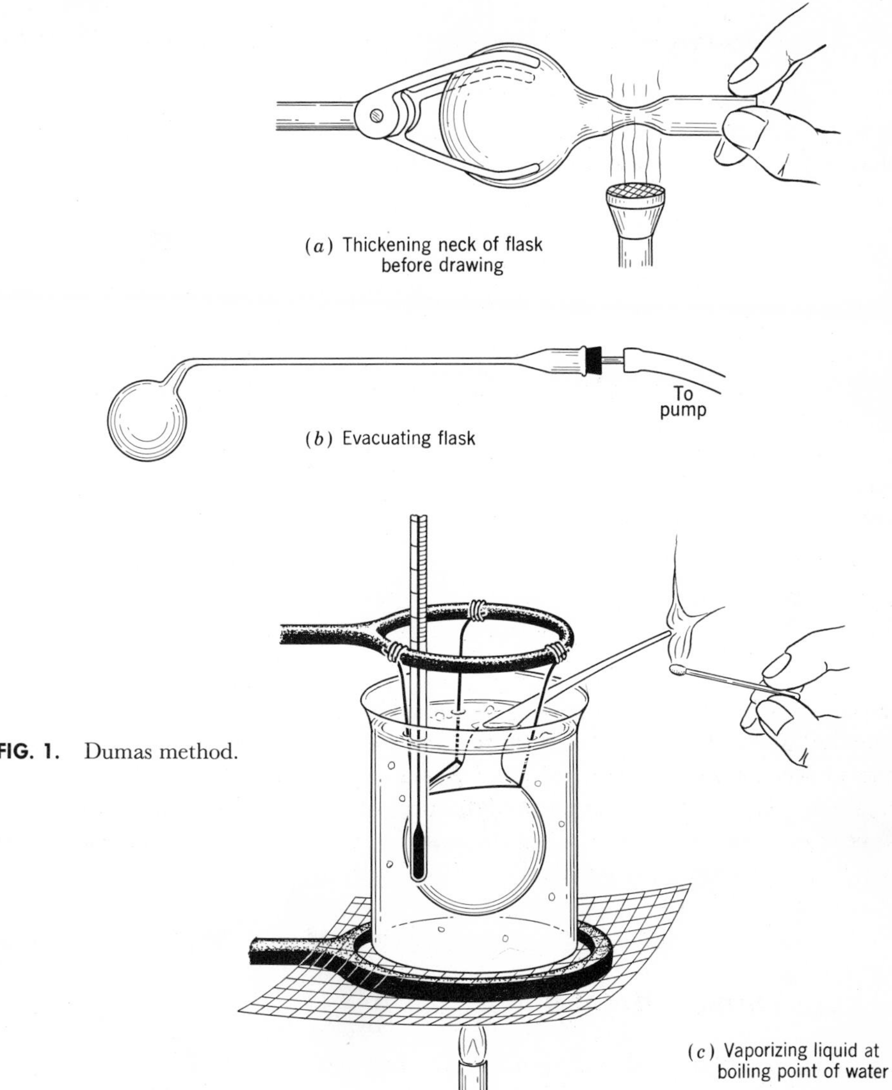

FIG. 1. Dumas method.

and break off the capillary to a convenient length, say 6 to 8 cm. During the drawing process the neck should be bent, at the point of constriction, to an angle of about 120°. The empty bulb should be weighed carefully to within 1 mg on an analytical balance.

If the bulbs are to be made rather than purchased, provision can conveniently be made for weighing them in an evacuated condition. The neck is drawn down as above, but not broken off. The mouth end of the original neck is then fitted with a one-hole rubber stopper and short glass tube, which is connected to a mechanical vacuum pump with a length of pressure tubing. After evacuating as well as possible (this can often be judged from the sound made by the mechanical pump), the capillary is sealed off at a point 8 to 10 cm from the bulb. The sealing should be done very cautiously with a small, cool flame to keep the thin glass from "sucking in." After the flask has cooled, it is carefully weighed. The tip can then be scratched and broken off as above, and air allowed to enter. The glass tip which was broken off must be saved and weighed with the flask in all subsequent weighings. With some ingenuity and the use of sealing wax, a commercial bulb can also be attached to a pump, evacuated, and sealed off.

The liquid to be studied should have a boiling point well above room temperature but below 100°C. A small quantity of the liquid is introduced by warming the bulb gently over a burner flame and then introducing the neck into the liquid; as the bulb cools, liquid is drawn into the bulb. Enough should be introduced to fill 2 to 5 per cent of the bulb volume.

The bulb is then positioned in a beaker of water so that only the neck protrudes from the water. To hold the bulb under water, a suitably bent crucible triangle can be slipped over the neck and held down by a small ring attached to a ring stand. To measure the temperature of the water, a thermometer should be clamped with its bulb at the side of the flask. Alternatively, the temperature of the water bath can be calculated from the measured barometric pressure. Boiling chips can be added to prevent bumping. The water is brought rapidly to a boil. Once the water is boiling, the flame should be reduced to the minimum required for steady boiling. The liquid in the bulb should vaporize completely, and the vapor should expel the air from the bulb. (The stream of vapor can be detected with a lighted match *provided the liquid is not flammable* or by its effect on the fumes from a glass rod dipped in concentrated hydrochloric acid and held near the open mouth of a small bottle containing concentrated ammonium hydroxide.) When vapor no longer streams from the opening, the entire neck should be cautiously warmed with a small burner flame to vaporize any condensed liquid droplets. Then the neck should be carefully heated with a small burner flame a few centimeters from the end until it collapses. The tip should be drawn off and carefully saved. The bulb should be cooled, dried, and weighed together with the drawn-off tip(s).

To determine the volume, as well as to check whether all the air was expelled by the vapor, the tip of the bulb is then broken below the surface of water (preferably water that has been boiled to drive off dissolved air) so that the bulb fills with water. The filling should be substantially complete; if an empty space more than 2 or 3 per cent of the bulb volume remains, the run should be rejected. The filled bulb together with broken-off tips should be weighed to 0.1 g. At least two complete runs should be made. Record the ambient temperature. If the "empty" bulb has been weighed with air in it, the barometric pressure and if possible the humidity should also be recorded.

CALCULATIONS

The density of dry air under standard conditions (0°C, 1 atm) is 0.001293 g cm^{-3}. The density at the temperature and pressure prevailing in the laboratory can be estimated with the perfect-gas law. Air density is slightly dependent on humidity, and it may be advisable to make a correction for this by taking the molecular weights of dry air and of water vapor to be respectively 28.8 and 18.0 and using the perfect-gas law. However, if room humidity has changed since the neck was drawn, one cannot be certain that the humidity in the bulb is the same as the room humidity, since gas diffusion through the neck is slow. The weight of the air in the bulb can then be calculated and subtracted from the weight of the bulb containing air to yield the weight of the empty bulb. All weights are uncorrected for the buoyant effect of room air *external* to the bulb; corrections for this buoyancy are not necessary.

From the difference of the weights of the bulb empty and filled with vapor, the weight of the vapor can be obtained. Using the known density of water at the appropriate temperature, calculate the volume of the bulb. The density of the vapor at the boiling temperature of water can then be obtained. By use of Eq. (2) the molecular weight of the vapor can be calculated.

From the weight composition of the volatile liquid (e.g., as given by microanalysis), its empirical formula can be derived and its formula weight obtained. On the assumption that the liquid is not associated or dissociated in its vapor state, the number of empirical formula weights in one molecular weight may be taken as the integer nearest to the ratio of the experimental molecular weight to the empirical formula weight. The true molecular formula and molecular weight should be reported.

DISCUSSION

The student should consider how the air buoyancy effect in weighing should be defined and why it is not necessary in this experiment to make corrections for it. Factors limiting the precision of the experiment should also be discussed.

B. Victor-Meyer Method

The Victor-Meyer method of vapor-density measurement is ordinarily capable of higher precision than the Dumas method but requires more elaborate apparatus. It consists of volatilizing a weighed sample of a liquid and measuring, with a gas burette, the volume of air at known temperature and pressure that is displaced by the vapor.

The apparatus is shown in Fig. 2. The liquid sample is sealed in a glass bulb with a fragile tip, which can be broken inside a chamber surrounded by a steam jacket whereupon the liquid (which should have a boiling point below 100°C) volatilizes completely. Connected to the chamber is a vertical tube tall enough to prevent the vapor, which should be denser than air, from diffusing to any significant extent to the top of the tube where the connection is made to a gas burette. The gas burette contains water as the indicating liquid and has associated with it a side tube of the same diameter open to the atmosphere. A leveling bulb permits equalization of the pressure inside and outside the apparatus before each reading of the burette.

Since the pressure, temperature, and volume inside the heated chamber are the same before and after the bulb is broken, the number of moles of gas (air or air plus vapor) in the chamber is essentially the same before and after volatilization, by Avogadro's law. The volume occupied by the liquid before volatilization is assumed to be negligible. Thus, a quantity of air, equal in number of moles to the quantity of liquid volatilized, is expelled into the gas burette.

EXPERIMENTAL

The apparatus should be assembled as in Figs. 2 and 3. As much space as possible should be left between the gas burette and the rest of the apparatus to minimize temperature variations in the neighborhood of the gas burette. Before the brass tube is fastened in place with copper wire as shown in Fig. 3, it should be positioned so that its bottom end is about 35 mm from the bottom of the inner chamber. The flushing hose should be connected to the vacuum line only when necessary for flushing between runs.

The sample bulb should be made of 3-mm soft-glass tubing (about 1.6 mm i.d.). It should be sealed and rounded at one end and drawn down to a 0.5-mm capillary at the other. The main body of the bulb should be 45 mm long, and the capillary should be bent at an angle of 120° about 10 mm from the body of the bulb.

The bulb is weighed empty to 0.1 mg and is then filled with the sample liquid by first warming it in a flame and immersing the capillary tip in the liquid. The first liquid drawn in is shaken down to the closed end, and the bulb again warmed gently. The vapor should expel most of the air, and when the bulb is again immersed, it should fill almost completely. It is desired to have an amount of liquid which will give a vapor volume of 20 to 40 ml. For carbon tetrachloride, the filled portion should be about 35 mm long; for ethyl acetate, the bulb should be substantially filled.

After the bulb has been filled to the desired level, it is sealed off carefully with a microburner 1 or 2 mm from the 120° bend, so as to leave a bent tip. It is then

FIG. 2. Victor-Meyer method.

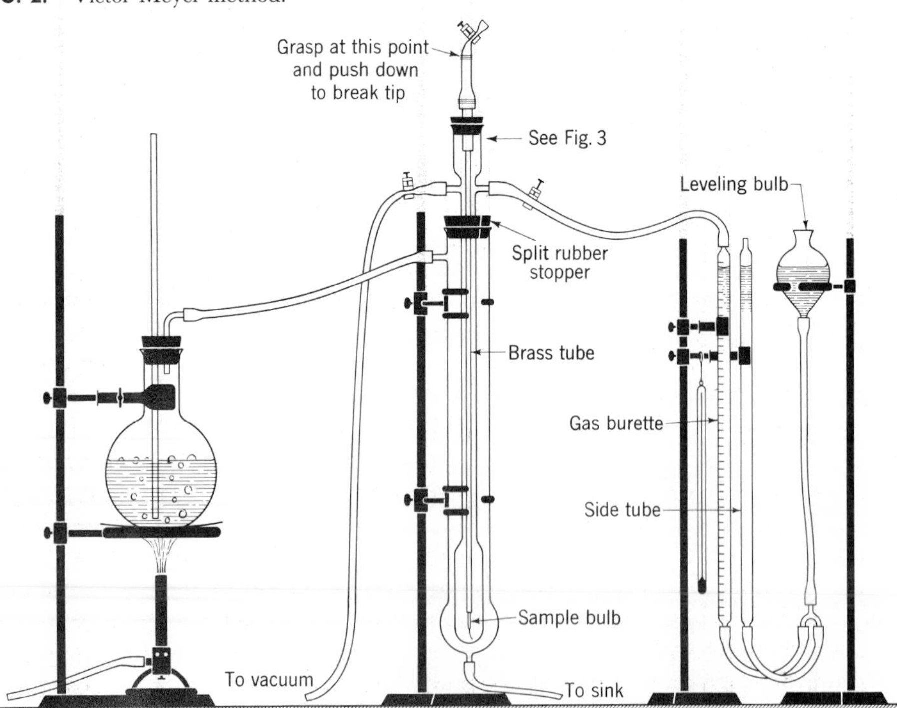

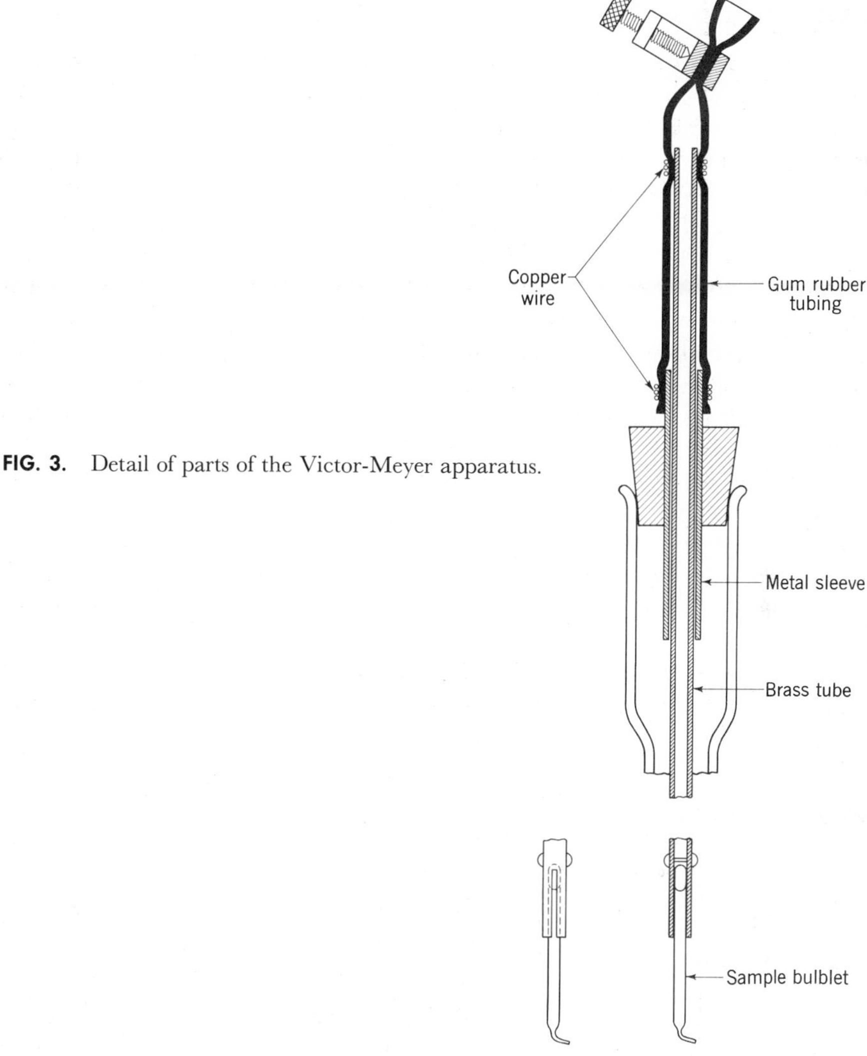

FIG. 3. Detail of parts of the Victor-Meyer apparatus.

weighed to 0.1 mg together with the remaining glass capillary; the difference of the two weighings gives the weight of the liquid.

The brass tube is now removed from the apparatus by detaching the rubber stopper from the top of the inner tube. The bulb is fitted into place in the lower end, which should be split so as to hold the bulb by friction. A rivet or pin through the brass tube 25 mm from the end provides a stop for the round end of the bulb. Lower the tube carefully into the apparatus, and reseat the rubber stopper.

At this point the screw clamp on the flushing hose should be closed tightly. The uppermost screw clamp and the one on the tube to the gas burette should be open. After steam has passed through the outer jacket and is emerging from the lower end, the leveling bulb is lowered from its highest to its lowest point, allowed to remain there for a minute or two, then raised to its highest point and allowed to remain there a minute; this process should be repeated several times. The purpose of this is to saturate the air in the upper part of the apparatus with water vapor at room temperature in order to avoid a volume increase due to water vaporization in the burette during the run. After the water level has been finally brought to a point near the top of the burette scale, the uppermost clamp is tightened.

The initial burette reading is taken after drift has ceased. Preparatory to taking a reading, the leveling bulb should be raised or lowered so that the water levels in the burette and in the side tube are the same. To test for leaks, the leveling bulb is lowered to its lowest position for a minute or so, then returned and the burette reread.

The tip of the bulb is broken by grasping the flexible connection at the upper wired position and pushing downward. Care should be exercised to see that it is returned to its initial position. As the water level in the burette falls, the leveling bulb should be lowered. When drift ceases (but not later than 1 or 2 min after breaking the bulb), the final burette reading is taken. The temperature in the vicinity of the burette should be recorded also.

To flush out the vapor in preparation for the next run, the screw clamp on the tube to the gas burette is tightened, the uppermost clamp opened, the connection to the vacuum line established, and the clamp on it opened. After the flushing, the brass tube is withdrawn, the broken bulb removed, and the bulb for the next run inserted.

Care should be exercised to prevent liquid water from getting into the inner tube, where it will vaporize and possibly condense later in the gas burette, resulting in loss of gas volume before the final reading.

The barometer should be read during the laboratory period. The reading should be corrected to 0°C for thermal expansion of the mercury and scale (see Appendix B).

At least two runs should be carried out.

CALCULATIONS

The volume of air displaced at 100°C can be calculated from that measured at room temperature by means of the perfect-gas equation. On the assumption that no great amount of mixing of the vapor with air has taken place, this can be assumed to be the volume of vapor at 100°C. (The exact temperature of the steam may deviate from this by a few tenths of a degree, but this is of no real consequence.) The value for the vapor density at 100°C, calculated from this volume and the weight of liquid volatilized, is not affected by gas imperfections other than the relatively small one for air.

The calculation of the molecular weight from the vapor density at 100°C is done with the perfect-gas equation as described for the Dumas method (and is, of course, subject to gas imperfections of the vapor). The use of the molecular weight so determined, to deduce the true molecular formula and precise molecular weight, is as described for the Dumas method.

DISCUSSION

If done with care this experiment gives results sufficiently precise to demonstrate deviations from ideal-gas behavior in the vapors concerned. For substances whose critical temperatures and pressures are known, the gas imperfections can be estimated roughly from Berthelot's equation,[1]

$$pV = NR^*T \tag{3}$$

where
$$R^* = R\left[1 + \frac{9}{128}\frac{p}{p_c}\frac{T_c}{T}\left(1 - 6\frac{T_c^2}{T^2}\right)\right] \tag{4}$$

and where p_c and T_c are the critical pressure and temperature, respectively. The equation corresponding to Eq. (2), yielding an improved molecular weight M^*, is

$$M^* = \rho\frac{R^*T}{p} \tag{5}$$

It is apparent that R^* should be less than R for any substances which might be studied in the present experiment, since T_c cannot be much lower than 373°K and is likely to be considerably higher.

If critical data are available for the liquid studied, one can use Eqs. (4) and (5) to estimate the effect of gas imperfections. (For carbon tetrachloride, for example, $T_c = 556.3$°K, $p_c = 45.0$ atm.)

APPARATUS

Dumas Method. Two Dumas bulbs (~200 ml); sharp triangular file; microburner; bunsen burner; ring stand; ring and gauze; one small and two large beakers; some means for positioning Dumas bulb; 50 to 105°C thermometer with clamp and clamp holder.

Carbon tetrachloride, ethyl acetate, or other liquid to be studied (50 ml); boiled distilled water (1 liter); boiling chips. If the bulb is to be evacuated, glass-blowing facilities and a vacuum pump are required.

Victor-Meyer Method. Victor-Meyer apparatus—steam jacket, inner vaporizer tube, brass plunger tube, rubber stopper with metal sleeve, large split rubber stopper—as shown in Figs. 2 and 3; steam generator; gas burette and side tube; leveling bulb; Y-tube; 0 to 30°C thermometer; three to four soft-glass sample bulblets; microburner; small vial; gum-rubber connecting tubes; three screw clamps; four ring stands; clamps and clamp holders, as required (five); bunsen burner; large ring clamp and gauze; small ring clamp.

Carbon tetrachloride, ethyl acetate, or other liquid to be studied (5 ml); copper wire (No. 18 or other convenient size); millimeter scale; vacuum pump or water aspirator.

REFERENCE

1. S. Glasstone, "Textbook of Physical Chemistry," p. 287, Van Nostrand, Princeton, N.J. (1940).

Experiment 3. Joule-Thomson Effect

The Joule-Thomson effect is a measure of the deviation of the behavior of a real gas from what is defined to be ideal-gas behavior. In this experiment a simple technique for measuring this effect will be applied to a few common gases.

THEORY

An ideal gas may be defined as one for which the following two conditions apply at all temperatures for a definite quantity of the gas: (1) Boyle's law is obeyed; i.e.,

$$pV = f(T)$$

and (2) the internal energy E is independent of volume. Accordingly E is independent of pressure as well, and in the absence of other pertinent variables (due to applied fields) E is therefore a function of the temperature alone:

$$E = g(T)$$

It is apparent that the enthalpy H of an ideal gas is also a function of temperature alone:

$$H \equiv E + pV = h(T)$$

Accordingly we can write for a definite quantity of an ideal gas at all temperatures

$$\left(\frac{\partial E}{\partial V}\right)_T = \left(\frac{\partial E}{\partial p}\right)_T = \left(\frac{\partial H}{\partial V}\right)_T = \left(\frac{\partial H}{\partial p}\right)_T = 0 \tag{1}$$

The absence of any dependence of the internal energy of a gas on volume was suggested by the early experiments of Gay-Lussac and Joule. They found that, when a quantity of gas in a container initially at a given temperature was allowed to expand into another previously evacuated container without work or heat flow to or from the surroundings ($\Delta E = 0$), the final temperature (after the two containers came into equilibrium with each other) was the same as the initial temperature. However, that kind of experiment (known as the Joule experiment) is of limited sensitivity, because the heat capacity of the containers is large in comparison with that of the gases studied. Subsequently Joule and Thomson[1] showed, in a different kind of experiment, that real gases do undergo small temperature changes on free expansion. This experiment utilized continuous gas flow through a porous plug under adiabatic conditions. Because of the continuous gas flow, the solid parts of the apparatus come into thermal equilibrium with the flowing gas and their heat capacities impose a much less serious limitation than in the case of the Joule experiment.

Let it be imagined that gas is flowing slowly from left to right through the porous plug in Fig. 1. To the left of the plug the temperature and pressure of the gas are T_1 and p_1, and to the right of the plug they are T_2 and p_2. The volume of a definite quantity of gas (say 1 mole) is V_1 on the left and V_2 on the right, and the internal energy is E_1 and E_2, respectively. When 1 mole of gas flows through the plug, the work done by the system on the surroundings is

$$w = p_2V_2 - p_1V_1$$

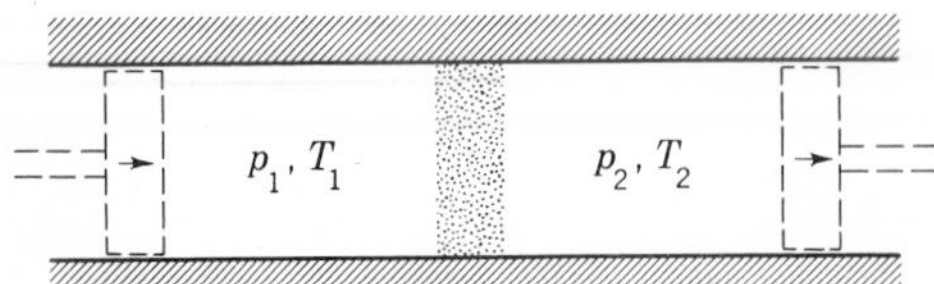

FIG. 1. Schematic diagram of the Joule-Thomson experiment.

Since the process is adiabatic, the change in internal energy is

$$\Delta E = E_2 - E_1 = q - w = -w$$

Combining these two equations we obtain

$$E_1 + p_1V_1 = E_2 + p_2V_2$$

or

$$H_1 = H_2 \tag{2}$$

Thus this process takes place at constant enthalpy.

For a process involving arbitrary infinitesimal changes in pressure and temperature, the change in enthalpy is

$$dH = \left(\frac{\partial H}{\partial p}\right)_T dp + \left(\frac{\partial H}{\partial T}\right)_p dT \tag{3}$$

In the present experiment dH is zero and dT and dp cannot be arbitrary but are related by

$$\mu \equiv \left(\frac{\partial T}{\partial p}\right)_H = -\frac{(\partial H/\partial p)_T}{(\partial H/\partial T)_p} \tag{4}$$

The quantity μ defined by this equation is known as the *Joule-Thomson coefficient.* It represents the limiting value of the experimental ratio of temperature difference to pressure difference as the pressure difference approaches zero:

$$\mu = \lim_{\Delta p \to 0} \left(\frac{\Delta T}{\Delta p}\right)_H \tag{5}$$

Experimentally ΔT is found to be very nearly linear with Δp over a considerable range; this is in accord with expectations based on the theory given below.

The denominator on the right side of Eq. (4) is the heat capacity at constant pressure C_p. The numerator is zero for an ideal gas [see Eq. (1)]. Accordingly for an ideal gas the Joule-Thomson coefficient is zero, and there should be no temperature difference across the porous plug. For a real gas, the Joule-Thomson coefficient is a measure of the quantity $(\partial H/\partial p)_T$ [which can be related thermodynamically to the quantity involved in the Joule experiment, $(\partial E/\partial V)_T$]. Using the general thermodynamic relation

$$\left(\frac{\partial H}{\partial p}\right)_T = -T\left(\frac{\partial V}{\partial T}\right)_p + V \tag{6}$$

it can be shown that, for an ideal gas satisfying the criteria already given,

$$pV = \text{const} \times T \tag{7}$$

where T is the absolute thermodynamic temperature. The coefficient $(\partial H/\partial p)_T$ is therefore a measure of the deviation from the behavior predicted by Eq. (7). On combining Eqs. (4) and (6), we obtain

$$\mu = \frac{T(\partial V/\partial T)_p - V}{C_p} \tag{8}$$

In order to predict the magnitude and behavior of the Joule-Thomson coefficient for a real gas, we can use van der Waals' equation of state,[2] which (for 1 mole) is

$$\left(p + \frac{a}{V^2}\right)(V - b) = RT \tag{9}$$

We can rearrange this equation (with neglect of the very small second-order term ab/V^2 and substitution of p/RT for $1/V$ in a first-order term) to obtain

$$pV = RT - \frac{ap}{RT} + bp$$

Thus
$$\left(\frac{\partial V}{\partial T}\right)_p = \frac{R}{p} + \frac{a}{RT^2}$$

Combination of these two equations yields

$$\left(\frac{\partial V}{\partial T}\right)_p = \frac{V - b}{T} + \frac{2a}{RT^2} \tag{10}$$

which on substitution into Eq. (8) gives the expression

$$\mu = \frac{(2a/RT) - b}{C_p} \tag{11}$$

This expression does not contain p or V explicitly, and C_p may be considered essentially independent of these variables. The temperature dependence of C_p is small, and accordingly that of μ is also small enough to be neglected over the ΔT's obtainable with a Δp of about 1 atm (namely about 1° or less for the gases considered here). Accordingly we may expect that μ will be approximately independent of Δp over a wide range, as stated previously.

For most gases under ordinary conditions, $2a/RT > b$ (the attractive forces predominate over the repulsive forces in determining the nonideal behavior) and the Joule-Thomson coefficient is therefore positive (gas cools on expansion). At a sufficiently high temperature the inequality is reversed, and the gas warms on expansion. The temperature at which the Joule-Thomson coefficient changes sign is called the *inversion temperature* T_I; for a van der Waals' gas

$$T_I = \frac{2a}{Rb} \tag{12}$$

This temperature is usually several hundred degrees above room temperature. However hydrogen and helium are exceptional in having inversion temperatures well below room temperatures. This results from the very small attractive forces in these gases (see Table 1 for values of van der Waals' constant a).

Other semiempirical equations of state can be used to predict Joule-Thomson coefficients. Perhaps the best of these is the Beattie-Bridgeman equation,[3, 4] which can be written (for 1 mole) as

$$p = \frac{RT(1 - \epsilon)}{V^2}(V + B) - \frac{A}{V^2} \tag{13}$$

where $A = A_0(1 - a/V)$, $B = B_0(1 - b/V)$, and $\epsilon = c/VT^3$. In this equation of state there are five constants which are characteristic of the particular gas: A_0, B_0, a, b, and c. In terms of these constants and the pressure and temperature, the Joule-Thomson coefficient is given[3] by

$$\mu = \frac{1}{C_p}\left\{-B_0 + \frac{2A_0}{RT} + \frac{4c}{T^3} + \left[\frac{2B_0b}{RT} - \frac{3A_0a}{(RT)^2} + \frac{5B_0c}{RT^4}\right]p\right\} \tag{14}$$

TABLE 1. Values of Constants in Equations of State[a]

	He	H_2	N_2	CO_2
van der Waals:[6]				
a	0.0341	0.244	1.39	3.59
b	0.0237	0.0266	0.0391	0.0427
Beattie-Bridgeman:[3]				
A_0	0.0216	0.1975	1.3445	5.0065
a	0.05984	−0.00506	0.02617	0.07132
B_0	0.01400	0.02096	0.05046	0.10476
b	0.0	−0.04359	−0.00691	0.07235
$10^{-4}c$	0.0040	0.0504	4.20	66.00

[a] Units assumed are: V in liters per mole, p in atmospheres, T in Kelvin degrees. ($R = 0.08206$ liter-atm deg^{-1}.)

This equation predicts a small dependence on pressure, not shown by Eq. (11) which is based on van der Waals' equation.

EXPERIMENTAL

The experimental apparatus is shown in Figs. 2 and 3. The "porous plug" is a fritted glass plate (porosity F is convenient) sealed in a 30-mm glass tube. The lower end of this tube is drawn down to 6 to 8 mm and connected by a short length

FIG. 2. The Joule-Thomson apparatus.

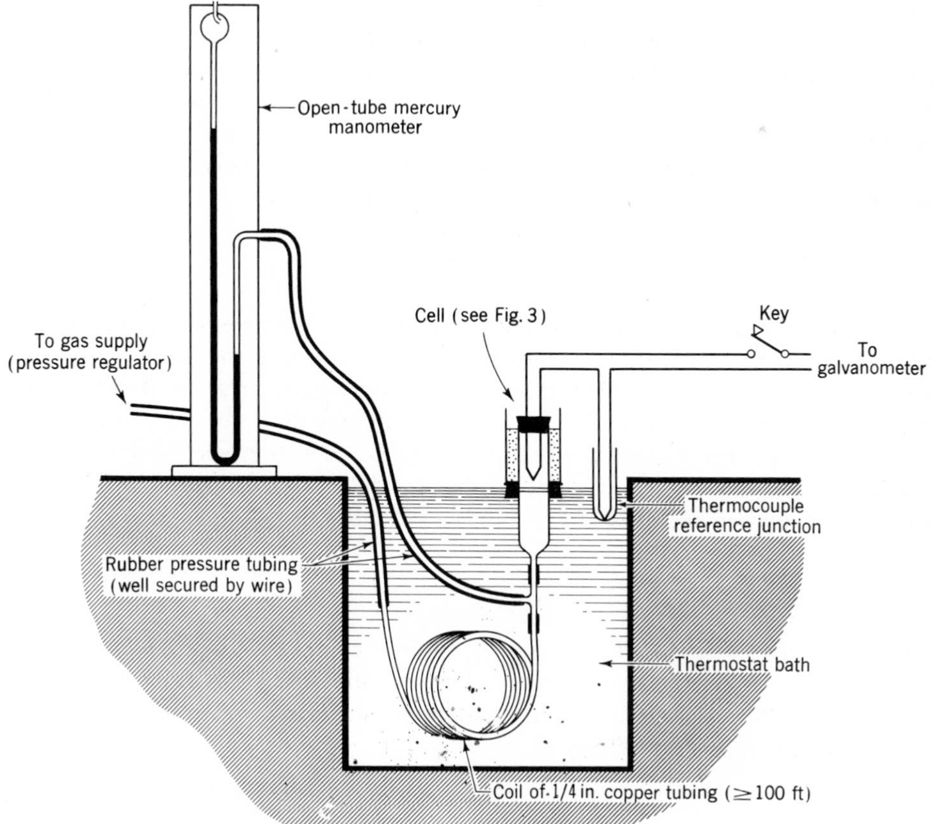

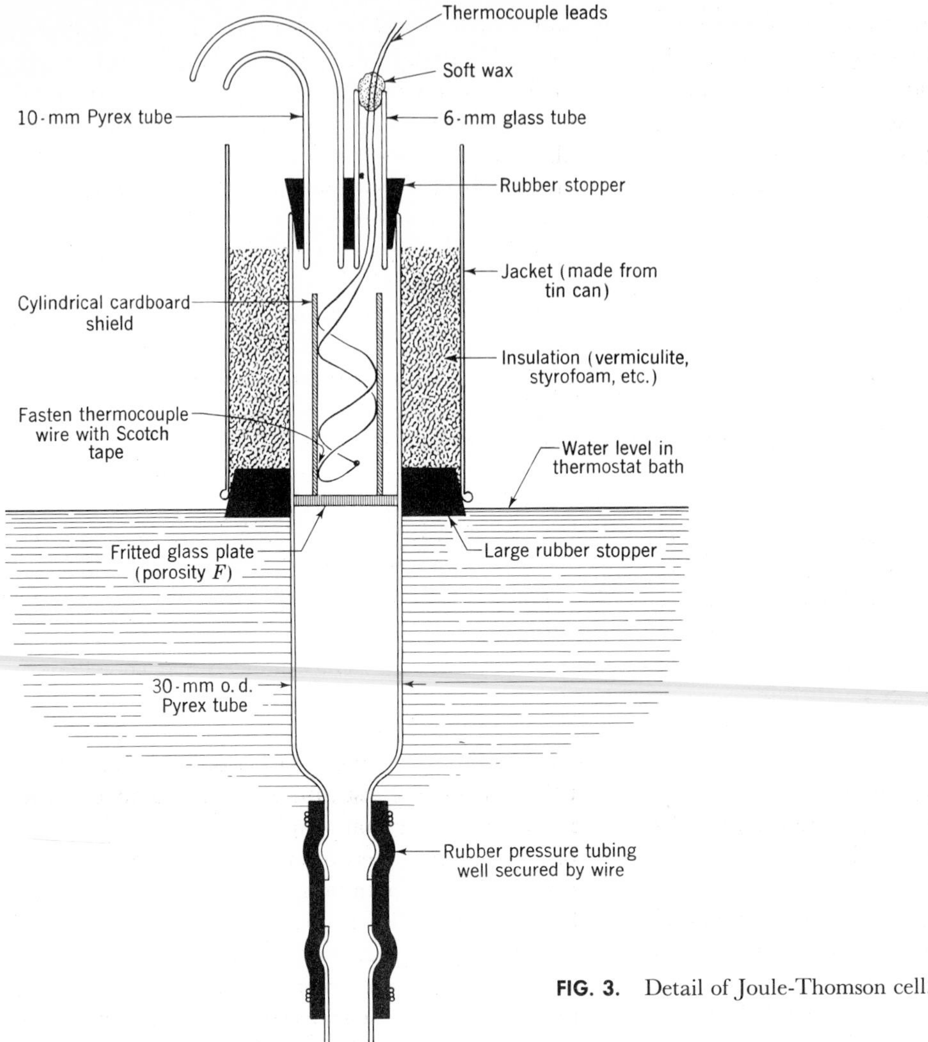

FIG. 3. Detail of Joule-Thomson cell.

of pressure tubing (securely clamped or wired) to at least 100 ft of ¼-in. copper tubing wound in a coil of convenient shape. This coil and the lower end of the glass tube (up to the fritted disk) are submerged in a constant-temperature bath in order to bring the gas to the bath temperature. The other end of the coil is connected to a supply of gas at a pressure ½ to 1 atm above atmospheric pressure. An open-tube mercury manometer is used to measure Δp. The upper end of the glass tube (above the frit) is always at atmospheric pressure but is thermally insulated with an outer jacket filled with a medium such as vermiculite or styrofoam. The temperature difference ΔT between the gas above the plate and the water in the bath is measured with a copper-constantan thermocouple (using the finest wires available). A sensitive galvanometer (such as Leeds and Northrup 2430d, having a sensitivity of 0.0005 μa mm^{-1} and an internal resistance of 550 ohms) is required. A potentiometer of sufficient sensitivity (± 0.1 μv) can be used, but it is not needed, since the galvanometer-thermocouple system can be calibrated directly against a Beckmann thermometer. An alternative design for a simple Joule-Thomson apparatus is described elsewhere.[5] The most obvious change in the cell design would involve mounting the "reference" junction in the high-pressure gas below the frit; this would require a change in the calibration procedure described below. For slow flow rates through a long coil, the assumption that the high-pressure gas is at bath temperature is well justified and the present design is adequate.

Procedure. Set up the apparatus as shown in Figs. 2 and 3. The gas supply should be a cylinder or supply line equipped with a pressure regulator and a needle valve. Be sure that the supply pressure is constant; if there are other demands on the gas supply, careful planning is required. All gas connections should be securely wired or clamped. **Warning:** All changes in pressure must be carried out **very slowly.**

For the *initial* equilibration of the system, close the needle valve and adjust the main gas supply valve until the regulator gauge reads about 40 psi. Then **very slowly** open the needle valve until the pressure in the system (as indicated by the manometer) is increasing at about the rate of 5 cm Hg min^{-1}. Continue to adjust the needle valve until Δp is about 75 cm (this should take *at least* 15 min). If the gas pressure is increased rapidly at the beginning, the coil will not be able to bring the initial surge of gas to bath temperature, and the porous frit will be cooled to below its steady-state value; this will cause a very slow (2 to 3 hr) attainment of the steady-state value of ΔT. With care in making all pressure changes, a steady state should be achieved in about 40 min.

While waiting for the system to come to a steady state, you should calibrate the thermocouple. The reference junction of the thermocouple should be embedded in a small amount of wax or oil at the bottom of a test tube which is mounted in the constant-temperature bath. The measuring junction should be removed from the Joule-Thomson cell and taped to the bulb of a Beckmann thermometer which is placed first in the bath and then in a Dewar containing water approximately 1° below the bath temperature. The temperature of the water in the Dewar can be raised or lowered by the addition of small amounts of hot or cold water, and enough thermometer and galvanometer readings can be obtained to yield a calibration curve. This curve should be obtained with the thermocouple leads connected directly across the galvanometer terminals. Another calibration curve should be obtained with an appropriate resistance in series to reduce the sensitivity by a factor of 4 or more. (With the L & N 2430d galvanometer, a 1500-ohm resistor is recommended.)

After calibration, the thermocouple wires are very carefully dried and installed in the cell. It is recommended that a cylindrical cardboard tube be placed in the cell so as to rest on the fritted disk. It may be roughly centered with a few tufts of glass wool. The thermocouple wires should be loosely coiled inside the tube and fastened near the bottom with a small piece of scotch tape in such a way that the junction is in the center of the tube and about 5 to 10 mm above the fritted disk.

Record values of the galvanometer deflection, the pressure differential Δp, and the time until no significant change in ΔT occurs over a 10- to 15-min interval. Then *very slowly* close the needle valve so as to reduce the pressure drop Δp to approximately 60 cm Hg. This change should require *at least* 5 min! Record Δp and ΔT values until a steady state is achieved at this new setting (about 20 min). Repeat the procedure to obtain data at $\Delta p = 45$, 30, and 15 cm Hg. If time is available, make measurements on both nitrogen and carbon dioxide.

CALCULATIONS

For each gas studied, plot Δp against ΔT and draw the best straight line through these points; this line should, of course, pass through the origin. From the slope evaluate the Joule-Thomson coefficient in degrees per atmosphere.

For comparison, calculate Joule-Thomson coefficients for these gases at this temperature from the van der Waals and/or the Beattie-Bridgeman constants given in Table 1. The molar heat capacities at constant pressure C_p of N_2 and CO_2 are 0.286 and 0.362 liter-atm deg^{-1}, respectively.

DISCUSSION

For the Joule experiment we can write

$$\eta \equiv -\left(\frac{\partial T}{\partial V}\right)_E = \frac{(\partial E/\partial V)_T}{(\partial E/\partial T)_V} = \frac{T(\partial p/\partial T)_V - p}{C_v} \tag{15}$$

This quantity is called the Joule coefficient. It is the limit of $-(\Delta T/\Delta V)_E$, corrected for the heat capacity of the containers, as ΔV approaches zero. With van der Waals' equation of state we obtain, for 1 mole, $\eta = a/V^2C_v$. The corrected temperature change when the two containers are of equal volume is found by integration to be $\Delta T = -a/2VC_v$, where V is the initial molar volume and C_v is the molar constant-volume heat capacity.

It will be instructive for the student to calculate this ΔT for a gas such as CO_2. In addition, he may consider the relative heat capacities of 10 liters of the gas at a pressure of 1 atm and that of the quantity of copper required to construct two spheres of this volume with walls (say) 1 mm thick and then calculate the ΔT expected to be observed with such an experimental arrangement.

APPARATUS

Joule-Thomson cell comprising glass tube with fritted disk, large rubber stopper with outer jacket, insulating medium such as vermiculite, rubber stopper with bent glass outlet tube and tube for thermocouple wires, and cardboard cylinder; clamp to hold cell in bath; thermocouple (insulated copper-constantan, No. 30) with test tube for reference junction; clamp for same; sensitive galvanometer (such as L & N 2430d); auxiliary resistance (e.g., 1500 ohms); tapping key; coil of ¼-in. copper tubing, at least 100 ft; open-tube manometer (80 cm) containing mercury; T-tube; two 4- and two 36-in. (or longer) pieces of rubber pressure tubing for making connections; Beckmann thermometer; thermometer clamp; 500-ml beaker.

Constant-temperature bath regulated at 25°C; cylinders or supply lines for gases (N_2, CO_2) equipped with pressure regulators and needle valves; copper wire for securing connections of rubber tubing; Scotch tape; soft wax; paraffin wax or oil; glass wool.

REFERENCES

1. J. P. Joule and W. Thomson (Lord Kelvin), *Phil. Trans.*, **143,** 357 (1853); **144,** 321 (1854). Reprinted in "Harper's Scientific Memoirs I, The Free Expansion of Gases," Harper, New York (1898).
2. W. J. Moore, "Physical Chemistry," 2d ed., pp. 16, 18, 171, Prentice-Hall, Englewood Cliffs, N. J. (1955).

3. J. A. Beattie and W. H. Stockmayer, The Thermodynamics and Statistical Mechanics of Real Gases, in H. S. Taylor and S. Glasstone (eds.), "A Treatise on Physical Chemistry," vol. II, pp. 187ff., esp. pp. 206, 234, Van Nostrand, Princeton, N.J. (1951).
4. J. A. Beattie and O. C. Bridgeman, *J. Am. Chem. Soc.*, **49,** 1665 (1927); *Proc. Am. Acad. Arts Sci.*, **63,** 229 (1928).
5. C. E. Hecht and G. Zimmerman, *J. Chem. Educ.*, **31,** 530 (1954).
6. Landolt-Börnstein *physikalisch-chemische Tabellen,* 5th ed., p. 254, Springer, Berlin (1923) [reprinted by Edwards, Ann Arbor, Mich. (1943)].

Experiment 4. Heat-capacity Ratios for Gases

The method of adiabatic expansion can be used to determine the ratio of the heat capacity of a gas at constant pressure to that at constant volume. Several gases will be studied, and the results interpreted in terms of the contribution made to the specific heat by various molecular degrees of freedom.

THEORY

For the reversible, adiabatic expansion of a gas, the change in energy content is related to the change in volume by

$$dE = -p\,dV \tag{1}$$

For a perfect gas,

$$p = \frac{NRT}{V} \tag{2}$$

Moreover, since E for a perfect gas is a function of temperature only, we can write

$$dE = C_v\,dT \tag{3}$$

where C_v is the constant-volume heat capacity. Substituting Eqs. (2) and (3) into Eq. (1) and integrating, we find that

$$\tilde{C}_v \ln \frac{T_2}{T_1} = -R \ln \frac{\tilde{V}_2}{\tilde{V}_1} \tag{4}$$

where $\tilde{C}_v$ and $\tilde{V}$ are molar quantities (that is, C_v/N, V/N). It has been assumed that C_v is constant over the temperature range involved. This equation predicts the decrease in temperature resulting from a reversible adiabatic expansion of a perfect gas.

Consider the following two-step process involving a perfect gas denoted by A:

Step I: Allow the gas to expand adiabatically and reversibly until the pressure has dropped from p_1 to p_2.

$$\mathrm{A}(p_1,\tilde{V}_1,T_1) \rightarrow \mathrm{A}(p_2,\tilde{V}_2,T_2) \tag{5}$$

Step II: At constant volume, restore the temperature of the gas to T_1.

$$\mathrm{A}(p_2,\tilde{V}_2,T_2) \rightarrow \mathrm{A}(p_3,\tilde{V}_2,T_1) \tag{6}$$

For step 1, we can use the perfect-gas law to obtain

$$\frac{T_2}{T_1} = \frac{p_2\tilde{V}_2}{p_1\tilde{V}_1} \tag{7}$$

Substituting Eq. (7) into Eq. (4) and combining terms in $\tilde{V}_2/\tilde{V}_1$, we write

$$\ln\frac{p_2}{p_1} = \frac{-(\tilde{C}_v + R)}{\tilde{C}_v}\ln\frac{\tilde{V}_2}{\tilde{V}_1} = -\frac{\tilde{C}_p}{\tilde{C}_v}\ln\frac{\tilde{V}_2}{\tilde{V}_1} \tag{8}$$

since for a perfect gas

$$\tilde{C}_p = \tilde{C}_v + R \tag{9}$$

For step 2;

$$\frac{\tilde{V}_2}{\tilde{V}_1} = \frac{p_1}{p_3} \tag{10}$$

Thus

$$\ln\frac{p_1}{p_2} = \frac{\tilde{C}_p}{\tilde{C}_v}\ln\frac{p_1}{p_3} \tag{11}$$

This can be rewritten in the form

$$\frac{\tilde{C}_p}{\tilde{C}_v} = \frac{\log p_1 - \log p_2}{\log p_1 - \log p_3} \tag{12}$$

Heat Capacities of Gases. Let us now consider the theoretical calculation of the heat capacities of gases. Since we are concerned with perfect gases and Eq. (9) applies, our discussion can be restricted to C_v.

The number of "degrees of freedom" for a molecule is the number of independent coordinates needed to specify its position and configuration. Hence a molecule of n atoms has $3n$ degrees of freedom. These could be taken as the three cartesian coordinates of the n individual atoms, but it is more convenient to classify them as follows:

1. Translational degrees of freedom: Three independent coordinates are needed to specify the position of the center of mass of the molecule.

2. Rotational degrees of freedom: All molecules containing more than one atom require a specification of their orientation in space. As an example, consider a rigid diatomic molecule; such a model consists of two point masses (the atoms) connected by a rigid massless bar (the chemical bond). Through the center of mass, which lies on the rigid bar, independent rotation can take place about two axes mutually perpendicular to each other and to the rigid bar. (The rigid bar itself does not constitute a third axis of rotation under ordinary circumstances for reasons based on quantum theory, there being no appreciable moment of inertia about this axis.) Rotation of a *diatomic* molecule or any linear molecule can thus be described in terms of *two* rotational degrees of freedom. *Nonlinear* molecules for which the third axis has a moment of inertia of appreciable magnitude and constitutes another axis of rotation require *three* rotational degrees of freedom.

3. Vibrational degrees of freedom: One must also specify the displacements of the atoms from their equilibrium positions (vibrations). The number of vibrational degrees of freedom is $3n$-5 for linear molecules and $3n$-6 for nonlinear molecules. These values are determined by the fact that the total number of degrees of freedom must be $3n$. For each vibrational degree of freedom there is a "normal mode" of vibration of the molecule, with characteristic symmetry properties and a charac-

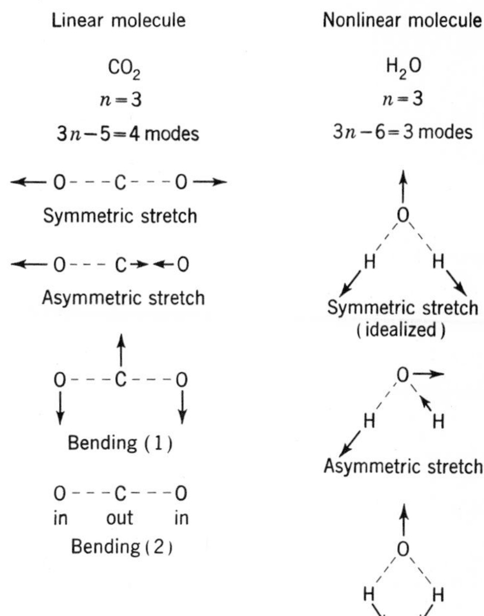

FIG. 1. Schematic diagrams of the vibrational normal modes for CO_2, a linear molecule, and H_2O, a bent molecule.

teristic harmonic frequency. The vibrational normal modes for CO_2 and H_2O are illustrated schematically in Fig. 1.

Using classical statistical mechanics one can derive the theorem of the equipartition of energy. According to this theorem $kT/2$ of energy is associated with each quadratic term in the expression for the energy.[1] Thus there is associated with each translational or rotational degree of freedom for a molecule a contribution to the energy of $kT/2$ of kinetic energy and for each vibrational degree of freedom a contribution of $kT/2$ of kinetic energy and $kT/2$ of potential energy. (The corresponding contributions to the energy per *mole* of gas are $RT/2$.)

Clearly a monatomic gas has no rotational or vibrational energy but does have a translational energy of $\frac{3}{2}RT$ per mole. The constant-volume heat capacity of a monatomic perfect gas is thus

$$\tilde{C}_v = \left(\frac{\partial \tilde{E}}{\partial T}\right)_v = \frac{3}{2}R \tag{13}$$

For diatomic or polyatomic molecules, we can write

$$\tilde{E} = \tilde{E}(\text{trans}) + \tilde{E}(\text{rot}) + \tilde{E}(\text{vib}) \tag{14}$$

In Eq. (14), contributions to the energy from electronic states have been neglected, since they are not significant at room temperature for most molecules. Also any small intramolecular energies which occur for imperfect gases are not considered.

The equipartition theorem is based on classical mechanics. Its application to translational motion is in accord with quantum mechanics as well. At ordinary temperatures the rotational results are also in accord with quantum mechanics. (The greatest deviation from the classical result is in the case of hydrogen, H_2; at temperatures below 100°K the rotational energy of H_2 is significantly below the equipartition value, as predicted by quantum mechanics.)

The vibrational energy is, however, highly quantized and depends strongly on temperature; the various vibrational modes are at ordinary temperatures only partially "active," and the degree of activity depends strongly on the temperature. As a general rule, the heavier the atoms or the smaller the force constant of the bond (i.e., the lower the vibrational frequency), the more "active" is a given degree of freedom at a given temperature and the greater is the contribution to the heat capacity. Moreover, the frequencies of modes that are predominantly bending of bonds tend to be much lower than those that are predominantly stretching of bonds. In the case of most gaseous *diatomic* molecules (where the one vibrational mode is a pure stretch) the vibrational contribution to $\tilde{C}_v$ is very small; e.g., N_2 would have its classical equipartition value for $\tilde{C}_v$ only above about 4000°K. Many polyatomic molecules, especially those containing heavy atoms, will at room temperature have significant *partial* vibrational contributions to $\tilde{C}_v$.

We are now in a position to calculate for polyatomic molecules approximate or at least limiting values for $\tilde{C}_v$ and for the ratio $\tilde{C}_p/\tilde{C}_v$. For monatomic gases and all ordinary diatomic molecules (where vibration is not important at room temperature) definite values can be calculated.

METHOD

This experiment, due to Clement and Desormes,[2] uses the very simple apparatus shown in Fig. 2. The change in state (5) is carried out by quickly removing and replacing the stopper of a large carboy containing the desired gas at a pressure initially somewhat higher than 1 atm pressure, so that the pressure of gas in the carboy momentarily drops to atmospheric pressure p_2. The change in state (6) consists of allowing the gas remaining in the carboy to return to its initial temperature. The initial pressure p_1 and the final pressure p_3 are read from an open-tube manometer.

The thermodynamic equations (1) to (12) apply only to that part of the gas that remains in the carboy after the stopper is replaced. We may imagine the gas initially in the carboy to be divided into two parts by an imaginary surface; the part above the surface leaves the carboy when the stopper is removed and presumably interacts irreversibly with the surroundings, but the part below the surface expands *reversibly* against this imaginary surface, doing work in pushing the upper gas out. The process is approximately adiabatic only because it is rapid; within a few seconds the gas near the walls will have received an appreciable quantity of heat by direct conduction from the walls, and the pressure can be seen to rise almost as soon as the stopper is replaced.

The experiment will presumably give a somewhat *low* result (low p_3 and therefore low $\tilde{C}_p/\tilde{C}_v$ ratio) if the expansion is to an appreciable degree irreversible, a somewhat *low* result if the stopper is left open so long that the conditions are not sufficiently adiabatic, and a somewhat *high* result if the stopper has not been removed for a long enough time to permit the pressure to drop momentarily to atmospheric. There should be no significant irreversibility if during the expansion there are no significant pressure gradients in the gas below the imaginary surface mentioned above, and such pressure gradients should not be expected if the throat area is small in comparison with the effective area of this imaginary surface. With an 18-liter carboy and a p_1 about 5 cm Hg above 1 atm, the volume of air forced out should be about 1 liter, which should provide a large enough surface area to fulfill this condition approximately if the throat diameter is not more than about

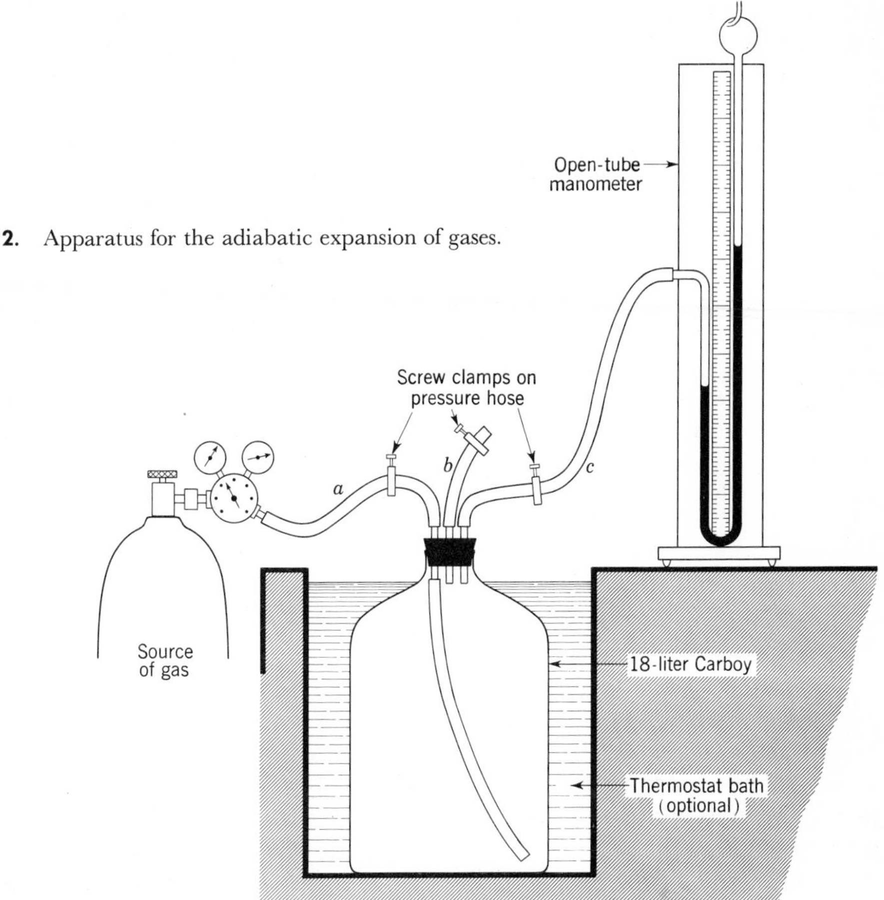

FIG. 2. Apparatus for the adiabatic expansion of gases.

2 or 3 cm. The effect of the length of time the stopper is removed is much more difficult to estimate by calculation; some idea can be obtained from the duration of the sound produced when the stopper is removed and from the rate of rise of the manometer reading immediately after the stopper is replaced. For the purpose of this experiment the student may assume that, if the stopper is removed completely from the carboy to a distance of 2 or 3 in. away and replaced tightly as soon as physically possible, the desired experimental conditions are approximately fulfilled. Some additional assurance may be gained from the reproducibility obtained in duplicate runs.

The method used in this experiment is not the best method of determining the heat-capacity ratio. Much better methods are based on measurements of the velocity of sound in gases. One such method consists of measuring the wavelength of sound of an accurately known frequency, by measuring the distance between nodes in a sonic resonance set up in a tube known as Kundt's tube, along one wall of which there is a fine powder that remains undisturbed only at these nodes. The velocity of sound U in a gas can be shown to be given by

$$U = \left(\frac{p}{\rho} \frac{\tilde{C}_p}{\tilde{C}_v}\right)^{1/2} \qquad (15)$$

where ρ is the density of the gas. The heat-capacity ratio enters because it is not the isothermal compressibility but the adiabatic compressibility that enters into description of sound-wave motion, for the rapid alternate rarefactions and compressions due to a sound wave are essentially adiabatic.

The method used here is not useful for obtaining good values for the heat capacities themselves and should be used only for getting approximate values of the $\tilde{C}_p/\tilde{C}_v$ ratio. Methods exist for determining the heat capacities directly,[3] although the measurements are not easy.

EXPERIMENTAL

The apparatus should be assembled as shown in Fig. 2. If desired, the carboy may be mounted in a thermostat bath; if so, it must be clamped securely to overcome buoyancy. The manometer is an *open-tube* manometer, one side of which is open to the atmosphere; the pressure that it measures, therefore, is the difference of pressure from atmospheric pressure. A suitable liquid for the manometer is dibutyl phthalate, which has a density of 1.046 g cm^{-3} at room temperature (20°C). To convert manometer readings (centimeters of dibutyl phthalate) to equivalent readings in centimeters of mercury, multiply by the ratio of this density to the density of mercury, which is 13.55 g cm^{-3} at 20°C. To find the total pressure in the carboy, the converted manometer reading should be added to atmospheric pressure as given by a barometer. It is unnecessary to correct all readings to 0°C, as all pressures enter the calculations as ratios.

Seat the rubber stopper firmly in the carboy and open the clamps on tubes *a* and *b*. Clamp off the tube *c*. The connections shown in Fig. 2 are based on the assumption that the gas to be studied is heavier than air (or the previous gas in the carboy) and therefore should be introduced at the bottom in order to force the lighter gas out at the top; in the event that the gas to be studied is lighter, the connections *a* and *b* should be reversed.

Allow the gas to be studied to sweep through the carboy for 15 min. The rate of gas flow should be about 6 liters min^{-1}, or 100 ml sec^{-1} (measure roughly in an inverted beaker held under water in the thermostat bath). Thus, five volumes of gas (90 liters) will pass through the carboy.

Retard the gas flow to a fraction of the flushing rate by partly closing the clamp on tube *a*. **Carefully** open the clamp on tube *c*, and then cautiously (to avoid blowing liquid out of the manometer) clamp off the exit tube *b*, keeping a close watch on the manometer. When the manometer has attained a reading of about 60 cm, clamp off tube *a*. Allow the gas to come to the temperature of the thermostat bath (about 15 min), as shown by a constant manometer reading. Record this reading; when it is converted to an equivalent mercury reading and added to the barometer reading, p_1 is obtained.

Remove the stopper *entirely* (a distance of 2 or 3 in.) from the carboy, and replace it *in the shortest possible time,* making sure that it is tight. As the gas warms back up to the bath temperature, the pressure will increase and finally (in about 15 min) reach a new constant value p_3, which can be determined from the manometer reading and the barometer reading. At some point in the procedure, a barometer reading (p_2) should be taken.

Repeat the steps above to obtain two more determinations with the same gas.

For these repeat runs, long flushing is not necessary; one additional volume of gas should suffice to check the effectiveness of the original flushing.

Measurements are to be made on both helium and nitrogen. If there is sufficient time, study carbon dioxide also.

CALCULATIONS

For each of the three runs on He, N_2 (and CO_2) calculate $\tilde{C}_p/\tilde{C}_v$ using Eq. (12). Also calculate the theoretical value of $\tilde{C}_p/\tilde{C}_v$ predicted by the equipartition theorem. In the case of N_2 and CO_2 calculate the ratio both with and without vibrational contribution to $\tilde{C}_v$.

DISCUSSION

Compare your experimental ratios with those calculated theoretically, and make any deductions you can about the presence or absence of rotational and vibrational contributions, taking due account of the uncertainties in the experimental values. For CO_2, how would the theoretical ratio be affected if the molecule were nonlinear (like SO_2) instead of linear? Could you decide between these two structures from the $\tilde{C}_p/\tilde{C}_v$ ratio alone?

APPARATUS

Large-volume vessel (such as 18-liter glass carboy); three-hole stopper fitted with three glass tubes; open-tube manometer, with dibutyl phthalate as indicating fluid (may contain a small amount of dye for ease of reading); three long and one short lengths of rubber pressure tubing; three screw clamps; cork ring and brackets, needed if vessel is to be mounted in a water bath; thermometer; 500-ml beaker.

Thermostat bath, set at 25°C (unless each vessel has an insulating jacket); cylinders of helium, nitrogen, and carbon dioxide.

REFERENCES

1. W. J. Moore, "Physical Chemistry," 2d ed., pp. 188–193, Prentice-Hall, Englewood Cliffs, N.J. (1955).
2. Lord Rayleigh, "The Theory of Sound," 2d ed., vol. II, pp. 15–23, Dover, New York (1945).
3. K. Schell and W. Heuse, *Ann. Physik,* **37,** 79 (1912); **40,** 473 (1913); **59,** 86 (1919).

GENERAL READING

J. R. Partington, "An Advanced Treatise on Physical Chemistry," vol. I, pp. 792ff., Longmans, London (1949).

IV

TRANSPORT PROPERTIES OF GASES

EXPERIMENTS

5. Viscosity of Gases
6. Thermal Conductivity of Gases
7. Diffusion of Gases
8. Low-pressure Effusion of Gases

KINETIC THEORY OF TRANSPORT PHENOMENA

In this section we shall be concerned with a molecular theory of the transport properties of gases. The molecules of a gas collide with each other frequently, and the velocity of a given molecule is usually changed by each collision that the molecule undergoes. However, when a one-component gas is in thermal and statistical equilibrium, there is a definite distribution of molecular velocities—the well-known Maxwellian distribution.[1] Figure 1 shows how molecular velocities are distributed in such a gas. This distribution is isotropic (the same in all directions) and can be characterized by a *root-mean-square velocity* u, which is given by

$$u = \left(\frac{3kT}{m}\right)^{1/2} = \left(\frac{3RT}{M}\right)^{1/2} \tag{1}$$

where k is Boltzmann's constant, R is the gas constant, m is the mass of one molecule, and M is the molecular weight. Sometimes it is more convenient to use the *mean speed* $\bar{c}$:

$$\bar{c} = \left(\frac{8kT}{\pi m}\right)^{1/2} = \left(\frac{8}{3\pi}\right)^{1/2} u \tag{2}$$

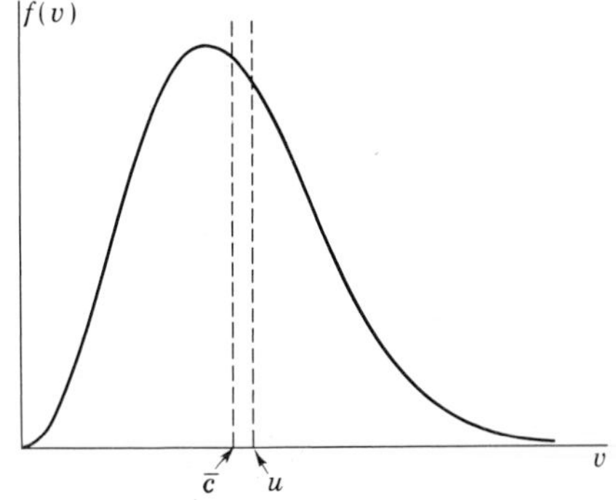

FIG. 1. Schematic Maxwellian velocity distribution: $f(v)\,dv$ is the fraction of the molecules with velocities between v and $v + dv$. Values of the rms velocity u and the mean speed $\bar{c}$ are shown.

Another very important concept in kinetic theory is the average distance a molecule travels between collisions—the so-called *mean free path.* On the basis of a very simple conception of molecular collisions, the following equation for the mean free path can be derived:

$$\bar{l} = \frac{1}{\pi \bar{n} d^2}$$

where d is the "molecular diameter," or center-to-center collision distance, and $\bar{n}$ is the number of molecules per unit volume. When the fact is properly taken into account that molecules do not all have the same velocities, a different numerical coefficient is obtained:[1]

$$\bar{l} = \frac{1}{\sqrt{2}\pi \bar{n} d^2} = 3.72 \times 10^{-25} \frac{RT}{pd^2} \qquad (3)$$

In this equation the perfect-gas law has been used, and the numerical coefficient assumes that d, the molecular diameter, is in centimeters. Some typical values of $\bar{l}$ are given in Table 1.

We shall here consider in detail the viscosity, thermal conductivity, and diffusion of gases; indeed, the kinetic theory treatment of these three transport properties is very similar. But first let us consider the simpler problem of molecular effusion.

Effusion of Gases. The theory of effusion (Knudsen flow) is quite straightforward, since only molecular flow is involved; i.e., in the process of effusing the molecules act independently of one another. For a Maxwellian distribution of velocities it can be shown[1, 2] that the number z of molecular impacts on a unit area of wall surface in unit time is

TABLE 1. Mean Free Paths of Various Gases[a] at 25°C

Gas	Mean free path, cm	
	At 1 atm	At 0.1 mm Hg
He	19.4×10^{-6}	14.7×10^{-2}
Ar	7.0×10^{-6}	5.3×10^{-2}
O_2	7.1×10^{-6}	5.4×10^{-2}
N_2	6.6×10^{-6}	5.0×10^{-2}
Air	6.7×10^{-6}	5.1×10^{-2}
CO_2	4.4×10^{-6}	3.3×10^{-2}

[a] E. H. Kennard, "Kinetic Theory of Gases," McGraw-Hill, New York (1938).

$$z = \frac{1}{\sqrt{6\pi}} u\bar{n} \tag{4}$$

where u is the rms velocity and $\bar{n}$ is the molecular concentration. Combining Eqs. (1) and (4) we obtain

$$z = \left(\frac{RT}{2\pi M}\right)^{1/2} \bar{n}$$

The number Z of *moles* colliding with 1 cm^2 of wall surface per second is

$$Z = \left(\frac{RT}{2\pi M}\right)^{1/2} \frac{N}{V} \tag{5}$$

where N/V is the number of moles per unit volume. For a perfect gas Eq. (5) becomes

$$Z = \frac{p}{\sqrt{2\pi MRT}} \tag{6}$$

Let two bodies of the same gas, at the same temperature but at two different pressures (p and p'), communicate through a small hole of area A, all dimensions of which are *small* in comparison with the mean free path of the gas molecules. It can then be assumed that the Maxwellian distribution of velocities is essentially undisturbed and that the same number of molecules will enter the hole as would otherwise have collided with the corresponding area of wall surface. It will also be assumed that all molecules entering the hole will pass through to the other side. The *net* rate of effusion through the hole will be the difference between the numbers of moles flowing through the hole in unit time in the two directions:

$$\frac{dN_{\text{eff}}}{dt} = \frac{A(p - p')}{\sqrt{2\pi MRT}} \tag{7}$$

This equation assumes that the gas is perfect, but it should be emphasized that the rate of effusion calculated from it is independent of the size and shape of the molecules provided only that these are such as to give a sufficiently long mean free path at the given temperature and pressure.

Gas Viscosity. Consider a body of gas under shear as shown in Fig. 5-1 and discussed in the introduction to Exp. 5. Assume that all the molecules in the gas are of one kind and that the gas undergoes laminar flow. By the mass velocity of the gas at each point, we understand the (vectorial) average velocity of all molecules passing through an infinitesimal region at that point. If the velocity gradient is substantially constant within one or a few mean free paths, we may also say that the mass velocity of the gas at a given point is the (vectorial) average velocity of all molecules that have suffered their most recent collision in an infinitesimal region at that point. We shall assume that, with respect to a system of coordinates moving at the mass velocity at a given point, the distribution of velocities of gas molecules which underwent their most recent collisions at that point is the same as it would be if the gas were not under shear (i.e., that the distribution is Maxwellian and therefore isotropic). We shall also assume, for simplicity, that all molecules travel the same distance $\bar{l}$ between collisions.

Let us focus our attention on a laminar plane $x = x'$, with $v = v'$. Molecules coming from below and colliding with molecules on this layer may be assumed (in a rough approximation) to have suffered their most recent previous collision on a plane at a distance $\bar{\ell}$ below the plane in question. The average momentum component in the shear direction parallel to the lamina (call it the y direction) for one of these molecules is therefore

$$m \cdot v(x - \bar{\ell}) = mv' - m\frac{dv}{dx}\bar{\ell}$$

where m is the mass of a molecule. Since by hypothesis the molecules have average momentum mv' after collision, an average amount of momentum

$$-m\frac{dv}{dx}\bar{\ell}$$

is transferred to the laminar plane x' from below, per collision. The number of molecules reaching a unit area of the plane from below per unit time is

$$\tfrac{1}{6}\bar{n}u$$

where $\bar{n}$ is the number of molecules per unit volume and u is their rms molecular velocity. Therefore, the rate of upward transfer of momentum to a unit area of the plane from below is

$$-\frac{1}{6}\bar{n}um\bar{\ell}\frac{dv}{dx}$$

Similarly it can be shown that the rate of downward transfer of momentum from a unit area of the plane x' to the plane at $(x' - \bar{\ell})$ is

$$+\frac{1}{6}\bar{n}um\bar{\ell}\frac{dv}{dx}$$

A downward flow of momentum is equivalent to an upward flow of momentum of the opposite sign. Thus the net rate of *upward* flow of momentum through any given plane, per unit area, is

$$-\frac{1}{3}\bar{n}um\bar{\ell}\frac{dv}{dx}$$

This rate of change of momentum must be balanced by a force in accordance with Newton's second law:

$$\frac{f}{A} = \frac{1}{3}\bar{n}um\bar{\ell}\frac{dv}{dx} \tag{8}$$

We can write Eq. (5-1), the defining equation for the viscosity coefficient η, as

$$\frac{f}{A} = \eta\frac{dv}{dx} \tag{9}$$

Combining Eqs. (8) and (9) we obtain an expression for η:

$$\eta = \tfrac{1}{3}m\bar{n}u\bar{\ell} \tag{10}$$

Since $m\bar{n}$ is the density of the gas, we have on the perfect-gas assumption

$$m\bar{n} = \rho = \frac{NM}{V} = \frac{pM}{RT}$$

and we obtain

$$\eta = \frac{1}{3}\sqrt{3}p\bar{\ell}\sqrt{\frac{M}{RT}} \tag{11}$$

where Eq. (1) has been used for u. Equation (11) can be rearranged to give

$$\bar{\ell} = \sqrt{3}\frac{\eta}{p}\left(\frac{RT}{M}\right)^{1/2} \tag{12}$$

This "mean-free-path treatment" involves several rough approximations; a more sophisticated derivation[1] gives a result identical with Eq. (12) except for the numerical factor:

$$\bar{\ell} = 1.256\frac{\eta}{p}\left(\frac{RT}{M}\right)^{1/2} \tag{13}$$

This equation can be used to calculate the mean free path in a gas from the experimentally observed viscosity.

If we combine Eqs. (3) and (13), a theoretical expression for the coefficient of gas viscosity is obtained:

$$\eta = 2.96 \times 10^{-25}\frac{\sqrt{MRT}}{d^2} \tag{14}$$

According to this equation, the gas viscosity coefficient should be independent of pressure and should increase with the square root of the absolute temperature. The viscosities of gases are, in fact, found to be substantially independent of pressure over a wide range. The temperature dependence generally differs to some extent from $T^{1/2}$ because the effective molecular diameter may be dependent on how hard the molecules collide and therefore may depend somewhat on temperature. Deviation from ideal behavior in the case of air (diatomic molecules, N_2 and O_2) is demonstrated by Eq. (5-19).

Equation (14) can also be used for the calculation of molecular diameters from experimental viscosity data. These can be compared with molecular diameters as determined by other experimental methods (molecular beams, diffusion, thermal conductivity, X-ray crystallographic determination of molecular packing in the solid state, etc.).

Thermal Conductivity. The mechanism of thermal conduction is analogous to that of viscous resistance to fluid flow. In the case of fluid flow, where a velocity gradient exists, momentum is transported from point to point by gas molecules; in thermal conduction, where a temperature gradient exists, it is kinetic energy that is transported from point to point by gas molecules. If in the mean-free-path treatment of viscosity the momentum is replaced by the average kinetic energy $\bar{\epsilon}$ of a molecule, we obtain for one-dimensional heat flow in the x direction an equation analogous to Eq. (8):

$$\dot{q} = \frac{1}{3}\bar{n}u\bar{\ell}\left(\frac{-d\bar{\epsilon}}{dx}\right) \tag{15}$$

where $\dot{q}$ is rate of heat flow per unit area, $\bar{n}$ is the number of molecules per unit volume (in cubic centimeters), u is the rms molecular velocity, and $\bar{\ell}$ is the mean free path. Now

$$\frac{d\bar{\epsilon}}{dx} = \frac{d\bar{\epsilon}}{dT}\frac{dT}{dx} = m\bar{C}_v\frac{dT}{dx}$$

where m is the mass of a molecule and $\bar{C}_v$ is the constant-volume specific-heat capacity (i.e., per gram) of the gas; thus we obtain

$$\dot{q} = \frac{1}{3} m\bar{n}u\bar{\ell}\,\bar{C}_v\left(\frac{-dT}{dx}\right) \tag{16}$$

By comparison with Eq. (6-2), the defining equation for the coefficient of thermal conductivity K, we find that

$$K = \tfrac{1}{3} m\bar{n}u\bar{\ell}\,\bar{C}_v \tag{17}$$

Using the expression [Eq. (10)] derived with the mean-free-path treatment for the coefficient of viscosity of a gas, we obtain the following relationship between coefficients of thermal conductivity and of viscosity:

$$\frac{K}{\eta} = \bar{C}_v \tag{18}$$

This simple expression is correct in form but requires a numerical coefficient different from unity; it must be remembered that the mean-free-path treatment is a simple treatment with several rough approximations. More advanced treatments[1] yield a modified relation

$$\frac{K}{\eta} = \frac{5}{2}\bar{C}_v \tag{19}$$

This result holds well only for monatomic gases. Interactions between diatomic and polyatomic molecules, involving transfer of rotational and vibrational energy, are difficult to treat theoretically and will not be discussed here. For monatomic gases, we can write

$$\frac{K}{\eta} = \frac{15}{4}\frac{R}{M} \tag{20}$$

where R is the gas constant and M is the molecular weight.

Diffusion. The theory of the diffusion of a gas is related to the theory of viscosity and of thermal conductivity in the sense that all three are concerned with a transport of some quantity from one point to another by the thermal motion of gas molecules. For diffusion, where a concentration gradient exists, chemical identity is transported.

Let there be two kinds of perfect gases, designated 1 and 2, present in a closed system of fixed total volume at concentrations of $\bar{n}_1$ and $\bar{n}_2$ molecules per cubic centimeter or $\bar{N}_1$ and $\bar{N}_2$ moles per cubic centimeter, respectively. These gases will have mean free paths of $\bar{\ell}_1$ and $\bar{\ell}_2$, respectively.

Let it be assumed that there is a concentration gradient in the x direction only. Consider a plane x_0, parallel to the y and z axes, and consider for a moment those molecules of kind 1 that pass through a small area $dA = dy\,dz$ on that plane. Assume for simplicity that these molecules suffered their most recent collision at or near the surface of an imaginary sphere of radius $\bar{\ell}_1$ with its center at dA. Now the mean distance from the plane x_0 up or down to the sphere is $2\bar{\ell}_1/3$. Therefore the mean concentration of these molecules, in the regions below the plane where they suffered their most recent collisions, is

$$\bar{n}_{-} = \bar{n}_1(x_0) - \frac{2\bar{l}_1}{3}\frac{d\bar{n}_1}{dx}$$

and the mean concentration similarly defined above the plane is

$$\bar{n}_{+} = \bar{n}_1(x_0) + \frac{2\bar{l}_1}{3}\frac{d\bar{n}_1}{dx}$$

The number of molecules passing through a unit area of a given plane surface depends on the concentration of the molecules;

$$z = \tfrac{1}{4}\bar{c}\bar{n} \tag{21}$$

where $\bar{c}$ is the mean speed [see Eqs. (2) and (4)]. The *net* number of molecules of kind 1 crossing the x_0 plane in the upward direction is therefore

$$z_1 = \frac{1}{4}\bar{c}_1(\bar{n}_{-} - \bar{n}_{+}) = -\frac{1}{3}\bar{c}_1\bar{l}_1\frac{d\bar{n}_1}{dx} \tag{22}$$

So far we have neglected the mass flow, if any, that is needed for the maintenance of constant and uniform pressure. If there is mass flow with a given velocity w_0 (which will be taken as positive when the mass flow is upward), the molecular velocities will be Maxwellian only with respect to a set of coordinate axes moving with that velocity, since the diffusing molecules suffered their recent collisions with molecules moving upward at that *mean* velocity. Equation (22) therefore represents the number of molecules per second crossing a unit area on a plane (parallel to the y and z axes) that is moving upward at velocity w_0. The number of molecules per second crossing a unit area on a *fixed* plane is then

$$\begin{aligned} z_1 &= \bar{n}_1 w_0 - \frac{1}{3}\bar{c}_1\bar{l}_1\frac{d\bar{n}_1}{dx} \\ z_2 &= \bar{n}_2 w_0 - \frac{1}{3}\bar{c}_2\bar{l}_2\frac{d\bar{n}_2}{dx} \end{aligned} \tag{23}$$

Now for maintenance of constant pressure we must have $z_1 = -z_2$; thus we obtain

$$\begin{aligned} w_0 &= \frac{1}{3(\bar{n}_1 + \bar{n}_2)}\left(\bar{c}_1\bar{l}_1\frac{d\bar{n}_1}{dx} + \bar{c}_2\bar{l}_2\frac{d\bar{n}_2}{dx}\right) \\ &= \frac{1}{3\bar{n}}\frac{d\bar{n}_1}{dx}(\bar{c}_1\bar{l}_1 - \bar{c}_2\bar{l}_2) \end{aligned} \tag{24}$$

and

$$z_1 = -\frac{1}{3\bar{n}}(\bar{n}_1\bar{l}_2\bar{c}_2 + \bar{n}_2\bar{l}_1\bar{c}_1)\frac{d\bar{n}_1}{dx} = -z_2 \tag{25}$$

where, since the pressure is constant, we have used the relation

$$-\frac{d\bar{n}_1}{dx} = \frac{d\bar{n}_2}{dx} \tag{26}$$

We can also write, in terms of moles,

$$\begin{aligned} Z_1 &= -\frac{1}{3\bar{N}}(\bar{N}_1\bar{l}_2\bar{c}_2 + \bar{N}_2\bar{l}_1\bar{c}_1)\frac{d\bar{N}_1}{dx} = -Z_2 \\ &= -\frac{1}{3}(X_1\bar{l}_2\bar{c}_2 + X_2\bar{l}_1\bar{c}_1)\frac{d\bar{N}_1}{dx} \end{aligned} \tag{27}$$

where X_1 and X_2 are mole fractions ($X_1 = \bar{N}_1/\bar{N}$, $X_2 = \bar{N}_2/\bar{N}$; $\bar{N} = \bar{N}_1 + \bar{N}_2$). By comparison with Eq. (7-2), the defining equation for the diffusion constant D_{12}, we find that

$$D_{12} = \tfrac{1}{3}(X_1\bar{l}_2\bar{c}_2 + X_2\bar{l}_1\bar{c}_1) \tag{28}$$

This equation appears to predict that D_{12} will be a function of the composition of the gas, although experimentally the diffusion constant is almost independent of composition. However, we must be careful in our definition of $\bar{l}_1$ and $\bar{l}_2$. We must take account of the fact that collisions of molecules of one species with one another can have no significant effect on the diffusion; such collisions do not affect the total momentum possessed by all the molecules of that species and thus do not affect the mean mass velocity of the species in its diffusion. Thus the total number of molecules of that species crossing the reference plane in a given period of time is not affected by such collisions and is the same as if such collisions did not take place at all. We should define $\bar{l}_1$ for our present purpose as the mean free path of molecules of species 1 between successive collisions with molecules of species 2 and *vice versa*. Accordingly we write [see Eq. (3)]

$$\bar{l}_1 = \frac{1}{\sqrt{2}\pi\bar{n}_2 d_{12}^2} \tag{29}$$

where by d_{12} we mean the center-to-center collision distance (assuming the molecules to be "hard spheres"). Equation (28) then becomes

$$D_{12} = \frac{1}{3\sqrt{2}\pi d_{12}^2\bar{n}}(\bar{c}_1 + \bar{c}_2) \tag{30}$$

which is independent of the composition. If we now introduce the kinetic theory expressions for $\bar{c}_1$ and $\bar{c}_2$ as given by Eq. (2) and make use of the perfect-gas expression for $\bar{n}$, namely,

$$\bar{n} = N_0\bar{N} = N_0\frac{p}{RT} \tag{31}$$

where N_0 is Avogadro's number, we obtain for the diffusion constant

$$D_{12} = \frac{2}{3\pi^{3/2}N_0}\,\frac{(RT)^{3/2}}{p}\,\frac{\sqrt{1/M_1} + \sqrt{1/M_2}}{d_{12}^2} \tag{32}$$

and for the *self-diffusion constant* (see Exp. 7)

$$D_1 = \frac{4}{3\pi^{3/2}N_0}\,\frac{(RT)^{3/2}}{p}\,\frac{\sqrt{1/M_1}}{d_1^2} \tag{33}$$

More advanced treatments[1] lead to a slightly different form of expression for D_{12} and different numerical coefficients for both D_{12} and D_1:

$$D_{12} = \frac{3}{8\sqrt{2\pi}N_0}\,\frac{(RT)^{3/2}}{p}\,\frac{\sqrt{1/M_1 + 1/M_2}}{d_{12}^2} \tag{34}$$

and

$$D_1 = \frac{3}{8\sqrt{\pi}N_0}\,\frac{(RT)^{3/2}}{p}\,\frac{\sqrt{1/M_1}}{d_1^2} \tag{35}$$

Equations (32) and (34), which are based on a "hard-sphere" model, are in agreement in predicting no dependence of the diffusion constant on gas composition. However, for real molecules a slight composition dependence should exist, which depends upon the form of the intermolecular potential.[1]

That Eqs. (32) and (34) differ in the dependence of D_{12} on the molecular weights should not be altogether surprising, since in our simple treatment we have assumed that the velocities of molecules after collisions are uncorrelated with their velocities before collisions, while, in fact, such correlations in general exist and are functions of the ratio of the masses of the colliding particles. To take this and other remaining factors properly into account would require a treatment that is beyond the scope of this book. It may suffice to point out here that the square-root quantity in Eq. (34) is equivalent to $\sqrt{1/\mu_{12}N_0}$, where

$$\mu_{12} = \frac{m_1 m_2}{m_1 + m_2}$$

is the "reduced mass" of a system comprising a molecule of kind 1 and a molecule of kind 2.

The diffusion constant is predicted by Eqs. (32) to (35) to be inversely proportional to the total pressure. Experimentally this is the case to roughly the degree to which the perfect-gas law applies. The equations appear to predict that the diffusion constant will be proportional to the three-halves power of the temperature; however, as in the case of viscosity, significant deviations from this behavior occur, as actual molecules are not truly "hard spheres" and have collision diameters that depend on the relative speeds with which molecules collide with one another.

By means of Eq. (34) it is possible to calculate center-to-center collision distances d_{12} from a measured diffusion constant D_{12}. If three diffusion constants D_{12}, D_{13}, and D_{23} can be measured, individual molecular diameters d_1, d_2, and d_3 can be obtained if it can be assumed that the collision distances are the arithmetic averages of the molecular diameters involved, as would be the case with hard spheres:

$$d_{ij} = \tfrac{1}{2}(d_i + d_j) \tag{36}$$

If a self-diffusion constant D_1 can be measured approximately through one of the approaches discussed in Exp. 7, a molecular diameter d_1 can be obtained directly from Eq. (35). Conversely, Eqs. (34) and (35) can be used to estimate a diffusion constant if molecular diameters are known from some other source or to calculate self-diffusion constants from binary diffusion constants (or vice versa) by calculating first the molecular diameters. In the latter case it can be argued that any remaining approximations in the treatment will largely cancel out.

As expected, the self-diffusion constant can be related to other transport coefficients. From Eq. (28) we can write for self-diffusion

$$D_1 = \frac{2}{3}\left(\frac{8}{3\pi}\right)^{1/2} u_1 \bar{l}_1 \tag{37}$$

where we now interpret $\bar{l}_1$ as the mean free path as customarily defined. The simple mean-free-path treatment of gas viscosity gave Eq. (10), which can be written as

$$\eta = \tfrac{1}{3}\rho u \bar{l} \tag{38}$$

where ρ is the mass density of the gas. Thus we obtain

$$\frac{D}{\eta} = 1.8\frac{1}{\rho} \tag{39}$$

More exact treatments[1] have shown that the coefficient of $1/\rho$ in this expression should be 1.20 for hard spheres and about 1.5 for spherical molecules with an inverse fifth-power repulsion. Clearly D may also be related to K; for monatomic gases, we can use Eq. (20) and obtain

$$\frac{D}{K} \simeq \frac{0.4M}{\rho R} \tag{40}$$

REFERENCES

1. E. H. Kennard, "Kinetic Theory of Gases," McGraw-Hill, New York (1938); R. D. Present, "Kinetic Theory of Gases," McGraw-Hill, New York (1958).
2. W. J. Moore, "Physical Chemistry," 2d ed., Prentice-Hall, Englewood Cliffs, N. J. (1955).

Experiment 5. Viscosity of Gases

It is a general property of fluids (liquids and gases) that an applied shearing force that produces flow in the fluid is resisted by a force that is proportional to the gradient of flow velocity in the fluid. This is the phenomenon known as *viscosity*.

Consider two parallel plates of area A, a distance D apart, as in Fig. 1. It is convenient to imagine that D is small in comparison with any dimension of the plates in order to avoid edge effects. Let there be a uniform fluid substance between the two plates. If one of the plates is held at rest while the other moves with uniform velocity v_0 in a direction parallel to its own plane, under ideal conditions the fluid undergoes a pure shearing motion and a flow velocity gradient of magnitude v_0/D exists throughout the fluid. This is the simplest example of *laminar flow*, or pure viscous flow, which takes place under such conditions that the inertia of the fluid plays no significant role in determining the nature of the fluid motion. The most important of these conditions is that the flow velocities be small. In laminar flow in a system with stationary solid boundaries, the paths of infinitesimal mass elements of the fluid do not cross any of an infinite family of stationary laminar surfaces that may be defined in the system. In the simple example above, these laminar surfaces are planes parallel to the plates. When fluid velocities become high, the flow becomes *turbulent* and the momentum of the fluid carries it across such laminar surfaces so that eddies or vortices form.

In the above example, with laminar flow, the force f resisting the relative motion of the plates is proportional to the area A and to the velocity gradient v_0/D:

$$f = \eta A \frac{v_0}{D} \tag{1}$$

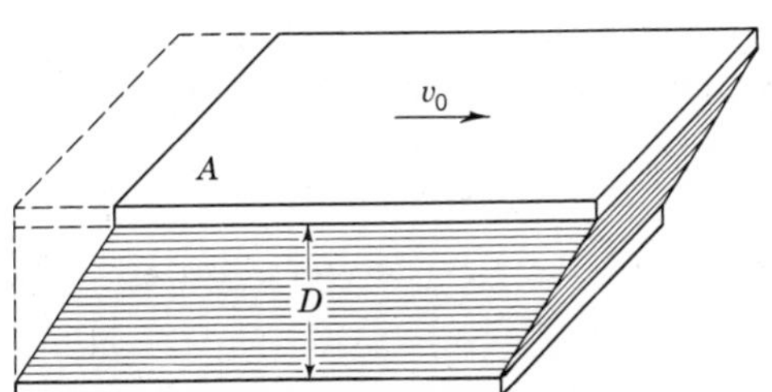

FIG. 1. Ideal plane-parallel laminar flow.

The constant of proportionality η is called the *coefficient of viscosity* of the fluid, or simply the *viscosity* of the fluid. The cgs unit of viscosity is the *poise,* which is equivalent to a dyne-second per square centimeter.

The viscosities of common liquids are of the order of a centipoise; at 20.20°C, the viscosity of water is 1.000 centipoise, while that of ethyl ether is 0.23 centipoise, and that of glycerin is 830 centipoises (8.3 poises). The viscosity of pitch or asphalt at room temperature is of the order of 10^{10} poises, and the viscosity of glass (a supercooled liquid) is many powers of 10 higher. The viscosities of gases are of the order of 100 or 200 micropoises. The viscosities of liquids and soft solids decrease with increasing temperature, while those of gases increase with increasing temperature. Viscosities of all substances are substantially independent of pressure at ordinary pressures but show change at very high pressures and apparently in the case of gases alone at very low pressures also.

METHOD

Among the various methods[1, 2] that have been used for determining the viscosities of liquids and gases are several that involve the measurement of viscous drag on a rotating disk or cylinder immersed in the fluid or a sphere falling through it. The simplest and most commonly used methods, however, depend on measurement of the rate of viscous flow through a cylindrical capillary tube, in relation to the pressure gradient along the capillary.

For absolute viscosity measurements the pressure should be constant at each end of the capillary. A simple but excellent method for gases has been described by A. O. Rankine[2] in which a constant-pressure difference is maintained across the ends of a capillary by a pellet of mercury falling in a parallel tube of considerably larger diameter (up to 3.5 mm). However, it is rarely necessary to make absolute determinations. Most viscosity measurements are made in "relative viscosimeters," in which the viscosity is proportional to the time required for the flow of a fixed quantity of fluid through the capillary, under a pressure differential that varies during the experiment *but always in the same manner.* If the pressure differential as a function of the volume of fluid passed through the capillary is accurately known, the viscosimeter can be used for absolute determinations. More commonly the unknown factors are lumped into a single apparatus constant, the value of which is determined by time-of-flow measurements on a reference substance of known viscosity. This is the principle of the Ostwald viscosimeter routinely used for measurements on liquids and solutions, in which capillary flow is induced by gravity (and accordingly the time of flow is proportional to the viscosity divided by the liquid density). It is also the principle of the method used for measurements on gases in this experiment, in which gas is caused to flow through the capillary by mercury displacement.

THEORY

Let us imagine a long cylindrical capillary tube, of length L and radius r. Let x denote the distance outward radially from the axis of the tube and z denote the distance along the axis. Under conditions of laminar flow, the laminar surfaces are a family of right circular cylinders coaxial with the tube.

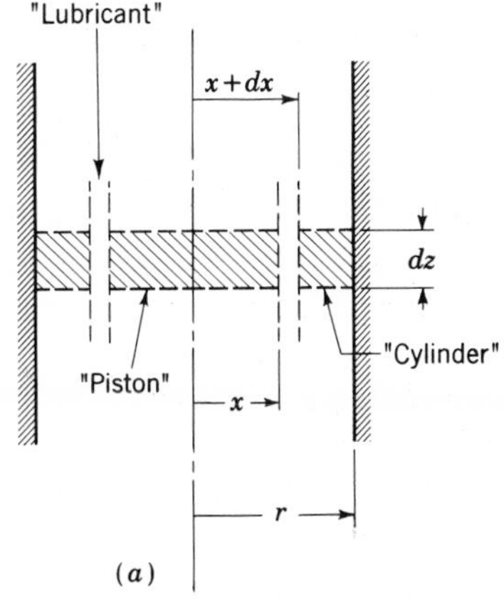

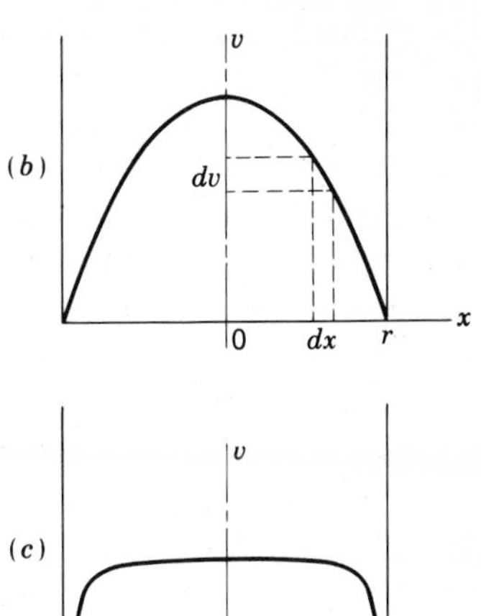

FIG. 2. (*a*) Definition of variables. (*b*) Parabolic velocity distribution. (*c*) Abnormal (approximately uniform) velocity distribution existing near inlet.

Consider two such cylindrical surfaces, of radius x and $x + dx$ and length dz as shown in Fig. 2*a*. What is the difference in velocity dv between the two cylinders when the flow rate is such as to produce a pressure gradient dp/dz along the tube?

The force tending to cause the inner cylinder to slide past the outer one is the same as it would be for a *solid* inner piston of radius x sliding with the same relative velocity in a *solid* cylinder of radius $x + dx$, with the fluid playing the role of a "lubricant" between. Since the spacing dx is infinitesimal in comparison with the radius of curvature, we may imagine that the conditions existing between the two surfaces resemble those of Fig. 1. The force acting on an element of length dz of the tube is

$$df = \frac{dp}{dz}\pi x^2\,dz$$

The corresponding cross-sectional area is

$$dA = 2\pi x\,dz$$

and the spacing D is dx. In order to determine the corresponding velocity difference dv, we substitute for f, A, D, and v_0 in Eq. (1) and rearrange to obtain

$$dv = \frac{\pi x^2}{\eta 2\pi x}\frac{dp}{dz}\,dx = -\frac{1}{2\eta}\left(-\frac{dp}{dz}\right)x\,dx \tag{2}$$

To find the velocity at any value of x, we integrate from $x = r$, where the velocity vanishes, to $x = x$:

$$v(x) = \int_r^x dv = \frac{1}{4\eta}\left(-\frac{dp}{dz}\right)(r^2 - x^2) \tag{3}$$

This equation predicts that the distribution of velocities in the tube can be represented by a parabola, as in Fig. 2*b*. The volume rate of flow past a given point (volume per unit time) is

$$\phi_V = \int_0^r v(x)2\pi x\,dx = \frac{\pi r^4}{8\eta}\left(-\frac{dp}{dz}\right) \tag{4}$$

and the mean velocity is

$$\bar{v} = \frac{\phi_V}{\pi r^2} = \frac{1}{8\eta}\left(-\frac{dp}{dz}\right)r^2 = \frac{1}{2}v_{\max} \tag{5}$$

If the fluid is incompressible, the volume rate of fluid flow must be constant along the tube and we find, where p_1 and p_2 are the pressures at the inlet and outlet of the tube respectively, that

$$\phi_V = \frac{\pi r^4(p_1 - p_2)}{8\eta L}$$

This equation, known as *Poiseuille's law,* can be applied under ordinary laminar-flow conditions to liquids, and also to gases in the limiting case where $(p_1 - p_2)$ is negligible in comparison with p_1 or p_2. For a more general treatment of gases, their compressibility must be taken into account. If we assume the perfect-gas law, we can write for the *molar* rate of flow (moles per unit time)

$$\phi_N = \frac{p}{RT}\phi_V = \frac{\pi r^4}{8\eta RT}p\left(-\frac{dp}{dz}\right) = \frac{\pi r^4}{16\eta RT}\left[-\frac{d(p^2)}{dz}\right] \tag{6}$$

Since conservation of matter requires that the mole rate of flow be constant along the tube, $d(p^2)/dz$ must be constant and accordingly we can write

$$-\frac{d(p^2)}{dz} = \frac{p_1{}^2 - p_2{}^2}{L} \tag{7}$$

We now obtain

$$\phi_N = \frac{\pi r^4(p_1{}^2 - p_2{}^2)}{16\eta LRT} \tag{8}$$

In the apparatus to be used in this experiment (see Fig. 3) the gas contained in a bulb B is forced through a capillary tube by mercury flowing into the bulb from an upper reservoir R. The time during which the mercury level rises from a lower fiducial mark a to an upper fiducial mark b is denoted as t_{ab}. For any such apparatus of given design and dimensions and containing a constant amount of mercury, the inlet pressure p_1 is a definite function of the volume V occupied by the gas in the bulb and tubing below the capillary; p_2 is a constant (atmospheric pressure). If N is the number of moles of gas below the capillary,

$$\frac{dN}{dt} = \frac{1}{RT}\frac{d(p_1V)}{dt} = \frac{1}{RT}\left(V\frac{dp_1}{dV} + p_1\right)\frac{dV}{dt}$$

Setting $(-dN/dt)$ to ϕ_N we obtain†

$$-\frac{dV}{dt} = \frac{\pi r^4(p_1{}^2 - p_2{}^2)}{16\eta L[V(dp_1/dV) + p_1]} \tag{9}$$

On inverting and integrating, we find that the time required for the mercury meniscus to rise from mark a to mark b is

$$t_{ab} = \eta\frac{16L}{\pi r^4}\int_{V_b}^{V_a}\frac{V(dp_1/dV) + p_1}{p_1{}^2 - p_2{}^2}\,dV \equiv K\eta \tag{10}$$

where the "apparatus constant" K contains a part $(16L/\pi r^4)$ determined by the

† The minus sign is necessary, since dN/dt is negative while ϕ_N is positive.

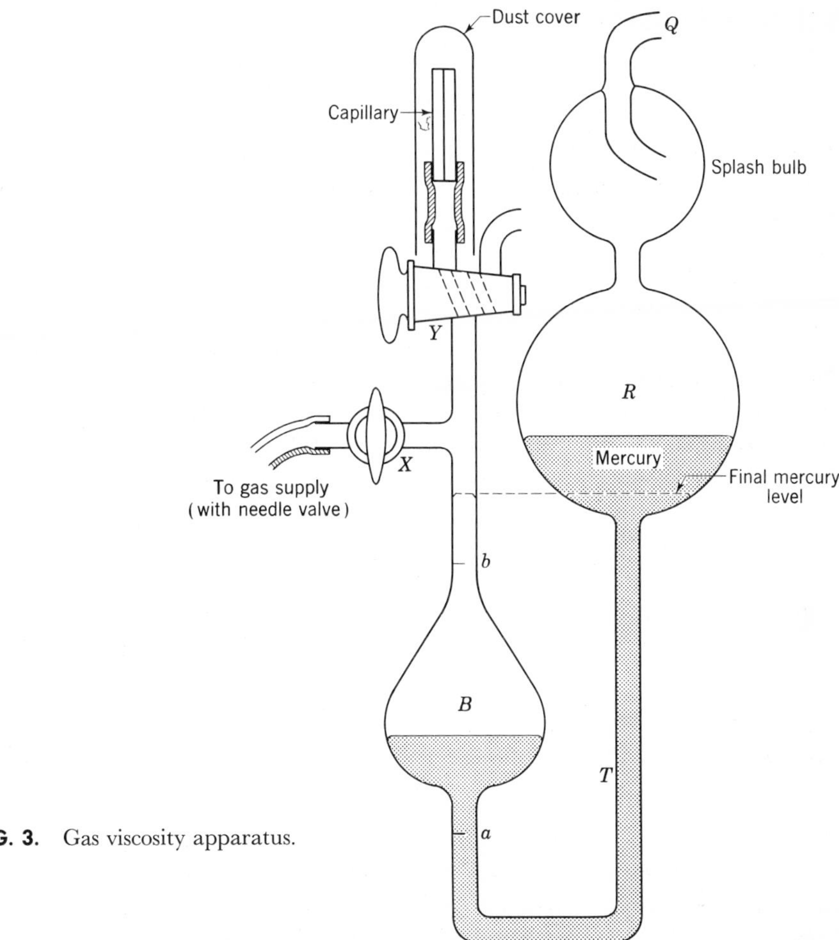

FIG. 3. Gas viscosity apparatus.

capillary tube and a part (the integral over V) determined by the shape and dimensions of the bulb and the mercury pressure system. While it is possible to determine K from capillary dimensions and measurements of p_1 as a function of V (as described later), more satisfactory results can be obtained by determining K from the time of flow of a gas of known viscosity.

Factors Influencing Apparatus Design. Practical application of the theory presented above depends on the validity of a number of assumptions. One, which has already been mentioned, is the assumption that the flow is laminar. It has been shown by dimensional analysis that for any given type of hydrodynamic experiment the conditions for onset of turbulent flow depend upon the magnitude of a certain combination of pertinent experimental variables that is a pure number, called the Reynolds number R. For flow through a long, round, straight tube,

$$R = r\bar{v}\frac{\rho}{\eta} \tag{11}$$

where ρ is the density of the fluid. It is found empirically that laminar flow is always obtained in such a tube when R is less than 1000 regardless of the magnitude of any of the individual variables r, $\bar{v}$, ρ, η. Laminar flow can be obtained with a

Reynolds number as high as 10,000 or even 25,000 if sufficiently careful attention is given to the smoothness of the walls and to the shape of the inlet, but ordinarily turbulent flow is obtained with Reynolds numbers in excess of a few thousand.[3]

Another important factor concerns the transition from a uniform velocity distribution at the inlet of the tube to the parabolic velocity distribution inside the tube (see Fig. 2*b* and *c*). The region in which this transition takes place may be of considerable length, and Eq. (8) will not apply very well over this region. Thus it is important that the length of the region be small in comparison with the length of the tube. Experiments have shown[3] that the length L' of the transition region is given approximately by the equation

$$L' = \tfrac{1}{4}Rr \tag{12}$$

where r is the radius of the tube and R is the Reynolds number.

It is important that the tube be very straight; the critical Reynolds number for onset of turbulence will be greatly reduced if the tube is appreciably curved. As a suitable criterion it might be specified that deviations from straightness should be negligible in comparison with r over distances of the order of L'.

Kinetic-energy Correction. In deriving Eq. (10) it was assumed that "end effects" are negligible. Such end effects are most likely to be important at the inlet of the capillary, where a pressure drop occurs as a result of the necessity of imparting kinetic energy to the fluid.

By the law of Bernoulli, the pressure drop is equal to the "flow-average" *kinetic-energy density* of the fluid (that is, the rate of flow of kinetic energy past a given fixed point divided by the volume rate of flow of fluid past this point). For flow through a pipe or capillary,

$$\Delta p = \frac{1}{\pi r^2 \bar{v}} \int_0^r \rho \frac{v^2}{2} v \; 2\pi x \, dx \tag{13}$$

Beyond the transitional region of length L' we may assume the parabolic velocity distribution given by Eqs. (3) and (5):

$$v = 2\bar{v}\left(1 - \frac{x^2}{r^2}\right) \tag{14}$$

The over-all kinetic-energy pressure drop from the inlet to the point where the distribution has become parabolic is obtained by substituting Eq. (14) into Eq. (13) and is

$$\Delta p = \rho(\bar{v})^2 = \frac{\rho}{\pi^2 r^4} \phi_V^2 \tag{15}$$

This quantity is called the *kinetic-energy correction.* In practice, it is subtracted from the over-all pressure difference $p_1 - p_2$, since no comparable pressure change need ordinarily be considered at the outlet end. This results from the fact that the kinetic energy of the fluid carries it in a jet stream far out into the body of fluid beyond the outlet, so that the kinetic energy is dissipated (as heat, rather than as potential energy) at a considerable distance from where it could otherwise be effective in producing a pressure change at the outlet.

To take into account the effect of kinetic energy on the time of flow t_{ab}, we can subtract Δp, as given by Eq. (15), from p_1 in Eqs. (8) and (9), then invert and integrate as before. We obtain the integral appearing in Eq. (10), plus additional terms which are small. To simplify the latter we assume that $(p_1 - p_2)$ and $V\,dp_1/dV$ are negligible in comparison with p_1. We obtain

$$t_{ab} = K\eta + \frac{\rho V_{ab}}{8\pi\eta L} \tag{16}$$

where V_{ab} is the volume of the bulb between the two fiducial marks and K is the same apparatus constant as previously defined.†

Slip Correction. It has been assumed throughout the above discussion that Eq. (1) is valid down to the smallest dimensions that are of any significant importance in the experiment. This assumption appears well founded for laminar *liquid* flow, but for gases it breaks down when the mean free path is not negligibly small in comparison with the apparatus dimensions. Thus, at very low pressures or at ordinary pressures in capillaries of very small diameter, gas viscosities appear to be lower than when measured under ordinary conditions. When the mean free path of a gas is small but not negligible in comparison with the radius of the capillary, the gas behaves as if it were "slipping" at the capillary walls, rather than having zero velocity at the walls as shown in Fig. 2*b* and given in Eq. (3). Indeed, the mean velocity of the gas infinitesimally close to the wall is not zero, for although half the molecules in this region have suffered their most recent collision at the wall the other half have suffered their most recent collision at some distance from the wall, of the order of a mean free path $\bar{l}$. Therefore the mass velocity, instead of being zero at the wall, is a fraction approximating $(4\bar{l}/r)$ of the average mass velocity $\bar{v}$. Thus, if Eq. (16) yields the "apparent viscosity" η_{app}, the true viscosity can be obtained from the equation

$$\eta = \eta_{app}\left(1 + \frac{4\bar{l}}{r}\right) \tag{18}$$

Dependence on Flow Velocity. With regard to the tacit assumption that the viscosity coefficient is independent of flow velocities and gradients of flow velocities, it must be remembered that the molecular velocities are essentially Maxwellian in a gas under shear only when variations in mass velocity over distances of the order of a mean free path are small in comparison with the molecular velocities themselves; if these differences are considerable, it is possible that the perturbed distribution of molecular velocities will manifest itself in an altered apparent viscosity coefficient. Without going into detail, it may be stated that if $\bar{v} \ll u$ (where u is the rms molecular velocity) and if $\bar{l} \ll r$, the error in η due to perturbation of the Maxwellian distribution will be negligible.

† One may ask whether the viscous drag and kinetic energy of the mercury in tube T of the apparatus shown in Fig. 3 will influence the experimental results. Simple calculations are likely to show that kinetic-energy effects (including possible turbulence) will be more important than viscous drag. A reasonable design criterion (for 0.1 per cent maximum error) might be based on the application of Eq. (15) to the mercury in tube T:

$$3\,\frac{\rho_{\mathrm{Hg}}}{\pi^2 r_T^4}\,\phi_{V\mathrm{max}}^2 \leqslant 0.001(p_{1\mathrm{max}} - p_2) \tag{17}$$

where the factor 3 appears reasonable, since there are three straight portions of the tube. If the Reynolds number is high enough to indicate turbulent flow of the mercury, the factor 3 may be too small. This formula assumes a parabolic velocity distribution; a nearly uniform distribution would appear more likely in view of Eq. (12) but is a less conservative assumption, since it would imply an additional factor of ½ on the left side of Eq. (17).

EXPERIMENTAL

Using the apparatus shown in Fig. 3, measure the flow times t_{ab} for dry air, helium, argon, carbon dioxide, and/or any other gases provided, at the same temperature in the same apparatus. Be careful not to disturb the leveling of the apparatus; the time of flow is rather sensitive to tipping of the apparatus, and it is important to have the same leveling for all gases studied. Moisture should be removed from the air by inserting a drying tube in the rubber hose line between the compressed-air supply and the viscosity apparatus. The drying tube (Fig. 4) should be full but not too tightly packed. It should be removed from the line when other gases are studied. If CO_2 is studied, be sure it is at room temperature before starting the run, as it cools considerably on expansion at the outlet of the cylinder.

Admit one of the gases to the bulb B by slowly opening stopcock X while stopcock Y remains closed; the mercury level in the bulb should drop quite slowly. Close stopcock X when the Hg level is about 2 cm below the lower fiducial mark. Carefully vent the bulb through the open outlet from the three-way stopcock Y to flush the system. Fill and flush a second time. Refill the bulb with gas, then open stopcock Y to the capillary and measure t_{ab} with a stopwatch. Four or more runs should be made if time permits.

Repeat the above procedure for each of the gases to be studied. Also record the temperature and the corrected barometric pressure p_2. Record at least approximate values for all the pertinent apparatus factors—L, r, V_B, maximum value of $p_1 - p_2$, radius of tube T.

Optional: Make an absolute determination of the apparatus constant K. Measure the length L of the capillary tube with a millimeter scale. Fill the capillary with mercury, measure the length of the pellet of mercury contained in the capillary, expel the mercury into a weighing bottle, and weigh it. From the results calculate r for the capillary. To find p_1 as a function of V, attach to the outlet tube Q a gas burette with a parallel leveling bulb (see Exp. 2). Use water as the indicating fluid. By means of one of the stopcocks (say Y) permit the mercury to rise a little at a time in bulb B. After each change measure the quantity introduced

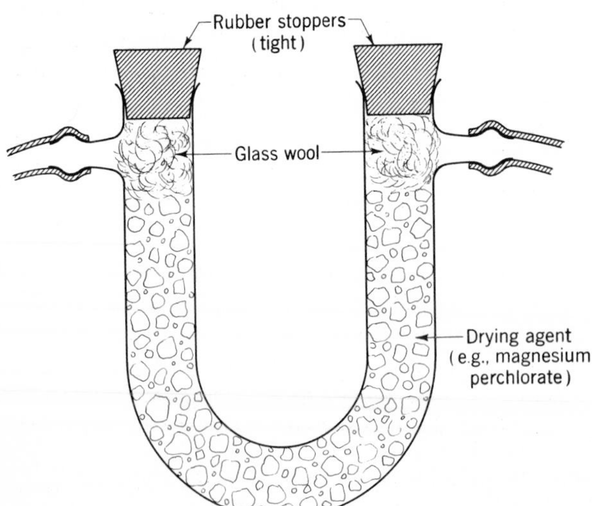

FIG. 4. U tube for drying air.

by adjusting and reading the gas burette, and measure the pressure difference $(p_1 - p_2)$ by measuring the difference in mercury levels, preferably with a cathetometer. Alternatively, connect the gas inlet tube P of the apparatus directly to an open-tube manometer, for measuring $(p_1 - p_2)$ directly. Plot p_1 against V and draw a curve through the points. Evaluate dp_1/dV at a number of points and calculate the integrand of Eq. (10). Evaluate the integral graphically and compute K. Then compare the value of K with the value obtained by calibration with dry air.

CALCULATIONS

For calibration purposes dry air was chosen as the standard, since it is easily available and has been carefully studied by many investigators. Data from many sources can be summarized in the empirical Sutherland expression[4]

$$\eta = \frac{(145.8 \times 10^{-7})T^{3/2}}{T + 110.4} \tag{19}$$

which gives the viscosity of dry air in poises at 1 atm as a function of absolute temperature T. At 25°C, the value is 183.7 micropoises (0.01837 centipoise). For the temperature of your experiment, calculate η for dry air from Eq. (19).

For each gas studied, average the flow times for the individual runs to obtain an average t_{ab}.

If Eq. (10) were valid, the ratio of viscosities for two gases would equal the corresponding ratio of flow times. Assuming Eq. (10) and using t_{air} and η_{air}, find approximate values of the viscosities of the other gases from their flow times.

For each gas (including air) calculate the maximum value of the Reynolds number from Eq. (11) and verify that it is below 1000. Use Eq. (12) to verify that L', the length of the transition region, is small compared with the length L of the capillary. Estimate the largest value of $\bar{v}$ from Eq. (5) and compare it with the rms molecular velocity u.

If the required conditions have been met, kinetic energy and slip corrections may now be made in order to get more precise values of η. First calculate $\bar{l}$ for each gas from Eq. (IV-13). With Eq. (18) find η_{app} for dry air and use this value in Eq. (16) to find the value of K. Now calculate η_{app} for the other gases from Eq. (16) (one can use the approximate value of η in evaluating the kinetic-energy correction term). Finally apply the slip correction to obtain the true viscosity.

Report the final values obtained for η together with the temperature at which they were determined. Report also for each gas the calculated mean free path at 1 atm and the effective molecular diameter as calculated from the viscosity.

APPARATUS

Gas viscosity apparatus, complete with capillary tube and mercury; gas supply outlet(s) with needle valve(s); glass U tube with rubber stoppers and policemen; two lengths of gum-rubber tubing; 0 to 30°C thermometer; stopwatch; millimeter scale. If an absolute determination is to be made: additional mercury; weighing bottle; gas burette and leveling bulb; ring stands and clamps; cathetometer or open-tube manometer.

Cylinders of argon, helium, and carbon dioxide; source of compressed air; glass wool; drying agent (such as magnesium perchlorate); stopcock grease.

REFERENCES

1. J. R. Partington, "An Advanced Treatise on Physical Chemistry," vol. I, pp. 876ff., Longmans, London (1949).
2. J. Reilly and W. N. Rae, "Physico-chemical Methods," 5th ed., vol. I, pp. 667, 690 and vol. III, p. 247, Van Nostrand, Princeton, N. J. (1953).
3. L. Prandtl, "Essentials of Fluid Dynamics," Blackie, Glasgow (1952).
4. NBS-NACA Tables of Thermal Properties of Gases, Table 2.39, Dry Air, compiled by F. C. Morey (December, 1950).

GENERAL READING

S. Pai, "Viscous Flow Theory," vol. I, Laminar Flow, Van Nostrand, Princeton, N. J. (1956).

Experiment 6. Thermal Conductivity of Gases

The thermal conductivity of a substance is a measure of its capacity to conduct heat. Heat tends to flow in a homogeneous body in the direction of the temperature gradient, from regions of higher temperature toward regions of lower temperature. The rate of heat flow, or amount of heat that flows through a given cross section per unit time, is proportional to the area of the cross section and to the magnitude of the temperature gradient normal to the cross section. Thus in an idealized experimental situation in which the temperature varies only in the x direction, the rate of heat flow $\dot{Q}$ through an area A normal to the x axis is given by

$$\dot{Q} = KA\left(\frac{-dT}{dx}\right) \tag{1}$$

The constant of proportionality K is called the *coefficient of thermal conductivity.* It is customarily expressed in units of cal cm^{-1} sec^{-1} deg^{-1}.

More generally, if $\dot{q}$ is the "heat flux" or rate of flow of heat per unit area $(\dot{Q}/A)$, we can write

$$\dot{q} = -K\frac{dT}{dx} \tag{2}$$

where x is a coordinate taken in the direction of the temperature gradient.

In this experiment, measurements are made in a hot-wire cell to obtain values of K for several gases.

THEORY OF STATIONARY-STATE CYLINDRICAL HEAT FLOW

Differential Equation. Let us assume that heat is flowing in an isotropic homogeneous nonflowing (nonconvecting) medium of thermal conductivity coefficient K, under conditions of cylindrical symmetry, so that the temperature is a function only of the distance r from the cylindrical axis and the direction of heat flow is everywhere perpendicular to that axis. Let us calculate the rate of accumulation of heat in a cylindrical ring of radius r, thickness dr, and *unit height* (in the axial direction).

The rate of heat flow into the region, at r, is

$$\dot{Q}(r) = 2\pi r\,\dot{q}(r) = -2\pi K\left(r\frac{\partial T}{\partial r}\right)_r$$

and the rate of heat flow out of the region, at $r + dr$, is

$$\begin{aligned}\dot{Q}(r+dr) &= 2\pi(r+dr)\,\dot{q}(r+dr) \\ &= -2\pi K\left(r\frac{\partial T}{\partial r}\right)_{r+dr} \\ &= -2\pi K\left[\left(r\frac{\partial T}{\partial r}\right)_r + \frac{\partial}{\partial r}\left(r\frac{\partial T}{\partial r}\right)dr\right]\end{aligned}$$

The net rate of accumulation of heat in this region is

$$\dot{Q}(r) - \dot{Q}(r+dr) = 2\pi K\frac{\partial}{\partial r}\left(r\frac{\partial T}{\partial r}\right)dr \tag{3}$$

Now if the specific heat is $\bar{c}$ and the mass density is ρ,

$$\dot{Q}(r) - \dot{Q}(r+dr) = \bar{c}\rho\frac{\partial T}{\partial t}2\pi r\,dr \tag{4}$$

Combining these two equations we obtain

$$\frac{\partial T}{\partial t} = \frac{K}{\bar{c}\rho}\frac{1}{r}\frac{\partial}{\partial r}\left(r\frac{\partial T}{\partial r}\right) \tag{5}$$

This is the partial differential equation for heat flow in the special case of cylindrical symmetry. In principle it can be integrated with any given set of boundary conditions to yield the temperature T as a function of r and t.

Stationary State. In what we shall describe as a stationary state, the temperature nowhere changes with time; that is,

$$\frac{\partial T}{\partial t} \equiv 0$$

Equation (5) then becomes

$$\frac{d}{dr}\left(r\frac{dT}{dr}\right) = 0 \tag{6}$$

This equation is a special case of Laplace's equation for the case of complete cylindrical symmetry.[1]

The boundary conditions that we shall impose are

$$\begin{aligned} T &= T_1 \qquad \text{at } r = r_1 \\ T &= T_2 \qquad \text{at } r = r_2 \end{aligned} \tag{7}$$

These boundary conditions apply to the flow of heat through a medium contained between two infinite concentric cylinders, each maintained at constant temperature. After two successive integrations of (6) we obtain

$$T = C_1 \ln r + C_2 \tag{8}$$

where C_1 and C_2 are constants of integration, which we can evaluate by means of the boundary conditions. Using Eqs. (7) we obtain

$$T = \frac{1}{\ln (r_2/r_1)} \left(T_2 \ln \frac{r}{r_1} + T_1 \ln \frac{r_2}{r} \right) \tag{9}$$

and accordingly

$$\dot{q} = -K \frac{dT}{dr} = \frac{K}{r \ln (r_2/r_1)} (T_1 - T_2) \tag{10}$$

For cylinders of length L,

$$\dot{Q} = \frac{2\pi KL}{\ln (r_2/r_1)} (T_1 - T_2) \tag{11}$$

METHOD

The thermal conductivity of a gas is usually measured in a cylindrical cell either containing an electrically heated wire coaxially mounted in a tube of comparatively large diameter as in the present apparatus or consisting of two concentric cylinders with the gas occupying the narrow gap between.[2, 3, 4] With accurate knowledge of the apparatus dimensions and electrical properties, absolute measurements of thermal conductivity can be made; as in the case of viscosity (Exp. 5) such apparatus can also be used for relative measurements.

Apparatus. The thermal-conductivity cell used in this experiment is shown in Fig. 1. A platinum wire (about 25 cm in length) is mounted coaxially in a long, accurately straight glass tube of uniform inside diameter between two metal "heat stations." The wire has a radius r_1 (about 0.005 cm), and the tube has an inner radius r_2 (about 0.4 cm). The temperature T_2 of the tube is maintained by a thermostat bath. The temperature T_1 of the wire is maintained at a value a few degrees higher by passing electric current through it; for measurements on gases, it is necessary to limit the temperature difference to a few degrees to prevent convection. The thermal-conductivity coefficient K obtained with this apparatus applies to a temperature intermediate between T_1 and T_2. Since the temperature dependence of K is small [see, for example, Eq. (20)], no great error is introduced by assuming that K applies to the bath temperature T_2.

Let us neglect for the moment the end effects at the heat stations and energy transfer by radiation. In the steady state the rate of dissipation of electrical energy as heat by the wire (i^2R) will be equal to the rate of heat flow from the wire to the glass wall:

$$\dot{Q} = i^2R = \frac{2\pi KL}{\ln (r_2/r_1)} (T_1 - T_2) \tag{12}$$

where R is the resistance of the wire and L is its length. Thus,

$$K = \frac{i^2R}{2\pi L} \frac{\ln (r_2/r_1)}{T_1 - T_2} \tag{13}$$

In actuality, the end effects are by no means negligible. The major effect is flow of heat along the wire to the heat stations. A secondary effect is a decrease in the heat flux through the gas near the heat stations due to the lower wire temperature in this region, but this effect is adequately taken into account by the fact that the resistance of the wire measures the *average* wire temperature.

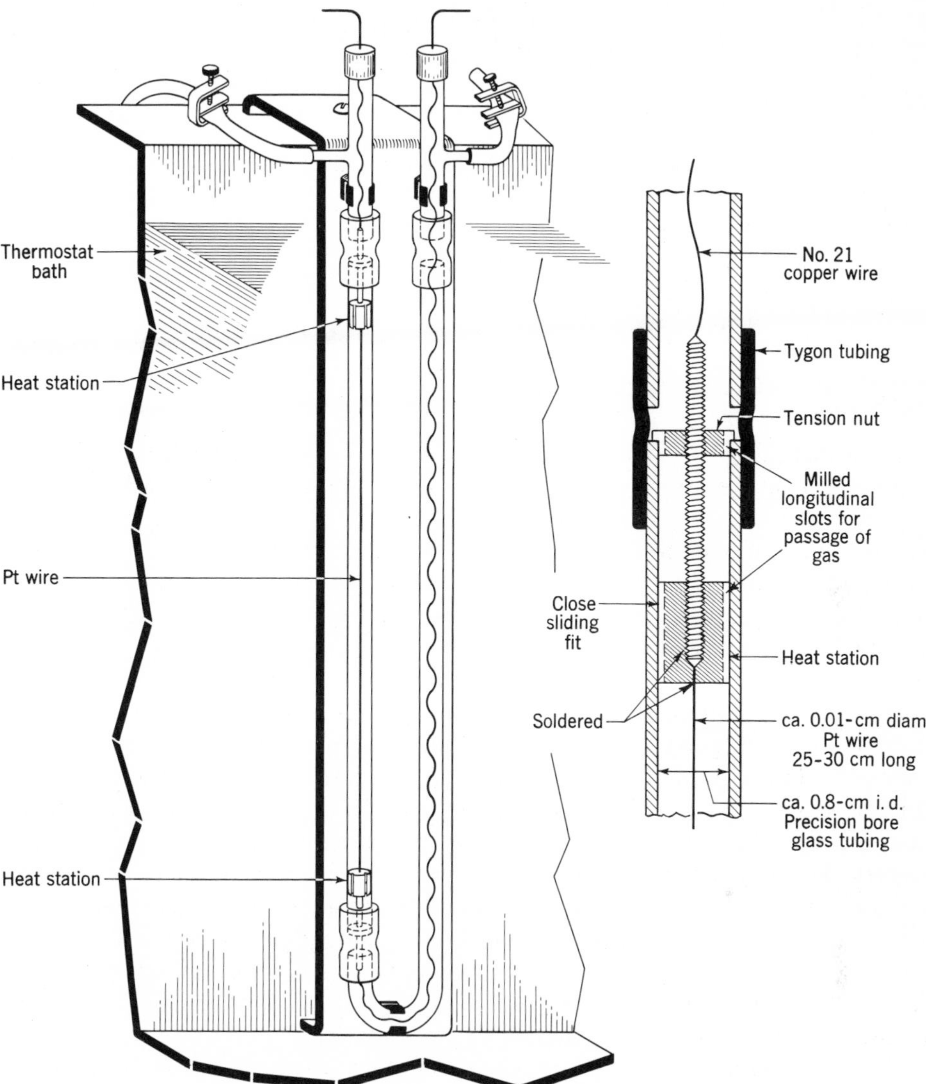

FIG. 1. Thermal-conductivity cell.

If we designate by α the fraction of the total supplied power that is conducted along the wire to the heat stations or transmitted by radiation, we can write

$$K = \frac{(1 - \alpha)i^2R}{2\pi L} \frac{\ln(r_2/r_1)}{T_1 - T_2} \tag{14}$$

When i is given in amperes, R in ohms, T_1 and T_2 in degrees Kelvin, and L in centimeters, the units of K are joule $\text{cm}^{-1}\ \text{sec}^{-1}\ \text{deg}^{-1}$; if K is desired in cal $\text{cm}^{-1}\ \text{sec}^{-1}\ \text{deg}^{-1}$ an additional factor of 4.184 must be placed in the denominator of (14).

Although, if r_2/r_1 and $(T_1 - T_2)$ are accurately known, Eq. (14) can be used for the determination of the thermal conductivity coefficient of the gas on an absolute basis, it is much easier experimentally to determine thermal-conductivity coefficients on a relative basis by the study of two or more gases in successive experiments in the same cell. It is then not necessary to know the value of $(T_1 - T_2)$

provided that this quantity has the same value for all gases for which relative thermal conductivities are desired. This can be accomplished by holding T_2 constant by means of a thermostat and keeping T_1 constant *by adjusting the current so that the wire always has the same electrical resistance as determined through balance of a Wheatstone bridge.* Then, if the two gases are denoted a and b,

$$\frac{K_a}{K_b} = \frac{1 - \alpha_a}{1 - \alpha_b} \frac{i_a^2}{i_b^2} \tag{15}$$

Radiation. An ideal "black body" radiates electromagnetic radiation[5] (practically all in the far infrared at room temperature) at a rate, per square centimeter of surface, equal to σT^4, where $\sigma = 5.67 \times 10^{-12}$ joule deg^{-4} sec^{-1} cm^{-2}. A body capable of partially reflecting such radiation, particularly a metal body, radiates at the rate $(1 - \beta)\sigma T^4$, where β is the coefficient of reflectivity (fraction of incident radiation reflected). A body of area A at temperature T_1 completely surrounded at some distance by bodies of vastly greater surface at a slightly lower temperature T_2 will lose energy by radiation to the surroundings at the rate

$$(1 - \beta)A\sigma(T_1^4 - T_2^4) \cong (1 - \beta)4A\sigma T^3(T_1 - T_2)$$

For a platinum wire ($\beta \approx 0.96$) of radius 0.005 cm and length 25 cm the energy loss by radiation is about 10^{-5} cal sec^{-1} at 300°K per degree of temperature difference. Since the total power input to the wire in this experiment is in excess of 0.01 cal sec^{-1}, the loss by radiation is clearly negligible.

Convection. Since a temperature gradient exists in the cell, and since the density of gas varies with the temperature, convection may take place in the cell. Under certain conditions convection can be responsible for a significant fraction of the energy transfer. Without going into detail it may be stated that with the apparatus dimensions and operating conditions here described convection is not experimentally significant.

End Conduction. It might seem preferable to maintain the ends of the wire at the temperature T_1 prevailing elsewhere in the wire rather than at the temperature T_2 of the wall of the tube. This is, however, experimentally very difficult to accomplish, and the temperatures of the ends of the wire are maintained at temperature T_2 because this is easy to do experimentally and because it presents an easily soluble mathematical problem.

Let us assume that the temperature T of the wire varies from T_2 at one end ($z = 0$) to T_1 some distance away. By a one-dimensional treatment analogous to that used in deriving the partial differential equation for cylindrical symmetry, we find that the rate of accumulation of heat in a region of the wire of length dz and cross section πr_1^2 is

$$K'\pi r_1^2 \frac{\partial^2 T}{\partial z^2} dz$$

(where K' is the coefficient of thermal conductivity of the wire), *plus* the amount produced by dissipation of electrical energy,

$$i^2 \frac{R}{L} dz$$

minus the amount conducted away by the gas, which we shall assume is given by

$$\frac{2\pi K\,dz}{\ln (r_2/r_1)}(T - T_2)$$

For the quantity i^2R/L we may make a substitution in accordance with Eq. (12). For the steady state we set the net rate of accumulation of heat equal to zero, and we obtain

$$K'\pi r_1^2 \frac{d^2T}{dz^2} + \frac{2\pi K}{\ln (r_2/r_1)}[(T_1 - T_2) - (T - T_2)] = 0$$

This can be written as

$$\frac{d^2\,\Delta T}{dz^2} - B^2\,\Delta T = 0 \tag{16}$$

where

$$\left.\begin{aligned} \Delta T &\equiv T_1 - T \\ B &= \left[\frac{2}{r_1^2 \ln (r_2/r_1)}\,\frac{K}{K'}\right]^{1/2} \end{aligned}\right\} \tag{17}$$

This differential equation is easily integrated with the appropriate boundary conditions, yielding

$$\Delta T = (T_1 - T_2)e^{-Bz}$$

The rate of flow of heat to a heat station at one end is given by

$$K'\pi r_1^2\left(\frac{dT}{dz}\right)_{z=0} = K'\pi r_1^2\left(-\frac{d\,\Delta T}{dz}\right)_{z=0}$$
$$= K'\pi r_1^2(T_1 - T_2)B \tag{18}$$

The fraction α of the total power that is lost to the two heat stations is then *twice* this quantity divided by the supplied electric power i^2R. For the latter quantity we can again use Eq. (12), and we then obtain

$$\alpha = \frac{r_1}{L}\left(2\frac{K'}{K}\ln\frac{r_2}{r_1}\right)^{1/2} \tag{19}$$

Wheatstone Bridge. The method for maintenance of a constant wire temperature depends upon the temperature dependence of the resistance of platinum wire; the electrical resistance increases about 0.3 per cent for each degree centigrade of temperature increase. The temperature of the wire in the cell can then be determined, in principle, by use of a Wheatstone bridge, of which the wire in the conductivity cell is one of the four arms, the other three having resistances which are essentially independent of current and temperature. In the present experiment such a bridge is used not to obtain an absolute measurement of the wire temperature but to enable the wire temperature to be maintained at a constant preset value. The general principles of a Wheatstone-bridge circuit are discussed in Chap. XV.

The electrical circuit used in this experiment is shown in Fig. 2. The resistors used in the bridge are wound of manganin wire, which has a negligible temperature coefficient of resistivity. One of the arms is partially shunted with a variable resistor to permit small adjustments to be made for the purpose of initially balancing the bridge. Once the bridge has been initially balanced, with a current passing through the wire, balancing at other times during the experiment is performed *only*

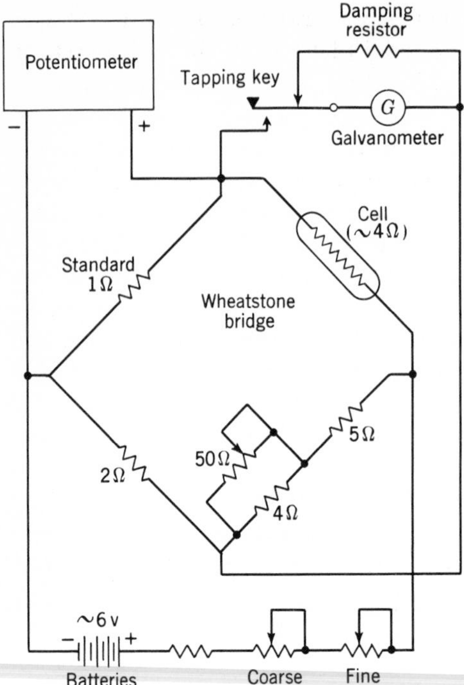

FIG. 2. Circuit diagram for the Wheatstone bridge. If a second galvanometer (in addition to that used in the potentiometer circuit) is not available, use a DPDT knife switch to permit a single galvanometer to be used for both purposes.

by adjustment of the total current through the bridge. The magnitude of the current through the wire is determined through potentiometric measurement of the potential across the arm of the bridge that is in series with the cell.

EXPERIMENTAL

For this experiment thermal conductivities will be measured relative to that of dry air, which is taken as a standard.

Set up the circuit as shown in Fig. 2. (Have it checked by an instructor before connecting the positive terminals of batteries and standard cell.) The conductivity cell should be mounted vertically and rigidly in a thermostat bath, in such a manner that it is not subject to vibration. It should not be moved during the experiment, and care should be taken not to get water into it. Check the thermostat bath at intervals during the experiment to make sure that it is regulating properly (within $\pm.01°C$) at $25°C \pm 1°$.

Runs are to be made on three gases: helium, argon, and dry air. Introduce each gas with sufficient flushing to eliminate all of the gas previously present; pass at least five volumes of the gas quickly through the cell.

For the dry-air runs, compressed air should be passed through a drying tube containing magnesium perchlorate or some other drying agent; such a drying tube is shown in Fig. 5-4. The tube should be full but not too tightly packed.

The first gas to be run should be dry air. After flushing and filling the cell, set the current through the wire at about 0.1 amp. After allowing some time for the wire and the gas to achieve steady-state conditions, adjust the variable resistance provided in the Wheatstone-bridge circuit so that the bridge is balanced. This, in effect, specifies the wire temperature for this and all later runs; **this bridge setting must not be disturbed again for any gas.** The bridge must be kept in balance at all times, and this is achieved by adjusting the current through the bridge circuit.

The steady-state current should now be determined with the bridge in balance. Having allowed sufficient time for a steady state to occur, make at least *four* measurements of the current through the cell (5 min apart) by potentiometric determination of the potential across the 1-ohm wire-wound standard resistor which forms the arm of the bridge in series with the cell. Each measurement should be preceded by a standardization of the potentiometer against the standard cell and by a check of the balance of the Wheatstone bridge and adjustment of the balance, if necessary, *by adjusting the current through the bridge.* No run should be considered complete until the steady-state current varies by less than 0.5 per cent in 10 min.

Flush the cell again with the same gas, check the bridge balance after a short wait for steady-state conditions, and repeat the current measurement. If the results of this run do not agree with those of the first, flush and repeat a third time.

Flush the cell thoroughly with the next gas to be studied, and carry out at least two runs as before. Be sure not to disturb the setting of the bridge. If time permits, make measurements on the third gas in the same way.

Record the dimensions of the cell (L, r_1, and r_2).

Absolute Measurement. If an absolute determination is to be made, an additional series of runs should be made on either dry air or argon with the bath temperature lowered a precisely known amount (about 5°). (If it is desired to make the additional run on helium, raise the bath temperature by about 2°.) If a precise value for the wire resistance R has not been given, measure it by substituting a decade resistance box for the cell without altering the bridge setting and then adjusting the decade box to balance the bridge. By writing Eq. (14) for each of the runs on a given gas at two different bath temperatures one obtains two equations in two unknowns T_1 and K. These can be solved to give K.

CALCULATIONS

For relative measurements based on air as a standard, calculate the thermal-conductivity coefficient of dry air from the expression[6]

$$K = \frac{0.632 \times 10^{-5} T^{1/2}}{1 + (245/T)10^{-12/T}} \quad \text{joule cm}^{-1}\,\text{sec}^{-1}\,\text{deg}^{-1} \tag{20}$$

where T is the absolute temperature. At 25°C, $K = 6.24 \times 10^{-5}$ cal cm^{-1} sec^{-1} deg^{-1} for dry air.

Ignoring end corrections, calculate approximate values for K for helium and argon from that given for dry air. Using these values of K, estimate α for each of the three gases by use of Eq. (19). For platinum, $K' = 0.17$ cal cm^{-1} sec^{-1} deg^{-1} at 25°C.

Determine corrected values of K for helium and argon, using Eq. (15).

If an absolute determination was made, solve the two equations (14) at the two known bath temperatures to find K for the gas studied. Calculate K for the other gases using Eq. (15) as above.

DISCUSSION

From your previous experimental results for gas viscosity in Exp. 5 (or from literature values) and your present results for thermal conductivity, calculate the ratio K/η for argon and helium, and compare the result with the theoretical value of $15R/4M$ given by kinetic theory in Eq. (IV-20).

Discuss qualitatively any complicating features of this experiment that occur to you which may be analogous to those discussed in Exp. 5 (e.g., kinetic energy, slip, Reynolds number, etc.).

APPARATUS

Thermal-conductivity cell with holder for mounting in bath; Wheatstone bridge; variable resistors to control bridge current; four 1.5-v dry cells or a 6-v storage battery to power bridge; galvanometer with high voltage sensitivity for bridge circuits; three-terminal tapping key; critical damping resistor; complete potentiometer setup (see Chap. XV); 24 electrical leads with lugs attached; two connectors for attaching leads to cell; glass U tube with rubber stopper and policemen; two long pieces of gum rubber tubing and one short piece; two screw clamps.

Cylinders of argon and helium gas; source of compressed air; glass wool; drying agent (such as magnesium perchlorate); constant-temperature bath set at 25°C.

REFERENCES

1. See, for example, H. M. Margenau and G. M. Murphy, "The Mathematics of Physics and Chemistry," pp. 217ff., Van Nostrand, Princeton, N.J. (1956).
2. J. R. Partington, "An Advanced Treatise on Physical Chemistry," vol. I, pp. 895ff., Longmans, London (1949).
3. L. A. Guildner, *Proc. Natl. Acad. Sci.,* **44,** 1149 (1958).
4. R. G. Vines, *J. Heat Transfer,* **1960,** 48.
5. See, for example, R. B. Leighton, "Principles of Modern Physics," pp. 60ff., 723, McGraw-Hill, New York (1959).
6. F. G. Keyes, *Trans. Am. Soc. Mech. Engrs.,* **73,** 589 (1951).

GENERAL READING

H. S. Carslaw, "Conduction of Heat in Solids," 2d ed., Dover, New York (1945).

Experiment 7. Diffusion of Gases

When a component of a continuous fluid phase (a liquid solution or a gas mixture) is present in nonuniform concentration, at uniform and constant temperature and pressure and in the absence of external fields, that component diffuses in such a way as to tend to render its concentration uniform. For simplicity, let the concentration of a given substance $\bar{N}_1$ be a function of only one coordinate x; that is, the concentration of substance 1 varies only along the x direction, which we shall take as the upward direction. The net "flux" Z_1 of the substance passing upward past a given fixed point x_0 (i.e., amount per unit cross-sectional area per unit time) is under most conditions found to be proportional to the negative of the concentration gradient:

$$Z_1 = -D\left(\frac{d\bar{N}_1}{dx}\right)_{x_0} \tag{1}$$

where D is the *diffusion constant,* which is characteristic of the diffusing substance and usually also of the other substances present. This is called "Fick's first law of diffusion."

When only two substances are present in a closed gaseous system of fixed total volume at uniform and constant temperature, the distribution of one of the substances is completely determined when the distribution of the other is specified. The sum of the partial pressures of the two components is equal to the total pressure, and if the two components are perfect gases, the total pressure is constant and the sum of the two concentrations is also constant. Designating the two substances by the subscripts 1 and 2, we can write

$$Z_1 = -D_{12}\frac{d\bar{N}_1}{dx} = D_{12}\frac{d\bar{N}_2}{dx} \tag{2}$$

$$Z_2 = -Z_1 = -D_{21}\frac{d\bar{N}_2}{dx} = D_{21}\frac{d\bar{N}_1}{dx} \tag{3}$$

from which it can be seen that D_{12}, the diffusion constant for the diffusion of component 1 into component 2, is equal to D_{21}, the diffusion constant for the diffusion of 2 into 1.

One can also define a diffusion constant for the diffusion of a substance into itself. Suppose that we have a single molecular species (substance 1, say) present in a vessel but that the molecules initially in a certain portion of the vessel can somehow be tagged or labeled (without changing their kinetic properties) so that later they can be distinguished from the others. After a period of time the distribution of the tagged molecules could then be determined experimentally and the *self-diffusion constant* D_1 calculated. In actuality, it is not possible to tag molecules without some effect on their kinetic properties. A close approach to such tagging can be obtained, however, with the use of different isotopes that may be distinguished with a mass spectrometer or a Geiger counter. Another close approach can be obtained in a few cases by the use of molecules that are very similar in size, shape, and mass but different in chemical constitution, for example, the pair N_2 and CO or the pair CO_2 and N_2O. For each of these pairs the diffusion constant D_{12} should constitute a reasonably good estimate of the self-diffusion constants D_1 and D_2.

In the case where the two gases are distinctly different in their diffusing tendencies, the mutual diffusion constant D_{12} lies somewhere between the two self-diffusion constants D_1 and D_2 in value. It is also found that, when the two self-diffusion constants are very different, the mutual diffusion constant is largely determined by the more rapidly diffusing substance rather than by the more slowly diffusing one; thus there is a greater difference between the diffusion constants for the systems Kr-He and Kr-H_2 than for Kr-He and CO_2-He. The gas having the high self-diffusion constant (He or H_2) diffuses rapidly into the gas having the low self-diffusion constant. But there must be a *mass flow* of the resulting mixture in the opposite direction to maintain uniform pressure, so the gas with the lower diffusion constant gives the appearance of diffusing, although in reality it is mainly undergoing displacement.

THEORY

Let the concentration of gas 1 be $\bar{N}_1(x)$, a function of x only, in a vertical tube of uniform cross section A (x increasing upward). Let us calculate the rate of accumulation of gas 1 in the region from x to $x + dx$. The net flow of the gas into the region from below, per square centimeter per second, is given by Fick's first law,

$$Z_1(x) = -D_{12}\left(\frac{\partial \bar{N}_1}{\partial x}\right)_x$$

The net flow of the gas out of the region in the upward direction, per square centimeter per second, is

$$Z_1(x + dx) = -D_{12}\left(\frac{\partial \bar{N}_1}{\partial x}\right)_{x+dx}$$

$$= -D_{12}\left[\left(\frac{\partial \bar{N}_1}{\partial x}\right)_x + \left(\frac{\partial^2 \bar{N}_1}{\partial x^2}\right)_x dx\right]$$

The rate of increase of the concentration $\bar{N}_1(x)$ is given by

$$\frac{\partial \bar{N}_1(x)}{\partial t} = \frac{Z_1(x) - Z_1(x + dx)}{dx}$$

and therefore

$$\frac{\partial \bar{N}_1}{\partial t} = D_{12}\frac{\partial^2 \bar{N}_1}{\partial x^2} \tag{4}$$

This is the differential equation for diffusion in one dimension† (called "Fick's second law").

Let two perfect gases be placed in a *Loschmidt apparatus*[1]—a vertical tube of length $2L$, of uniform cross section, closed at both ends, and containing a removable septum in the center. The heavier of the two gases (gas 1, say) is initially confined to the lower half and the lighter (gas 2) to the upper half in order to avoid convective mixing. Both gases are at initial concentration $\bar{N}_0$. At time $t = 0$ the septum is removed, so that the gases are free to interdiffuse. Let us define a quantity $\Delta\bar{N}$ as follows:

$$\Delta\bar{N} = \bar{N}_1 - \bar{N}_2 \equiv 2\bar{N}_1 - \bar{N}_0 \tag{5}$$

The differential equation to be solved,

$$\frac{\partial\, \Delta\bar{N}}{\partial t} = D\frac{\partial^2\, \Delta\bar{N}}{\partial x^2} \tag{6}$$

is the differential equation (4) in $\bar{N}_1$ minus a similar one in $\bar{N}_2$, and

$$D = D_{12} = D_{21}$$

Taking the origin at the middle of the tube, we write the boundary conditions

† It is also the differential equation for *one-dimensional* heat flow when N_1 is replaced by temperature T and D_{12} is replaced by $K/\bar{c}\rho$; compare with Eq. (6-5).

$$
\begin{aligned}
t = 0:\quad & \Delta\bar{N} = \bar{N}_0 & -L \leqslant x < 0 \\
& \Delta\bar{N} = -\bar{N}_0 & 0 < x \leqslant L
\end{aligned}
\tag{7}
$$

$$
t = \infty:\quad \Delta\bar{N} = 0 \qquad -L \leqslant x \leqslant L \tag{8}
$$

$$
\begin{aligned}
\text{All } t:\quad & \frac{\partial\,\Delta\bar{N}}{\partial x} = 0 & x = -L \\
& \frac{\partial\,\Delta\bar{N}}{\partial x} = 0 & x = L
\end{aligned}
\tag{9}
$$

The last boundary condition follows from the fact that there is no flow of gas through the two ends of the tube; see Eq. (1). Boundary condition (7) can be expressed in terms of a Fourier series expansion[2] of $\Delta\bar{N}$:

$$
t = 0:\quad \Delta\bar{N} = -\frac{4}{\pi}\bar{N}_0\left(\sin\frac{\pi}{2L}x + \frac{1}{3}\sin\frac{3\pi}{2L}x + \frac{1}{5}\sin\frac{5\pi}{2L}x + \cdots\right) \tag{7'}
$$

This is the Fourier series for a "square wave" of amplitude $\bar{N}_0$ and wavelength $2L$.

We shall omit the procedure for finding the solution of Eq. (6) and simply give the result:

$$
\begin{aligned}
\frac{\Delta\bar{N}}{\bar{N}_0} = \frac{\bar{N}_1 - \bar{N}_2}{\bar{N}_1 + \bar{N}_2} = -\frac{4}{\pi}\bigg(& e^{-\pi^2 Dt/4L^2}\sin\frac{\pi}{2L}x + \frac{1}{3}e^{-9\pi^2 Dt/4L^2}\sin\frac{3\pi}{2L}x \\
& + \frac{1}{5}e^{-25\pi^2 Dt/4L^2}\sin\frac{5\pi}{2L}x + \cdots\bigg)
\end{aligned}
\tag{10}
$$

The reader can easily verify that the solution satisfies the differential equation and the boundary conditions (7) or (7′), (8) and (9). The behavior of $\Delta\bar{N}$ with x and t is shown qualitatively in Fig. 1*a*.

After time t, let us replace the removable septum and analyze the two portions of the tube for total quantity of one of the gases, say gas 1. The total amount of gas 1 in the upper part will be equal to the total amount of gas 2 in the lower part. Let M_1 and N_1 be the mass and number of moles of gas 1 in the lower part and M_1' and N_1' be the mass and number of moles of gas 1 in the upper part, and let similar symbols with subscript 2 pertain to gas 2. Define a quantity f by

$$
f \equiv \frac{N_1 - N_2}{N_1 + N_2} = \frac{(\bar{N}_1 - \bar{N}_2)_{\text{av}}}{\bar{N}_0} = \frac{1}{L}\int_{-L}^{0}\frac{\Delta\bar{N}}{\bar{N}_0}\,dx \tag{11}
$$

Since $N_1' = N_2$, we have also

$$
f = \frac{N_1 - N_1'}{N_1 + N_1'} = \frac{M_1 - M_1'}{M_1 + M_1'} \tag{12}
$$

This expression permits the calculation of f from the results of analyzing separately the upper and lower parts of the tube for gas 1. Integrating Eq. (11), we obtain

$$
f = \frac{8}{\pi^2}\left(e^{-\pi^2 Dt/4L^2} + \frac{1}{9}e^{-9\pi^2 Dt/4L^2} + \frac{1}{25}e^{-25\pi^2 Dt/4L^2} + \cdots\right) \tag{13}
$$

At $t = 0$, the sum of the series in parentheses is equal to $\pi^2/8$, so the quantity f is initially unity. After a short time all terms except the first become negligible, and f thereafter decays with time in a simple exponential manner.

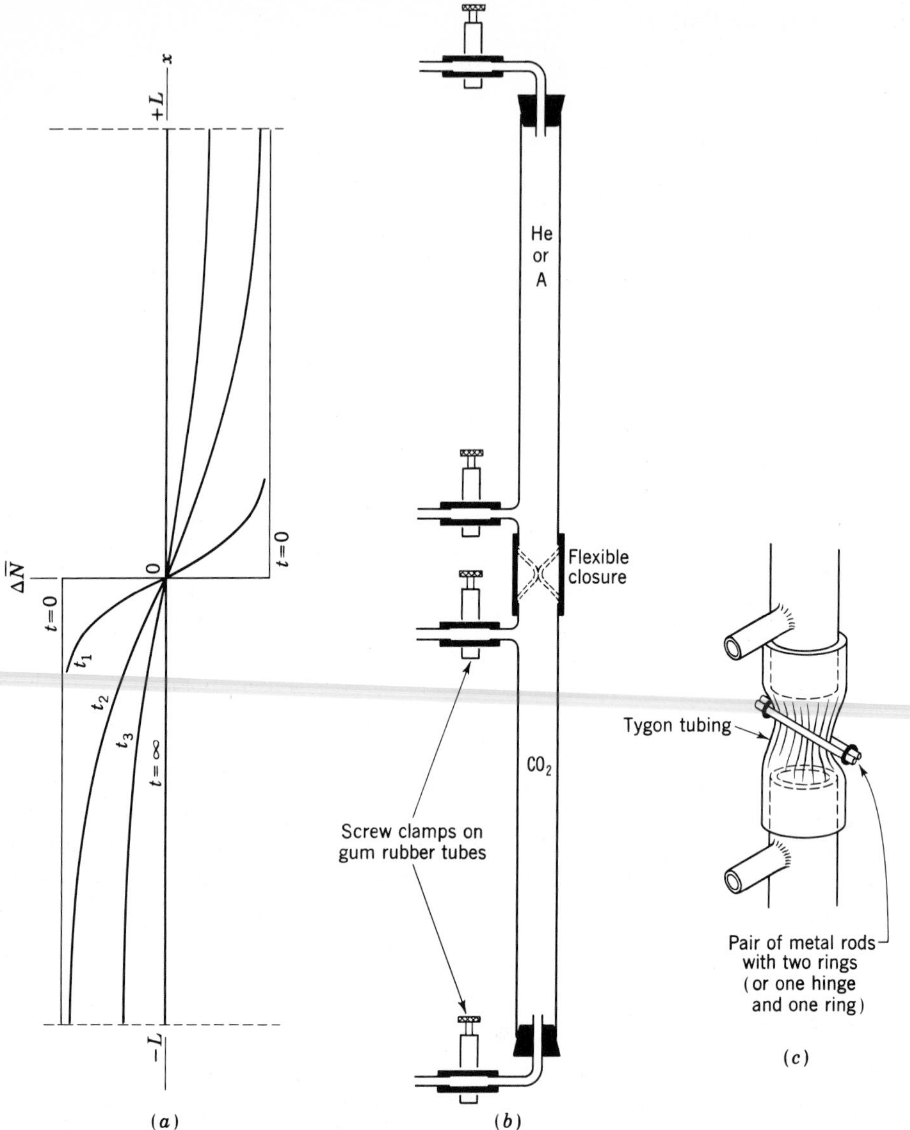

FIG. 1. Loschmidt diffusion apparatus. (*a*) Curves showing schematically the quantity $\Delta\bar{N} = \bar{N}_1 - N_2$. (*b*) Cell. (*c*) Detail of flexible closure.

At what time t should the run be stopped in order to obtain the most precise value of D, assuming that the only significant errors are those in determining f and that the uncertainty in f is constant (independent of the time)? Neglecting all but the first term of Eq. (13), we find, on solving for D and differentiating, that

$$\frac{\partial D}{\partial f} = -\frac{1}{t}\frac{4L^2}{\pi^2}\frac{1}{f}$$

We wish to find at what value of t the derivative $\partial D/\partial f$ is at a minimum:

$$0 = \frac{\partial^2 D}{\partial t\,\partial f} = \frac{4L^2}{\pi^2}\left(\frac{1}{t}\frac{1}{f^2}\frac{\partial f}{\partial t} + \frac{1}{t^2}\frac{1}{f}\right) = \frac{4L^2}{\pi^2 ft}\left(-\frac{\pi^2 D}{4L^2} + \frac{1}{t}\right)$$

thus the optimum time is

$$t_{\text{opt}} = \frac{4L^2}{\pi^2 D} \tag{14}$$

At this optimum time, Eq. (13) gives

$$f = 0.81057\ (0.367879 + 0.000014 + \cdot\cdot\cdot) = 0.2982$$

Note that neglect of the second and higher terms of Eq. (13) proves to be justified if the experiment is run for any time in the neighborhood of the optimum time or for any greater time.

METHOD

In this experiment we shall measure the diffusion constants for the systems CO_2-He and CO_2-Ar at room temperature. In each run, CO_2, the heavier gas, will be initially in the lower portion of a vertical tube. The gas in the two portions at the end of the run will be analyzed for CO_2 by sweeping it through absorption tubes (U tubes) filled with Ascarite (asbestos impregnated with NaOH, which reacts with CO_2) and with magnesium perchlorate (to absorb the water liberated in the first reaction). These tubes are weighed before and after sweeping the gas through them.

The diffusion cell, a modified Loschmidt type, is shown in Fig. 1*b*. In place of a removable septum at the center, the two halves of this tube are joined by a flexible plastic (Tygon) sleeve of approximately the same inner diameter as the glass, which can be pinched tight to achieve a closure as shown in Fig. 1*c*.

In round numbers the length L in the apparatus to be employed is 50 cm, and the two diffusion constants are of the order of magnitude 0.6 $cm^2\ sec^{-1}$ for CO_2-He and 0.15 $cm^2\ sec^{-1}$ for CO_2-Ar. Using these figures the optimum diffusion times can be estimated from Eq. (14). The actual time should approximate this optimum time but in any case should not differ from it by more than 50 per cent.

EXPERIMENTAL

In carrying out the experiment the student should follow a careful plan worked out with his partner, taking into account the following:

1. Even a tiny leak is serious; all stoppers and clamps *must be tight.* Rubber and Tygon tubing must be in good condition.

2. When one gas is being flushed out by another, the gas being introduced should enter at the lower end of the vessel if it is the heavier and at the upper end if it is the lighter.

3. Considerable heat is evolved in the reaction of CO_2 with Ascarite; a U tube that has absorbed a considerable amount of CO_2 should be allowed to cool for about 15 min before it is weighed.

4. Carbon dioxide gas emerges rather cool from the tank valve. Time should be allowed for it to warm to room temperature before the diffusion run is started. It is wise to vent the lower chamber, containing CO_2, momentarily at the side arm before the run to restore atmospheric pressure.

5. If the cylinder is not equipped with a regulator valve, turn off the gas supply at the cylinder before closing off the system. The inlet of the system should be clamped off before the outlet.

6. The CO_2-containing gas should be swept into the drying tubes no faster than five bubbles per second. Use a dibutyl-phthalate bubbler for metering gas flow. One bubble is approximately 0.1 cm^3. This rate can be obtained by synchronization with the ticking of a watch. It is well to adjust the flow rate (with the outlet valve on the compressed air line) *before* attaching to the system. The sweeping air should go *first* through the bubbler and *then* through a purifying tube (to remove CO_2 and H_2O) before it enters the system. In case the flow rate is preadjusted, it is important to make sure that the system is open at both ends at the moment the air tube is attached.

7. Drying tubes should be closed off with rubber policemen when gas is not being passed through them. Take care that the drying tube always has the same two policemen.

8. Do not neglect the volumes of gas that are contained in any significant lengths of rubber tubing. Before using a rubber tube that may previously have contained CO_2, flush it out momentarily with air. Also, do not neglect the possibility of a heavy gas spilling out of the system if it is open at two places at different levels for more than a second or two.

Procedure. Prepare as shown in Fig. 2 and weigh two U tubes, A and B. It is not necessary to correct weights to vacuum readings. A third U tube, which need not be weighed, should be prepared for purification of the air to be used for sweeping.

Flush out the lower half of the cell with CO_2, using a flushing rate of at least 10 to 15 bubbles per second through the bubbler. *Make sure the center partition is closed* before flushing. Pass at least six volumes of gas through to be sure of complete replacement.

Connect the lower half-cell to U tubes A and B in series, and sweep out the gas in the lower half-cell into the U tubes with three or four volumes of air (purified with the third U tube), at five bubbles per second. Without stopping the sweeping, *quickly* pull off tube A and reconnect tube B. Immediately close the ends of tube A. After one or two more additional volumes have been swept through tube B, weigh tube B first, then tube A. Tube B should not have gained more than a few milligrams. Add the two gains in weight; this quantity is $M_1 + M_1'$, the total weight of CO_2 in the cell.

Now flush out the lower half-cell with CO_2 and the upper one with the other gas (He or Ar) to be studied, as above. This should be done during the above weighings to save time.

Begin the diffusion by *carefully* (not too suddenly) opening the center partition and simultaneously starting a stopwatch. After the estimated optimum time, close the partition.

Sweep the contents of the lower tube into U tubes A and B as before. After the weighings, repeat with the upper tube. The value of $M_1 + M_1'$ should agree with the value obtained above to within a very few milligrams; if greater disagreement is obtained, a leak must be suspected.

Repeat the procedure with the second gas combination. If time permits, repeat each of the above runs, with the diffusion cell inverted, and in each case take as your value of f the mean of the two values obtained.

Measure the length L as precisely as possible. Also record the barometric pressure and the ambient temperature.

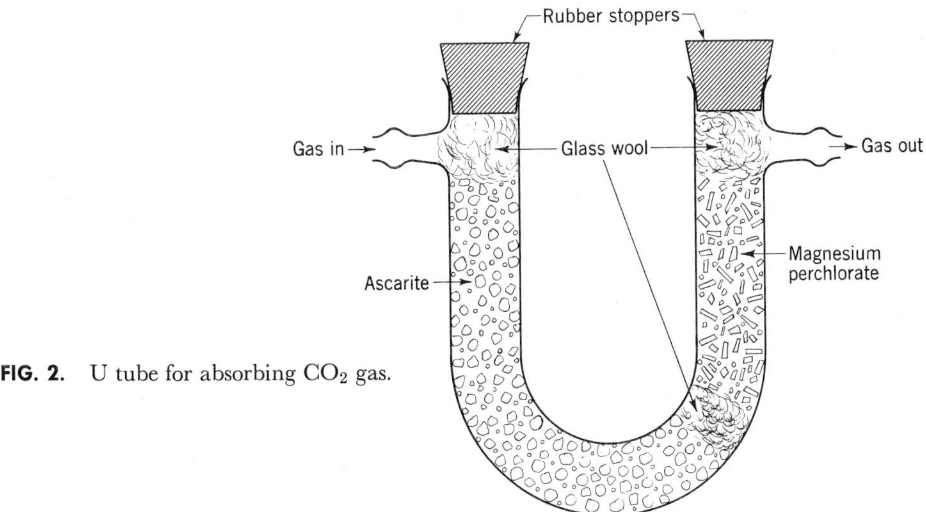

FIG. 2. U tube for absorbing CO_2 gas.

CALCULATIONS

By use of Eqs. (12) and (13) neglecting all but the first term in the series, calculate D for each gas combination. Then, with this value of D, calculate the second term in the series; if it is more than 1 per cent of the first term, recalculate D. The resulting values of D are to be designated D_{12} for CO_2-He, D_{13} for CO_2-Ar.

Gas viscosity measurements yield hard sphere diameters of 2.58 A (angstroms) for helium, 3.42 A for argon, and 4.00 A for carbon dioxide. With these values, calculate d_{12} and d_{13} from Eq. (IV-36), and calculate D_{12} and D_{13} using Eq. (IV-34). Compare with your experimental values.

Optional: At 273°K, D_{23} (for He-Ar) is 0.653 cm² sec⁻¹. From D_{12}, D_{13}, and D_{23} at *room temperature* calculate d_{12}, d_{13}, and d_{23}. (To correct diffusion constants from one temperature to another, assume a $T^{3/2}$ dependence if the temperature change is small. This is only approximate, since the d's may vary in some degree with the temperature.) Then obtain d_1, d_2, and d_3 and use these to calculate D_1, D_2, and D_3 from Eq. (IV-35). Determine the ratios of the self-diffusion constants to their respective viscosities. How do these compare with the theoretical ratios discussed in Chap. IV?

DISCUSSION

The flexible closure used here, though simple and convenient, is admittedly less satisfactory than a removable diaphragm closure would be. Discuss its disadvantages from the points of view of (1) mixing produced in the opening and closing operations, (2) inexactness of the matching of its diameter with that of the tubes, and (3) any other defects that occur to you. Try wherever possible to employ arguments that are not wholly qualitative; estimate orders of magnitude where you can. If possible, suggest an improved closure design. What additional techniques might be used with this experimental method to enable D_{23} (for He-Ar) to be measured directly? Using your value for D_{13} estimate the time necessary for a diffusion run on CO_2-Ar in the present apparatus to achieve a state where $M_1 = 1.01\ M_1'$

(i.e., where the concentration of CO_2 is only 1 per cent greater in the lower half than in the upper half).

APPARATUS

Diffusion cell (Loschmidt type) with sturdy support; clamping device for flexible closure; two one-hole rubber stoppers, with short bent tubes, for ends of cell; four 1-in. lengths of rubber tubing; four screw clamps; four short glass tubes; three glass U tubes with rubber stoppers and policemen; bubbler, containing dibutyl phthalate; three long and two short lengths of rubber tubing; needle valve; two ring stands; four clamps with clamp holders; 0 to 30°C thermometer; stopwatch; meter stick.

Cylinders of helium, argon, and carbon dioxide; source of compressed air; glass wool; Ascarite; drying agent (such as magnesium perchlorate).

REFERENCES

1. J. R. Partington, "An Advanced Treatise on Physical Chemistry," vol. I, Longmans, London (1949).
2. Any text on advanced calculus, such as R. Courant, "Differential and Integral Calculus," Blackie, Glasgow (1934); or P. Franklin, "Methods of Advanced Calculus," McGraw-Hill, New York (1944).

GENERAL READING

E. H. Kennard, "Kinetic Theory of Gases," McGraw-Hill, New York (1938).
R. D. Present, "Kinetic Theory of Gases," McGraw-Hill, New York (1958).

Experiment 8. Low-pressure Effusion of Gases

In Exp. 5 we were concerned with the viscous flow of gas through a capillary tube. One of the conditions for that experiment was that the mean free path of the gas must be small compared with the diameter of the tube. Actually, the flow ceases to be purely viscous and begins to assume some molecular character when the slip correction becomes significant. When the mean free path becomes very large in comparison with the diameter of a tube or hole, the flow is completely molecular in character.

At a given temperature, the mean free path $\bar{l}$ is inversely proportional to the pressure; for most gases, $\bar{l}$ is of the order of 10^{-5} cm at 1 atm and about 0.05 cm at a pressure 0.1 mm Hg (see Table IV-1). Clearly, it is difficult to obtain the necessary conditions for molecular flow at 1 atm pressure, since extremely small holes or pores are needed. Demonstrations of molecular flow at 1 atm with pinholes punched in foils are of no value, although they may appear to give correct flow time ratios for two gases if the choice of a pair of gases for study is fortuitously such that the molecular diameters are about the same. In general the results of such experiments show a dependence of flow time on molecular diameter, which is a property of viscous flow and not true of pure molecular flow. Valid molecular flow can be achieved, however, using holes with diameters of about 0.01 cm if the gas pressure is 0.10 mm of mercury or less.[1] Such low-pressure effusion of helium, argon, and carbon dioxide will be studied in this experiment.

METHOD AND THEORY

Effusion will be studied for gas at low pressure flowing through a small pinhole into a vacuum. The experimental apparatus is shown in Fig. 1. The important features of this apparatus are: (1) a system for obtaining high vacuum; (2) a large bulb B (about 5 liters), to contain the gas to be studied, at an initial pressure of 0.1 to 0.2 mm; (3) an orifice O in the form of a pinhole of the order of 0.1 mm in diameter in very thin platinum foil, through which the gas in bulb B may effuse into the high-vacuum part of the system; (4) a vacuum gauge for measuring periodically the pressure of the gas remaining in bulb B; and (5) an expansion system for filling bulb B with gas at the desired initial pressure.

For this method we can write Eq. (IV-7) as

$$-\frac{dN}{dt} = \frac{Ap}{\sqrt{2\pi MRT}} \tag{1}$$

where N is the number of moles of gas in the bulb B at pressure p and temperature T, A is the area of the pinhole, and M is the molecular weight of the gas. In Eq. (1) we have made use of the fact that the pressure outside the pinhole is essentially zero (10^{-5} mm Hg or less). Applying the perfect-gas law to the gas in the bulb B (volume V) we write

$$dN = \frac{V}{RT}\,dp \tag{2}$$

Combining Eqs. (1) and (2) gives

$$\frac{dp}{p} = -\frac{A}{V}\sqrt{\frac{RT}{2\pi M}}\,dt = -\frac{dt}{\tau} \tag{3}$$

where τ is the "relaxation time" for the system and is

$$\tau = \frac{V}{A}\sqrt{\frac{2\pi M}{RT}} \tag{4}$$

For a given apparatus and choice of gas, τ is a constant if T does not vary; therefore, Eq. (3) can be integrated to give

$$\ln\frac{p}{p_0} = -\frac{1}{\tau}t$$

or

$$\log p = \log p_0 - \frac{t}{2.303\tau} \tag{5}$$

where p is the pressure in bulb B at time t and p_0 is the initial pressure (at $t = 0$). A plot of $\log p$ vs. t should be a straight line. From the slope we can evaluate τ and then use Eq. (4) with known values of A, V, and T to calculate the molecular weight of the gas. Even if we do not know the value of A/V, if we obtain data for two different gases, we can determine the ratio of their molecular weights.

EXPERIMENTAL

Before the run is started, the entire system should be evacuated to a pressure of 10^{-5} mm Hg or less and liquid nitrogen should be placed in the Dewar flask around trap P. Either this will be done by an instructor before the period, or

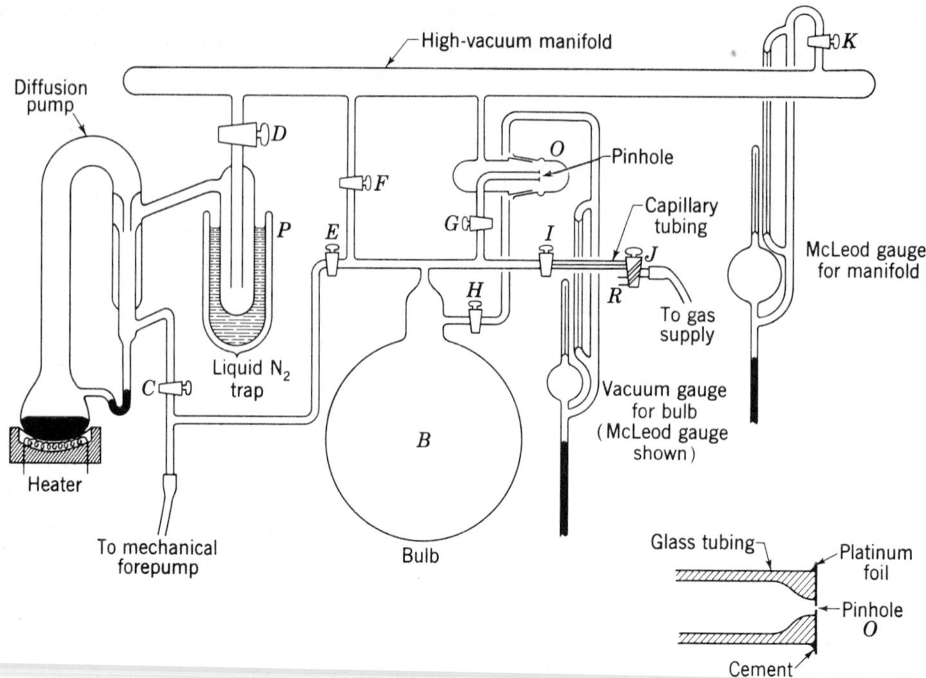

FIG. 1. Apparatus for the low-pressure effusion of gases.

instructions will be issued for the proper procedure to be used. The pressure should be checked with the McLeod gauge which connects to the manifold through stopcock *K*. For a general discussion of high-vacuum systems and components see Chap. XVII.

The actual apparatus may differ from that shown in Fig. 1, in which case special operating instructions will be available. The procedure given here will refer to the system shown. When the system is completely evacuated, all stopcocks will be open except *E* and *J*.

The pressure gauge which is connected to the bulb by stopcock *H* will be either a small-volume McLeod gauge or a thermocouple gauge. If it is a McLeod gauge, readings during the run should be taken as quickly as possible, since a small amount of gas is cut off in the gauge during a pressure reading. If the gauge is a thermocouple gauge, this precaution is not necessary but the gauge must be calibrated against the manifold McLeod gauge with each gas used. This calibration can be done after the run by the following procedure: Close *D* and *E*; open *H*, *F*, and *K*; admit gas to the entire line at the highest required pressure through *J* and *I*. Now read both the McLeod and the thermocouple gauge. Reduce the pressure by opening *D* momentarily and repeat the measurements; continue until the desired range has been covered, and plot a calibration curve. (For precise calibration at very low pressures, one can insert a cold trap between the manifold and the McLeod gauge to eliminate mercury vapor.) A discussion of the thermocouple gauge is given in Chap. XVII.

Procedure. Connect the gas inlet hose to a cylinder of helium, argon, or carbon dioxide which has a regulator valve, and adjust the pressure to about 2 psi above 1 atm. Carefully turn stopcock *J* so that the hose can be flushed out through outlet R of this stopcock. Close stopcock I and turn J so as to fill the short length of capillary tubing with the gas. Now close J, F, G and open I to allow the slug of gas to expand into the bulb B and its associated pressure gauge. Close I and measure the pressure in bulb B. If the pressure is between 100 to 150 μ (microns) (0.10 to 0.15 mm Hg), the run can be started; if above 150 μ, open stopcock E *momentarily* to reduce the pressure to the range 100 to 150 μ.

To start the effusion, open stopcock G which connects the bulb B to the high-vacuum manifold through the pinhole at O. Take pressure readings on the gas in B at 5-min intervals. Continue readings until the pressure is down to about 5 per cent of its initial value. Record the ambient temperature near bulb B. At least once during the run, check the manifold pressure (with the McLeod gauge at K) to verify that it is less than 10^{-4} mm Hg. Except for this measurement, keep stopcock K closed during the run.

To terminate a run, open F and I to allow the diffusion pump to evacuate the system to a high vacuum.

Repeat this procedure with one or both of the other gases. When this experiment has been completed, leave the apparatus evacuated unless otherwise instructed.

Record the necessary apparatus constants A and V.

CALCULATIONS

Convert all pressure gauge readings obtained during a run to microns of mercury (p) and plot log p against the time in *seconds*. Alternatively, if a McLeod gauge was used, one can simplify the calculation by plotting 2 log h vs. t, since the pressure is proportional to h^2, where h is the gauge reading.

From each plot, determine τ from the slope and p_0 from the intercept at $t = 0$. Compare this p_0 value with the pressure measured prior to opening stopcock G. Using Eq. (4) compute the molecular weight M for each gas studied. Also compute the ratio of molecular weights from the ratio of τ values. The agreement with accepted values is expected to be better for the ratio than for the individual values because the effect of uncertainties in A and V has been eliminated.

DISCUSSION

Calculate the mean free path of each gas at pressure p_0. How does this compare with the pinhole diameter?

Estimate the effect of neglecting the back effusion from the manifold into the bulb.

For the highest effusion rates attained in this experiment, what is the minimum pumping speed required for the vacuum system to maintain a manifold pressure no higher than 10^{-4} mm?

An alternative method employs effusion through a pinhole from one bulb to another of equal volume. How would you define a relaxation time τ' for this method, and what relationship would τ' bear to τ?

Suggest how an effusion experiment could be designed and carried out to measure a very low vapor pressure for a solid.

APPARATUS

High-vacuum system; effusion apparatus such as that shown in Fig. 1; heavy-wall rubber tubing; stopwatch; Dewar flask for cold trap.

Cylinders of helium, argon, and carbon dioxide; stopcock grease; liquid nitrogen (1 liter).

REFERENCE

1. M. Knudsen, *Ann. Physik,* **28,** 75 (1909).

GENERAL READING

E. H. Kennard, "Kinetic Theory of Gases," McGraw-Hill, New York (1938).

V

THERMOCHEMISTRY

EXPERIMENTS

PRINCIPLES OF CALORIMETRY

We are concerned here with the problem of determining experimentally the enthalpy change ΔH or the energy change ΔE accompanying a given isothermal change in state of a system, normally one in which a chemical reaction occurs. We can write the reaction schematically in the form

$$\underbrace{A(T_0) + B(T_0)}_{\text{initial state}} = \underbrace{C(T_0) + D(T_0)}_{\text{final state}} \tag{1}$$

In practice we do not actually carry out the change in state isothermally; this is not necessary because ΔH and ΔE are independent of the path. In calorimetry we usually find it convenient to use a path composed of two steps:

Step I. A change of state is carried out *adiabatically* in the calorimeter vessel to yield the desired products but in general at another temperature:

$$A(T_0) + B(T_0) + S(T_0) = C(T_1) + D(T_1) + S(T_1) \tag{2}$$

where S represents those parts of the system (e.g., inside wall of the calorimeter vessel, stirrer, thermometer, solvent) that are always at the same temperature as the reactants or products because of the experimental arrangement; these parts, plus the reactants or products, constitute the system under discussion.

Step II. The products of Step I are brought to the initial temperature T_0 by adding heat to (or taking it from) the system:

$$C(T_1) + D(T_1) + S(T_1) = C(T_0) + D(T_0) + S(T_0) \tag{3}$$

As we shall see, it is often unnecessary to carry out this step in actuality.

By adding Eqs. (2) and (3) we obtain Eq. (1) and verify that these two steps describe a complete path connecting the desired initial and final states. Accordingly, ΔH or ΔE for the change in state (1) is the sum of the values of this quantity pertaining to the two steps:

$$\Delta H = \Delta H_{\mathrm{I}} + \Delta H_{\mathrm{II}} \tag{4a}$$

$$\Delta E = \Delta E_{\mathrm{I}} + \Delta E_{\mathrm{II}} \tag{4b}$$

The particular convenience of the path described is that the heat q for Step I is zero, while the heat q for Step II can be either measured or calculated. It can be measured directly by carrying out Step II (or its inverse) through the addition to the system of a measurable quantity of heat or electrical energy, or it can be calculated from the temperature change $(T_1 - T_0)$ resulting from adiabatic Step I if the heat capacity of the product system is known. For Step I,

$$\Delta H_{\mathrm{I}} = q_p = 0 \qquad \text{constant pressure} \tag{5a}$$

$$\Delta E_{\mathrm{I}} = q_v = 0 \qquad \text{constant volume} \tag{5b}$$

Thus, if *both* steps are carried out at constant pressure,

$$\Delta H = \Delta H_{\mathrm{II}} \tag{6a}$$

and if *both* are carried out at constant volume,

$$\Delta E = \Delta E_{\mathrm{II}} \tag{6b}$$

Whether the process is carried out at constant pressure or at constant volume is a matter of convenience. In nearly all cases it is most convenient to carry it out at constant pressure; the experiments on heats of ionic reaction and heats of solution are examples. An exception to the general rule is the determination of a heat of combustion, which is conveniently carried out at constant volume in a bomb. However, we can easily calculate ΔH from ΔE as determined from a constant-volume process (or ΔE from ΔH as determined from a constant-pressure process) by use of the equation

$$\Delta H = \Delta E + \Delta(pV) \tag{7}$$

When all reactants and products are condensed phases, the $\Delta(pV)$ term is negligible in comparison with ΔH or ΔE, and the distinction between these two quantities is unimportant. When gases are involved, as in the case of combustion, the $\Delta(pV)$ term is likely to be significant in magnitude, though still small, in comparison with ΔH or ΔE. Since it is small, we can employ the perfect-gas law and rewrite Eq. (7) in the form

$$\Delta H = \Delta E + RT\,\Delta N_{\mathrm{gas}} \tag{8}$$

where ΔN_{gas} is the *increase* in the number of moles of gas in the system.

We must now concern ourselves with procedures for determining ΔH or ΔE for Step II. We might envisage Step II being carried out by adding heat to the system or taking heat away from the system and measuring q for this process.†

† This could be done by placing the system in thermal contact with a heat reservoir (such as a large water bath) of known heat capacity until the desired change has been effected and calculating q from the measured change in the temperature of the reservoir.

Usually, however, it is much easier to measure work than heat. In particular, electrical work, which can be degraded to "Joule heat" by a heating coil in the system, can be used conveniently in carrying out either Step II or its inverse, whichever is endothermic. Since the heat is dissipated *inside* the system, the work is negative:

$$-w_{el} = \int E\,dq = \int Ei\,dt$$

For very precise work, one should measure both E and i during the heating period. In many instances, however, it is possible to assume that the resistance of the heating coil R_H is constant and make only measurements of i by determining the potential drop E_s across a standard resistance R_s in series with the heating coil. In such a case, one can write

$$-w_{el} = \int i^2 R_H\,dt = \frac{R_H}{R_s^2}\int E_s^2\,dt \qquad (9)$$

Note that the electrical work as given by Eq. (9) is in joules when resistance is in ohms, potential in volts, and time in seconds. To convert this to calories, it must be divided by 4.184. If the electric heating is done adiabatically,

$$\Delta H_{\mathrm{II}} = -w_{el} \qquad \text{constant pressure} \qquad (10a)$$

$$\Delta E_{\mathrm{II}} = -w_{el} \qquad \text{constant volume} \qquad (10b)$$

Our discussion so far has been limited to determining ΔH_{II} or ΔE_{II} by directly carrying out Step II (or its inverse). However, it is often not necessary to carry out this step in actuality. If we know or can determine the heat capacity of the system, the temperature change $(T_1 - T_0)$ resulting from Step I provides all the additional information we need:

$$\Delta H_{\mathrm{II}} = \int_{T_1}^{T_0} C_p(\mathrm{C + D + S})\,dT \qquad (11a)$$

$$\Delta E_{\mathrm{II}} = \int_{T_1}^{T_0} C_v(\mathrm{C + D + S})\,dT \qquad (11b)$$

The heat capacities ordinarily vary only slightly over the small temperature ranges involved; accordingly we can write

$$\Delta H_{\mathrm{II}} = C_p(\mathrm{C + D + S})\cdot(T_0 - T_1) \qquad (12a)$$

$$\Delta E_{\mathrm{II}} = C_v(\mathrm{C + D + S})\cdot(T_0 - T_1) \qquad (12b)$$

where C_p and C_v are average values over the temperature range or to a good approximation may be regarded as constants independent of temperature.

The heat capacity, if not known, must be determined. A direct method, which depends on the assumption of the constancy of heat capacities over a small range of temperature, is to measure the temperature rise $(T_2' - T_1')$ produced by the dissipation of a measured quantity of electrical energy. We then obtain

$$\left.\begin{matrix} C_p \\ C_v \end{matrix}\right\} = \frac{-w_{el}}{T_2' - T_1'} \qquad \begin{matrix} (13a) \\ (13b) \end{matrix}$$

at constant pressure or at constant volume, respectively. This method is exemplified in the experiments on heats of ionic reaction and heats of solution.

An indirect method of determining the heat capacity is to carry out another reaction altogether, for which the heat of reaction is known, in the same calorimeter under the same conditions. This method depends on the fact that in most calorimetric measurements on chemical reactions the heat-capacity contributions of the actual product species (C and D) are very small, and often negligible, in comparison with the contribution due to the parts of the system denoted by the symbol S. In a bomb calorimeter experiment the reactants or products amount to a gram or two, while the rest of the system is equivalent to about 2500 g of water. In calorimetry involving dilute aqueous solutions, the heat capacities of such solutions can in a first approximation be taken equal to that of equivalent weights or volumes of water. Thus we may write, in place of Eqs. (12*a*) and (12*b*),

$$\left.\begin{array}{l}\Delta H_{\mathrm{II}} \quad (14a)\\ \Delta E_{\mathrm{II}} \quad (14b)\end{array}\right\} = C(\mathrm{S})\cdot(T_0 - T_1)$$

for constant-pressure and constant-volume processes, respectively. In Eqs. (14*a*) and (14*b*) we have omitted any subscript from the heat capacity as being largely meaningless, since only solids and liquids, with volumes essentially independent of pressure, are involved. The value of $C(\mathrm{S})$ can be calculated from the heat of the known reaction and the temperature change $(T_2' - T_1')$ produced by it, as follows:

$$C(\mathrm{S}) = \begin{cases} \dfrac{-\Delta H_{\mathrm{known}}}{T_2' - T_1'} & \text{constant pressure} \quad (15a) \\[2ex] \dfrac{-\Delta E_{\mathrm{known}}}{T_2' - T_1'} & \text{constant volume} \quad (15b) \end{cases}$$

This method is exemplified in the experiment on heats of combustion by bomb calorimetry.

Let us now consider Step I, the adiabatic step, and the measurement of the temperature difference $(T_1 - T_0)$ which is the fundamental measurement of calorimetry. It is an idealization to assume that Step I is truly adiabatic; as no thermal insulation is perfect, some heat will in general leak into or out of the system during the time required for the change in state to occur and for the thermometer to come into equilibrium with the product system.

In addition, we usually have a stirrer present in the calorimeter to aid in the mixing of reactants or for hastening thermal equilibration. The mechanical work done on the system by the stirrer results in the continuous addition of energy to the system at a small, approximately constant rate. During the time required for the change in state and thermal equilibration to occur, the amount of energy introduced can easily be significant.

The following are the most important experimental approaches aimed at minimizing the effect of nonadiabatic conditions and the effect of the stirrer; they can be used separately or in combination:

1. The calorimeter may be built in such a way as to minimize heat conduction in or out of the system. A vessel with an evacuated jacket (Dewar flask), often with silvered surfaces to minimize the effect of heat radiation, may be used.

2. One may interpose between system and surroundings an "adiabatic jacket," reasonably well insulated from both. This jacket is so constructed that its temperature can be adjusted at will from outside, as, for example, by supplying electrical

energy to a heating circuit. In use, the temperature of the jacket is continuously adjusted so as to be as close as possible to that of the system, so that no significant quantity of heat will tend to flow between the system and the jacket.

3. The stirring system may be carefully designed to produce the least rate of work consistent with the requirement of thorough and reasonably rapid mixing.

4. We may assume that the rate of gain or loss of energy by the system resulting from heat leak and stirrer work is reasonably constant with time at any given temperature. We may therefore assume that the temperature, as a function of time, should be initially and finally linear. Thus we can estimate what the temperature T_1 would be in the event of instant equilibration by plotting temperature against time for a period long enough to obtain a curve with a long portion that is essentially linear and extrapolating this linear portion back to the time of initiation of the reaction, as shown in Fig. 1. Where the time required for the change in state is long, as in the case of determining the heat capacity by electrical heating, the rate of heat leak presumably changes continuously from the initiation of electrical heating to its termination, and it would be improper to extrapolate to the time of initiation of the heating. The appropriate procedure in this case would be to extrapolate the linear portions of the heating curves for the periods before initiation and after termination to the middle of the heating period.

In the experiment on heats of combustion we make use of approaches 2 (optionally), 3, and 4. In the experiments on heats of ionic reaction and heats of solution we make use of 1, 3, and 4.

In the above discussion, we have been concerned with determining ΔH or ΔE for a chemical change, with arbitrary amounts of reactants. The quantities in which we are interested are the molar quantities $\Delta\tilde{H}$ or $\Delta\tilde{E}$ corresponding to one formula of reaction. The number of formulas of reaction N can be calculated from the quantity of the limiting reactant. Thus we have

$$\Delta\tilde{H} = \frac{\Delta H}{N} \tag{16a}$$

or

$$\Delta\tilde{E} = \frac{\Delta E}{N} \tag{16b}$$

FIG. 1. (*a*) Schematic plot of temperature T vs. time t showing the extrapolation for obtaining T_1. (*b*) Plot with interrupted temperature axis and greatly expanded temperature scale. Such a plot will eliminate the contribution of graphical errors to the uncertainty in $T_1 - T_0$.

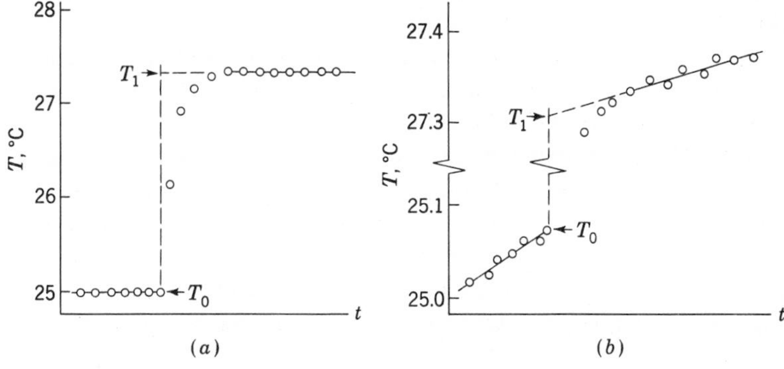

GENERAL READING

J. M. Sturtevant, Calorimetry, in Weissberger (ed.), "Techniques of Organic Chemistry," 2d ed., vol. I, part I, chap. XIV, Interscience, New York (1949).

G. N. Lewis and M. Randall (revised by K. S. Pitzer and L. Brewer), "Thermodynamics," 2d ed., McGraw-Hill, New York (1961).

F. H. MacDougall, "Thermodynamics and Chemistry," 3d ed., Wiley, New York (1939).

Experiment 9. Heats of Combustion

In this experiment a bomb calorimeter is employed in the determination of the heat of combustion of an organic substance such as naphthalene, $C_{10}H_8$. The heat of combustion of naphthalene is $-\Delta\tilde{H}$ for the reaction at constant temperature and pressure

$$C_{10}H_8(s) + 12O_2(g) = 10CO_2(g) + 4H_2O(l) \qquad (1)$$

THEORY

A general discussion of calorimetric measurements is presented in the section Principles of Calorimetry. That material should be reviewed as background for this experiment. It should be noted that no specification of pressure is made for the reaction in Eq. (1) other than that it is constant. (Indeed, in this experiment the reaction is not actually carried out at constant pressure, though the results are corrected to constant pressure in the calculations.) In fact energy and enthalpy changes attending physical changes are generally small in comparison with those attending chemical changes, and those involved in pressure changes on condensed phases (owing to their small molal volumes and low compressibilities) and even on gases (owing to their resemblance to perfect gases) at constant temperature are very small. Thus, energy and enthalpy changes accompanying chemical changes can be considered as being independent of pressure for nearly all practical purposes.

EXPERIMENTAL

The calorimeter (Emerson design), shown in Fig. 1, consists of a high-pressure stainless-steel bomb which sits in a calorimeter pail containing 2000 ml of water. Projecting downward into this pail through a hole in the cover is a motor-driven stirrer and a precision thermometer. All these parts constitute what has been denoted by the letter S in the Principles of Calorimetry. The bomb contains a pair of electrodes to which are attached a short length of fine iron wire in contact with the specimen. Electrical ignition of this wire provides the means of initiating combustion of the sample, which burns in a small metal pan. The bomb is constructed in two parts, which are put together by means of a large ring nut and a lead gasket. A needle valve at the top is provided for filling the bomb with oxygen to about 300 psi.

The system as shown in Fig. 1 is surrounded by the Daniels adiabatic jacket,[1] which consists of two concentric metal cans with a space in between that can be filled with water. Adjustment of the temperature of the jacket is done by passage

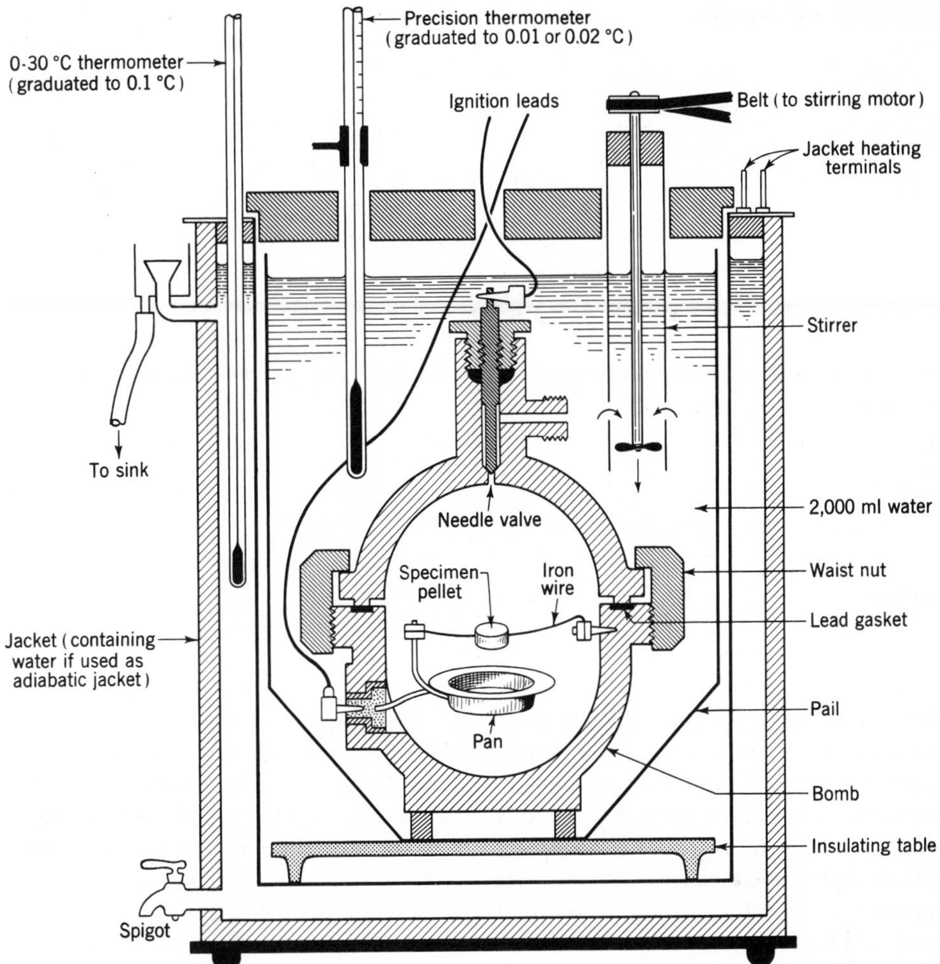

FIG. 1. Bomb calorimeter (Emerson design), shown with Daniels adiabatic jacket which may also be used empty as an air jacket.

of electric current between the two cans, by conduction through the water. The water must have a certain degree of electrical conductivity. Often ordinary tap water or a mixture of tap water and distilled water can be used; more predictable performance can be obtained by adding a small quantity of electrolyte to distilled water (0.05 g of NaCl per liter of water). The electric current is controlled by a tapping key to maintain the jacket temperature [as measured by an ordinary laboratory thermometer (graduated to 0.1°) immersed in the water between the two cans] as nearly as possible at the temperature registered by the calorimeter thermometer. It is also possible to operate the calorimeter without controlling the temperature of the Daniels adiabatic jacket. In this case the space between the two cans is left empty to provide thermal insulation. The heat leak that does occur can be compensated for very well by the extrapolation technique illustrated in Fig. V-1. Either technique of operation is satisfactory. In principle it is better to use the adiabatic jacket; in practice it is usually easier not to use it.

Following the procedure given below, two runs should be made with benzoic acid to determine the heat capacity of the calorimeter and two runs should be made with naphthalene or another substance (perhaps an unknown).

Procedure. The successful operation of this experiment requires close attention to detail, as there are possible sources of trouble that may prevent the experiment from working properly. It is for this reason, and because laboratory scheduling usually does not allow the student to work out his own technique by trial and error, that the procedure is presented in considerable detail.

The student's attention is particularly drawn to the following **warning:** There is a hazard of electric shock and of short circuit from exposed terminals and metal parts of the calorimeter, especially when outer jacket heating is employed. Keep the working space dry. The bomb is expensive and should be handled carefully. In particular, be careful not to scratch or dent the ring gasket or the steel surface that contacts it.

Condition of apparatus: The bomb must be clean and dry with no bits of iron wire in the terminals. Make sure that the jacket is completely empty and that all switches on the control box are off. Check to see that the inside of the calorimeter is dry; then place the insulating table in the bottom, flat side up. By testing in a beaker of water, verify that the stirrer is operating so as to impel the water *downward.*

Filling of the bomb: Cut the iron wire, free from sharp bends or kinks, to the correct length and weigh it accurately. Press pellets of the substance concerned, of weight 0.5 ± 0.1 g for naphthalene and 0.8 ± 0.1 g for benzoic acid. Shave them to the desired weight with a spatula if necessary. Fuse the wire into the pellet by heating the wire with current provided by a 1.5-v dry cell. Blow gently on the wire to prevent it from overheating. The pellet should be at the center of the wire. Weigh it accurately. The weight of the pellet alone is obtained by difference. Handle it very carefully after weighing.

Install the pellet and wire in the bomb with the terminal nuts thumb tight. The pellet should be over the pan, and the wire should touch *only* the terminals. Carefully assemble the bomb and tighten the waist nut with a wrench.

Attach the bomb to the filling apparatus. Line up the fitting carefully before tightening, as misalignment may result in damaged threads. Open the needle valve *one turn* only. For opening and closing the needle valve, use the handwheel provided. *Carefully* open the supply valve, and fill the bomb to 300 psi. Release the pressure to flush out most of the atmospheric nitrogen originally present in the bomb. Retighten and refill to the same pressure. Close the needle valve hand-tight only and remove the bomb. If trouble is encountered in filling the bomb, check the condition of the gasket on the filling apparatus. Check the bomb for leaks by immersion in water. If a leak is found around the waist, retighten the waist nut with the wrench and try again. An occasional bubble—one every 5 or 10 sec—is inconsequential.

Assembly of calorimeter: Dry the bomb. Make electrical connections *tightly* to the top and side; the side connector *must not touch the waist ring nut.* Place the bomb in the dry pail. Check to see that the side connector does not touch the pail. Set the pail in the calorimeter, making sure that it is centered and does not touch the inner wall of the calorimeter.

Fill a 2000-ml volumetric flask with water at 25°C. A convenient way of doing this is to use both hot and cold water; add the two as required, swirling and checking with a thermometer until the flask is almost full, then make up to the mark. Pour the water from the flask carefully into the pail; avoid splashing. Allow the flask to drain a minute.

Put the calorimeter lid in place and introduce the stirrer as far as it will go. Clamp the precision thermometer in place as low as it will go without obscuring the scale. The clamp should be as low as possible and *not too tight.* The jaws of the clamp should be rubber-covered to protect the thermometer. The thermometer should register within half a degree of 25°C.

If a test meter or an improvised tester consisting of a flashlight bulb and a dry cell is available, it is advisable to check the electrical continuity between the two prongs of the plug on the ignition cord. With all switches off, plug the stirrer and ignition cords into the control box (see Fig. 2).

Adiabatic jacket: The following procedure is omitted if the jacket is used only as an insulating air jacket. Close the spigot on the outside of the calorimeter, and fill the jacket to the top of the filling funnel with water of the required conductivity from the supply provided. The overflow drain should be provided with a length of rubber tubing to carry the overflow to a sink. The temperature of the water should be *below* 25°C. This step should be performed concurrently with those described above to save time. Mount an ordinary laboratory thermometer (0 to 30°, graduated to 0.1 or 0.2°) in the jacket so that the bulb is about halfway down. Plug the heater circuit into the control box.

Making the run: The instructions below should be reviewed prior to starting the run; those steps enclosed in brackets ([ ]) should be omitted if the adiabatic jacket is not used.

Recheck the wiring and then plug the control box into a 110-v ac outlet. Turn on the stirrer and be sure it runs smoothly. [Make sure that the tapping key is open, and turn on the switch to the jacket heating circuit. Read the precision thermometer, and by careful use of the tapping key bring the jacket temperature up to the pail temperature. Be very careful not to overshoot.]

Begin time-temperature readings, reading the precision thermometer once

FIG. 2. Electrical circuit for bomb calorimeter.

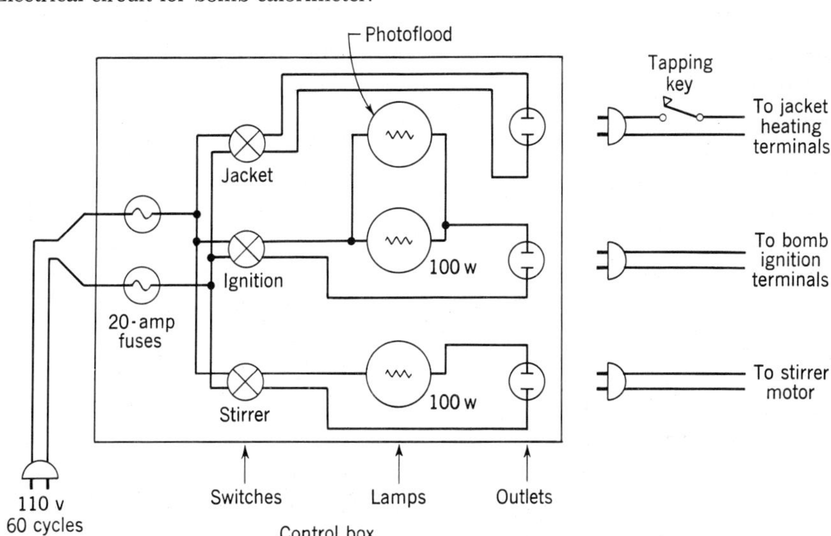

every 30 sec and recording both the time and the temperature. Estimate the temperature to thousandths of a degree if feasible. Tap the thermometer *gently* before each reading. *Do not interrupt the time-temperature readings until the run is over.* [In between readings, check the jacket temperature, and if it is low, correct with tapping key. This procedure must be followed throughout the entire run, especially immediately after ignition.] The calorimeter pail temperature should increase at a very slow linear rate (of the order of $0.001°\ min^{-1}$) due to the stirrer. After this steady rate has persisted for at least 5 min, the bomb may be ignited.

To ignite, turn the ignition switch on and then immediately off. Record the exact time. A dull brief flash may be observable in the light bulbs indicating the passage of current for the instant required to burn the wire through. In nearly all such cases the burning wire will ignite the pellet, and after a delay of 10 or 15 sec the temperature will begin to rise. [As soon as the temperature begins to rise following ignition, depress the tapping key and endeavor to keep the jacket temperature continuously equal to the pail temperature.] After a few minutes the pail temperature should again show a slow, steady rate of change. Do not discontinue readings; continue them until the time since ignition has been at least four times the period required for attainment of this steady rate. The purpose of this is to provide a valid basis for extrapolation. When readings are completed, turn all switches off.

Disassemble the apparatus, release the bomb pressure, and open the bomb with a wrench. Remove and weigh any unburned iron wire; ignore "globules" unless attempts to crush them reveal that they are fused metal rather than oxide. Subtract the weight of unburned iron wire from the initial iron-wire weight to obtain the net weight of iron burned. If the inside of the bomb is found to be coated with soot, the amount of oxygen present at the time of ignition was presumably insufficient to give complete combustion and the run should be discarded. Wipe dry all bomb parts, especially the waist ring nut. [Empty the jacket completely (tilt if necessary).]

CALCULATIONS

For each run, plot temperature vs. time using an expanded, interrupted temperature scale as shown in Fig. V-1*b* and perform the indicated extrapolation to determine the temperature change.

The heat capacity $C(S)$ is found by determining the temperature rise $(T_2' - T_1')$ obtained in the combustion of a known weight of benzoic acid (and, of course, a known weight of iron wire) and making use of Eq. (V-15*b*). For calculating the energy change produced, the specific (i.e., per gram) energies of combustion of benzoic acid (BA) and iron wire (Fe) given below can be used:[3]

$$\begin{aligned} \Delta\bar{E}_{BA} &= -6316 \text{ cal g}^{-1} \\ \Delta\bar{E}_{Fe} &= -1600 \text{ cal g}^{-1} \end{aligned} \tag{2}$$

In this experiment ΔE for the combustion of a weighed specimen of naphthalene or other substance is determined from the rise in temperature $(T_1 - T_0)$ and the heat capacity $C(S)$ by use of Eqs. (V-6*b*) and (V-14*b*). The value of ΔE obtained includes a contribution for the combustion of the iron wire; this must be subtracted to yield the contribution from the naphthalene alone. The molar energy change $\Delta\tilde{E}$ is then obtained from the number of moles of the reactant that is present in the least equivalent amount (in this case, naphthalene) in accordance with Eq. (V-16*b*). The molar enthalpy change $\Delta\tilde{H}$ can then be obtained by use of Eq. (V-8).

Report the individual and average values of the heat capacity $C(S)$ and the individual and average values of the molar enthalpy change $\Delta\tilde{H}$ for the combustion of naphthalene, calculated using the average $C(S)$.

DISCUSSION

How does the order of magnitude of the error introduced into the experimental result by the assumption of the perfect-gas law in Eq. (V-8) compare with the uncertainties inherent in the measurements in this experiment? What is the magnitude of the uncertainty introduced by lack of knowledge of the specific heat of the sample? Does your ΔH value pertain to the initial or the final temperature?

APPARATUS

Bomb calorimeter complete with bomb, pail, jacket, insulating table, cover, and stirring motor with power cord; one set of electrical leads which connect to bomb; 110-v power source unit, equipped with fuse and bulbs; precision calorimeter thermometer covering range from 19 to 35°C; magnifying thermometer-reader; 0 to 30° thermometer; stopwatch; 2000-ml volumetric flask; 1.5-v dry cell; 500-ml beaker. If adiabatic jacket is to be used: tapping key and set of leads for jacket heating; water of proper conductivity for filling jacket.

Bomb-filling apparatus on table securely bolted to the floor; long-handled wrench for closing and opening bomb; cylinder of oxygen with appropriate fittings; large pail for leak-testing bomb; benzoic acid (5 g); naphthalene (5 g) or other solid to be studied; pellet press; spatula; 0.004-in.-diameter iron wire (50 cm); device for checking electrical continuity (optional).

REFERENCES

1. F. Daniels, *J. Am. Chem. Soc.*, **38,** 1473 (1916); T. W. Richards, *J. Am. Chem. Soc.*, **31,** 1275 (1909).
2. H. C. Dickinson, *Natl. Bur. Standards Bull.*, **11,** 189 (1915).
3. Handbook of Chemistry and Physics, 41st ed., Chemical Rubber Publishing Co., Cleveland (1960).

GENERAL READING

J. M. Sturtevant, Calorimetry, in Weissberger (ed.), "Techniques of Organic Chemistry," 2d ed., vol. I, part I, chap. XIV, pp. 783–802, Interscience, New York (1949).

Experiment 10. Heats of Ionic Reaction

It is desired in this experiment to determine the heat of ionization of water:

$$H_2O(l) = H^+(aq) + OH^-(aq),\ \Delta\tilde{H}_1 \tag{1}$$

and the heat of the second ionization of malonic acid ($HOOC—CH_2—COOH$, hereafter designated H_2R):

$$HR^-(aq) = H^+(aq) + R^=(aq),\ \Delta\tilde{H}_2 \tag{2}$$

These will be obtained by studying experimentally with a solution calorimeter the heat of reaction of an aqueous HCl solution with an aqueous NaOH solution, for which the ionic reaction is

$$H^+(aq) + OH^-(aq) = H_2O(l),\ \Delta\tilde{H}_3 \tag{3}$$

and that of the reaction of an aqueous NaHR solution with an aqueous NaOH solution,

$$HR^-(aq) + OH^-(aq) = R^=(aq) + H_2O(l),\ \Delta\tilde{H}_4 \tag{4}$$

The last two equations can be written in the general form

$$A + B = \text{products} \tag{5}$$

where A represents the acid ion and B the basic ion.

THEORY

A general discussion of calorimetric measurements is presented in the section Principles of Calorimetry, which should be reviewed in connection with this experiment. We shall not here consider the concentration dependence of these enthalpy changes. Such concentration dependence is generally a small effect, since the heats of dilution involved are usually much smaller than the heats of chemical reaction (indeed they are zero for perfect solutions). Since we are here dealing with solutions of moderate concentration, particularly in the case of the NaOH solution, it may be useful to make parallel determinations of heats of dilution of the solutions concerned by a procedure similar to that described here if time permits.

EXPERIMENTAL

In this experiment 500 ml of solution *A*, with a precisely known concentration in the neighborhood of 0.25 *M*, is reacted with 50 ml of solution *B* at a concentration sufficient to provide a slight excess over the amount required to react with solution *A*. The reaction is carried out in the solution calorimeter shown in Fig. 1. The calorimeter is a vacuum bottle (Dewar flask) containing a thermometer, a motor-driven stirrer, a heating coil of precisely known electrical resistance, and a precision thermometer. Various methods of mixing the two solutions might be employed; here we use an inner vessel having an outlet hole plugged by stopcock grease which can be blown out by applying air pressure at the top.

For determining the heat capacity, a dc electric current of about 1.5 amp is passed through the heating coil during a known time interval. The magnitude of the current is measured as a function of time by determining the potential difference developed across a standard resistance in series with the coil. The electric circuit is shown in Fig. 2.

It is recommended that two complete runs be made with HCl and NaOH and two with NaHR and NaOH.

Procedure. It is advisable to carry out a test of the electrical heating procedure in advance of the actual runs. Place roughly 600 ml of water in the calorimeter and introduce the stirrer-heater unit and thermometer. Make the electrical

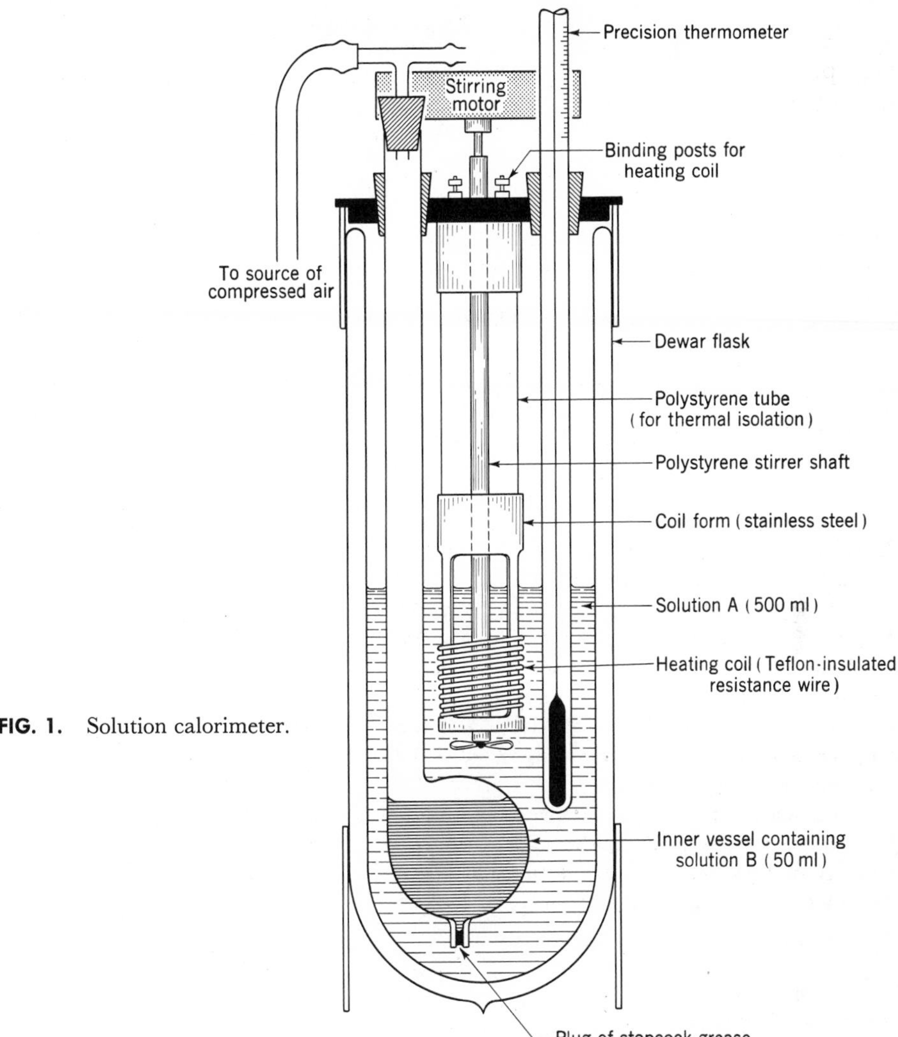

FIG. 1. Solution calorimeter.

connections as shown in Fig. 2. Turn on the stirring motor and then turn on the current to the heater; **never** pass current through the heating coil when it is not immersed in a liquid, as it will overheat and may burn out. Standardize the potentiometer and record the potential difference across the resistor in series with the heating coil. Also note the rate of temperature rise during heating. Both of these observations will be useful during the actual runs.

Fill a 500-ml volumetric flask with solution *A*, the temperature of which should be within a few tenths of a degree of 25.0°C. (Adjust the temperature by swirling under running hot or cold water before the flask has been entirely filled, then make up to the mark.) Pour the solution into the clean and reasonably dry calorimeter and allow the flask to drain for a minute. Work a plug of stopcock grease into the capillary hole in the bottom of the inner vessel. The glass must be absolutely dry, or the grease will not stick. Pipette in 50 ml of solution *B*. Place the inner vessel in the calorimeter carefully.

Introduce the stirrer-heater unit and thermometer into the calorimeter making

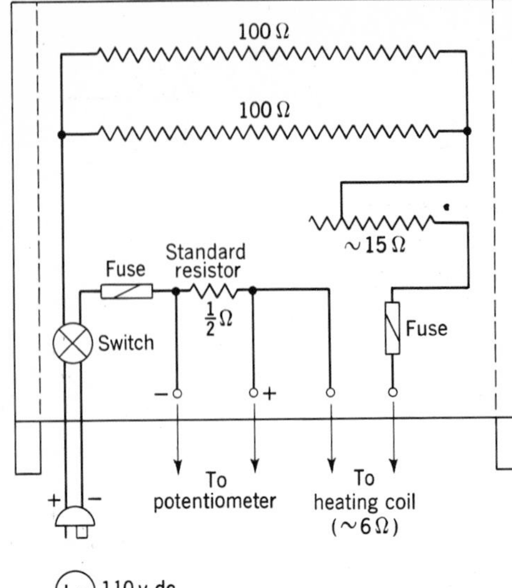

FIG. 2. Electrical heating circuit for solution calorimeter. The unit should stand upright on the two extended ends as shown; this will permit air cooling and prevent overheating of the standard resistor. If a heating coil of higher resistance (say ~60 ohms) is to be used, the current can be reduced (to say ~0.5 amp) and a 1-ohm standard resistor should be used.

sure that the thermometer bulb is completely immersed (level with or just below the heating coil). The inner vessel should be held in a hole in the calorimeter cover by a split stopper so that it does not rest on the bottom of the Dewar flask. Check the electrical connections to the heating coil. Connect the T tube to a compressed-air supply; turn on the air, adjust to barely audible flow, and attach the T tube to the top of the inner vessel. Turn on the stirring motor.

Start temperature-time measurements. Read the thermometer every 30 sec, estimating to thousandths of a degree if feasible. Tap the thermometer stem *gently* before each reading. After a slight but steady rate of temperature change due to stirring and heat leak has been observed for 5 min, initiate the reaction by blowing the contents of the inner vessel into the surrounding solution. This is done by placing a finger over the open end of the T tube. Release the pressure as soon as bubbling is heard. Record the time. After 15 sec, blow out the inner vessel again to ensure thermal equilibrium throughout all the solution.

After a plateau with a slight, steady rate of temperature change has prevailed for 5 min, turn on the current to the heater and *record the exact time.* Immediately measure the potential difference across the standard resistor in series with the heater. The potentiometer should be standardized and set to the expected potential (as determined above) a minute or so before the current is turned on. Repeat the potential measurement at least once every minute while the current is on.

When a temperature rise of about 1.5°C has been obtained by electric heating, turn off the current, again noting the exact time. Simultaneously blow out the inner vessel again to mix the contents with the surrounding solution. After a final plateau with a slight, steady temperature change has been achieved for 5 min, the run may be terminated. Record the resistance of the heating coil used.

CALCULATIONS

For each run, plot the temperature vs. time, preferably using a greatly expanded temperature scale with an interrupted temperature axis (see Fig. V-1*b*). Perform

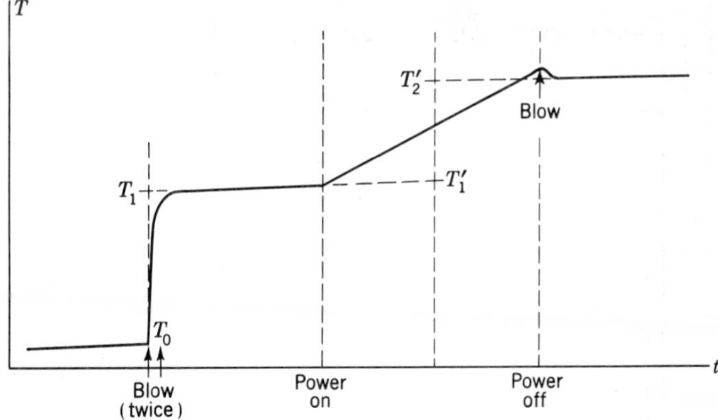

FIG. 3. Schematic plot of temperature vs. time: heat of ionic reaction.

the extrapolations indicated in Fig. 3 and obtain the temperature differences ($T_0 - T_1$) and ($T_2' - T_1'$). The heat capacity is calculated by use of Eqs. (V-9) and (V-13*a*); the integral in Eq. (V-9) should be evaluated graphically unless the current is constant during the heating period. The enthalpy change of the ionic reaction is calculated from Eqs. (V-6*a*) and (V-12*a*). Calculate the number of formulas of reaction from the number of moles of A (the limiting reactant) present and calculate the molal enthalpy change $\Delta\tilde{H}_3$ or $\Delta\tilde{H}_4$, by use of Eq. (V-16*a*).

From the average values of $\Delta\tilde{H}_3$ and $\Delta\tilde{H}_4$ obtained, calculate $\Delta\tilde{H}_1$ and $\Delta\tilde{H}_2$.

DISCUSSION

Using literature data,[1, 2] estimate the difference between the $\Delta\tilde{H}_3$ value for the concentrations employed in this experiment and the value which would apply at infinite dilution. Compare this effect with a qualitative estimate of the experimental uncertainty in the measured $\Delta\tilde{H}_3$. Indicate why there should be a large percentage error in $\Delta\tilde{H}_4$ as determined here.

APPARATUS

Solution calorimeter (1-qt Dewar); stirrer-heater unit complete with motor and power cord; inner vessel; precision calorimeter thermometer covering range from 19 to 35°C; magnifying thermometer reader; 0 to 30°C thermometer; two split rubber stoppers; glass T tube with stopper and rubber tubing; stopwatch; dc power-supply unit for heater (see Fig. 2); complete potentiometer setup (see Chap. XV); 15 electrical leads with lugs attached; 250-ml beaker; 500-ml volumetric flask; a 50- and a 10-ml pipette; 100-ml beaker; rubber pipetting bulb.

Solutions: NaOH, concentration slightly greater than 2.5 *M* (0.4 liter); 0.25 *M* HCl (1.5 liters); 0.25 *M* $NaHC_3H_2O_4$ (1.5 liters; the sodium acid malonate solution can be prepared by neutralizing malonic acid with sodium hydroxide to a point just past the $NaHC_3H_2O_4$ end point); stopcock grease; source of compressed air.

REFERENCES

1. F. R. Bichowsky and F. D. Rossini, "Thermochemistry of Chemical Substances," Reinhold, New York (1936).
2. Selected Values of Chemical Thermodynamics Properties, *Natl. Bur. Standards Circ.* 500 (1952).

Experiment 11. Heats of Solution

In this experiment, techniques very similar to those used in Exp. 10 will be employed to determine the integral and differential heats of solution of a salt in aqueous solution.

THEORY

The general background for calorimetric measurements has been developed in the section Principles of Calorimetry, but it is necessary here to define and distinguish the terms *integral heat of solution* and *differential heat of solution.*[1, 2]

For a given solution of specified concentration m, the integral heat of solution per mole of solute $\Delta\tilde{H}_{int}$ is the heat absorbed when one mole of solute is dissolved isothermally in enough solvent to form a final solution of concentration m. In other words, it is the enthalpy change for the change in state at constant p and T

$$\mathrm{A} + x\mathrm{S} = \mathrm{A}\cdot x\mathrm{S}\ (\textit{solution, conc. } m) \tag{1}$$

where A is the pure solute and S is the pure solvent. This quantity $\Delta\tilde{H}_{int}$ varies with the concentration m. As x in Eq. (1) approaches infinity (m approaches zero), $\Delta\tilde{H}_{int}$ asymptotically approaches a constant value $\Delta\tilde{H}_{\infty}$, the integral heat of solution at infinite dilution.

In many thermodynamic calculations, it is necessary to know the enthalpy change for the change in state at constant p and T

$$\mathrm{A} = \mathrm{A}\ (\textit{solution } \mathrm{S}, \textit{ conc. } m) \tag{2}$$

where A and S have the same meaning as in Eq. (1). This quantity is known as the differential heat of solution of the solute and may be thought of as the heat absorbed when one mole of solute is dissolved isothermally in an infinite amount of solution of concentration m. The differential heat of solution could in principle be obtained by measuring the heat absorbed per mole ($\delta Q/\delta n$) when a very small number of moles (δn) of solute is dissolved in a finite amount of solution. In practice, however, it is much easier to calculate the differential heat of solution from the integral heat of solution determined as a function of concentration. The enthalpy change ΔH for the dissolving of N_2 moles of solute in N_1 moles of solvent will be a function of both N_1 and N_2. The differential heat of solution of the solute $\Delta\overline{H}_2$ is given by

$$\Delta\overline{H}_2 = \left(\frac{\partial\,\Delta H}{\partial N_2}\right)_{N_1} \tag{3}$$

Now consider the solution of m moles of solute in 1000 g of solvent to give a solution of molality m. The enthalpy change ΔH will be $m\Delta\tilde{H}_{int}$; therefore,

$$\Delta\overline{H}_2 = \frac{\partial(m\,\Delta\tilde{H}_{int})}{\partial m} \tag{4a}$$

$$= \Delta\tilde{H}_{int} + m\frac{d\,\Delta\tilde{H}_{int}}{dm} \tag{4b}$$

Once $\Delta\tilde{H}_{int}$ is known as a function of concentration m, the differential heat of solution $\Delta\overline{H}_2$ can be calculated for any given concentration by use of Eq. (4a) or (4b).

The differential heat of solution is equal to the *partial molal enthalpy* of solute A in solution minus that for pure A.[1,2] A brief discussion of partial molal quantities is given in Exp. 12.

EXPERIMENTAL

The experimental method to be used is very similar to that described in Exp. 10. The apparatus is identical with that shown in Figs. 10-1 and 10-2 *except* that the inner vessel of the solution calorimeter is replaced by a short (~3 in.) length of glass tubing flared at the top to serve as a funnel for adding the solid salt. This funnel should not come in contact with the liquid below.

The experiment is carried out in five successive runs, in each of which an aliquot of solid KNO_3, weighing approximately 2.8 g, is introduced into the calorimeter. In the first run the salt is dissolved in distilled water and in other runs it is dissolved in the solution resulting from the previous run. The calorimeter should originally contain a known amount of water (about 600 g). The solution of KNO_3 in water is endothermic, and the temperature therefore drops; after each addition of KNO_3 electrical energy is dissipated inside the calorimeter by means of a heating coil. This heating accomplishes two purposes simultaneously: the temperature is returned to its initial value at the end of each run prior to the next addition of KNO_3, and the heat capacity is determined for each resulting solution.

Procedure. After the equipment has been set up, a test of the electrical heating circuit should be carried out in advance of the actual runs. Follow the procedure described in Exp. 10. Be careful **never** to pass current through the heating coil when it is not immersed in a liquid.

Place approximately 2.8 g of dry KNO_3 powder (accurately weighed on an analytical balance) in each of five small well-dried and numbered weighing bottles or erlenmeyer flasks. Stopper these flasks, and if possible, keep them thermostated at 25°C until used.

Fill a 500- and a 100-ml volumetric flask with distilled water. Adjust the temperature of the water to within a few tenths of a degree of 25.0°C by swirling the flasks under running hot or cold water. Then pour the distilled water into the clean and dry calorimeter (Dewar) and allow the flasks to drain briefly. (If desired, the flasks may be weighed before and after delivery.)

Introduce the stirrer-heater unit and thermometer into the calorimeter making sure that the thermometer bulb is completely immersed (level with or just below the heating coil). Place the funnel (*dry*) in an opening provided in the cover of the calorimeter. Make electrical connections to the heating coil and start the stirring motor.

Begin temperature-time measurements. Read the thermometer, estimating to thousandths of a degree if feasible, every 30 sec throughout the run. After a small, steady rate of temperature change due to stirring and heat leak has been observed for 5 min, one of the weighed samples of KNO_3 is emptied into the funnel and the time is recorded. The funnel should be tapped to ensure that all the salt drops into the liquid below. As the salt dissolves, the temperature will fall and then level off.

After a plateau with a steady rate of temperature change has prevailed for 5 min, turn on the current to the heating coil and *record the exact time.* Immediately measure the potential difference across the standard resistor in series with the heater.

The potentiometer should be standardized and set to the expected potential a minute or so before the current is turned on. Repeat the potential measurement at least once every minute while the current is on. The current is turned off when the temperature is about 0.1°C below the initial temperature (before the salt was added) in order to allow for some "overshoot." Record the exact time. After a plateau with a small, steady rate of temperature change has been achieved for 5 min, the run is complete.

The next run can be started immediately by adding another weighed sample of KNO_3 to the solution in the calorimeter and proceeding as before. Five successive runs are to be carried out. Record the resistance of the heating coil used.

CALCULATIONS

For each run plot the temperature vs. time, preferably using a greatly expanded temperature scale with an interrupted temperature axis (see Fig. V-1*b*). Perform the extrapolations indicated in Fig. 1 and obtain the temperature differences $(T_0 - T_1)$ and $(T_2' - T_1')$. The heat capacity is calculated by use of Eqs. (V-9) and (V-13*a*); the integral in Eq. (V-9) should be evaluated graphically unless the current is constant during the heating period. The C_p values for the individual runs should agree closely with each other. If an untrustworthy value of C_p is obtained for one run, discard that result and replace it with the mean of the C_p values for the preceding and following runs. The enthalpy change of the *i*th run ΔH_i is calculated from Eqs. (V-6*a*) and (V-12*a*). Tabulate your values of C_p and ΔH for each run.

The integral heat of solution for all the salt dissolved up to and including the *n*th run is given by

$$\Delta \tilde{H}_{int} = \frac{\sum_{i=1}^{n} \Delta H_i}{\sum_{i=1}^{n} N_i} \tag{5}$$

where N_i is the number of moles of KNO_3 added in the *i*th run. The molality of the solution (moles of salt per 1000 g of water) *m* is calculated for each of the five solutions obtained after an addition of salt. From Eq. (5) the corresponding $\Delta \tilde{H}_{int}$ values are calculated and tabulated.

FIG. 1. Schematic plot of temperature vs. time: heat of solution.

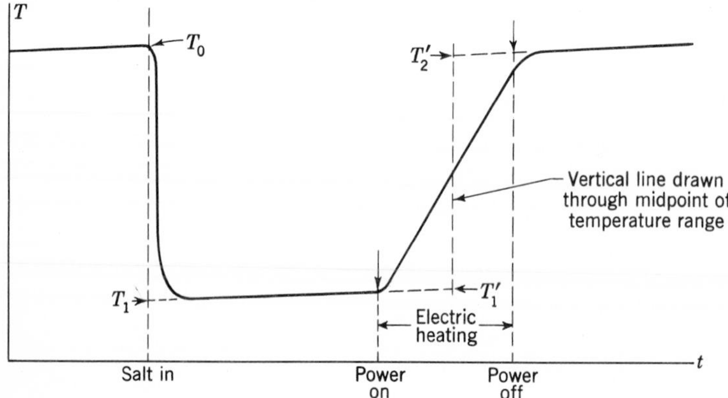

Plot $\Delta\tilde{H}_{int}$ vs. m and extrapolate the curve to zero molality to obtain the integral heat of solution at infinite dilution $\Delta\tilde{H}_{\infty}$. The slope of the curve should be zero at $m = 0$. Using Eq. (4*b*), determine the differential heat of solution, $\Delta\overline{H}_2$, at intervals of 0.05 molal over the concentration range studied.

DISCUSSION

Describe any necessary changes in the experimental equipment and/or procedure for heat of solution measurements which are exothermic.

APPARATUS

Solution calorimeter (1-qt Dewar); stirrer-heater unit complete with motor and power cord; short, wide funnel; precision calorimeter thermometer covering range from 19 to 35°C; magnifying thermometer-reader; 0 to 30°C thermometer; two split rubber stoppers; stopwatch; dc power-supply unit for heater (see Fig. 10-2); complete potentiometer setup (see Chap. XV); 15 electrical leads with lugs attached; one 500- and one 100-ml volumetric flask; five small flasks or weighing bottles to hold solid salt.

Distilled water; pure, dry KNO_3 solid (20 g); thermostat bath at 25°C (optional).

REFERENCES

1. F. H. MacDougall, "Thermodynamics and Chemistry," chap. VI, Wiley, New York (1939).
2. G. N. Lewis and M. Randall (revised by K. S. Pitzer and L. Brewer), "Thermodynamics," 2d ed., McGraw-Hill, New York (1961).

GENERAL READING

J. M. Sturtevant, Calorimetry, in Weissberger (ed.), "Techniques of Organic Chemistry," 2d ed., vol. I, part I, chap. XIV, pp. 817–827, Interscience, New York (1949).

VI
SOLUTIONS

EXPERIMENTS

Experiment 12. Partial Molal Volume

In this experiment the partial molal volumes of sodium chloride solutions will be calculated as a function of concentration from densities measured with a pycnometer.

THEORY

Most thermodynamic variables fall into two types. Those representing *extensive* properties of a phase are proportional to the amount of the phase under consideration; they are exemplified by the thermodynamic functions V, E, H, S, A, G. Those representing *intensive* properties are independent of the amount of the phase; they include p and T. Variables of both types may be regarded as examples of homogeneous functions of degree n, that is, functions having the property

$$f(kN_1, \ldots, kN_i, \ldots) = k^n f(N_1, \ldots, N_i, \ldots) \tag{1}$$

where N_i represents for our purposes the number of moles of component i in a phase. Extensive variables are functions of degree one and intensive variables are functions of degree zero.

Among intensive variables important in thermodynamics are *partial molal quantities,* defined by the equation

$$\bar{Q}_i = \left(\frac{\partial Q}{\partial N_i}\right)_{p,T,N_j \neq i} \tag{2}$$

where Q may be any of the extensive quantities already mentioned. For a phase of one component, partial molal quantities are identical with so-called molal quantities, $\tilde{Q} = Q/N$. For an ideal gaseous or liquid solution, certain partial molal quantities ($\bar{V}_i$, $\bar{E}_i$, $\bar{H}_i$) are equal to the respective molal quantities for the pure components while others ($\bar{S}_i$, $\bar{A}_i$, $\bar{G}_i$) are not. For nonideal solutions, all partial molal quantities differ in general from the corresponding molal quantities, and the differences are frequently of interest.

A property of great usefulness possessed by partial molal quantities derives from Euler's theorem for homogeneous functions, which state that, for a homogeneous function $f(N_1, \ldots, N_i, \ldots)$ of degree n,

$$N_1 \frac{\partial f}{\partial N_1} + N_2 \frac{\partial f}{\partial N_2} + \cdots + N_i \frac{\partial f}{\partial N_i} + \cdots = nf \tag{3}$$

Applied to an extensive thermodynamic variable Q, we see that

$$N_1\bar{Q}_1 + N_2\bar{Q}_2 + \cdots + N_i\bar{Q}_i + \cdots = Q \tag{4}$$

Equation (4) leads to an important result. If we form the differential of Q in the usual way,

$$dQ = \frac{\partial Q}{\partial N_1}\,dN_1 + \cdots + \frac{\partial Q}{\partial N_i}\,dN_i + \cdots + \frac{\partial Q}{\partial p}\,dp + \frac{\partial Q}{\partial T}\,dT$$

and compare it with the differential derived from Eq. (4),

$$dQ = \bar{Q}_1\,dN_1 + \cdots + \bar{Q}_i\,dN_i + \cdots + N_1\,d\bar{Q}_1 + \cdots + N_i\,d\bar{Q}_i + \cdots$$

we obtain

$$N_1\,d\bar{Q}_1 + \cdots + N_i\,d\bar{Q}_i + \cdots - \left(\frac{\partial Q}{\partial p}\right)_{N_i,T} dp - \left(\frac{\partial Q}{\partial T}\right)_{N_i,p} dT = 0 \tag{5}$$

For the important special case of constant pressure and temperature,

$$N_1\,d\bar{Q}_1 + \cdots + N_i\,d\bar{Q}_i + \cdots = 0 \qquad (\text{const } p \text{ and } T) \tag{6}$$

This equation tells us that changes in partial molal quantities (resulting of necessity from changes in the N_i) are not all independent. For a binary solution one can write

$$\frac{d\bar{Q}_2}{d\bar{Q}_1} = -\frac{X_1}{X_2} \tag{7}$$

where the X_i are *mole fractions*, $X_i = N_i/\Sigma N_i$. In application to free energy this equation is commonly known as the Gibbs-Duhem equation.

We are concerned in this experiment with the partial molal volume $\bar{V}_i$, which may be thought of as the increase in the volume of an infinite amount of solution (or an amount so large that insignificant concentration change will result) when 1 mole of component i is added. This is by no means necessarily equal to the volume of 1 mole of pure i.

Partial molal volumes are of interest in part through their thermodynamic connection with other partial molal quantities such as partial molal free energy, known also as chemical potential. An important property of chemical potential is that for any given component it is equal for all phases that are in equilibrium with each other. Consider a system containing a pure solid substance (e.g., NaCl) in equilibrium with the saturated aqueous solution. The chemical potential of the solute is the same in the two phases. Imagine now that the pressure is changed isothermally. Will solute tend to go from one phase to the other, reflecting a change in solubility? For an equilibrium change at constant temperature, involving only expansion work,

$$dG = V\,dp \tag{8}$$

Differentiating with respect to N_2, the number of moles of solute, we obtain

$$d\bar{G}_2 = \bar{V}_2\,dp \tag{9}$$

where the partial molal free energy (chemical potential) and partial molal volume appear. For the change in state

$$\mathrm{NaCl}(s) = \mathrm{NaCl}(aq)$$

we can write

$$d(\Delta\bar{G}_2) = \Delta\bar{V}_2\,dp$$

or

$$\left[\frac{\partial(\Delta\bar{G}_2)}{\partial p}\right]_T = \Delta\bar{V}_2 \tag{10}$$

Thus if the partial molal volume of solute in aqueous solution is greater than the molal volume of solid solute, an increase in pressure will increase the chemical potential of solute in solution relative to that in the solid phase; solute will then leave the solution phase until a lower, equilibrium solubility is attained. Conversely, if the partial molal volume in the solution is less than that in the solid, the solubility will increase with pressure.

Partial molal volumes, and in particular their deviations from the values expected for ideal solutions, are of considerable interest in connection with the theory of solutions, especially as applied to binary mixtures of liquid components where they are related to heats of mixing and deviations from Raoult's law.

METHOD[1]

We see from Eq. (4) that the total volume of an amount of solution containing 1000 g (55.51 moles) of water and m moles of solute is given by

$$V = N_1\bar{V}_1 + N_2\bar{V}_2 = 55.51\bar{V}_1 + m\bar{V}_2 \tag{11}$$

where the subscripts 1 and 2 refer to solvent and solute, respectively. Let $\tilde{V}_1{}^0$ be the molal volume of pure water ($=18.016/0.997044 = 18.069$ cm^3 at 25.00°C). Then we define the *apparent molal volume* ϕ of the solute by the equation

$$V = N_1\tilde{V}_1{}^0 + N_2\phi = 55.51\tilde{V}_1{}^0 + m\phi \tag{12}$$

which can be rearranged to give

$$\phi = \frac{1}{N_2}(V - N_1\tilde{V}_1{}^0) = \frac{1}{m}(V - 55.51\tilde{V}_1{}^0) \tag{13}$$

Now
$$V = \frac{1000 + mM_2}{d} \tag{14}$$

and
$$N_1\tilde{V}_1{}^0 = \frac{1000}{d_0} \tag{15}$$

where d is the density of the solution, d_0 is the density of pure solvent, and M_2 is the solute molecular weight. Substituting Eqs. (14) and (15) into Eq. (13), we obtain

$$\phi = \frac{1}{d}\left(M_2 - \frac{1000}{m}\frac{d - d_0}{d_0}\right) \tag{16}$$

$$= \frac{1}{d}\left(M_2 - \frac{1000}{m}\frac{W - W_0}{W_0 - W_e}\right) \tag{17}$$

In Eq. (17), the directly measured weights of the pycnometer—W_e when empty, W_0 when filled to the mark with pure water, and W when filled to the mark with solution—are used. This equation is preferable to Eq. (16) for calculation of ϕ, as it avoids the necessity of computing the densities to the high precision that would otherwise be necessary in obtaining the small difference $d - d_0$.

Now by the definition of partial molal volumes and by use of Eqs. (11) and (12),

$$\bar{V}_2 = \left(\frac{\partial V}{\partial N_2}\right)_{N_1,T,p} = \phi + N_2\frac{\partial \phi}{\partial N_2} = \phi + m\frac{d\phi}{dm} \tag{18}$$

Also,
$$\bar{V}_1 = \frac{1}{N_1}\left(N_1\tilde{V}_1{}^0 - N_2{}^2\frac{\partial \phi}{\partial N_2}\right) = \tilde{V}_1{}^0 - \frac{m^2}{55.51}\frac{d\phi}{dm} \tag{19}$$

We might proceed by plotting ϕ vs. m, drawing a smooth curve through the points, and constructing tangents to the curve at the desired concentrations in order to measure the slopes. However, for solutions of simple electrolytes, it has been found that many apparent molal quantities such as ϕ vary linearly with $\sqrt{m}$, even up to moderate concentrations.[2] This behavior is in agreement with the prediction of the Debye-Hückel theory for dilute solutions.[3] Since

$$\frac{d\phi}{dm} = \frac{d\phi}{d\sqrt{m}}\frac{d\sqrt{m}}{dm} = \frac{1}{2\sqrt{m}}\frac{d\phi}{d\sqrt{m}} \tag{20}$$

we obtain from Eqs. (18) and (19)

$$\bar{V}_2 = \phi + \frac{m}{2\sqrt{m}}\frac{d\phi}{d\sqrt{m}} = \phi + \frac{\sqrt{m}}{2}\frac{d\phi}{d\sqrt{m}} = \phi^0 + \frac{3\sqrt{m}}{2}\frac{d\phi}{d\sqrt{m}} \tag{21}$$

$$\bar{V}_1 = \tilde{V}_1{}^0 - \frac{m}{55.51}\left(\frac{\sqrt{m}}{2}\frac{d\phi}{d\sqrt{m}}\right) \tag{22}$$

where ϕ^0 is the apparent molal volume extrapolated to zero concentration. Now one can plot ϕ vs. $\sqrt{m}$ and draw the best *straight* line through the points. Unless the experimental data are unusually good, deviations of experimental points from the best straight line are not significant. From the slope $d\phi/d\sqrt{m}$ and the value of ϕ^0, both $\bar{V}_1$ and $\bar{V}_2$ can be obtained.

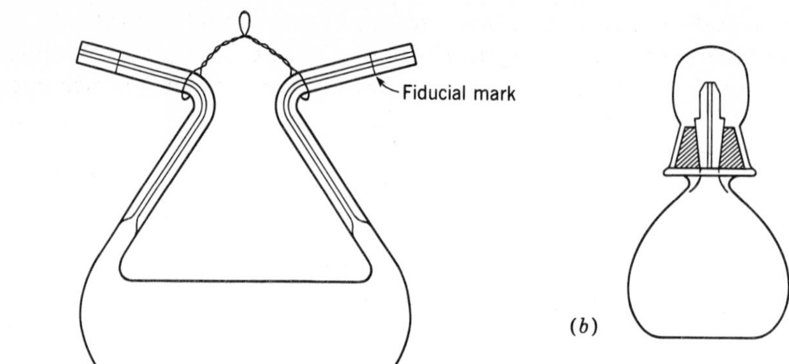

FIG. 1. Pycnometers: (*a*) Ostwald-Sprengel type; (*b*) stopper type.

EXPERIMENTAL

Make up 200 ml of approximately 3.2 *m* (3.0 *M*) NaCl in water. Weigh the salt accurately and use a volumetric flask; then pour the solution into a dry flask. If possible, prepare this solution in advance (since the salt dissolves slowly). Solutions of ½, ¼, ⅛, and 1⁄16 of the initial molarity are to be prepared by successive volumetric dilutions; for each dilution pipette 100 ml of solution into a 200-ml volumetric flask and make up to the mark with distilled water.

The pycnometer is rinsed with distilled water and thoroughly dried before each use. Use an aspirator, and rinse and dry by suction; use a few rinses of acetone to expedite drying. The procedure given here is for the Ostwald-Sprengel type pycnometer; the less accurate but more convenient stopper type can be used with a few obvious changes in procedure. To fill, dip one arm of the pycnometer into the vessel containing the solution (preferably at a temperature *below* 25°C) and apply suction by mouth with a piece of rubber tubing attached to the other arm. Hang the pycnometer in the thermostat bath (25.0°C) with the main body below the surface but with the arms emerging well above. Allow at least 15 min for equilibration. While the pycnometer is still in the bath, adjust menisci to fiducial marks with the aid of a piece of filter paper. Remove the pycnometer from the bath and quickly but thoroughly dry the outside surface with a towel and filter paper. Weigh the pycnometer, hanging it from the hook above the balance pan.

The pycnometer should be weighed empty and dry (W_e), and also with distilled water in it (W_0), as well as with each of the solutions in it (W). It is advisable to repeat W_e and W_0 as a check, inasmuch as the results of all runs depend upon them.

All weighings are to be done on an analytical balance to the highest possible precision. Record the values of all weights, then apply any weight calibration corrections. It is unnecessary to correct the weights to vacuum readings in this experiment, although for very precise work this must be done.

CALCULATIONS

The success of this experiment depends greatly upon the care with which the computations are carried out. Careful judgment should be used as to when slide-rule accuracy is sufficient and when five-place logarithms should be used. All calculations should be checked; a slide-rule check may suffice for logarithmic computations. If the work is done by two or more students, the partners are encouraged to work together, performing the same calculations independently and checking results with each other after each step.

Although to a great extent the weights themselves enter into the calculations, it is necessary also to have the density d of every solution to at least *good* slide-rule accuracy:

$$d = \frac{W_{\text{soln}}}{V} = \frac{W - W_e}{V_p} \tag{23}$$

The volume of the pycnometer V_p is obtained by use of the density of water at 25°C, d_0 (with the value 0.997044 g cm^{-3}), and $W_0 - W_e$.

The molalities m which are needed for the calculations can be obtained from the molarities M obtained from the volumetric procedures by use of the equation

$$m = \frac{1}{1 - \dfrac{(M)}{d}\dfrac{M_2}{1000}} \cdot \frac{(M)}{d} = \frac{1}{\dfrac{d}{(M)} - \dfrac{M_2}{1000}} \tag{24}$$

where M_2 is the solute molecular weight (58.45) and d is the experimental density.

Calculate ϕ for each solution using Eq. (17) and plot ϕ vs. $\sqrt{m}$. Draw the best straight line and obtain $d\phi/d\sqrt{m}$ from the slope. Record the value of ϕ^0, the intercept at m equal zero.

Calculate $\bar{V}_2$ and $\bar{V}_1$ for $m = 0$, 0.5, 1.0, 1.5, 2.0, and 2.5. Plot them against m and draw a smooth curve for each of the two quantities.

In your report, present the curves (ϕ vs. $\sqrt{m}$, $\bar{V}_2$ and $\bar{V}_1$ vs. m) mentioned above. Present also in tabular form the quantities d, M, m, $\dfrac{1000}{m}\dfrac{W - W_0}{W_0 - W_e}$, and ϕ for each solution studied. Give the values obtained for the pycnometer volume V_p and for ϕ^0 and $d\phi/d\sqrt{m}$.

DISCUSSION

The density of NaCl(s) is 2.165 g cm^{-3} at 25°C. How will the solubility of NaCl in water be affected by an increase in pressure?

Discuss qualitatively whether the curves of $\bar{V}_1$ and $\bar{V}_2$ vs. m behave in accord with Eq. (7).

APPARATUS

Pycnometer (approximately 70 ml) with wire loop for hanging in bath; large weighing bottle; short-stem funnel; 200-ml volumetric flask; 250-ml erlenmeyer flask; one 250- and one 100-ml beaker; gum-rubber tube (1 to 2 ft long); one piece of filter paper; 100-ml pipette; spatula.

Constant-temperature bath set at 25°C; bath hardware for holding flasks and pycnometer; reagent-grade sodium chloride (30 to 40 g, or 200 ml of solution of an accurately known concentration); acetone to be used for rinsing; cleaning solution.

REFERENCES

1. F. T. Gucker, Jr., *J. Phys. Chem.*, **38,** 307 (1934).
2. D. O. Masson, *Phil. Mag.*, **8,** 218 (1929).
3. O. Redlich and P. Rosenfeld, *Z. physik. Chem.*, **A155,** 65 (1931).

GENERAL READING

G. N. Lewis and M. Randall (revised by K. S. Pitzer and L. Brewer), "Thermodynamics," 2d ed., chap. 17, McGraw-Hill, New York (1961).

F. H. MacDougall, "Thermodynamics and Chemistry," 3d ed., chap. III, Wiley, New York (1939).

N. Bauer, Determination of Density, in Weissberger (ed.), "Technique of Organic Chemistry," 2d ed., vol. I, part I, chap. VI, Interscience, New York (1949).

Experiment 13. Cryoscopic Determination of Molecular Weight

When a substance is dissolved in a given liquid solvent, the freezing point of the solvent is nearly always lowered. This phenomenon constitutes a so-called *colligative* property of the substance—a property that depends in its magnitude primarily on the number of moles of the substance that are present in relation to a given amount of solvent. In the present case, the amount by which the freezing point is lowered, called the *freezing-point depression* ΔT_f, is approximately proportional to the number of moles of solute dissolved in a given amount of the solvent. Other colligative properties are vapor-pressure lowering, boiling-point elevation, and osmotic pressure.

THEORY

In Fig. 1, T_0 and p_0 are, respectively, the temperature and vapor pressure at which the pure solvent freezes. Strictly speaking, T_0 is the temperature at the "triple point" with a total pressure equal to p_0 rather than the freezing point at 1 atm. However, the pressure effect is small—of the order of a few thousandths of a degree—and moreover, as it is essentially the same for a dilute solution as for the pure solvent, it will cancel out in the calculation of ΔT_f. The curve labeled p_l is the vapor pressure of the pure liquid solvent as a function of temperature, and that labeled p_s is the vapor pressure ("sublimation pressure") of the pure solid solvent. The dashed curve labeled p_x is the vapor pressure of a solution containing solute in mole fraction X. We now introduce Assumption 1: *The solid in equilibrium with a solution at its freezing point is essentially pure solid solvent.* The validity of this assumption results primarily from the crystalline structure of the solid solvent, in which the molecules are packed in a regular manner closely dependent upon their shape and size. The substitution of one or more solute molecules for solvent molecules, to yield a solid solution, is usually accompanied by a very large increase in free

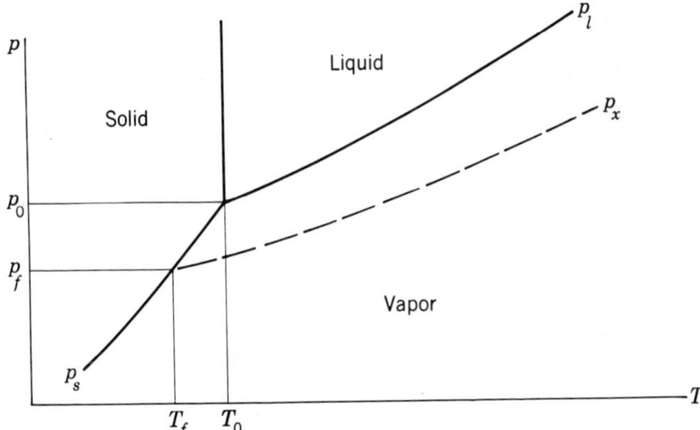

FIG. 1. Pressure-temperature diagram for solvent and solution.

energy, for the solute molecule usually has a size and shape poorly adapted to filling suitably the cavity produced by removing a solvent molecule. Exceptions occur when solute and solvent molecules are very similar, as in the toluene-chlorobenzene, benzene-pyridine, and other similar systems and in some inorganic salt mixtures and many metal alloys.

By the second law of thermodynamics, when a solution is in equilibrium with solid solvent, the solvent vapor pressures of the two must be equal. Therefore for a solution containing solute at mole fraction X, the freezing point T_f and the corresponding equilibrium vapor pressure p_f are determined by the intersection of the sublimation-pressure curve p_s with the solution vapor-pressure curve p_x. To determine the point of intersection we write the equations for the two curves and solve them simultaneously for p and T.

The equation of the sublimation curve is conveniently obtained from the integrated Clausius-Clapeyron equation:

$$\ln \frac{p_s}{p_0} = \frac{\Delta \tilde{H}_s}{R}\left(\frac{1}{T_0} - \frac{1}{T}\right) \tag{1}$$

where $\Delta \tilde{H}_s$ is the molar heat of sublimation of the solid solvent. In order to use this equation we must introduce Assumption 2: *All assumptions required in the derivation of the integrated Clausius-Clapeyron equation may be here assumed.* These are that (a) the vapor obeys the perfect-gas law, (b) the volume of a condensed phase is negligible in comparison with that of an equivalent amount of vapor, and (c) the enthalpy change accompanying vaporization or sublimation is independent of temperature. Part c of this assumption may be dispensed with, as we shall see later. The vapor-pressure curve p_x for the solution may be related to that for the liquid p_l, the equation of which we may take in accordance with the above assumption as

$$\ln \frac{p_l}{p_0} = \frac{\Delta \tilde{H}_v}{R}\left(\frac{1}{T_0} - \frac{1}{T}\right) \tag{2}$$

where $\Delta \tilde{H}_v$ is the molar heat of vaporization of the liquid solvent. To obtain the equation for the p_x curve we introduce Assumption 3: *Raoult's law applies.* Raoult's law is applicable to ideal solutions and, in the limit of infinite dilution, to real solutions. It is usually a fairly good approximation for moderately dilute real solutions.

According to this law,

$$\frac{p_x}{p_l} = X_0 = 1 - X \tag{3}$$

where X_0 is the mole fraction of solvent and X is the mole fraction of solute in the solution. Combining Eqs. (2) and (3) we obtain, as the equation for p_x as a function of T,

$$\ln \frac{p_x}{p_0} = \ln \frac{p_x}{p_l} + \ln \frac{p_l}{p_0} = \ln (1 - X) + \frac{\Delta \tilde{H}_v}{R}\left(\frac{1}{T_0} - \frac{1}{T}\right) \tag{4}$$

Now we are ready to solve for the coordinates of the intersection point p_f, T_f. Setting p_x equal to p_s, we obtain from Eqs. (1) and (4)

$$\ln (1 - X) = \frac{\Delta \tilde{H}_s - \Delta \tilde{H}_v}{R}\left(\frac{1}{T_0} - \frac{1}{T_f}\right)$$

or

$$\ln (1 - X) = -\frac{\Delta \tilde{H}_f}{R T_0 T_f} \Delta T_f \tag{5}$$

where

$$\Delta T_f \equiv T_0 - T_f \tag{6}$$

and $\Delta \tilde{H}_f$ is the molar heat of fusion of the liquid solvent.

It is worth noting here that Eq. (5) may be derived more elegantly on a somewhat different set of assumptions, in which those pertaining to properties of the solvent vapor do not appear. Those assumptions, together with Raoult's law, may be replaced by the single assumption that the *activity of the solvent is directly proportional to the mole fraction of the solvent in the solution.*

We wish to derive expressions for calculating the molality m of the solution (or the molecular weight M of the solute) from a measured freezing-point depression ΔT_f. The molality of the solution is given by

$$m = \frac{1000}{M_0} \frac{X}{1 - X} \tag{7}$$

where M_0 is the molecular weight of the solvent. If g is the weight of solute and G is the weight of solvent,

$$\frac{X}{X_0} = \frac{g/M}{G/M_0}$$

thus

$$M = M_0 \frac{g}{G} \frac{X_0}{X} = M_0 \frac{g}{G} \frac{1 - X}{X}$$

Combining this with Eq. (7) we obtain

$$M = \frac{g}{G} \frac{1000}{m} \tag{8}$$

The expressions commonly used for determination of molalities or molecular weights from freezing-point depressions are derived with the following approximations:

$$\begin{aligned} \ln (1 - X) &\cong -X \\ T_0 T_f &\cong T_0^2 \\ 1 - X = X_0 &\cong 1 \end{aligned} \tag{9}$$

With the aid of these approximations, Eq. (5) becomes

$$X = \frac{\Delta\tilde{H}_f}{RT_0^2}\,\Delta T_f \tag{10}$$

Combining Eq. (10) with Eqs. (7) and (8) we obtain

$$m = \frac{1000\,\Delta\tilde{H}_f}{M_0RT_0^2}\,\Delta T_f = \frac{\Delta T_f}{K_f} \tag{11}$$

and

$$M = \frac{M_0gRT_0^2}{G\,\Delta\tilde{H}_f\,\Delta T_f} = 1000\frac{g}{G}\,\frac{K_f}{\Delta T_f} \tag{12}$$

where

$$K_f \equiv \frac{M_0RT_0^2}{1000\,\Delta\tilde{H}_f} \tag{13}$$

K_f is called the *molal freezing-point depression constant,* since it is equal to the freezing-point depression predicted by Eq. (11) for a 1-molal solution.

It will often be the case that no further refinement of these expressions is justified. In some cases, however, the use of a higher order of approximation is worthwhile. In the treatment that follows, we shall retain terms representing no more than two orders in ΔT.

Let the right-hand side of Eq. (5) be called y,

$$y \equiv -\frac{\Delta\tilde{H}_f}{RT_0T_f}\,\Delta T_f$$

and express e^y in a Maclaurin series, so that Eq. (5) becomes

$$1 - X = e^y = 1 + y + \frac{y^2}{2!} + \cdots$$

Since y is small in comparison with unity,

$$X \cong -y\left(1 + \frac{y}{2}\right) \cong -\frac{y}{1 - y/2} \tag{14}$$

The other approximations of Eq. (9) are replaced by

$$T_0T_f = T_0^2\frac{T_f}{T_0} = T_0^2\left(1 - \frac{\Delta T_f}{T_0}\right) \cong \frac{T_0^2}{1 + \Delta T_f/T_0} \tag{15}$$

and

$$1 - X = X_0 = 1 + y \cong \frac{1}{1 - y} \tag{16}$$

In addition, if it is not desired to retain Assumption 2*c* that $\Delta\tilde{H}_f$ is strictly constant, we can replace it in the expression for y by its mean value over the temperature range ΔT_f:

$$\overline{\Delta\tilde{H}_f} = \Delta\tilde{H}_f^0 - \Delta\tilde{C}_p\frac{\Delta T_f}{2} = \Delta\tilde{H}_f^0\left(1 - \frac{\Delta\tilde{C}_p}{2\,\Delta\tilde{H}_f^0}\,\Delta T_f\right) \tag{17}$$

where $\Delta\tilde{H}_f^0$ is the molar heat of fusion of the pure solvent at its freezing point.

In combining the above equations we follow the usual rules for multiplying and dividing binominals and reject terms of second and higher order in ΔT_f in comparison with unity. We obtain

$$\frac{X}{1-X} = \frac{\Delta\tilde{H}_f{}^0}{RT_0{}^2}\,\Delta T_f(1 + k_f\,\Delta T_f) \tag{18}$$

where
$$k_f = \frac{1}{T_0} + \frac{\Delta\tilde{H}_f{}^0}{2RT_0{}^2} - \frac{\Delta\tilde{C}_p}{2\Delta\tilde{H}_f{}^0} \tag{19}$$

We further obtain, by use of Eqs. (7) and (8),

$$m = \frac{\Delta T_f}{K_f}(1 + k_f\,\Delta T_f) \tag{20}$$

$$M = 1000\frac{g}{G}\,\frac{K_f}{\Delta T_f}(1 - k_f\,\Delta T_f) \tag{21}$$

In Table 1 are given values of the pertinent constants for two common solvents: benzene and water. It will be seen that for freezing-point depressions of 1 or 2°, omission of the correction term $k_f\,\Delta T_f$ leads to errors of the order of 1 per cent in m or M.

TABLE 1

		Benzene	*Water*
Molecular weight (g)	M_0	78.11	18.02
Celsius freezing point (°C)	t_0	5.51	0.00
Absolute freezing point (°K)	T_0	278.7	273.2
Molar heat of fusion at T_0 (cal mole^{-1})	$\Delta\tilde{H}_f{}^0$	2360	1436
Molar heat-capacity change on fusion (cal deg^{-1} mole^{-1})	$\Delta\tilde{C}_p$	~1	9.1
Molal freezing-point depression constant (deg molal^{-1})	K_f	5.12	1.855
Correction constant (deg^{-1})	k_f	0.011	0.005

Where Raoult's law fails, we may expect in the case of a nondissociating and nonassociating solute that the experimental conditions will at least lie in a concentration range over which the deviation in vapor pressure can be expressed fairly well by a quadratic term in the solute mole fraction X. Within this range the main effect on the above equations will be to change k_f by a small constant amount. Thus we may expect that a plot of M [calculated either with Eq. (12) or with Eq. (21)] against ΔT_f, with a number of experimental points obtained at different concentrations, should yield an approximately straight line which, on extrapolation to $\Delta T_f = 0$, should give a good value for M. In the event of failure of the assumption of no solid solution, however, the limiting value of M itself should be expected to be in error.†

METHOD

In this experiment the freezing point of a solution containing a known weight of an "unknown" solute in a known weight of benzene is determined from cooling curves. From the result at each of two concentrations, the molecular weight of the unknown is determined.

† This can easily be shown by a treatment parallel to the derivation here given, taking account of the facts that the equilibrium concentration of solute in the solid phase increases (and that of solvent decreases) with increasing solute concentration in the liquid phase and that the solvent vapor pressure of the solid decreases as the solvent concentration in the solid decreases. Thus for the solid a new vapor-pressure curve should be drawn below p_s in Fig. 1, and its intersection point with p_x is to the right of that shown.

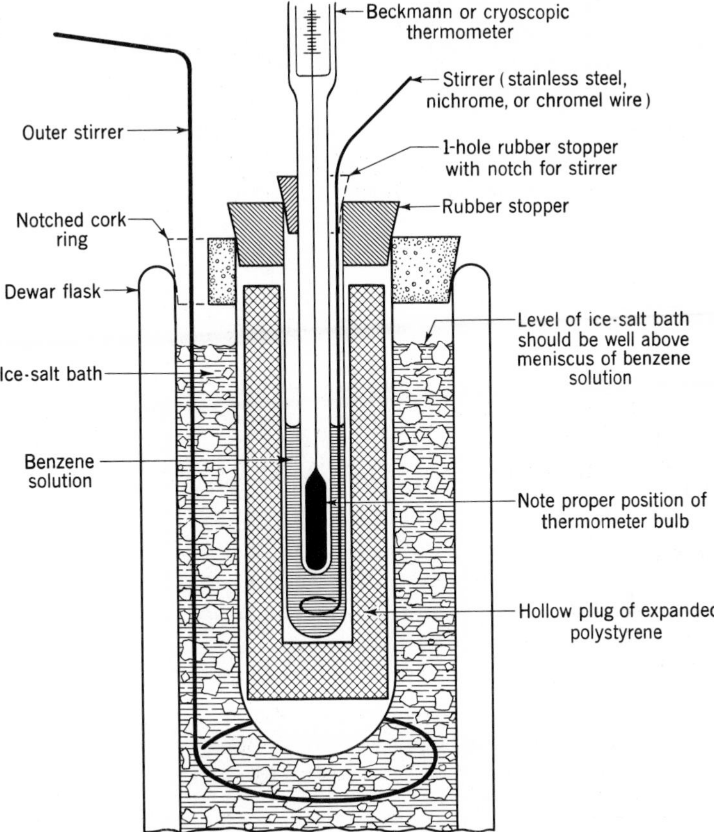

FIG. 2. Apparatus for cryoscopic determination of molecular weight.

The apparatus is shown in Fig. 2. The inner test tube, containing the solution, stirrer, and thermometer, is partially insulated from a surrounding ice-salt cooling bath through being suspended in a larger test tube with an air space in between. To provide additional insulation the space between may be filled by a hollow plug of expanded polystyrene foam. The thermometer is either a Beckmann thermometer with a 5 or 6° range adjusted to cover the temperature range expected in the experiment or a special cryoscopic thermometer of the appropriate range. The thermometer should be graduated to 0.02 or 0.01°C.

Under the conditions of the experiment, heat flows from the inner system, at temperature T, to the ice-salt bath, at temperature T_b, at a rate which is approximately proportional to the temperature difference:

$$-\frac{dH}{dt} = A(T - T_b) \tag{22}$$

where H is the enthalpy of the inner system and A is a constant incorporating shape factors and thermal-conductivity coefficients. If $(T - T_b)$ is sufficiently large in comparison with the temperature range covered in the experiment, we can write

$$-\frac{dH}{dt} \cong \text{const} \tag{23}$$

In the absence of a phase change, the rate of change of the temperature is given by

$$-\frac{dT}{dt} = \frac{1}{C}\left(-\frac{dH}{dt}\right) \tag{24}$$

where C is the heat capacity of the inner system. When a pure liquid freezes, dT/dt vanishes as long as two phases are present and we have a "thermal arrest." When pure solid solvent separates from a liquid solution on freezing, the temperature does not remain constant because the solution becomes continually more and more concentrated and the freezing point T_f correspondingly decreases. It can be shown that in this case

$$-\frac{dT}{dt} = \frac{1}{(N_0\,\Delta\tilde{H}_f/\Delta T_f) + C}\left(-\frac{dH}{dt}\right) \tag{25}$$

where N_0 is the number of moles of solvent present in the liquid phase. Thus, when solid solvent begins to freeze out of solution on cooling, the slope changes discontinuously from that given by Eq. (24) to the much smaller slope given by Eq. (25), and we have what is called a "break" in the cooling curve.

Figure 3 shows schematically the types of cooling curves that are expected as a result of these considerations. It will be noted that the solutions may "supercool" before solidification of solvent takes place. In the present experiment, supercooling rarely exceeds about 2° and is best kept below 1° by seeding—introducing a small crystal of frozen solvent.

When supercooling occurs, the recommended procedure for estimating the true freezing point of the solution (the temperature at which freezing would have started in the absence of supercooling) is to extrapolate back that part of the curve that

FIG. 3. Schematic cooling curves: (*a*) and (*c*) show the cooling curves for pure solvent; (*b*) and (*d*) show the cooling curves for a solution.

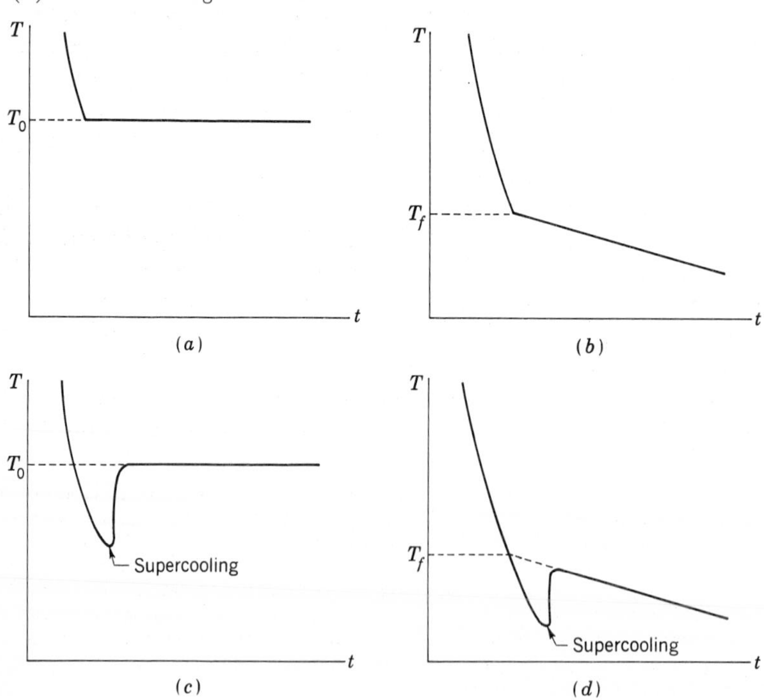

corresponds to freezing out of the solvent until the extrapolate intersects the cooling curve of the liquid solution. To a good approximation the extrapolation may be taken as a linear one.†

This procedure is valid only when the extent of supercooling is small in comparison with the difference in temperature between the system and the ice-salt cooling bath. When this is not the case, Eq. (22) must be used in place of Eq. (23), and it is then seen that the rate of decrease of enthalpy is dependent in significant degree on whether or not supercooling takes place. Therefore the amount of supercooling must be kept small, and the bath must be kept as cold as possible.

EXPERIMENTAL

The success of this experiment depends primarily on a careful experimental technique. The solvent to be used is benzene, which must be of reagent-grade purity (thiophene-free) and scrupulously dry. Pour about 25 ml of benzene into a clean, dry, glass-stoppered flask for your own use. During the experiment, take care to keep the inner part of the apparatus dry and to expose the inner test tube to the air as little as possible in order to avoid condensation of moisture inside.

The ice-salt mixture should be made up freshly for each run. Mix about one part by volume of coarse rock salt with about four parts by volume of finely crushed ice in a beaker or battery jar. Allow it to stand a few minutes to become slushy, and then pour the desired amount into the Dewar flask. (This ice-salt mixture can be replaced by a mixture of ten parts ice with one part denatured alcohol.)

Fill a small beaker with crushed ice and a little water, and place in it a test tube containing 1 or 2 ml of benzene and a very thin glass rod. Stopper the tube with cotton or glass wool to keep out moist air from the room. This frozen benzene is to be used for seeding. When it is desired to seed the system during a run, remove the glass rod, making sure it carries a small amount of frozen benzene, and carefully insert it into the solution with the least possible disruption of the experiment.

Benzene should be introduced into the inner test tube from a weighing bottle (weighed before and after delivery) or from a pipette. *Do not pipette benzene by mouth;* use a rubber bulb. The quantity normally required is 15 ml. If a pipette is used, record the ambient temperature.

The thermometer and stirrer should be inserted with the thermometer carefully mounted in such a way that the bulb is about halfway between the bottom of the test tube and the upper surface of the liquid and concentric with the tube so that the stirrer can easily pass around it. If the thermometer is too close to the bottom, a bridge of frozen solvent can easily form which will conduct heat away from the thermometer and result in low readings.

Much depends on the technique of stirring the solution. The motion of the stirrer should carry it from the bottom of the tube up to near the surface of the liquid;

† To justify this extrapolation procedure, consider two experiments starting at the same temperature and the same time under conditions identical in all respects except that in one case supercooling is allowed to take place and in the other it is somehow prevented. By Eq. (23) the enthalpies of the two systems remain identical throughout the experiment. Except during the interval of supercooling, both systems are in equilibrium, and therefore when their enthalpies are equal, they are identical in all respects, including temperature. Therefore, except for the interval of supercooling, the two curves when superimposed are congruent throughout their entire length. The dashed line representing the extrapolation in Fig. 3*c* or *d* is therefore part of the curve for the hypothetical experiment in which supercooling was prevented.

before assembling the apparatus, it is well to observe carefully how high the stirrer can be raised without too frequent splashing. The stirring should be continuous throughout the run and should be at the rate of about one stroke per second. The outer bath should be stirred a few times per minute.

The test tube containing benzene, stopper, thermometer, and stirrer is held in the beaker of ice water, and the benzene is stirred until it visibly starts to freeze. The outside of the tube is wiped dry, and the tube is allowed to warm up at least 1° above the freezing point. Then the tube is placed in the assembled apparatus and temperature readings are taken every 30 sec. Tap the thermometer gently before each reading, and estimate the temperature readings to tenths of the smallest scale division. If the temperature falls 0.5°C below the normal freezing point without evidence of freezing, seed the liquid. Once freezing has occurred, continue temperature readings for about 5 min. If the benzene and apparatus are suitably dry, the temperature should remain constant or fall by no more than about 0.01 or 0.02°C during that time.

The inner test tube is removed and warmed (with stirring) in a beaker of water until the benzene has completely melted. The stopper is lifted, and an *accurately weighed* pellet of the unknown compound, of about 0.6 g, is introduced. The pellet is dissolved by stirring, the inner tube is cooled with stirring in an ice bath to about the freezing temperature of pure benzene and then dried on the outside, and the apparatus is reassembled. Temperature readings are taken every 30 sec throughout the run. After a depression of about 2° has been reached, it is advisable to seed the system at intervals of about 0.5° until freezing starts. After freezing has begun, temperature readings should be continued for a period at least four times as long as the estimated period of supercooling to provide data for an adequate extrapolation.

The inner tube is removed, the benzene melted as before, and a second weighed pellet of the unknown is added and stirred into solution. Before this pellet is added, it is well to make a rough calculation, based on the results of the first run, to make sure that the temperatures in the second run will remain on scale and, if necessary, to modify the weight of the pellet accordingly. The second run is carried out as before, after cooling in an ice bath to about the temperature at which freezing was obtained in the first run.

If the results from these two runs are not in agreement and time allows, a repeat of both runs should be made using somewhat different pellet weights.

CALCULATIONS

If the benzene was introduced with a pipette, its weight G can be calculated using the density:

$$\rho(\text{benzene}) = 0.879 - 0.001(t - 20)$$

where t is the centigrade temperature. Plot the cooling-curve data for pure benzene and for each solution studied. If supercooling took place, perform the extrapolations as shown in Fig. 3. Report the weight g of solute and the freezing-point depression ΔT_f for each run.

Calculate the molecular weight from both Eqs. (12) and (21) using the appropriate constants in Table 1. An extrapolated value of M can be obtained from the calculated values from either equation by plotting the calculated molecular weight against the depression ΔT_f. If the elementary analysis or empirical formula of the unknown is given, deduce the molecular formula and the exact molecular weight.

APPARATUS

Dewar flask; notched cork ring to fit top of Dewar; large test tube with polystyrene-foam insert; large ring stirrer; inner test tube which fits into polystyrene insert; large rubber stopper with hole for inner test tube; medium stopper with hole for thermometer and a notch for small ring stirrer; 1-qt battery jar or 1000-ml beaker; 250-ml beaker; 125-ml glass-stoppered flask for storing benzene; small test tube; glass rod (3 mm diameter and 20 cm long); 15-ml pipette; small rubber pipetting bulb; precision cryoscopic thermometer; magnifying thermometer reader; stopwatch.

Dry reagent-grade benzene (50 ml); glass wool; naphthalene or an unknown solid; pellet press; acetone for rinsing; ice (3 lb); ice grinder or shaver; coarse rock salt (2 lb).

GENERAL READING

E. L. Skau and H. Wakeham, Determination of Melting and Freezing Temperatures, in Weissberger (ed.), "Techniques of Organic Chemistry," 2d ed., vol. I, part I, chap. III, Interscience, New York (1949).

F. H. MacDougall, "Thermodynamics and Chemistry," 3d ed., Wiley, New York (1939).

Experiment 14. Freezing-point Depression of Strong and Weak Electrolytes

In this experiment, the freezing-point depression of aqueous solutions is used to determine the degree of dissociation of a weak electrolyte and to study the deviation from ideal behavior which occurs with a strong electrolyte.

THEORY

Use will be made of the theory developed in Exp. 13 for the freezing-point depression ΔT_f of a given solvent containing a known amount of an ideal solute; this material should be reviewed.

In the case of a dissociating (or associating) solute, the molality given by Eq. (13-11) or (13-20) is ideally the *total* effective molality—the number of moles of all solute species present, whether ionic or molecular, per 1000 g of solvent. As we shall see, ionic solute species at moderate concentrations do not form ideal solutions and, therefore, do not obey these equations. However, for a weak electrolyte the ionic concentration is often sufficiently low to permit treatment of the solution as ideal.

Weak Electrolytes. As an example, let us discuss a weak acid HA with nominal molality m. Due to the dissociation

$$HA = H^+ + A^-$$

the equilibrium concentrations of HA, H^+ and A^- will be $m(1 - \alpha)$, $m\alpha$, and $m\alpha$, respectively, where α is the fraction dissociated. The total molality m' of all solute species is

$$m' = m(1 + \alpha) \tag{1}$$

This molality m' can be calculated from the observed ΔT_f using Eq. (13-20). Thus, freezing-point measurements on weak electrolyte solutions of known molality m enable the determination of α.

The equilibrium constant in terms of concentrations can be calculated from

$$K_c = \frac{(H^+)(A^-)}{(HA)} = m\frac{\alpha^2}{(1 - \alpha)} \tag{2}$$

In this experiment α and K_c are to be determined at two different molalities. Since these will be obtained at two different temperatures, the values of K_c should be expected to differ slightly.

Strong Electrolytes. These are now generally believed to be completely dissociated in ordinary dilute solutions. However, their colligative properties when interpreted in terms of ideal solutions appear to indicate that the dissociation is a little less than complete. This fact led Arrhenius to postulate that the dissociation of strong electrolytes is indeed incomplete. Subsequently, this deviation in colligative behavior has been demonstrated to be an expected consequence of interionic attractions.

For a nonideal solution, Eq. (13-5) is replaced by

$$\ln a_0 = -\frac{\Delta\tilde{H}_f}{RT_0T_f}\Delta T_f \cong -\frac{\Delta\tilde{H}_f}{RT_0^2}\Delta T_f \tag{3}$$

where a_0 is the *activity* of the solvent and is related to the mole fraction of solvent X_0 by

$$a_0 = \gamma_0 X_0 \tag{4}$$

The quantity γ_0 is the activity coefficient for the solvent and in electrolytic solutions differs from unity even at moderately low concentrations. Let us write $\ln a_0$ as $(\ln \gamma_0 + \ln X_0)$ in Eq. (3) and divide both sides by $\ln X_0$ to obtain

$$-\frac{\Delta\tilde{H}_f}{RT_0^2}\frac{\Delta T_f}{\ln X_0} = 1 + \frac{\ln \gamma_0}{\ln X_0} \equiv g \tag{5}$$

where g is called the *osmotic coefficient* of the solvent. Now

$$X_0 = \frac{N_0}{N_0 + \nu N_1} \tag{6}$$

where N_0 is the number of moles of solvent and νN_1 is the total number of moles of ions formed from N_1 moles of solute (for example, $\nu = 2$ for HCl). Thus,

$$-\ln X_0 \equiv \ln\left(1 + \frac{\nu N_1}{N_0}\right) \cong \frac{\nu N_1}{N_0} \tag{7}$$

for dilute solutions. Substituting this expression for $\ln X_0$ into Eq. (5), we have

$$\frac{\Delta\tilde{H}_f}{RT_0^2}\frac{N_0}{\nu N_1}\Delta T_f = g \tag{8}$$

For a solution of molality m in a solvent with molecule weight M_0, we can replace $(N_0/\nu N_1)$ by $(1000/M_0\nu m)$. Equation (8) can then be written as

$$\left(\frac{\Delta \tilde{H}_f}{R T_0^2} \frac{1000}{M_0}\right)\frac{\Delta T_f}{\nu m} = \frac{\Delta T_f}{\nu m K_f} = g \tag{9}$$

where K_f is the molal freezing-point depression constant defined by Eq. (13-13).

For an ideal solution, $\gamma_0 = 1$ and g is unity. Then Eq. (9) is identical with Eq. (13-11), since the total molality of all solute species is νm for a completely dissociated solute of molality m. For ionic solutions, the Debye-Hückel theory predicts a value of γ_0 different from unity and therefore a deviation of g from unity. A treatment of this aspect of the Debye-Hückel theory is beyond the scope of this book, and we shall merely state the result. The osmotic coefficient g at 0°C for dilute solutions of a single strong electrolyte in water is given[1] by

$$g = 1 - 0.376\sigma |z_+ z_-| \mu^{1/2} \tag{10}$$

where z_+ is the valence of the positive ion, z_- is the valence of the negative ion, and μ is the ionic strength:

$$\mu = \tfrac{1}{2} \sum_i m_i z_i^2 \tag{11}$$

the sum being taken over all ionic species present. The quantity σ is a function of κa where, for aqueous solutions at 0°C, κ is given by MacDougall[1] as

$$\kappa = 0.324 \times 10^8 \mu^{1/2}$$

and a is the effective ionic diameter. For a small ion, a is approximately 3×10^{-8} cm and we can take $\kappa a \simeq \mu^{1/2}$. For a uni-univalent electrolyte (such as HCl) this becomes simply

$$\kappa a \cong m^{1/2} \tag{12}$$

Therefore Eq. (10) can be written

$$g = 1 - 0.38\sigma m^{1/2} \tag{13}$$

Values of the function σ are given for several values of κa in Table 1. For a known value of m, κa for a uni-univalent electrolyte is given by Eq. (12) and one can find the appropriate value of σ by interpolating in the table. Use of this value in Eq. (13) allows one to calculate g. It should be emphasized that Eq. (13) is an approximation based on the Debye-Hückel theory and valid only in dilute solution.

EXPERIMENTAL

The apparatus used in this experiment is shown in Fig. 1. The thermometer is either a Beckmann thermometer adjusted to cover the temperature range expected in the experiment or a special cryoscopic thermometer of the appropriate range. The thermometer should be graduated to 0.01 or 0.02°C. In the experiment, an aqueous solution of a weak or strong acid is mixed with crushed ice until equilibrium is attained. The temperature is recorded, and two or more aliquots of the

TABLE 1

κa	0.20	0.25	0.30	0.35	0.40	0.45	0.50	0.55
σ	0.7588	0.7129	0.6712	0.6325	0.5988	0.5673	0.5376	0.5108

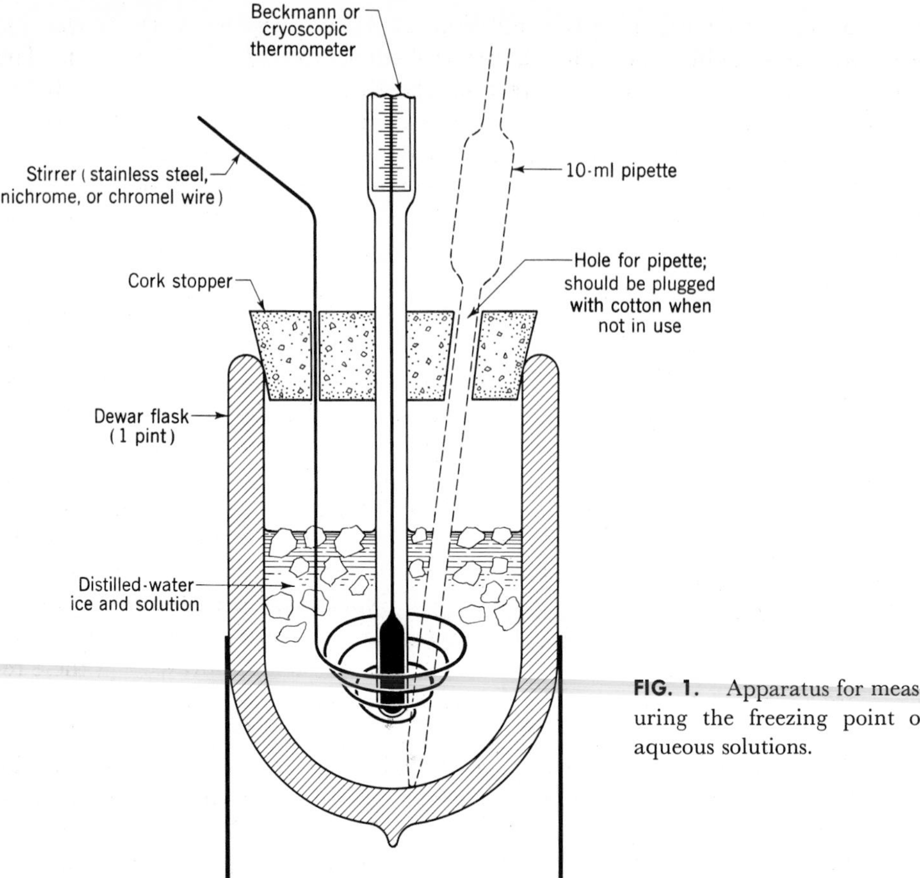

FIG. 1. Apparatus for measuring the freezing point of aqueous solutions.

liquid phase are withdrawn for titration to determine the equilibrium nominal concentration m_0. The ice to be used should preferably be distilled-water ice.

The most difficult part of the experimental technique is the achievement of thorough mixing. This difficulty is aggravated by the fact that water has a maximum density near 4°C and solution at that temperature tends to settle to the bottom of the Dewar flask while colder solution tends to float near the top with the ice. The stirring must therefore be *vigorous and prolonged.* A good technique is to work the stirrer frequently above the mass of ice and with a vigorous downward thrust propel the ice all the way to the bottom of the flask. *It must not be assumed that equilibrium has been obtained until the temperature shown by the thermometer has become quite stationary and does not change when the stirring is stopped or when the manner or vigor of stirring is changed.*

Procedure. The solutions to be studied are the strong electrolyte HCl and weak electrolyte monochloroacetic acid, each at two concentrations—roughly 0.25 and 0.125 m. About 150 ml of each solution will be needed, and the 0.125 m solutions required should be prepared by diluting the 0.25 m stock solutions with distilled water. Place each solution in a clean, glass-stoppered flask packed in crushed ice. A flask of distilled water should also be packed in ice.

Wash about 300 ml of crushed, distilled-water ice with several small amounts of the chilled distilled water, then fill the Dewar flask about one-third full with this washed ice. About 100 ml of the chilled distilled water is added to the Dewar, the apparatus is assembled, and the mixture well stirred to achieve equilibrium. The temperature T_0 is recorded. In reading the thermometer, tap it gently before reading and estimate to tenths of the smallest division. It should be realized that a cryoscopic thermometer may not read exactly zero at this point and may deviate by several hundredths of a degree without coming under suspicion of being defective. The important function of a thermometer of this kind is to measure temperature *differences* accurately, and it is not primarily intended to give an accurate measurement of an actual temperature.

The water is poured off and replaced by 100 ml of chilled 0.25 *m* HCl solution. After stirring to achieve equilibrium, as described previously, the temperature is read and a 10-ml aliquot withdrawn with a pipette. Introduce the pipette quickly, while blowing a gentle stream of air through it to prevent solution from entering it until the tip touches the bottom of the flask. This will prevent small particles of ice from being drawn into the pipette. Alternatively, attach to the tip of the pipette a filter consisting of a short length of rubber tubing containing a wad of cotton or glass wool. This aliquot is discharged into a clean weighing bottle, warmed to room temperature, and accurately weighed. It is then quantitatively transferred to a flask and titrated with 0.1 *M* NaOH to a methyl red or phenolphthalein end point. Stirring should be resumed vigorously for about 5 min, then another temperature reading taken and a second aliquot withdrawn. If these results are not consistent with each other, a third aliquot should be taken after further stirring.†

The solution is poured off and the experiment repeated with 0.125 *m* HCl. Be sure that an adequate amount of ice is present. If time permits, a run should be made with 0.0625 *m* HCl also.

Similar runs are carried out with the solutions of monochloroacetic acid, preferably repeating the measurement of T_0.

CALCULATIONS

Calculate the equilibrium molality m (in moles per 1000 g of water) for each aliquot. If the results for the two aliquots from a given run are consistent, the average values of m and ΔT_f may be used in further calculations. For monochloroacetic acid, a weak electrolyte, calculate the effective total molality m' from Eq. (13-20) using the appropriate constants in Table 13-1. Then calculate α and K_c for each of the two concentrations studied.

For hydrochloric acid, a strong electrolyte, calculate an experimental value of g with Eq. (9) for each of the concentrations studied. In addition, use Eq. (13) to obtain a value of the osmotic coefficient g based on the Debye-Hückel theory for each concentration. Compare these experimental and theoretical values.

DISCUSSION

The colligative behavior of strong electrolytes is often expressed in terms of the van't Hoff factor[2]

† The temperatures and the concentrations of the two aliquots may differ slightly, owing to some melting of ice, but the differences should be consistent. If they are not consistent, at least one of the aliquots was presumably not withdrawn at equilibrium.

$$i = \frac{m_{app}}{m}$$

where m_{app} is the "apparent" total molality as deduced from any colligative property when the solution is treated as ideal. Using the expressions for freezing point depression, show the relation between i and g.

What additional data would be required in order to compare the values of K_c obtained for monochloroacetic acid at two different temperatures? Can you predict the direction of the change in K_c with T; i.e., the sign of dK_c/dT?

APPARATUS

Dewar flask (short, wide mouth, 1 pt); cork stopper with three holes; coil-type stirrer; precision cryoscopic thermometer; magnifying thermometer reader; stopwatch; two 10-ml weighing bottles; 50-ml burette; burette clamp and stand; two 100-ml volumetric flasks; one 10-, one 25-, and one 50-ml pipette; battery jar; wash bottle.

Distilled-water ice (500 g); 0.1 M sodium hydroxide solution (500 ml); 0.25 m HCl solution (400 ml) and 0.25 m monochloroacetic acid solution (400 ml); phenolphthalein indicator; stopcock grease.

REFERENCES

1. F. H. MacDougall, "Thermodynamics and Chemistry," 3d ed., Wiley, New York (1939).
2. W. J. Moore, "Physical Chemistry," 2d ed., Prentice-Hall, Englewood Cliffs, N.J. (1955).

GENERAL READING

E. L. Skau and H. Wakeham, Determination of Melting and Freezing Temperatures, in Weissberger (ed.), "Techniques of Organic Chemistry," 2d ed., vol I, part I, chap. III, Interscience, New York (1949).

Experiment 15. Solubility and Ionic Strength

The solubility of a salt in water can be influenced by the presence of other electrolytes in several ways: by a "common-ion effect," by the occurrence of a chemical reaction involving one of the ions of the salt, or by a change in the activity coefficients of the ions of the salt (which is caused by a change in the ionic strength of the solution). The first two effects are familiar ones and are often encountered in elementary treatments which make use of equilibrium constants expressed in terms of concentrations. In the present experiment we shall be concerned with the third effect and shall show how an equilibrium constant in terms of activities can be obtained by extrapolation of solubility data to zero concentration. This constant is used in conjunction with the measured solubilities in solutions of different ionic strengths to obtain experimental values for the activity coefficient of silver acetate as a function of ionic strength. These are compared with theoretical values for activity coefficients as calculated by means of the Debye-Hückel theory.

THEORY

We are concerned here with the following equilibrium,[1] which occurs in the presence of excess solid silver acetate:

$$\text{AgAc}(s) = \text{Ag}^+ \text{ (in soln.)} + \text{Ac}^- \text{ (in soln.)} \qquad 25°\text{C, 1 atm} \tag{1}$$

Recent work[2] has shown that silver acetate exists in solution not only as Ag^+ and Ac^- but also as undissociated silver acetate AgAc and as complex-ions $AgAc_2^-$ and Ag_2Ac^+ and possibly other complex ionic forms. For our purposes complex ions may be neglected, and silver acetate will be assumed to be in solution as the undissociated neutral molecules AgAc and as the free ions Ag^+ and Ac^-. The determination of the equilibrium constant K' for the change in state

$$\text{AgAc}(s) = \text{AgAc (undiss., in soln.)} \tag{2}$$

will not be attempted as a part of this experiment. From extensive electrochemical measurements[2] the value

$$K' = 1.05 \times 10^{-2} \text{ mole liter}^{-1} \tag{3}$$

has been obtained at 25°C and 1 atm.† The concentration of undissociated AgAc may then be subtracted from the total concentration of silver found by titration to give the concentration c of Ag^+ ion.

For the equilibrium given in Eq. (1) the product of the *activities* of Ag^+ and Ac^- ions at the given temperature and pressure is a constant, regardless of the concentrations of these ions or of the presence of other ionic or molecular species in solution:

$$a_{\text{Ag}^+} a_{\text{Ac}^-} = K \tag{4}$$

The experimentally measurable concentrations are related to the activities by the *activity coefficients* γ:

$$a_{\text{Ag}^+} = \gamma_{\text{Ag}^+} c_{\text{Ag}^+} \qquad a_{\text{Ac}^-} = \gamma_{\text{Ac}^-} c_{\text{Ac}^-}$$

Thus,

$$K = \gamma_{\text{Ag}^+} \gamma_{\text{Ac}^-} c_{\text{Ag}^+} c_{\text{Ac}^-} = \gamma_\pm^2 c_{\text{Ag}^+} c_{\text{Ac}^-} \tag{5}$$

where $\gamma_\pm$, the *mean activity coefficient* for AgAc in the solution concerned, is the geometric mean of the two ionic activity coefficients. If there is no common ion present from another solute, and if there is no reagent present which reduces the concentration of either ion by chemical reaction, the concentrations of Ag^+ and Ac^- will be equal to each other and to the ionic solubility c, so that we can write

$$\gamma_\pm^2 c^2 = K \tag{6}$$

Measurements of the ionic solubility can therefore be used to determine the mean

† Since the concentration of complex ions is very small, an adequate approximation to K' could be obtained from the difference between the total solubility of AgAc in pure water and the ionic concentration of Ag^+ and Ac^- in a saturated solution as obtained from an independent measurement. For example, the concentration of dissolved ions could be determined from conductance measurements made on a saturated AgAc solution and on $AgNO_3$, $NaNO_3$, and NaAc solutions of about the same ionic concentration (see Exp. 22). Or the concentration of Ag^+ could be determined from the emf of an electrochemical cell with a silver electrode and a salt bridge to a calomel reference electrode if the activity coefficients are known.

activity coefficient $\gamma_\pm$ for AgAc in solutions containing other ions in various concentrations, provided the constant K can be determined.

Debye-Hückel Theory.[3] In the limit of zero ionic strength the activities of ions are equal to their concentrations, the activity coefficients thus becoming unity in the limit. The ionic strength μ is defined by the expression

$$\mu = \tfrac{1}{2} \sum_i c_i z_i^2 \tag{7}$$

where c_i is the concentration of the ith ionic species, z_i is the charge of the ion in units of the electronic charge, and the sum is taken over all ionic species present. The simple Debye-Hückel "limiting law"

$$\log \gamma_j = -A z_j^2 \sqrt{\mu}$$

predicts the activity coefficient of ion j at low ionic strengths but becomes seriously inexact at even moderate ionic strengths. A more complete form of the Debye-Hückel theory, which holds well for low and moderate ionic strengths, is represented by the equation[3]

$$\log \gamma_j = -z_j^2 \frac{A\sqrt{\mu}}{1 + B_j\sqrt{\mu}} \tag{8}$$

where A and B_j are constants. The value of A can be calculated theoretically; it depends on characteristics of the solvent and on the temperature. If logarithms to the base 10 are used, it has a value of about 0.509 for aqueous solutions at 25°C. B_j depends in addition on the diameter of the ion concerned and also on the diameters of other ions of opposite sign that may be present in the solution. To a good approximation, it can be shown that the *mean* activity coefficient of a given electrolyte is

$$\log \gamma_\pm = -|z_+z_-| \frac{A\sqrt{\mu}}{1 + B\sqrt{\mu}} \tag{9}$$

where B is a mean of the B_j of the two ions; the limiting law is, of course,

$$\log \gamma_\pm = -|z_+z_-| A\sqrt{\mu} \tag{10}$$

When μ is calculated using concentrations in moles per *liter of solvent* (or, in the case of dilute aqueous solutions, molality which is moles per 1000 g of solvent), the constant B is found to be close to unity for many salts at 25°C.[4] For $\gamma_\pm$ of AgAc in the system to be studied, B has been found empirically[5] to be about 1.25 at 25°C when μ is expressed in moles *per liter of solution.*

Determination of K. If we combine Eq. (9) with Eq. (6) we obtain for the case where the z's are unity

$$\log c = \frac{1}{2} \log K + \frac{A\sqrt{\mu}}{1 + B\sqrt{\mu}} \tag{11}$$

If $\log c$ is plotted against $\sqrt{\mu}$, a smooth curve should be obtained, and when this curve is extrapolated to $\sqrt{\mu} = 0$, the intercept will give $\tfrac{1}{2} \log K$. A more nearly linear curve can be obtained by plotting $\log c$ vs. $A\sqrt{\mu}/(1 + B\sqrt{\mu})$; this facilitates extrapolation to zero concentration from data at moderate ionic strengths.

By means of this extrapolation the activity product K can be determined, and by application of Eq. (6) the activity coefficient $\gamma_\pm$ for AgAc can be calculated for each solution studied.

EXPERIMENTAL

It is desired to measure the equilibrium solubility of AgAc in several solutions of different ionic strengths. In order to achieve rapid equilibrium, one should dissolve an excess of AgAc by heating the solution; on cooling to the desired temperature this excess will readily crystallize out.

Place about 2 g of AgAc in each of five clean, dry sample bottles. The AgAc should be weighed out roughly; the sample bottles should be suitable for mounting on a tumbler or agitator in a thermostat bath. Each bottle should be indelibly numbered or tagged to provide identification. Fill each bottle three-quarters full with one of the following solutions:†

1. Distilled water
2. 0.05 M $NaNO_3$
3. 0.1 M $NaNO_3$
4. 0.2 M $NaNO_3$
5. 0.5 M $NaNO_3$

Set the sample bottles in a large beaker of hot water until the solutions have warmed up to 50 to 60°C. Then stopper the bottles *tightly* and shake vigorously for 2 min. Place the bottles on a tumbler or agitator in a 25°C thermostat bath and allow 1 hr for equilibration. If mechanical agitation is not possible, one may clamp the bottles in the bath and shake them by hand about once every 5 min.

At the end of the hour remove the bottles from the tumbler and clamp them in the bath for 5 or 10 min to allow the solid to settle. *Without removing the bottles from the bath,* withdraw two 25-ml samples from each bottle; use a pipette fitted at the tip with a filter consisting of a short (1-in.) piece of rubber tubing packed with cotton. Remove the filter before adjusting the level of the liquid in the pipette to the mark. Use a clean, dry filter for each sample, and rinse out the pipette with a few milliliters of filtered solution before taking each sample. Discharge each sample into a 200-ml erlenmeyer flask containing 15 ml of distilled H_2O and 5 ml of 6 M HNO_3. The amount of silver ion in each sample is then determined by titration with 0.1 N KSCN solution. Add about 1 ml of 0.1 M ferric alum solution to each flask as an indicator; titrate to the appearance of a faint reddish-brown color which does not disappear on shaking. While waiting for the AgAc solutions to equilibrate, make at least one practice titration using the $AgNO_3$ solution provided. Once standardized by this practice titration, the $AgNO_3$ can be used for "back-titrations" if necessary.

CALCULATIONS

Data obtained for solutions of AgAc in water and in aqueous $NaNO_3$ should be treated in the following way:

Calculate the total solubility of AgAc from your titration results. Subtract the concentration of undissociated AgAc obtained from Eq. (3) to find the ionic solubility c in moles per liter of solution. Also calculate the ionic strength μ of each

† If it is desired to investigate, in addition, the effect on solubility of the presence of a common ion or of a reagent which reacts with one of the ions, an additional sample may be prepared with 0.1 M NaAc or 0.05 M HNO_3 solution.

solution from concentrations in moles per liter of solution, remembering that the summation in Eq. (7) is over *all* ionic species present.

Plot $\log_{10} c$ vs. $A\sqrt{\mu}/(1 + B\sqrt{\mu})$, where A is taken as 0.509, B as 1.25. Extrapolate to $\mu = 0$, taking pains to make the slope of the line as close to unity in the region of low ionic strength as the data will permit, and determine K. By means of Eq. (6) calculate the value of the mean activity coefficient $\gamma_\pm$ for AgAc for each solution.

The value of K determined above is in principle largely independent of the Debye-Hückel theory, in the sense that this theory has been used mainly as a convenience in extrapolating to zero ionic strength with limited data. Therefore the values of activity coefficients obtained with Eq. (6) are essentially *experimental* values. These values should be compared with *theoretical* activity coefficients calculated with the Debye-Hückel theory, using both the limiting law, Eq. (10), and the more complete expression, Eq. (9). The experimental value and both theoretical values of $\gamma_\pm$ for each ionic strength should be presented in tabular form.

APPARATUS

Five (or six) sample bottles (tall with narrow mouth, approximately 125 cm^3); rubber stoppers to fit; tags or labels for the sample bottles; tripod and wire gauze; bunsen burner, complete with hose; one 0 to 100°C thermometer; one 1- and one 25-ml pipette; two short (~1-in.) pieces of gum rubber tubing; two to four 200-ml erlenmeyer flasks; 15- or 25-ml graduated cylinder; one large (1500 to 2000 ml) beaker and one 250-ml beaker; one small (25 to 50 ml) beaker or flask; one 50-ml burette; burette clamp and stand; spatula.

Reagent-grade silver acetate (15 g); triple-beam balance; absorbent cotton or glass wool; spool of copper wire, for securing stoppers on sample bottles; constant-temperature bath at 25°C; bath clamps; tumbler or agitator for sample bottles.

The following solutions (100 ml each) should be made with precisely known concentrations: 0.05, 0.1, 0.2, 0.5 *M* sodium nitrate; 0.05 *M* silver nitrate; (0.1 *M* sodium acetate and 0.05 *M* nitric acid, if required). Also needed: standardized 0.1 *N* potassium thiocyanate (500 ml); approximately 6 *M* nitric acid (100 ml); ferric alum solution as indicator (25 ml).

REFERENCES

1. F. H. MacDougall, *J. Am. Chem. Soc.,* **52,** 1390 (1930).
2. F. H. MacDougall and L. E. Topol, *J. Phys. Chem.,* **56,** 1090 (1952).
3. W. J. Moore, "Physical Chemistry," Prentice-Hall, Englewood Cliffs, N.J. (1955).
4. G. Scatchard, *Chem. Rev.,* **19,** 309 (1936).
5. F. H. MacDougall and J. Rehner, Jr., *J. Am. Chem. Soc.,* **56,** 368 (1934).

GENERAL READING

R. D. Vold and M. J. Vold, Determination of Solubility, in Weissberger (ed.), "Techniques of Organic Chemistry," 2d ed., vol. I, part I, chap. VII, Interscience, New York (1949).

Experiment 16. Diffusion in Solution

The self-diffusion constant of liquid water will be determined by the use of isotopic labeling, i.e., by investigating the diffusion of heavy water (D_2O) into light water (H_2O). We shall also be concerned with the diffusion of solute molecules or ions, since the method to be used requires a calibration with some solution of known diffusion constant. This method gives only an average diffusion constant but is rapid, convenient, and widely applicable.

THEORY

The diffusion of gases has been discussed previously in Exp. 7 and should be reviewed, since it provides an important background for a discussion of diffusion in liquids.

Diffusion in liquids differs from diffusion in gases in two important respects. First, diffusion is much slower in liquids. In gases at ordinary pressures molecules travel over mean free paths of the order of 10^{-5} cm between collisions, while in liquids the distance of travel is of the order of 10^{-8} cm. Moreover, a molecule in the liquid usually undergoes many collisions with the few molecules that form a transient "cage" around it before it succeeds in escaping from that cage into another one. The second respect in which liquid diffusion differs from gas diffusion is that diffusion in liquids is typically less ideal; departure from the behavior expressed by Fick's laws, Eqs. (7-1) and (7-4), is usually much greater. However, for a "true" self-diffusion there is no reason to expect deviation from Fick's laws either for gases or for liquids.

As is pointed out in Exp. 7, self-diffusion can be investigated only by labeling some of the molecules in a way that enables them to be distinguished from the others by some physical or chemical method without producing by such labeling any drastic change in their kinetic behavior. Isotopic substitution is the most common form of labeling. In this experiment, the concentration of the labeled molecules (D_2O) will be determined from the liquid density; in other cases, it might be determined with a mass spectrometer or a Geiger counter if a radioactive isotope is used. Unfortunately, isotopic labeling introduces some change in kinetic behavior; the mean kinetic velocity of a molecule varies inversely with the square root of the molecular mass. Light and heavy water differ by about 10 per cent in mass and therefore by about 5 per cent in mean molecular velocity.† Moreover, some properties of a hydrogen-bonded medium such as water are significantly altered by replacement of hydrogen by deuterium on account of the altered amplitudes and frequencies of molecular and intermolecular vibrations. Clearly, a diffusion constant determined under these conditions is only an approximation to the true self-diffusion constant of water and may even be subject to significant nonidealities which may make it a function of concentration of the labeled component.

When two interdiffusing components (such as H_2O and K^+Cl^-) differ significantly in kinetic and molecular properties, it may be expected that the diffusive behavior of the system will depend on the concentrations of the components. The diffusion constant D in Fick's first law, Eq. (7-1), and second law, Eq. (7-4), is then not a constant but a function of the concentration(s). For a constant-volume, binary system only the concentration of one component N_1 needs to be specified. For a particular value of this concentration, $D(N_1)$ must be regarded as a *differential* diffusion constant. By contrast, an *integral* diffusion constant can be defined for a definite interval between two concentrations or between zero and a given concentration by an equation analogous to Eq. (7-1):

† The fact that, largely as a matter of convenience, the present system is described as D_2O interdiffusing with H_2O should not be taken to imply that these are the only two species present. The species HDO is also present, in rapid equilibrium with the other two.

$$Z_1 = -D_{12}{}^{int}\frac{\Delta N_1}{\Delta x} = -D_{12}{}^{int}\frac{N_1 - N_1'}{x - x'} \tag{1}$$

provided the conditions between x and x' are defined in an appropriate way. Thus, we might specify that a one-dimensional steady state exists whereby the flux Z_1 is constant between x and x'. In this case the integral diffusion constant can be expressed in terms of the differential diffusion constant by the equation

$$D_{12}{}^{int} = \frac{\int_0^{N_1} D_{12}(N)\, dN}{N_1} \tag{2}$$

where the minimum concentration has been taken to be zero. Thus, the integral diffusion constant is an average of the instantaneous or differential diffusion constant over the concentration range. An alternative specification, more directly applicable to the type of experiment performed here, might be that diffusion is one-dimensional with Z_1 varying in such a way that the rate of change of N_1 with time is approximately proportional to N_1:

$$\frac{dZ_1}{dx} = -\frac{dN_1}{dt} \propto N_1$$

This becomes approximately true in the present experiment after initial transient effects have damped out. In this case we have

$$D_{12}{}^{int} = \frac{\int_0^{N_1{}^2} D_{12}(N)\, d(N^2)}{N_1{}^2} \tag{3}$$

as the "integral" diffusion constant determined by the instantaneous behavior of the system at any particular time; it corresponds to the concentration interval between zero and the maximum concentration existing in the system at that time. Clearly an effective diffusion constant determined from the average behavior over a period of time is a more complicated kind of average. Such an effective diffusion constant might also be considered an "integral" diffusion constant. Clearly an integral diffusion constant might be defined in many other ways as well.

METHOD

A large variety of methods for measuring diffusion in liquids has been used.[1, 2] In many methods concentration changes occurring in a diffusion cell are determined by standard analytical techniques, but the rate of observable change in concentration is often quite slow. Other methods use an optical technique for following concentration change, but the equipment necessary is usually complex and expensive. In this experiment, a relative method which is both rapid and inexpensive will be used. This method, first used by Schulze,[3] has been revived by Wall,[4] who tested it with diffusion of electrolytes in aqueous solution and has also used it for investigation of the diffusion of polymer molecules.

A porous, unglazed porcelain disk (frit) is filled with a liquid or a solution and then placed in a large bath of another liquid (pure solvent) or a solution of different concentration. The frit is suspended in the bath by a wire from one arm of an analytical balance which has been modified for this purpose, and the progress of diffusion is followed by recording the apparent weight of the frit with time. Consider the diffusion out of a homogeneous cylindrical disk with plane parallel faces. If the faces are large and the disk is quite thin, the problem can be simplified to one-dimensional diffusion[4] [compare with Eq. (7-4)]

$$\frac{\partial c}{\partial t} = \frac{\partial(D\,\partial c/\partial x)}{\partial x} \tag{4}$$

where c is the concentration at time t and at a distance x from the center of the disk along the normal to the faces. For a porous disk containing solution, Eq. (4) will still hold if one defines an *effective* cross-sectional area A and an *effective* thickness $2L$ so that the integral over these dimensions of $c(t)$ equals $Q(t)$, the amount of solute contained in the frit at time t. Clearly these effective dimensions will be less than the actual external dimensions of the disk, since the volume of solution held by the frit is less than the volume of the disk.

If the diffusion constant is assumed independent of concentration or understood to be an average integral diffusion constant over the concentration range involved, Eq. (4) can be readily solved. In terms of $Q(t)$, the result is[4]

$$\begin{aligned} Q(t) &= A\int_{-L}^{L} [c(x,t) - c_0]\,dx \\ &= 2LA(c_1 - c_0)\frac{8}{\pi^2}\sum_{n=0}^{\infty}\frac{1}{(2n+1)^2}\exp[-Dt(2n+1)^2\pi^2/4L^2] \end{aligned} \tag{5}$$

where c_1 is the initial concentration in the frit at time $t = 0$ and c_0 is the concentration in the bath, which is assumed to be constant. If D is a function of concentration, the proper solution of Eq. (4) is much more difficult. A numerical integration of Eq. (4) for the case where D depends on concentration has been carried out by Wall and Wendt,[5] but this question will not be considered here, and we shall base our treatment on Eq. (5), which is essentially identical with Eq. (7-13) derived for diffusion of gases. Except for a short initial time period the sum in Eq. (5) is dominated by the first term ($n = 0$). For times sufficiently long that $t > 0.2(4L^2/\pi^2 D)$, $Q(t)$ can be written as simply

$$Q(t) = 2LA(c_1 - c_0)\frac{8}{\pi^2}\exp(-D\pi^2 t/4L^2) \tag{6}$$

Now let us define a quantity W_t by

$$W_t = W(t) - W(\infty) \tag{7}$$

where $W(t)$ is the apparent weight of the frit suspended in the bath at time t and $W(\infty)$ is the apparent weight after equilibrium has been reached. Clearly W_t is given by

$$W_t = A\int_{-L}^{L} [d(x,t) - d_0]\,dx \tag{8}$$

where $d(x,t)$ is the density of solution at point x and time t and d_0 is the density of the liquid in the bath. If the density of a solution as a function of concentration can be represented by a linear function $d(c) = d(0) + kc$, where $d(0)$ is the solvent density, then one obtains

$$W_t = Ak \int_{-L}^{L} [c(x,t) - c_0]\, dx = kQ(t) \tag{9}$$

Substituting Eq. (9) into Eq. (6) and rearranging to a more convenient form, we find that

$$\log W_t = -\frac{D\pi^2 t}{2.303(4L^2)} + \log \left[2LAk(c_1 - c_0)\frac{8}{\pi^2} \right] \tag{10}$$

Thus a plot of log W_t vs. t should give a straight line of slope $(-\alpha D)$, where α is an "apparatus constant" characteristic of the frit used. A calibration of the frit with a solution of known diffusion properties is required to evaluate the constant α. It should be noted that for short times (at the beginning of the diffusion) the points should lie above the straight line determined by the log W_t vs. t points for longer times.

On the basis of a more detailed analysis,[5] one finds that the diffusion constant D obtained from Eq. (10) should lie between $D(c_1)$, the differential diffusion constant at concentration c_1 (initial concentration in the frit), and $D(c_0)$, the value at concentration c_0 in the bath. Indeed, D should be closer to $D(c_0)$ than $D(c_1)$. For convenience, we shall assume that D is approximately equal to $D(c_1/2)$.

Although Eq. (10) was obtained for the case of one-dimensional diffusion, it has been shown that for *sufficiently long times* all transient terms in the solution to the differential diffusion equation for this experimental method effectively vanish and that a linear log W_t vs. time plot should be obtained, no matter how irregular the shape of the frit used.[6] Use of a thin, flat disk should, however, result in a more rapid appearance of this linear region.

Wall et al.[4] have discussed the effect of (1) bulk flow of the more dense solution out of the frit due to gravity, (2) mechanical mixing of the solution caused by vigorous stirring, (3) failure to achieve a sharp initial boundary, and (4) neglect of the change in composition of the large volume of bath liquid. It has been concluded that none of these effects contributes significant error to the results obtained with this technique. The results are also not very sensitive to temperature variation; regulation of the bath temperature within $\pm 0.1\,^\circ$C is adequate.

EXPERIMENTAL

The experimental setup to be used is shown in Fig. 1. An analytical balance is mounted above a 25°C thermostat bath. A Chainomatic type of balance is most convenient for this work and should be modified by drilling a hole in the center of the left-hand pan and pan arrest and a somewhat larger hole in the base directly below the left pan. This will allow the porous disk to hang by a fine wire from the left pan of the balance into a solvent bath which is mounted in the thermostat. A convenient solvent bath vessel consists of a 1- or 2-gal screw-top jar which has a sufficiently wide mouth to permit introduction of the porous disk; this can be mounted in the thermostat by clamping around the neck with a Varigrip clamp.

The edges of the porous disk may be sealed with a cement or resin to prevent radial diffusion, although this is not necessary to achieve good results. A small hole may be drilled through the porous disk near the edge to permit attaching a fine (~0.01 in.) wire.

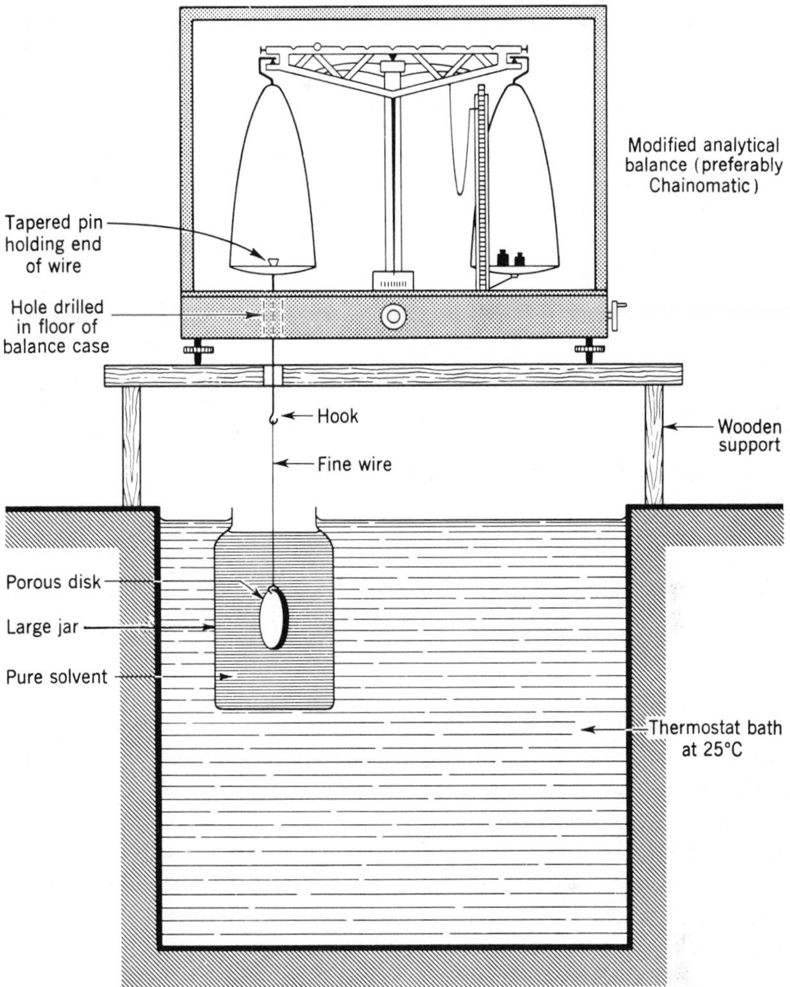

FIG. 1. Experimental arrangement for measuring the diffusion from a porous frit.

No provision need be made for stirring the solvent bath; indeed, mechanical stirring is not permissible while actual weighings are being made. Apparently for rapidly diffusing solutions, sufficient agitation results from the natural motion of the disk during the run. Perhaps, for very slow diffusion, the solvent bath should be stirred between weight readings.

Porous Disks. Selas† unglazed porous plates have been found satisfactory. These plates are available in a convenient size, having an external geometric volume of about 20 cm^3 and a dry weight of about 25 g. Such a disk will hold approximately 12 ml of liquid and has a porosity which allows diffusion of D_2O into H_2O to be complete in about 6 hr. Other porous plates are commercially available. Some may be as satisfactory as the Selas disk, but with some the diffusion is much slower and the experiment becomes unnecessarily tedious. Record the dimensions of the porous disk to be used.

After the supporting wire has been attached, the *dry* frit is immersed in D_2O for at least 12 hr to ensure a complete filling of the pores. Only a small volume of

† Selas Corporation of America, Philadelphia 34, Pa. Unglazed, microporous filter plates: 3 in. diameter, 3⁄16 to 1⁄4 in. thick, grade 10 porosity.

liquid is required to fill the disk when initially dry, but a large volume is needed to replace the liquid in a wet disk with a new liquid of different composition. About 25 to 30 ml of D_2O (at least 90 per cent) is placed in a shallow culture dish, and the disk is laid flat in the dish and covered. If convenient, the disk should be carefully turned over periodically during this soaking. When the soaking is complete, the disk is transferred to the solvent bath in the thermostat and the run is carried out as described below. After the D_2O run is complete, the disk is suspended in about 1 liter of a 1.5 M KCl solution and allowed to soak for at least 6 hr. A run is then made for calibration purposes to determine the apparatus constant α.

After use, the disk should be soaked overnight in distilled water to remove KCl completely and dried in air at room temperature for about 5 days or in a drying oven at 100°C for 1 day.

Procedure for a Run. While the frit is soaking in the solution or liquid to be studied, the solvent bath vessel is filled and mounted in the thermostat. Allow at least 1 hr for thermal equilibration if there is no stirring, and check periodically with a thermometer. If the solvent bath remains in the thermostat for a long period, cover it to prevent evaporation and possible contamination. In this experiment, the solvent bath always contains distilled H_2O.

When the frit has been adequately soaked, allow any excess liquid to drop off, quickly transfer the frit to the solvent bath, and hang it from a hook which is supported from the left-hand pan of the balance. Start a stopwatch. After an initial period of about 5 min has been allowed for transients to die out, readings of the apparent weight are begun and recorded at regular intervals. It is recommended that weighings be made at 1-min intervals until the difference between successive readings is one-fifth of its initial value (about 1 hr). If care is taken to make all readings at exactly 1-min intervals, a value for $W(\infty)$ is not needed, since the data may be treated using Guggenheim's method (see Exp. 27). Otherwise continue to record the weight approximately every hour until there is no significant change (4 to 6 hr), and take this value as $W(\infty)$.

CALCULATIONS

For a Guggenheim treatment, calculate the quantities $[W(t + \Delta t) - W(t)]$ using a constant Δt of about 15 min; a plot of log $[W(t + \Delta t) - W(t)]$ vs. time should be a straight line with a slope of $(-\alpha D)$. Alternatively, convert all the $W(t)$ readings to W_t as defined by Eq. (7) and then plot log W_t vs. time. For each run, draw the best straight line through the plotted points (ignore any initial curvature) and determine the slope $(-\alpha D)$ in units of seconds^{-1}.

Values of the differential diffusion constant for KCl solutions at 25°C are given in Table 1. From the αD value obtained from the calibration run, determine the value of the apparatus constant α. Use the differential diffusion constant given for

TABLE 1. Differential Diffusion Constants for KCl in H_2O at 25°C[7]

$c(M)$	D, 10^{-5} cm^2 sec^{-1}
0.75	1.87
1.25	1.92
1.50	1.94
2.50	2.06

one-half the initial concentration of KCl in the frit. Calculate the value of D for the diffusion of D_2O into H_2O.

DISCUSSION

Discuss the choice of the KCl diffusion constant used and the effect of alternative choices on the calculated value of D for D_2O-H_2O.[5]

From your value of α, calculate the effective thickness $2L$. How does this dimension compare with the actual external thickness of the porous disk?

It is necessary to be careful in making comparison of this D value for D_2O-H_2O with other values in the literature. The effective concentration of the diffusing solution varies from an initial high value (at least 90 per cent D_2O) to a final value of essentially 0 per cent D_2O. Roughly speaking, the diffusion constant found here is a mean value corresponding to a differential diffusion constant for a solution approximately 50 per cent in D_2O. It should be noted that a linear plot, as obtained with this method, does not necessarily imply that D is independent of concentration over the range.

Indeed, the diffusion constant for D_2O-H_2O systems appears to be dependent upon relative concentration of species. The same holds true for systems of H_2O^{16} with other isotopic water molecules (i.e., labeled with O^{18}, H^3, etc.). Thus it is necessary to be as explicit as possible about conditions and concentrations in making comparisons. Longsworth[8] has found a value of 2.26×10^{-5} cm^2 sec^{-1} for the self-diffusion constant of water using the interference method, with trace amounts of D_2O present. Wang and coworkers[9] have found values of 2.14×10^{-5} by a capillary method and 2.12×10^{-5} by a diaphragm method for the integral diffusion constant of 99.8 per cent D_2O into water and 2.34×10^{-5} for tracer diffusion of HDO, as well as a value of 3.01×10^{-5} for tracer diffusion of H_2O^{18}. Wang has found the activation energy for self-diffusion of water to be about 4.58 kcal mole^{-1} between 10 and 50°C.

APPARATUS

Analytical balance (Chainomatic) modified to permit hanging porous disk from left pan; stand for supporting balance over a bath; dry porous disk with fine wire attached; large screw-top jar (1- or 2-gal size); Varigrip clamp; shallow culture dish for soaking disk; 1-liter beaker; stopwatch.

Constant-temperature bath set at 25°C; heavy water, at least 90 per cent D_2O (30 ml); 1.5 *M* KCl solution (1.5 liters).

REFERENCES

1. W. Jost, "Diffusion in Solids, Liquids, Gases," chap. XI, Academic Press, Inc., New York (1952).
2. A. L. Geddes, Determination of Diffusivity, in A. Weissberger (ed.), "Technique of Organic Chemistry," 2d ed., vol. I, part I, chap. XII, Interscience, New York (1949).
3. G. Schulze, *Z. physik. Chem.*, **89**, 168 (1914).
4. F. T. Wall, P. F. Grieger, and C. W. Childers, *J. Am. Chem. Soc.*, **74**, 3562 (1952); F. T. Wall and C. W. Childers, *ibid.*, **75**, 3550 (1953); G. B. Taylor and F. T. Wall, *ibid.*, **75**, 6340 (1953).

5. F. T. Wall and R. C. Wendt, *J. Phys. Chem.,* **62,** 1581 (1958).
6. F. Grun and C. Blatter, *J. Am. Chem. Soc.,* **80,** 3838 (1958).
7. L. J. Gosting, *J. Am. Chem. Soc.,* **72,** 4418 (1950).
8. L. G. Longsworth, *J. Phys. Chem.,* **58,** 770 (1954).
9. J. H. Wang, C. V. Robinson, and I. S. Edelman, *J. Am. Chem. Soc.,* **73,** 510, 4181 (1951); **75,** 466 (1953).

VII

EQUILIBRIA

EXPERIMENTS

Experiment 17. Vapor Pressure of a Pure Liquid

When a pure liquid is placed in an evacuated bulb, molecules will leave the liquid phase and enter the gas phase until the pressure of the vapor in the bulb reaches a definite value which is determined by the nature of the liquid and its temperature. This pressure is called the vapor pressure of the liquid at a given temperature. The equilibrium vapor pressure is independent of the quantity of liquid and vapor present as long as both phases exist in equilibrium with each other at the specified temperature. As the temperature is increased, the vapor pressure also increases up to the critical point, at which the two-phase system becomes a homogeneous, one-phase fluid.

If the pressure above the liquid is maintained at a fixed value (say by admitting air to the bulb containing the liquid), then the liquid may be heated up to a temperature at which the vapor pressure is equal to the external pressure. At this point, vaporization will occur by the formation of bubbles in the interior of the liquid as well as at the surface; this is the boiling point of the liquid at the specified external pressure. Clearly the temperature of the boiling point is a function of the external pressure; in fact, the variation of the boiling point with external pressure is seen to be identical with the variation of the vapor pressure with temperature.

In this experiment the variation of vapor pressure with temperature will be measured and used to determine the molar heat of vaporization.

THEORY

We are concerned here with the equilibrium between a pure liquid and its vapor:

$$X(l) = X(g) \qquad (p,T) \tag{1}$$

It can be shown thermodynamically[1] that a definite relationship exists between the values of p and T at equilibrium as given by

$$\frac{dp}{dT} = \frac{\Delta S}{\Delta V} \tag{2}$$

In Eq. (2) dp and dT refer to infinitesimal changes in p and T for an equilibrium system composed of a pure substance with both phases always present; ΔS and ΔV refer to the change in S and V when one phase transforms to the other at constant p and T. Since the change in state (1) is isothermal and ΔG is zero, ΔS may be replaced by $\Delta H/T$. The result is

$$\frac{dp}{dT} = \frac{\Delta H}{T\Delta V} \tag{3}$$

Equation (2) or (3) is known as the Clapeyron equation. It is an exact expression which may be applied to phase equilibria of all kinds although it has been presented here in terms of the one-component liquid-vapor case. Since the heat of vaporization ΔH_v is positive and ΔV is positive for vaporization, it is seen immediately that the vapor pressure must increase with increasing temperature.

For the case of vapor-liquid equilibria in the range of vapor pressures less than 1 atm, one may assume that the molal volume of the liquid $\tilde{V}_l$ is negligible in comparison with that of the gas $\tilde{V}_g$, so that $\Delta\tilde{V} = \tilde{V}_g$. This assumption is very good in the low-pressure region, since $\tilde{V}_l$ is usually only a few tenths of a per cent of $\tilde{V}_g$. Thus we obtain

$$\frac{dp}{dT} = \frac{\Delta\tilde{H}_v}{T\tilde{V}_g} \tag{4}$$

Since $d \ln p = dp/p$ and $d(1/T) = -dT/T^2$, we can rewrite Eq. (4) in the form

$$\frac{d \ln p}{d(1/T)} = -\frac{\Delta\tilde{H}_v}{R}\frac{RT}{p\tilde{V}_g} = -\frac{\Delta\tilde{H}_v}{Rz} \tag{5}$$

where we have introduced a *compressibility factor* z for the vapor:

$$z = \frac{p\tilde{V}_g}{RT} \tag{6}$$

Equation (5) is a convenient form of the Clapeyron equation. We can see that *if* the vapor were a perfect gas ($z \equiv 1$) and $\Delta\tilde{H}_v$ were independent of temperature, then a plot of $\ln p$ vs. $1/T$ would be a straight line the slope of which would determine $\Delta\tilde{H}_v$. Indeed, for many liquids $\ln p$ is almost a linear function of $1/T$, which implies at least that $\Delta\tilde{H}_v/z$ is almost constant.

Let us now consider the question of gas imperfections, i.e., the behavior of z as a function of temperature for the saturated vapor. It is difficult to carry out p-V-T measurements on gases close to condensation and such data are scarce, but

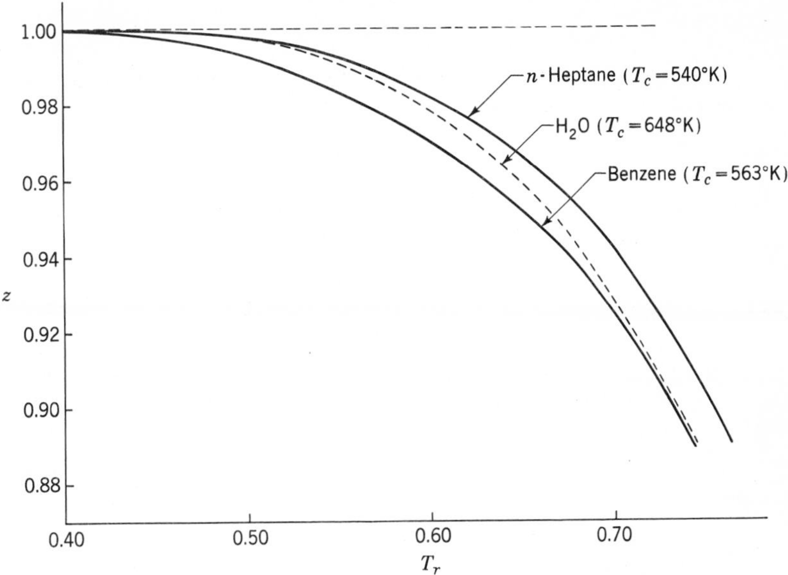

FIG. 1. The compressibility factor z of saturated vapor as a function of reduced temperature T_r for water, benzene, and n-heptane.

data are available for water,[2] and theoretical extrapolations[3] have been made for the vapor of "normal" liquids based on data obtained at higher temperatures. Figure 1 shows the variation of the compressibility factor z for a saturated vapor as a function of temperature in the case of water and two normal liquids, benzene and n-heptane. For the temperature axis, a "reduced" temperature T_r is used; $T_r = T/T_c$, where T_c is the critical temperature. This has the effect of almost superimposing the curves of many different substances; indeed, by the law of corresponding states such curves would be exactly superimposed. In general, it is clear that z decreases as the temperature increases. Water, due to its high critical temperature, is a reasonably ideal gas even at 100°C where z equals 0.986. But n-heptane at its 1-atm boiling point of 98°C has a value of z equal to 0.95 and is relatively nonideal. For many substances, sizable gas imperfections are present even at pressures below 1 atm.

Next we must consider the variation of $\Delta\tilde{H}_v$ with temperature. For a change in state such as Eq. (1),

$$\Delta H_{T_2} = \Delta H_{T_1} + \int_{T_1}^{T_2} \Delta C_p \, dT + \int_{p_1}^{p_2} \left(\frac{\partial H}{\partial p}\right)_T dp \tag{7}$$

Since the final term is zero for a perfect gas and small for most real gases, it is possible to approximate Eq. (7) by

$$\Delta H_{T_2} \simeq \Delta H_{T_1} + \overline{\Delta C_p}(T_2 - T_1) \tag{8}$$

where the average value over the temperature interval, $\overline{\Delta C_p}$, is used. For $\Delta\tilde{H}_v$ to be independent of temperature, $\Delta\tilde{C}_p$ must be very close to zero, which is generally not true. Heat capacities for water, benzene, and n-heptane are given on p. 162 as typical examples.[4, 5] For n-heptane, the specific heat of both gas and liquid changes rapidly with temperature; use of average values will give only an order-of-magnitude result. In general, the value of $\Delta\tilde{H}_v$ will decrease as the temperature increases.

Compound	Temp. range, °C	Average values, cal deg^{-1} mole^{-1}		
		$\tilde{C}_p(g)$	$\tilde{C}_p(l)$	$\Delta\tilde{C}_p$
Water	25–100	8	18	−10
Benzene	25–80	22	35	−13
n-Heptane	25–100	~47	~58	−11

Since both $\Delta\tilde{H}_v$ and z decrease with increasing temperature, it is possible to see why $\Delta\tilde{H}_v/z$ might be almost constant and give a nearly linear plot of $\ln p$ vs. $1/T$.

METHODS

There are several experimental methods of measuring the vapor pressure as a function of temperature.[6] In the *gas-saturation method* a known volume of an inert gas is bubbled slowly through the liquid, which is kept at constant temperature in a thermostat. The vapor pressure is calculated from a determination of the amount of vapor contained in the outcoming gas or from the loss in weight of the liquid. A common *static method* makes use of an *isoteniscope,* a bulb with a short U tube attached. The liquid is placed in the bulb, and some liquid is placed in the U tube. When the liquid is boiled under reduced pressure, all air is swept out of the bulb. The isoteniscope is then placed in a thermostat. At a given temperature the external pressure is adjusted so that both arms of the U tube are at the same height. At this setting, the external pressure, which is equal to the pressure of the vapor in the isoteniscope, is measured with a mercury manometer. A common *dynamic method* is one in which the variation of the boiling point with external applied pressure is measured. The total pressure above the liquid can be varied and maintained at a given value by use of a large-volume ballast bulb; this pressure is then measured with a mercury manometer. The liquid to be studied is heated until boiling occurs, and the temperature of the refluxing vapor is measured in order to avoid any effects of superheating. The experimental procedure for both the isoteniscope method and a boiling-point method is given below.

EXPERIMENTAL

1. Boiling-point Method. The apparatus should be assembled as shown in Fig. 2. A Claissen distilling flask can be used in this experiment by closing off the side arm with a rubber policeman. Use pressure tubing for connecting the condenser and the manometer to the ballast bulb. Fill the flask about one-third full (just above the level of the baffle) with the liquid to be studied. A few carborundum boiling chips should be added to reduce "bumping." Be sure that the thermometer scale is visible over a range of at least 50°C below the boiling point at 1 atm. Heating should be accomplished with either a bunsen burner or an electric heating mantle placed directly below the flask *F*. The baffle is used to prevent superheating of the vapor.

Use the manometer with the greatest care; be careful not to allow liquid to condense in it. Stopcock *X* should be open only when the manometer is to be read and closed immediately after each reading. Stopcock *X* should not be open at the same time as stopcock *S* is open, either to vacuum or to the air.

To make a reading, adjust the heating so as to attain steady boiling of the liquid,

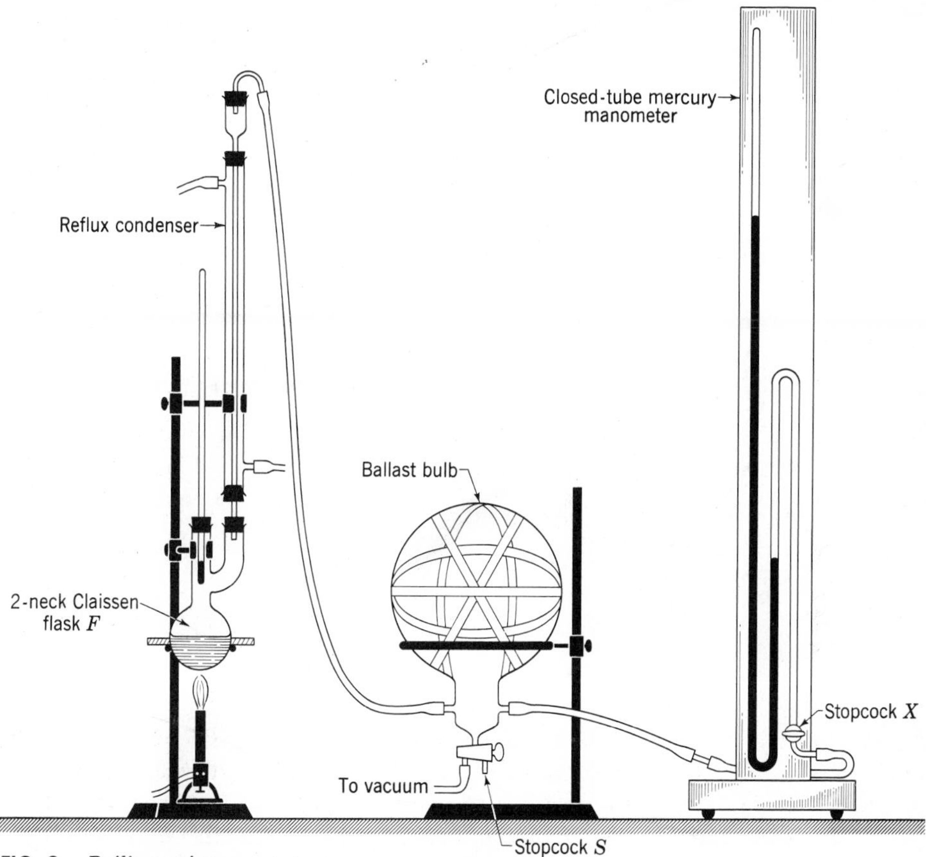

FIG. 2. Boiling-point apparatus.

but avoid heating too strongly. Preferably, heat the flask at a point an inch or so to one side of center. When conditions appear to be steady, open stopcock X carefully and watch the manometer. When manometer and thermometer appear to be as steady as they can be maintained, read them as nearly simultaneously as possible. The thermometer scale should be read to the nearest 0.1°C, and vapor should be condensing on and dripping from the thermometer bulb to ensure that the equilibrium temperature is obtained. In reading the manometer, record the position of each meniscus (h_1 and h_2), keeping your line of slight level with the meniscus to avoid parallax error. Estimate your readings to the nearest 0.1 mm. Record the ambient air temperature at the manometer several times during the run.

To change the pressure in the system between measurements, first remove the heater, then check to make sure that stopcock X is closed. After a short time admit some air or remove some air by opening stopcock S for a few seconds. Be especially careful in removing air from the ballast bulb to avoid strong bumping. Then open stopcock X carefully to measure the pressure on the manometer. Repeat as often as necessary to attain the desired pressure. Close stopcock X and restore the heater to its position under the flask.

Take readings at approximately the following pressures:

Pressure descending: 76, 60, 45, 35, 26, 20, 16, 13, 10, 8 cm
Pressure ascending: 9, 11, 14, 18, 23, 30, 40, 52, 67 cm

2. *Isoteniscope Method.* In this technique much of the equipment shown in Fig. 2 is used, but the distilling flask and reflux condenser are replaced by an isoteniscope mounted in a glass thermostat as shown in Fig. 3. The heater is operated from a Variac voltage control, and the water bath should be vigorously stirred to ensure thermal equilibrium. The liquid to be studied is placed in the isoteniscope so that the bulb is about one-half full and there is about 3 cm of liquid in each arm of the U tube. Then the isoteniscope is placed in the thermostat (which should be at room temperature) and is connected to the ballast bulb and manometer (which are assembled and connected as in Fig. 2).

Air is swept out of the bulb by **cautiously** reducing the pressure in the ballast bulb until air bubbles through the U-tube liquid at a reasonable rate; avoid evaporating too much of the liquid in the U tube. After 2 or 3 min carefully admit air through stopcock S until the liquid levels in both arms of the U tube are equal; then read the temperature and the pressure on the mercury manometer. (The procedure for operating and reading this manometer is described in section 1.) To ensure removal of all the air, repeat the procedure above until successive vapor-pressure readings are in good agreement. If the amount of liquid in the U tube becomes inadequate, tilt the isoteniscope so that some liquid from the bulb is transferred over into the U tube.

Once the air is removed and a good pressure reading at room temperature is obtained, heat the thermostat bath to a new temperature about 5°C above room

FIG. 3. Isoteniscope. This is connected to the ballast bulb and manometer shown in Fig. 2.

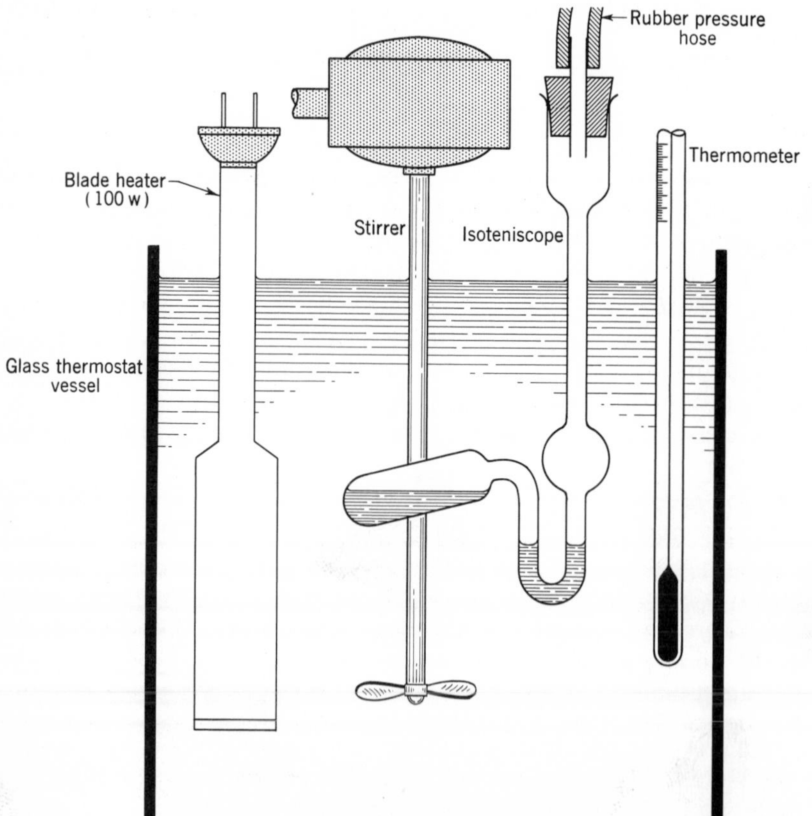

temperature. Keep the liquid levels in the U tube approximately equal at all times. When the bath temperature is steady at its new value, adjust the pressure in the ballast bulb until the levels in the U tube are equal and record both temperature and pressure.

Take readings at approximately 5°C intervals until the bath is at about 75°C, and then take readings at decreasing temperatures which are between the values obtained on heating.

CALCULATIONS

Correct all manometer pressure readings $(h_2 - h_1)$ for the fact that the mercury is not at 0°C by multiplying by $(1 - 1.8 \times 10^{-4}t)$, where t is the centigrade temperature of the manometer. If t has been reasonably constant during the experiment, use an average value and apply the same correction factor to all pressures.

Convert all centigrade temperature readings to absolute temperatures T and plot $\log_{10} p$ vs. $1/T$. If there is no systematic curvature, draw the best straight line through the points. If there is noticeable curvature, draw a smooth curve through the points and also draw a straight line tangent to the curve at about the mid-point.

Determine the slope of the straight line or tangent. From Eq. (5) it follows that this slope is $-\Delta\tilde{H}_v/2.303Rz$. Estimate the value of z for the saturated vapor at the appropriate temperature from Fig. 1 and calculate $\Delta\tilde{H}_v$ in calories per mole. Report the value of the heat of vaporization and of the vapor pressure for the liquid together with the applicable temperature (corresponding to the mid-point of the range studied).

DISCUSSION

Using Fig. 1 and Eq. (8), estimate the variation in $\Delta\tilde{H}_v/z$ over the range of temperatures studied. Indicate clearly whether $\Delta\tilde{H}_v/z$ should increase or decrease with increasing temperature. Does your $\log p$ vs. $1/T$ plot show a curvature of the correct sign?

Evaluate a quantitative uncertainty in your value of $\Delta\tilde{H}_v/z$ by the method of "limiting slopes." Comment on this uncertainty in relation to the variation with temperature calculated above.

Discuss possible systematic sources of error.

APPARATUS

Ballast bulb (5 liters); closed-tube manometer; double-neck distillation flask (if Claissen flask is used, a rubber policeman is needed to close off side arm); a centigrade thermometer to cover the desired range, with one-hole rubber stopper to fit flask; reflux condenser with large-hole rubber stopper to fit flask; bent glass tube in a rubber stopper to fit top of condenser; bunsen burner with hose; two long pieces of rubber tubing for circulating water through condenser; three long pieces of heavy-wall, rubber pressure tubing; two condenser clamps and clamp holders; ring stand; iron ring (and clamp holder, if necessary); transite baffle with center hole to fit around bottom of flask; 0 to 30°C thermometer.

If isoteniscope is used: a glass thermostat (e.g., large battery jar); mechanical stirrer; electric blade heater; Variac; isoteniscope.

Liquid, such as water, benzene, or n-heptane.

REFERENCES

1. Any standard text on chemical thermodynamics, such as F. H. MacDougall, "Thermodynamics and Chemistry," 3d ed., Wiley, New York (1939).
2. J. H. Keenan and F. G. Keyes, "Thermodynamic Properties of Steam," Wiley, New York (1936).
3. K. S. Pitzer, D. Z. Lippmann, R. F. Curl, Jr., C. M. Huggins, and D. E. Petersen, *J. Am. Chem. Soc.,* **77,** 3433 (1955).
4. Selected Values of Properties of Hydrocarbons, *Natl. Bur. Standards Circ.* C461 (1947).
5. "Handbook of Chemistry and Physics," 40th ed., Chemical Rubber Publishing Co., Cleveland (1958).
6. G. W. Thomson, Determination of Vapor Pressure, in A. Weissberger (ed.), "Technique of Organic Chemistry," 2d ed., vol. I, part I, Interscience, New York (1949).

GENERAL READING

G. W. Thomson, Determination of Vapor Pressure, in A. Weissberger (ed.), *op. cit.*

Experiment 18. Binary Liquid-Vapor Phase Diagram

This experiment is concerned with the heterogeneous equilibrium between two phases in a system of two components. The particular system to be studied is acetone-chloroform at 1 atm pressure. This system exhibits a strong negative deviation from Raoult's law, resulting in a maximum boiling point.

THEORY

For a system of two components (A and B) we have from the phase rule[1]

$$F = C - P + 2 = 4 - P \tag{1}$$

where C is the number of *components* (minimum number of chemical constituents necessary to define the composition of every phase in the system at equilibrium), P is the number of *phases* (number of physically differentiable parts of the system at equilibrium), and F is the *variance* or number of *degrees of freedom* (number of intensive variables pertaining to the system that can be independently varied at equilibrium without altering the number or kinds of phases present).

When a single phase is present the pressure p, the temperature T, and the composition X_B (mole fraction of component B) of that phase can be independently varied; thus a single-phase two-component system at equilibrium is defined, except for its size,† by a point in a three-dimensional plot in which the coordinates are the intensive variables p, T, and X_B (see Fig. 1). When two phases are present at equilibrium, e.g., liquid L and vapor V, there are four variables but only two of them can be independently varied. Thus, if p and T are specified, X_{BL} and X_{BV} (the mole fractions of B in L and V) are fixed at their *limiting* values ($X_{BL}{}^0$ and $X_{BV}{}^0$) for the respective phases at this p and T. The loci of points $X_{BL}{}^0(p,T)$ and

† The complete definition of the system would, of course, include also its shape, description of surfaces, specification of fields, etc.; ordinarily these have negligible effects as far as our present discussion is concerned.

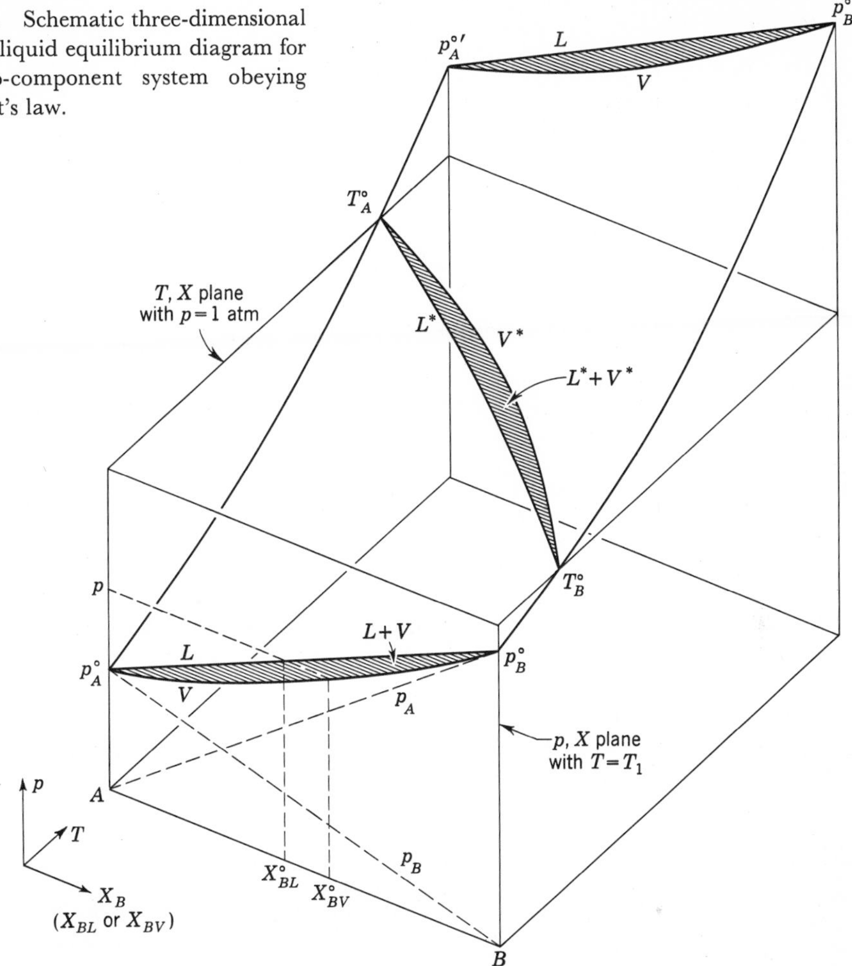

FIG. 1. Schematic three-dimensional vapor-liquid equilibrium diagram for a two-component system obeying Raoult's law.

$X_{BV}{}^0(p, T)$ constitute two surfaces, shown in Fig. 1. The shaded region between them may be interpreted as representing the coexistence of two phases L and V *if* in this region X_B is interpreted as a mole fraction of B *for the system as a whole.* Within the two-phase region X_B is *not* to be regarded as one of the intensive variables constituting the variance (although in a single-phase region it is indeed one of these variables). In a two-phase region the value of X_B determines the relative proportions of the two phases in the system; as X_B varies from $X_{BL}{}^0$ to $X_{BV}{}^0$, the molar proportion x_V of vapor phase varies from zero to unity:

$$x_V = 1 - x_L = \frac{X_B - X_{BL}{}^0}{X_{BV}{}^0 - X_{BL}{}^0} \tag{2}$$

Figure 1 is drawn for the special case of two components which form a complete range of *ideal solutions,* i.e., solutions which obey Raoult's law with respect to both components at all compositions. According to this law the vapor pressure (or partial pressure in the vapor) of a component at a given temperature T_1 is proportional to its mole fraction in the liquid. Thus, in Fig. 1 the light dashed lines representing the partial pressures p_A and p_B and the total vapor-pressure line (L, joining $p_A{}^0$ and $p_B{}^0$) are straight lines when plotted against the liquid composition.

However, the total vapor pressure as plotted against the *vapor* composition is not linear. The curved line V, joining $p_A{}^0$ and $p_B{}^0$, is convex downward, lying *below* the straight line on the constant-temperature section; its slope has everywhere the same sign as the slope of L.

The vapor pressures $p_A{}^0$ and $p_B{}^0$ of the pure liquids increase with temperature (in accord with the Clapeyron equation) as indicated by the curves joining $p_A{}^0$ with $p_A'^0$ and $p_B{}^0$ with $p_B'^0$. At a constant pressure, say 1 atm, the boiling points of the pure liquids are indicated as $T_A{}^0$ and $T_B{}^0$. The boiling point of the solution, as a function of X_{BL} or X_{BV}, is represented by the curve L^* or V^* joining these two points. Neither curve is in general a straight line. If Raoult's law is obeyed, both are convex upward in temperature, the vapor curve lying above the liquid curve in temperature and being the more convex.

In most binary liquid-vapor systems Raoult's law is a good approximation for a component only when its mole fraction is close to unity. Large deviations from this law are commonplace for the dilute component, or for both components when the mole fraction of neither is close to unity. If at a given temperature the vapor pressure of a solution is higher than that predicted by Raoult's law, the system is said to show a *positive deviation* from that law. For such a system the boiling-point curve L^* at constant pressure is usually convex downward in temperature. If at a given temperature the vapor pressure of the solution is lower than that predicted by Raoult's law, the system is said to show a *negative deviation;* in this case the curve L^* is more convex upward. These deviations from Raoult's law are often ascribed to differences between "heterogeneous" molecular attractions (A---B) and "homogeneous" attractions (A---A and B---B). Thus, the existence of a positive deviation implies that homogeneous attractions are stronger than heterogeneous attractions, and a negative deviation implies the reverse. This interpretation is consistent with the fact that positive deviations are usually associated with positive heats of mixing and volume expansions on mixing while negative deviations are usually associated with negative heats and volume contractions.[2]

In many cases the deviations are large enough to result in maxima or minima in the vapor-pressure and boiling-point curves, as shown in Fig. 2. Systems for which the boiling-point curves have a maximum include acetone-chloroform and hydrogen chloride-water; systems with a minimum include methanol-chloroform, water-ethanol, and benzene-ethanol. At a maximum or a minimum the compositions of the liquid and of the vapor are the same; accordingly there is a *point of tangency* of the curves L and V and of the curves L^* and V^* at the maximum or minimum. At every value of X_B the slope of V (or V^*) has the same sign as the slope of L (or L^*); one is zero where and only where the other is zero, at the point of tangency. (A common error in curves of this kind, found even in some textbooks, is to draw a cusp—point of discontinuity of slope—in one or both curves at the point of tangency; both curves are, in fact, smooth and have continuous derivatives.)

If the homogeneous attractions are very much stronger than the heterogeneous ones, phase separation may occur in the liquid; i.e., there is a limited mutual solubility of the two liquid components over certain pressure and temperature ranges. If the pressures and temperatures at which two liquid phases coexist include those at which equilibrium also exists with the vapor phase, a boiling-point diagram of a type similar to that shown in Fig. 19-1 is found. (That figure is a *melting-point* diagram, showing two solid phases in equilibrium with a liquid phase, but the prin-

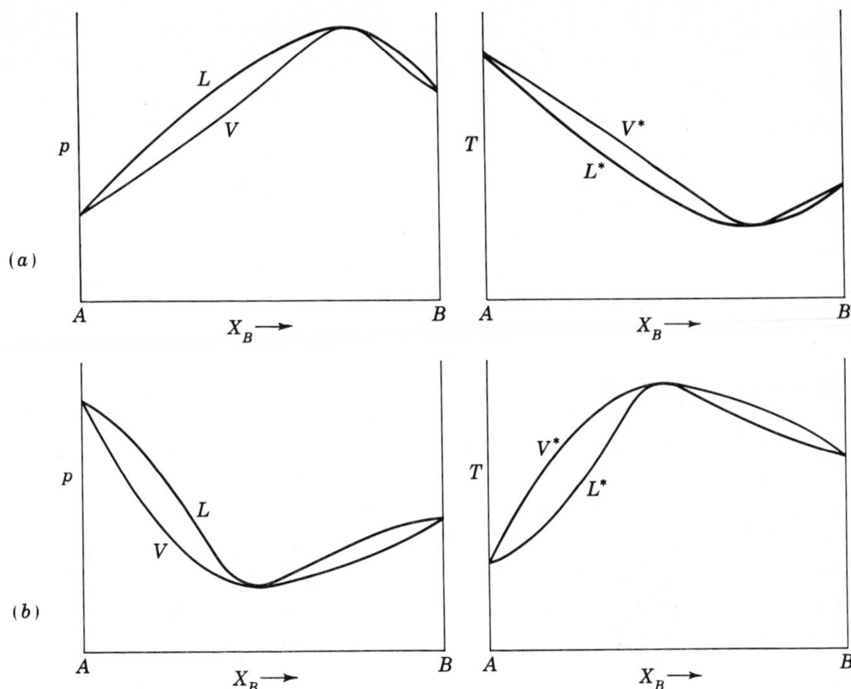

FIG. 2. Schematic vapor-pressure and boiling-point diagrams for systems showing (*a*) a strong positive deviation and (*b*) a strong negative deviation from Raoult's law.

ciples are the same. It will be noted that boundaries of fields show discontinuities in slope at points representing the coexistence of three phases.)

Liquid-vapor phase diagrams, and boiling-point diagrams in particular, are of importance in connection with *distillation,* which usually has as its object the partial or complete separation of a liquid solution into its components.[3] Distillation consists basically of boiling the solution and condensing the vapor into a separate receiver. A simple "one-plate" distillation of a binary system having no maximum or minimum in its boiling-point curve can be understood by reference to Fig. 3. Let the mole fraction of B in the initial solution be represented by X_{BL1}. When this is boiled and a small portion of the vapor condensed, a drop of distillate is obtained, with mole fraction X_{BV1}. Since this is richer in A than is the residue in the

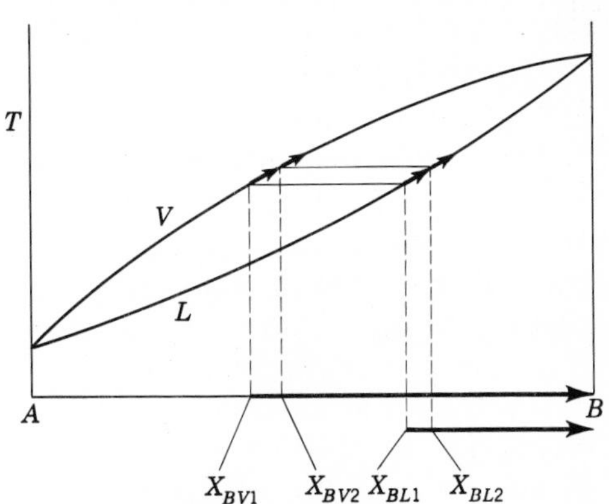

FIG. 3. Variation of liquid and vapor compositions during distillation.

flask, the residue becomes slightly richer in B, as represented by X_{BL2}. The next drop of distillate X_{BV2} is richer in B than was the first drop. If the distillation is continued until all the residue has boiled away, the last drop to condense will be virtually pure B. To obtain a substantially complete separation of the solution into pure A and B by distillations of this kind it is necessary to separate the distillate into portions by changing the receiver during the distillation, then subsequently to distill the separate portions in the same way, and so on, a very large number of successive distillations being required. The same result can be achieved in a single distillation by use of a fractionating column containing a large number of "plates"; discussion of the operation of such a column is beyond the scope of this book. If there is a maximum in the boiling-point curve (Fig. 2*b*) the compositions of vapor and residue do not approach pure A or pure B, but rather the composition corresponding to the maximum. A mixture with this composition will distill without change in composition and is known as a "constant-boiling mixture" or "azeotrope." These terms are also applied to a mixture with a minimum boiling point. Azeotropes are important in chemical technology. Occasionally they are useful (as in constant-boiling aqueous hydrochloric acid, used as an analytical standard); often they are nuisances (as in the case of the azeotrope of 95 per cent ethanol with 5 per cent water, the existence of which prevents preparation of absolute ethanol by direct distillation of dilute solutions of ethanol in water). Extensive lists of azeotropes have been compiled.[4]

METHOD

A boiling-point curve can be constructed from data obtained in actual distillations in an ordinary "one-plate" distilling apparatus. Small samples of the distillate are taken directly from the condenser, after which small samples of the residue are withdrawn with a pipette. The samples of distillate and residue are analyzed, and their compositions are plotted on a boiling-point diagram against the temperatures at which they were taken. In the case of the distillate the temperature to be plotted for each sample should be an average of the initial and final values during the taking of the sample. In the case of the residue the temperature to be plotted should be that recorded at the point where the distillation is stopped to take the sample of residue.

For analysis of the samples, a physical method is often preferable to chemical methods. Chemical analysis usually is appropriate only when a simple titration of each sample is involved, as in the case of the system HCl-H_2O. If a physical property is chosen as the basis for an analytical method, it should be one which changes significantly and sensitively over the entire composition range to be studied. For the system acetone-chloroform, the use of a refractometer is recommended for analyzing the specimens. In Table 1 the refractive index is given at various compositions for this system.

EXPERIMENTAL

A simple distilling apparatus that can be used for this experiment is shown in Fig. 4. The thermometer bulb should be about level with the side arm to the condenser. Except when samples of distillate are being taken for analysis, an adequate receiving flask should be placed at the lower end of the condenser.

TABLE 1. Refractive-index Composition for Acetone-Chloroform Mixtures

n_D^{25}	$M\%$ $CHCl_3$	n_D^{25}	$M\%$ $CHCl_3$	n_D^{25}	$M\%$ $CHCl_3$	n_D^{25}	$M\%$ $CHCl_3$
1.3562	0.00	1.3780	23.50	1.4000	47.55	1.4220	72.85
1.3570	0.75	1.3790	24.60	1.4010	48.70	1.4230	74.10
1.3580	1.75	1.3800	25.65	1.4020	49.80	1.4240	75.30
1.3590	2.75	1.3810	26.70	1.4030	50.90	1.4250	76.50
1.3600	3.80	1.3820	27.80	1.4040	52.00	1.4260	77.70
1.3610	4.85	1.3830	28.85	1.4050	53.10	1.4270	78.95
1.3620	5.90	1.3840	29.95	1.4060	54.20	1.4280	80.20
1.3630	7.00	1.3850	31.00	1.4070	55.30	1.4290	81.40
1.3640	8.10	1.3860	32.05	1.4080	56.45	1.4300	82.65
1.3650	9.20	1.3870	33.15	1.4090	57.60	1.4310	83.90
1.3660	10.30	1.3880	34.25	1.4100	58.75	1.4320	85.15
1.3670	11.40	1.3890	35.30	1.4110	59.90	1.4330	86.40
1.3680	12.50	1.3900	36.40	1.4120	61.05	1.4340	87.70
1.3690	13.60	1.3910	37.50	1.4130	62.25	1.4350	89.00
1.3700	14.70	1.3920	38.60	1.4140	63.40	1.4360	90.35
1.3710	15.80	1.3930	39.75	1.4150	64.55	1.4370	91.65
1.3720	16.90	1.3940	40.85	1.4160	65.75	1.4380	93.00
1.3730	18.00	1.3950	42.00	1.4170	66.90	1.4390	94.35
1.3740	19.10	1.3960	43.10	1.4180	68.10	1.4400	95.75
1.3750	20.20	1.3970	44.25	1.4190	69.30	1.4410	97.20
1.3760	21.30	1.3980	45.35	1.4200	70.50	1.4420	98.55
1.3770	22.40	1.3990	46.45	1.4210	71.70	1.4431	100.00

Before beginning the distillations, prepare twenty 5-ml shell vials for taking samples. Write on the corks the designations $1L$, $1V$, $2L$, . . . , $10V$ (L = *liquid* residue; V = condensed *vapor* or distillate). The samples to be taken are about 2 ml in size.

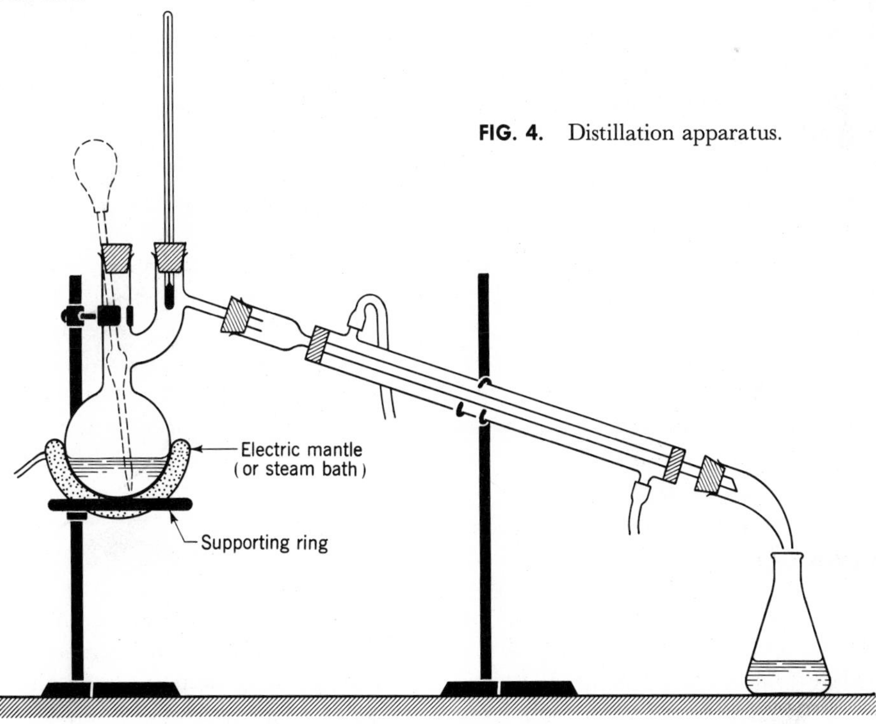

FIG. 4. Distillation apparatus.

When the distillation is proceeding at a normal (not excessive) rate at about the desired temperature, quickly replace the receiver with a vial and read the thermometer. After about 2 ml has been collected, read the thermometer again, replace the receiver, and cork the vial tightly. Turn off and lower the heating mantle to halt the distillation. At the point where the temperature just begins to fall, record another thermometer reading. After the flask has cooled 10 or 20°, remove the stopper at the top of the flask and insert a 2-ml pipette equipped with a rubber bulb. Fill the pipette, discharge it into the appropriate vial, and stopper the vial.

The following procedure is recommended for economical use of materials in carrying out this experiment. The paragraph numbers correspond to sample numbers. A graduated cylinder is adequate for measuring liquids. The temperatures recommended are those appropriate for 760 mm; at ambient pressures differing markedly from this the temperatures should be adjusted accordingly.

1. Pure Acetone. Introduce 180 ml of acetone into the flask. Determine the boiling point by distilling to constant temperature. (This temperature should be close to 56.3°C at 760 mm.) Collect samples ($1V$ and $1L$) for analysis if desired.

2. 58°C (acetone-rich side of azeotrope). Cool the distilling flask, and return the distillate of paragraph 1 to the flask. Add 20 ml of chloroform. Begin distillation. When the temperature reaches about 58°C, collect about 2 ml of distillate ($2V$) and 2 ml of residue ($2L$).

3. 60°C. Resume the distillation. Take samples ($3V$, $3L$) at about 60°C.

4. 62°C. Resume the distillation and continue to about 61°. Cool the flask somewhat and add 35 ml of chloroform and 65 ml of acetone. Resume the distillation. Take samples ($4V$, $4L$) at about 62°.

5. 63.5°C. Resume the distillation and continue to about 63°. Cool the flask somewhat and add 50 ml of chloroform and 50 ml of acetone. Resume the distillation, saving the distillate for later use. Take samples ($5V$, $5L$) at about 63.5°.

6. Azeotrope. Resume the distillation, continue distilling until the boiling point ceases to change significantly, and take samples ($6V$, $6L$). (If the boiling point does not become sufficiently constant, analyze the remaining residue with the refractometer and make up 100 ml of solution to the composition thereby found. Distill this to constant temperature and take samples.) Combine the residue with the distillate of paragraphs 5 and 6, and set it aside.

7. Pure Chloroform. Rinse the flask with a little chloroform. Introduce 80 ml of chloroform and determine the boiling point as in paragraph 1.

8. 62.5°C (chloroform-rich side of azeotrope). Cool the flask. Return the distillate of paragraph 7 and add 20 ml of the combined distillate and residue of paragraphs 5 and 6. Resume the distillation, and take samples at about 62.5°.

9. 63.5°C. Cool the flask, return the distillate of paragraph 8, and add about 50 ml of the distillate and residue of 5 and 6. Resume the distillation, and take samples ($9V$, $9L$) at about 63.5°.

10. Azeotrope (to check paragraph 6 from the other side). Resume the distillation, continue to constant boiling point, and take samples ($10V$, $10L$).

At any convenient time after the samples have been taken, their indices of refraction should be measured and recorded. The refractometer and the procedure for its use are described in Chap. XVIII. (If the experiment is being done by several teams using the same refractometer, it is wise to take samples to the refractometer as soon as six or eight samples are ready, or fewer if the instrument happens to be free.) If careful attention is given to the proper technique of using the refractometer, it should be possible to take readings at the rate of one sample per minute.

At the end of the experiment all acetone-chloroform mixtures should be poured into a designated waste vessel.

At some time during the laboratory period, the barometer should be read. The ambient temperature should be recorded for the purpose of making thermometer stem corrections.

CALCULATIONS

By interpolation in Table 1 convert the refractive indices to mole fractions. Plot the temperatures (after making any necessary stem corrections; see Chap. XVI) against the mole fractions. Draw one smooth curve through the distillate points V and another through the residue points L. Label all fields of the diagram to indicate what phases are present. Report the azeotropic composition and temperature, together with the atmospheric pressure (i.e., the properly corrected barometer reading).

APPARATUS

Claissen distilling flask; 0 to 100 or 50 to 100°C thermometer, graduated to 0.1°C; one-hole cork stopper for thermometer to fit flask; solid cork stopper; straight-tube condenser with one-hole stopper to fit distilling side arm; two lengths of rubber hose for condenser cooling water; distilling adapter with one-hole stopper to fit end of condenser; two clamps and clamp holders; two ring stands; one iron ring; electrical heating mantle (or steam bath); 20 small vials (screw-top or with corks to fit); 100-ml graduated cylinder; two wide-mouth 250-ml flasks; 2-ml pipette; pipetting bulb; two 500-ml glass-stoppered erlenmeyer flasks.

Refractometer, thermostated at 25°C; sodium-vapor lamp (optional); eye droppers; *clean* cotton-wool; acetone wash bottles; reagent-grade acetone (300 ml) and reagent-grade chloroform (200 ml); acetone for rinsing; large bottle for disposal of waste solutions.

REFERENCES

1. W. J. Moore, "Physical Chemistry," 2d ed., chap. 5, Prentice-Hall, Englewood Cliffs, N.J. (1955).
2. A. A. Noyes and M. S. Sherrill, "A Course of Study in Chemical Principles," 2d ed., p. 260, Macmillan, New York (1938).
3. A. J. Teller, *Chem. Eng.,* **61,** 168 (1954).
4. L. H. Horsley, "Azeotropic Data" (No. 6 of "Advances in Chemistry"), American Chemical Society, Washington (1952).
5. J. C. Chu, S. L. Wang, S. L. Levy, and R. Paul, "Vapor-Liquid Equilibrium Data," Edwards, Ann Arbor, Mich. (1956).

GENERAL READING

A. Findlay, "The Phase Rule and its Applications," 9th ed. (by A. N. Campbell and N. O. Smith), Dover, New York (1951).

C. S. Robinson and E. R. Gilliland, "Elements of Fractional Distillation," 4th ed., McGraw-Hill, New York (1950).

E. Hála, J. Pick, V. Fried, and O. Vitím (translated by G. Standart), "Vapour-Liquid Equilibrium," Pergamon Press, New York (1958).

Experiment 19. Binary Solid-Liquid Phase Diagram

In this experiment we are concerned with the heterogeneous equilibrium between solid and liquid phases in a two-component system. From the many systems[1, 2, 3] that are suitable for study, the system naphthalene-diphenylamine has been selected for this experiment because of the simplicity of its phase diagram and the convenience of its temperature range.

THEORY

The principles underlying this experiment are identical with those discussed in Exp. 18. For our discussion here we can merely replace *L* (liquid) in that experiment by *S* (solid) and *V* (vapor) by *L* (liquid). Solid-liquid equilibria differ from liquid-vapor equilibria in being essentially independent of pressure changes of the order of a few atmospheres. This is a consequence of the Clapeyron equation, Eq. (17-3), owing to the small molar volume change associated with fusion. Accordingly we shall be concerned only with temperature-composition diagrams at 1 atm pressure.

All types of phase diagrams that have been found for liquid-vapor equilibria are also possible for solid-liquid equilibria. (The reverse of this statement, however, is not true.) In some binary systems (particularly metal systems) the two components may form *solid solutions,* sometimes covering the entire composition range from pure *A* to pure *B*. Examples of systems with solid solutions covering the entire range include copper-nickel,[4] which has a phase diagram of the type shown in Fig. 18-3, with a nearly linear dependence of melting point on composition; *d*- and *l*-carvoxime ($C_{10}H_{14}NOH$),[5] which has a maximum melting point (analogous to the maximum boiling point shown in Fig. 18-2*b*); and bromobenzene-iodobenzene,[6] which has a minimum melting point (analogous to Fig. 18-2*a*). An important condition for the existence of a complete range of solid solutions is that *A* and *B* have the same type of crystal structure. The solid solutions must also have the same crystal structure as *A* and *B*, the atomic sites being occupied largely at random by the two kinds of atoms or molecules.

More often when solid solutions exist, they are limited in the range of their compositions. This may result from a difference between the crystal structures of pure *A* and pure *B*, or from differences in atomic or molecular size and shape resulting in "lattice incompatibility," or from factors analogous to those resulting in strong positive deviations from Raoult's law in liquids, or from any combination of these. Thus we may have two solid solutions at equilibrium, one (α) consisting predominantly of component *A* and the other (β) consisting predominantly of component *B*. These phases are often described as a solid solution of *B* in *A* and one of *A* in *B*, respectively.

Solid-liquid equilibria in a system of limited solid solubilities may yield a phase diagram of the type shown in Fig. 1. For this diagram, the compositions of the two phases (α and β, α and *L*, or β and *L*) coexisting at equilibrium at a given temperature and 1 atm pressure are found in the same way as in Exp. 18. A new feature is the possibility of the coexistence, at equilibrium, of three phases: α, β, and *L*. According to the phase rule, Eq. (18-1), with two components and three phases there is but one degree of freedom, and that is taken up in the arbitrary specifica-

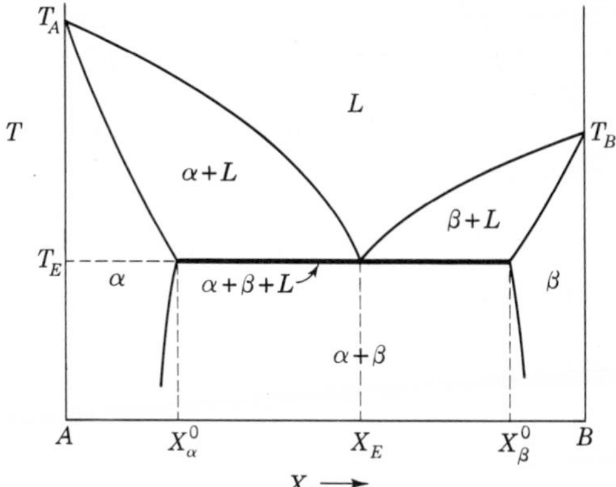

FIG. 1. Schematic solid-liquid phase diagram at 1 atm for a binary system with limited solid solubilities and no compound formation.

tion of the pressure as 1 atm. Thus the temperature is fixed (T_E) and the compositions of all phases are fixed ($X_B = X_\alpha{}^0, X_\beta{}^0, X_E$). A system of three phases coexisting at equilibrium is represented by any point on the heavy solid horizontal line of Fig. 1. The point T_E, X_E is called the "eutectic point"; its significance will be discussed later. Diagrams of the kind shown in Fig. 1, exhibiting limited solid solubility, exist for many systems, including azobenzene-azoxybenzene,[7] bismuth-tin, and lead-tin.

Very commonly, particularly in organic systems, where a high degree of lattice incompatibility is almost always present, solid solubility is so small that it may be regarded as negligible. Here the solid-solution regions α and β shrink to the vertical lines A and B and the type of phase diagram shown in Fig. 2*a* is obtained. The principal features of this type of diagram can be understood at least semiquantitatively from the theory of freezing-point depression. (It will be recalled that an essential requirement for the theory of freezing-point depression developed in Exp. 13 is the absence of appreciable solid solubility.) From Eq. (13-5) we obtain the

FIG. 2. (*a*) Schematic solid-liquid phase diagram at 1 atm for a binary system with negligible solid solubilities and no compound formation. (*b*) Schematic cooling curves for this system at various over-all compositions.

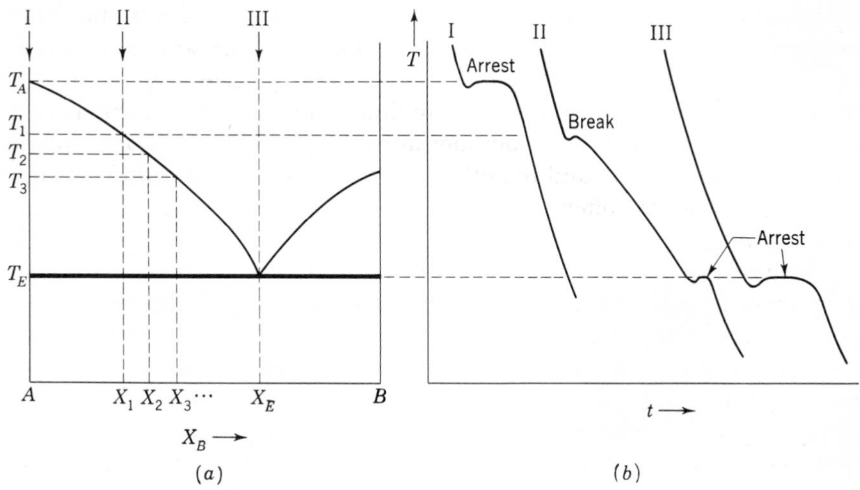

following equation for the solid-liquid curve ("liquidus curve") starting from the left at T_A, the melting point of A:

$$T \cong T_A + \frac{RT_A{}^2}{\Delta \tilde{H}_A} \ln (1 - X_B) = T_A - \frac{RT_A{}^2}{\Delta \tilde{H}_A} (X_B + \frac{X_B{}^2}{2} + \cdots) \qquad (1)$$

where $\Delta \tilde{H}_A$ is the heat of fusion of A. Clearly this curve starts with a finite negative slope determined by the melting point and heat of fusion of pure component A; the slope increases in steepness with increasing X_B, so that the curve is convex upward. Similarly, for the liquidus curve starting from the right at T_B we obtain

$$T \cong T_B + \frac{RT_B{}^2}{\Delta \tilde{H}_B} \ln X_B = T_B - \frac{RT_B{}^2}{\Delta \tilde{H}_B} [(1 - X_B) + \frac{(1 - X_B)^2}{2} + \cdots] \quad (2)$$

The eutectic composition and eutectic temperature are given by the intersection of the two liquidus curves and can be estimated by solving simultaneously Eqs. (1) and (2), on the assumption that the liquid represents an ideal solution with respect to both components over its entire composition range. This assumption is often not even roughly valid, especially in metal systems.

With the aid of Fig. 2*a* we can predict the general nature of the cooling curves in a system of this kind. These curves, examples of which are shown in Fig. 2*b*, are plots of temperature against time obtained when liquid solutions of various compositions are allowed to cool by slow leakage of heat to the surroundings; some features of such curves are discussed in Exp. 13. When a liquid consisting of pure A is cooled, the temperature falls until solid A begins to form; the temperature then remains constant until solidification is complete, whereupon it falls again. Thus, the curve shows a "thermal arrest." While two phases are present in this one-component system, there is only one degree of freedom, which is taken up in the arbitrary specification of the pressure, and the temperature is fixed. When a liquid having the eutectic composition is cooled, the behavior is similar in that a thermal arrest is obtained. Although the number of components is increased from one to two, the number of phases at the eutectic point is increased from two to three, and again we have a single degree of freedom which is taken up in the arbitrary specification of the pressure. When a liquid of some other composition—say X_1 in Fig. 2*a*—is cooled, solid A begins to form at temperature T_1. This tends to deplete the liquid of component A, so that its composition passes through X_2, X_3, . . . , and the temperature falls as long as solid A alone continues to come out of solution. With two components and two phases there are two degrees of freedom; thus, at constant pressure the temperature is not fixed but varies with the composition of the liquid. However, the slope of the cooling curve is much less than that for cooling of a single phase, owing to the heat liberated by the formation of solid A; see Eqs. (13-24) and (13-25). The abrupt change in slope, which occurs when solid A begins to form, is called a "break." When the composition of the solution finally reaches X_E, solid B begins to form together with solid A, and the two solids continue to separate from solution at the temperature T_E until no liquid remains; thus we have an arrest.

It is beyond the scope of this book to consider all possible types of solid-liquid binary phase diagrams. It will suffice here to mention two other important features, which arise when A and B can combine to form a solid compound of some stoichiometric composition A_mB_n or a solid solution varying in some degree from such

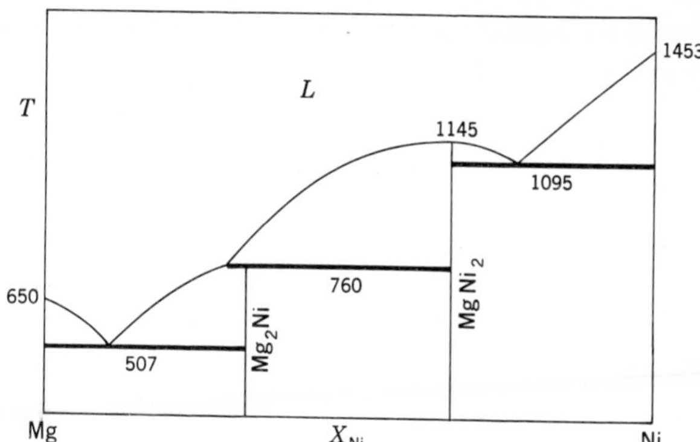

FIG. 3. Phase diagram for the system Mg-Ni at 1 atm.

a composition. Usually this compound or solid solution will differ in crystal structure both from *A* and from *B*. In Fig. 3 the phase diagram for the system Mg-Ni is shown. There are two solid compounds, Mg_2Ni and $MgNi_2$, with no appreciable solid solubility. The compound $MgNi_2$ has a sharp melting point and melts to give a liquid of the same composition. The liquidus curve has a maximum (horizontal tangent, no cusp) at this composition. The compound Mg_2Ni does not melt in this way; instead it undergoes a decomposition, or "peritectic transformation," to another solid phase, namely, $MgNi_2$, and to a liquid poorer in Ni than was the original compound. During this transformation, three phases are present—liquid, Mg_2Ni, and $MgNi_2$—and the temperature (at 1 atm) is therefore fixed. Some binary phase diagrams, particularly in metal systems, are exceedingly complicated and show many distinct compounds or phases.[1]

METHOD

The relation of cooling curves to phase diagrams (as illustrated by Fig. 2) forms the basis of "thermal analysis," an important technique for determining phase diagrams. This technique consists of cooling liquid mixtures of various compositions, making plots of temperature against time, and drawing inferences from features of these curves such as thermal arrests and breaks. A thermal arrest indicates the solidification temperature of a pure component, a compound, or a eutectic mixture (under favorable circumstances it may also indicate a peritectic transformation). A break indicates a point on the liquidus curve, corresponding to the temperature at which solid first appears at the given composition.

The interpretation of such curves is often subject to experimental difficulties. A frequent difficulty is supercooling (see Fig. 13-3), which tends to obscure breaks or make them difficult to distinguish from short arrests. When the initial composition is far from the eutectic, the thermal arrest at the eutectic temperature is often hard to observe, since the amount of liquid is small relative to the amount of solid already formed and stirring becomes very difficult. When solid solubility exists, it is often very difficult to obtain the true "solidus" curve from cooling curves. This is owing to the difficulty of maintaining solid-liquid equilibrium, which requires a continuous variation in the composition of the solid. As such a variation requires either diffusion in the solid or continuous dissolution and reprecipitation of the solid, it is ordinarily very slow or nonexistent except at elevated temperatures. Owing to these difficulties, thermal analysis must often be supplemented by other techniques in elucidating a phase diagram; these include microscopic examination of solidified specimens (to determine the number of solid phases present or to distinguish regions of small crystals that form at the eutectic temperature from regions of larger crystals that form while only one solid phase is precipitating) and X-ray diffraction analysis (which enables identification of the crystalline phases that are present).

For the system naphthalene-diphenylamine, a reasonable number of cooling curves can be easily obtained using either a mercury thermometer or a thermocouple to measure the temperature. Systems with phase diagrams of greater complexity, such as phenol-α-naphthylamine, require a larger number of cooling curves; in this case, it may be necessary to assign different composition ranges to several groups who will pool their data. Work at higher temperatures on systems such as lead-tin or bismuth-tin involves no basic change in the experimental method, although some changes in the experimental arrangement may be made for convenience.[8] Low-temperature work on systems such as chlorobenzene-cyanobenzene requires a refrigerant bath (see Chap. XVI for details about several such baths). Use of a thermocouple is recommended for both high- and low-temperature systems.

EXPERIMENTAL

The materials to be used should be of reagent grade. Diphenylamine is subject to discoloration resulting from air oxidation; it should preferably be obtained in containers packed in an argon atmosphere and should be taken from a freshly opened container.

The apparatus consists of an inner test tube with a 20-ml capacity, a thermometer or thermocouple mounted in a notched one-hole rubber stopper fitting the test tube, a wire stirrer, a larger test tube to serve as an outer jacket, a large one-hole rubber stopper to support the inner test tube in the outer one, and a bath of cold water or ice and water. If a 0 to 100°C thermometer is used, it should have a stem long enough to permit all readings above 25°C to be visible above the stopper. If a thermocouple (such as copper-constantan or chromel-alumel) is used, the junction should be immersed in wax or oil at the bottom of a closed glass tube 6 to 8 mm in diameter. This tube can be mounted in the stopper in the same way as a thermometer. The reference junction should be in a similar tube immersed in a slushy mixture of ice and distilled water contained in a Dewar flask, and the thermoelectric potential should be measured with a potentiometer (see Chap. XV).

Make up mixtures in accordance with Table 1. Weigh materials to 0.01 g on a triple-beam balance. Note that in most instances the mixture to be studied is

TABLE 1. Suggested Compositions for Thermal Analysis
(A = diphenylamine; B = naphthalene)

Run No.	Wt. % B	Prepare by adding . . .	. . . to sample used in run No.
1	100	5 g B	
2	83.3	1 g A	1
3	66.7	1.5 g A	2
4	50.0	2.5 g A	3
5	33.3	5 g A	4
6	0	5 g A	
7	16.7	1 g B	6
8	25.0	0.67g B	7
9	Eutectic	(See text)	

made by adding A or B to the previous mixture in order to minimize the quantities of materials required.

To obtain a cooling curve, heat the inner test tube containing the mixture in a beaker of hot water until the solid is completely melted, wipe the tube dry, place it in the outer jacket, and place the assembly in cold water or ice and water. Stir continuously, and read the temperature at regular intervals (say 30 sec). Continue readings to below 30° if possible.†

Plot each temperature reading against time as soon as it is obtained. After each run determine break and/or arrest temperatures and plot them against weight per cent B. From the results of runs 1 through 8 draw the liquidus curves and extrapolate them to an intersection at a point on the eutectic line. Determine the eutectic composition, and make up a mixture having this composition. Run a cooling curve on this mixture.

At the end of the experiment dispose of the mixtures and clean the glassware thoroughly. First liquefy the mixture by warming the test tube in a beaker of warm water, and then pour the contents into a designated disposal container. Remove the large rubber stopper, and wash the test tube, thermometer, and stirrer with benzene or toluene. Use several small portions in succession in order to minimize the amount of solvent required, and pour the used solvent into the designated container. Dry the apparatus.

CALCULATIONS

Convert weight-per cent compositions to mole fractions. Plot the break and arrest temperatures against the over-all composition X_B. Draw the eutectic line and the liquidus curves. Label all fields to show the phases present.

From the limiting slopes of the liquidus curves estimate the heats of fusion of A and B, assuming that there is no appreciable solid solubility. With these values for the heats of fusion plot ideal curves using Eqs. (1) and (2). Compare the calculated intersection temperature and composition with the eutectic temperature and composition found by experiment.

DISCUSSION

Why does the liquidus curve have a horizontal tangent at the melting point of a pure compound while it has a finite slope at the melting point of either of the two pure components?

A method sometimes used for obtaining the liquidus curve in a system of sufficient optical transparency is the determination of the "clear point" (the temperature at which the last solid disappears on warming) and of the "cloud point" (the temperature at which the first solid appears on cooling) for each of a number of compositions. What would you expect to be the limitations of this procedure?

APPARATUS

Test tube with notched one-hole stopper; 0 to 100° thermometer (all the stem above 25° should be above the stopper); wire ring stirrer; outer test tube with large stopper (see Exp. 13

† If time is limited, discontinue the cooling on all runs except 4, 8, and 9 shortly after the first definite break has occurred.

for above items); two 500-ml beakers; bunsen burner; tripod and wire gauze. A thermocouple with potentiometer and a small Dewar flask for the reference junction may be provided in place of the thermometer.

Diphenylamine (30 g); naphthalene (15 g); benzene or toluene (for washing glassware); ice (if needed for cold junction); waste vessel.

REFERENCES

1. M. Hansen, "Constitution of Binary Alloys," McGraw-Hill, New York (1958).
2. J. Timmermans, "Les Solutions concentrées," Masson et Cie, Paris (1936).
3. International Critical Tables (I.C.T.), vols. II (pp. 400–455) and IV (pp. 22–215), McGraw-Hill, New York (1928).
4. M. Hansen, *op. cit.,* p. 602.
5. J. Timmermans, *op. cit.,* p. 30.
6. *Ibid.,* p. 88.
7. *Ibid.,* p. 348.
8. F. Daniels, J. H. Mathews, J. W. Williams, P. Bender, and R. A. Alberty, "Experimental Physical Chemistry," 5th ed., pp. 108–115, McGraw-Hill, New York (1956).

Experiment 20. Chemical Equilibrium in Solution

In this experiment a typical homogeneous equilibrium in aqueous solution is investigated and the validity of the law of mass action is demonstrated. The equilibrium to be studied is that which arises when iodine is dissolved in aqueous KI solutions:

$$I_2 + I^- = I_3^- \tag{1}$$

In determining the concentrations of the species present at equilibrium in the aqueous solution use is made of a heterogeneous equilibrium: the distribution of molecular iodine I_2 between two immiscible solvents, water and carbon tetrachloride.

THEORY

Homogeneous Equilibrium. The thermodynamically exact equilibrium constant K_a (which must be expressed in terms of the activities of the chemical species involved) may be given to a good approximation in the case of the present reaction by the analogous expression involving concentrations.

$$K_a = \frac{a_{I_3^-}}{a_{I_2}a_{I^-}} = \frac{(I_3^-)}{(I_2)(I^-)}\,\frac{\gamma_{I_3^-}}{\gamma_{I_2}\gamma_{I^-}} \cong \frac{(I_3^-)}{(I_2)(I^-)} = K_c \tag{2}$$

where the a's are activities, the γ's are activity coefficients, K_c is the equilibrium constant in terms of concentration, and the parentheses denote concentrations in moles per liter. A commonly used approximate form of the Debye-Hückel theory for the activity coefficients of ionic species[1] is

$$\log \gamma_i = -0.509 z_i^2 \frac{\sqrt{\mu}}{1 + \sqrt{\mu}} \tag{3}$$

Since both I^- and I_3^- have the same charge z and are influenced by the same ionic strength μ, the activity coefficients γ_{I^-} and $\gamma_{I_3^-}$ are equal within the accuracy of Eq. (3). It should, however, be pointed out that Eq. (3) does not take account of variations in size and shape of ions. Also the I_2 concentration in aqueous solution is very small; thus γ_{I_2} is approximately unity, since the activity coefficient of a neutral solute species in dilute solution does not deviate greatly from its limiting value at infinite dilution. Therefore, the approximation given in Eq. (2) may be expected to be good to the order of 1 per cent or better in moderately dilute solutions, and K_c should be a constant independent of the concentrations of the species.

If, then, one starts with a solution of KI whose concentration C is known accurately and dissolves in it iodine, at equilibrium the iodine will be present partly as I_2 molecules and partly as I_3^- ions (a part of the I^- ions initially present having reacted to form the I_3^- ions). The total iodine concentration, $T = (I_2) + (I_3^-)$, can be found by titration with standard thiosulfate solution. If at equilibrium there is a way of measuring (I_2) separately, then K_c can be calculated, since

$$(I_3^-) = T - (I_2) \tag{4}$$

and

$$(I^-) = C - (I_3^-) \tag{5}$$

We can measure (I_2) at equilibrium by taking advantage of the fact that CCl_4, which is immiscible with aqueous solutions, dissolves molecular I_2 but not any of the ionic species involved.

Heterogeneous Equilibrium. We are concerned here with the distribution of molecular iodine I_2 as the solute between two immiscible liquid phases, aqueous solution and CCl_4. At equilibrium, the concentrations of I_2 in the two phases, $(I_2)_w$ and $(I_2)_{CCl_4}$, are related by a distribution constant k:

$$k = \frac{(I_2)_w}{(I_2)_{CCl_4}} \tag{6}$$

This distribution law applies only to the distribution of a definite chemical species, as does Henry's law. The distribution constant k is not a true thermodynamic equilibrium constant, since it involves concentrations rather than activities. Thus it may vary slightly with the concentration of the solute (particularly because of the relatively high concentration of I_2 in the CCl_4 phase); it is therefore advantageous to determine k at a number of concentrations. It can be determined directly by titration of both phases with standard thiosulfate solution when I_2 is distributed between CCl_4 and pure water. Once k is known, (I_2) in an aqueous phase containing I_3^- can be obtained by means of a titration of the I_2 in a CCl_4 layer that has been equilibrated with this phase. The use of a distribution constant in this manner depends upon the assumption that its value is unaffected by the presence of ions in the aqueous phase.

EXPERIMENTAL

Distribution Ratio. Measure the distribution constant $k = (I_2)_w/(I_2)_{CCl_4}$, using CCl_4 and pure H_2O as solvents and I_2 as solute. Distilled water (200 ml) and solutions of I_2 in CCl_4 (50 ml) should be put into 500-ml glass-stoppered erlenmeyer flasks and equilibrated with frequent shaking at 25°C. The quantities to use are given in Table 1 (runs 1 to 3); three sets of conditions are used in order to check the variation of the distribution constant with concentration. The flasks

TABLE 1[a]

Run No.	CCl_4 layer (50 ml), molarity I_2	Aqueous layer (200 ml), molarity KI	CCl_4 layer (Use 20-ml pipette)		Aqueous layer (Use 50-ml pipette)	
			Burette size, ml	Molarity $S_2O_3^=$	Burette size, ml	Molarity $S_2O_3^=$
1	0.080	0.0	50	0.1	10	0.01
2	0.040	0.0	50	0.1	10	0.01
3	0.020	0.0	10	0.1	10	0.01
4	0.080	0.15	10	0.1	50	0.1
5	0.040	0.15	10	0.1	10	0.1
6	0.080	0.03	50	0.1	10	0.1

[a] The table shows the nominal *initial* concentrations and volumes of the aqueous Kl solutions and of the solutions of I_2 in CCl_4 to be used. Also given are the nominal concentrations of the thiosulfate solutions to be used for titrating and the sizes of burettes and pipettes to be used. The *actual,* precise concentrations of the solutions used should be read from the labels on the respective bottles.

containing the solutions should be vigorously shaken for 5 min and clamped in a thermostat bath. After 10 min of thermal equilibration, remove the flasks one at a time, wrap them in a dry towel, shake them vigorously for 3 to 5 min, and then return to the thermostat bath. Repeat this procedure for at least an hour. Before removing samples for analysis let the flasks remain in the bath for 10 min after the last shaking to allow the liquid layers to separate completely. After equilibration is complete, remove one flask at a time from the thermostat bath and place in a battery jar containing water at 25°C as shown in Fig. 1. A sample of the aqueous layer and a sample of the CCl_4 layer are removed with pipettes, and the flask is stoppered and returned to the bath for an additional half hour of the above treatment, after which a second sample of each phase is removed for titration. Additional information is given in Table 1.

The purpose of taking a second sample after further equilibration is to verify that equilibrium has been achieved. If the two titrations are in substantial agreement, the average value can be used. If the results of the titrations indicate that equilibrium had not been reached when the first samples were taken, the results of the second titrations should be used although proof of equilibrium is in this case lacking.

In removing the samples for titration, it is important to avoid contamination of the sample by drops of the other phase, especially when the other phase is very much more concentrated as is the CCl_4 layer in this case. When pipetting samples of the CCl_4 solutions, blow a slow stream of air through the pipette while it is being introduced into the solution in order to minimize the contamination by the aqueous layer. It is advisable to use a rubber bulb with the pipette for these solutions; do not pipette by mouth. Between samples rinse the pipette well with acetone and dry it before taking the next sample.

Each sample is transferred from the pipette to a 250-ml erlenmeyer flask containing 10 ml of 0.1 *N* KI and titrated with the appropriate thiosulfate solution (see Table 1). The iodide is added to reduce loss of I_2 from the aqueous solution by evaporation during the titration, by forming the nonvolatile I_3^-. The reaction taking place during the titration is

$$2S_2O_3^= + I_3^- \rightarrow S_4O_6^= + 3I^-$$

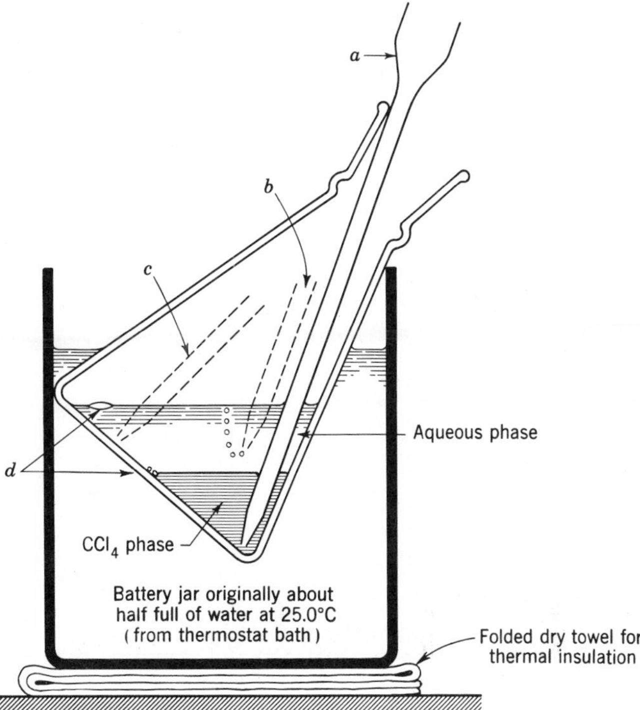

FIG. 1. Arrangement for withdrawing samples. Use a rubber bulb for drawing up liquid in the pipette. (*a*) Position of pipette for withdrawing sample of CCl_4 phase. Tip should touch bottom at deepest point and should not be moved around. (*b*) On inserting pipette, blow *small* stream of air to keep aqueous phase from entering tip. (*c*) Position of pipette for withdrawing aqueous sample. (*d*) On inserting pipette, avoid contact with drops of CCl_4 phase (spheres on bottom or lenses floating on top).

Near the end point, as indicated by a very light yellow color of aqueous iodine solution, 1 ml of starch solution is added; this acts as an indicator by adsorbing iodine and giving a deep blue color. At the end point this blue color disappears sharply. If the starch has been added too soon, the color may slowly redevelop after an apparent end point owing to diffusion of iodine from the interior of the colloidal starch particles; the titration should always be continued until no blue color reappears. In the two-phase titration, shake the flask vigorously after adding each portion of thiosulfate solution.

If desired, an excellent end point for the two-phase titration can be taken as the disappearance of the reddish-violet iodine color from the CCl_4 layer. This may even be done in the titration of the aqueous sample by adding 1 or 2 ml of pure CCl_4. In this case, do not add the starch indicator.

It is recommended that a practice titration be performed with one of the stock solutions of I_2 in CCl_4.

Equilibrium Constant. To determine the concentrations of I_2 and I_3^- in equilibrium in aqueous solutions we equilibrate aqueous KI solutions (200 ml) with solutions of I_2 in CCl_4 (50 ml) as shown in Table 1 (runs 4 to 6). The equilibration and titration procedures are identical with those described above; additional information is given in Table 1. With the distribution constant determined above and the initial I^- concentration, the equilibrium concentrations of I_2, I_3^-, and I^- can be calculated.

Adequate time for equilibration is of great importance; the flasks should be placed in the thermostat bath as soon as possible. The temperature of the thermostat bath should be checked several times throughout the equilibration.

CALCULATIONS

Calculate the distribution constant k from the results of runs 1 to 3. If more than one run was performed, plot k vs. the iodine concentration in the CCl_4 solution, $(I_2)_{CCl_4}$. If k is not constant, discuss its variation with concentration.

Using Eqs. (4), (5), and (6) and the results of runs 4 to 6, calculate the equilibrium concentrations of I_2, I_3^-, and I^- in each of the aqueous solutions. In each case use the appropriate value of k as read from the smooth curve of k vs. $(I_2)_{CCl_4}$. Calculate the equilibrium constant K_c for each run. If any variation of K_c with concentration is found, do you regard it as experimentally significant?

APPARATUS

Three to six 500-ml glass-stoppered erlenmeyer flasks; 1-qt battery jar or 1500-ml beaker; three pipettes—20, 50, 100 (or 200) ml; one 10- and one 50-ml burette; six 250-ml erlenmeyer flasks; 10-ml graduated cylinder; three 250-ml beakers; burette clamp and stand; large rubber bulb for pipetting; wash bottle.

Constant-temperature bath set at 25°C; bath clamps for holding 500-ml erlenmeyer flasks; pure CCl_4; acetone for rinsing; large carboy for waste liquids. Solutions: 0.08 M solution of I_2 in CCl_4 (300 ml); 0.04 M I_2 in CCl_4 (250 ml); 0.02 M I_2 in CCl_4 (100 ml); 0.15 M KI solution (800 ml); 0.03 M KI solution (400 ml); 0.1 M $Na_2S_2O_3$ solution (500 ml); 0.01 M $Na_2S_2O_3$ solution (100 ml); approximately 0.1 M KI solution (500 ml); 0.2 per cent soluble starch solution, containing a trace of HgI_2 as preservative (50 ml).

REFERENCE

1. W. J. Moore, "Physical Chemistry," 2d ed., Prentice-Hall, Englewood Cliffs, N.J. (1955).

GENERAL READING

G. N. Lewis and M. Randall (revised by K. S. Pitzer and L. Brewer), "Thermodynamics," 2d ed., McGraw-Hill, New York (1961).

L. C. Craig and D. Craig, Extraction and Distribution, in A. Weissberger (ed.), "Technique of Organic Chemistry," vol. III, Interscience, New York (1950).

VIII

ELECTROCHEMISTRY

EXPERIMENTS

Experiment 21. Transference of Ions: Moving-boundary Method

When electric current is passed through a solution, the fraction of the current carried by each migrating ion is called the transference number of that ion. A very generally applicable technique for measuring these transference numbers is the Hittorf method, in which the net change in the content of a particular ion in an anode or cathode region is determined by chemical analysis. Details of the Hittorf method are described elsewhere.[1] In this experiment, the *moving-boundary method*[2] is used to study an aqueous solution of HCl. Although more limited in applicability, this method has the great advantage of providing good precision and a direct visual indication of the motion of an ionic species in solution.

THEORY AND METHOD

Let the transference number of H^+ and Cl^- ions in aqueous HCl solution be denoted by T_H and T_{Cl}, respectively. Consider a vertical tube of uniform cross section, with electric current flowing upward. For every N faradays of electricity that pass a given stationary horizontal plane in the tube, NT_H equivalents of H^+ pass this plane going upward and NT_{Cl} equivalents of Cl^- pass the plane going downward.

If there existed in the tube a definite lower boundary below which H^+ ions were absent (some other cation being present instead), this boundary would move upward as the H^+ ions move upward. The position of the boundary may be determined as the position at which there is a difference in some property of the solution such as pH (shown by an indicator previously added to the HCl solution) or index of refraction. Under proper conditions the boundary remains sharp, the composition of the solution above the boundary remains uniform, and the mean velocity of upward migration of the H^+ ions may be taken as equal to the observed upward velocity of the boundary.

When the boundary sweeps through some volume V in a given time t, a number of equivalents of H^+ ion equal to the number contained in such a volume passes through a given fixed horizontal plane during that time. If the total electric current flowing upward through the tube has the constant value of i amp during this time, this number of H^+ ions is equal to NT_{H} or $(it/\mathcal{F})T_{\mathrm{H}}$. Therefore,

$$\frac{Vc_+}{1000} = N_{\mathrm{H}} = NT_{\mathrm{H}} = \frac{itT_{\mathrm{H}}}{\mathcal{F}} \tag{1}$$

where c_+ is the concentration of H^+ ions in *equivalents* per liter, V is the volume in milliliters swept through by the boundary in t sec, and $\mathcal{F}$ is the Faraday constant. Equation (1) can be written as

$$T_{\mathrm{H}} = \frac{\mathcal{F}c_+}{1000i}\,\frac{dV}{dt} \tag{2}$$

in the more general case in which i is not necessarily constant. In very precise measurements, it is necessary to correct the transference number calculated from Eq. (2) by taking account of volume changes (caused by electrode reactions and ionic migration) which produce a motion of the solvent relative to the tube.[3]

The transference number of the chloride ion (if it is the only other ion present above the boundary) can be determined from the relation

$$T_{\mathrm{H}} + T_{\mathrm{Cl}} = 1 \tag{3}$$

Conditions for Boundary Stability. The choice of the electrolyte below the boundary is governed by the necessity of maintaining the proper conditions for a stable, sharp boundary. In this experiment $CdCl_2$, generated at a cadmium anode at the bottom of the tube, is an electrolyte that satisfies these conditions. For a stable boundary there must be no tendency for mixing of the electrolytes. Convective mixing is avoided by having the heavier $CdCl_2$ solution lie below the HCl solution. It is also necessary that the effective mobility αU_+ (the migration velocity of the "ion constituent" under a unit potential gradient, α being the fraction ionized) be smaller for the lower cation Cd^{++} than for the upper cation H^+. It is then impossible for the lower cations to overtake the upper ones or for any significant amount of diffusive mixing to occur. If in the boundary region some mixing should happen to occur, the upper cations will move upward faster than the lower ones (both being affected, in this region, by the same potential gradient) and the boundary will be reestablished. In the present system this condition holds:

$$(\alpha U)_{\mathrm{Cd^{++}}} < (\alpha U)_{\mathrm{H^+}} \tag{4}$$

This inequality is largely due to the very high mobility of H^+ ions in aqueous solutions. In addition, the fraction ionized in the $CdCl_2$ solution is less than unity, while α for the HCl solution is essentially unity.

It is also necessary that the lower cation, in the solution just below the boundary, move upward with the same mean velocity as the upper cation. If there were a gap between the top of the lower cation region and the bottom of the upper cation region, the gap must be devoid of anions also, and thereby unable to carry current. Since the velocity of an ion, u_i, is given by

$$u_i = U_i \frac{dE}{dz} \tag{5}$$

where dE/dz is the potential gradient, we find that

$$U_{Cd^{++}} \frac{dE'}{dz} = U_{H^+} \frac{dE}{dz} \tag{6}$$

In the above, the prime indicates the value below the boundary. From Eqs. (4) and (6) it is seen that the potential gradient, which for a tube of uniform cross section is constant over a region of uniform composition, is different on the two sides of the boundary; indeed,

$$\frac{dE'}{dz} > \frac{dE}{dz} \tag{7}$$

Thus the solution below the boundary has the lower specific conductance (since $dE/dz = i/A\bar{L}$). Equation (7) shows that any H^+ ions which diffuse below the boundary not only will move faster than the Cd^{++} ions in that region due to Eq. (4) but will also move faster than H^+ ions above the boundary and will catch up with the boundary and keep it sharp. Also as the boundary moves upward, the potential difference over the entire cell, at constant current, increases; that is, the effective resistance of the cell increases. To enable constant current to be maintained, it is convenient to place a variable resistor in series with the cell.

EXPERIMENTAL

The transference cell, shown in Fig. 1, is constructed from a 1-ml Mohr capillary pipette, with a reservoir at the top and a metallic cadmium electrode which can be inserted at the bottom. The cell is surrounded by a jacket in which water should be placed to absorb the heat generated by the passage of electric current through the cell and thus prevent a significant rise in the temperature of the solution. The temperature of the jacket water should be checked occasionally during the run.

Into the reservoir at the top is introduced an Ag-AgCl electrode, made by anodizing a silver wire in HCl solution. This is surrounded around the sides and bottom by a glass cup, which serves the dual purpose of preventing AgCl particles from falling down into the capillary and of retarding the more concentrated HCl solution (accumulating by Hittorf transference at that electrode) from convectively mixing with the solution in the capillary.

The electrical circuit is shown in Fig. 2. The source of current is 110-v dc, which is controlled by a variable resistor. The current that passes through the cell also passes through a 1-ohm (nominal) standard resistor, the precise value of which

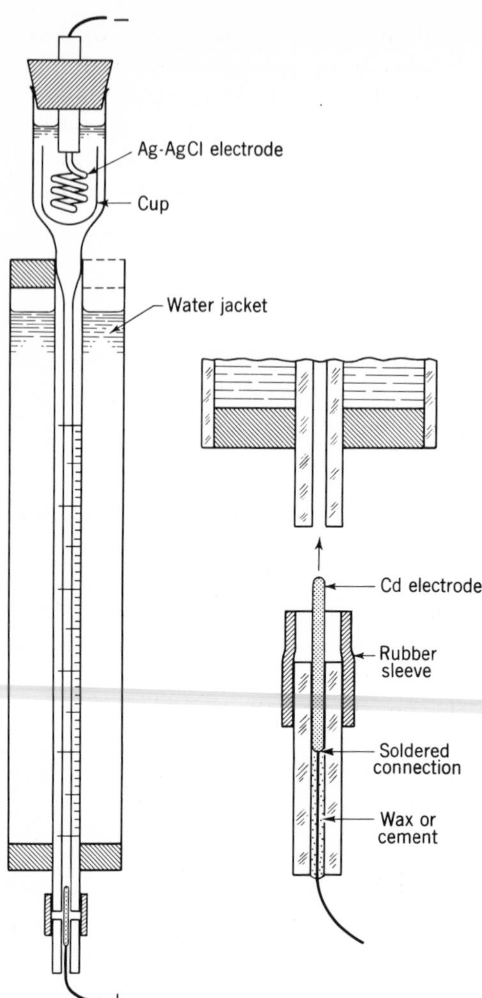

FIG. 1. Moving-boundary transference cell.

is known. The potential difference developed across this resistor is measured by use of a potentiometer. Because the potential to be measured is very small, a potentiometer circuit is used which differs from that usually employed in that the scale divisions are smaller by a factor of 100; this circuit is described in Chap. XV. *Thus the potentiometer readings must be multiplied by* 0.01 *to give the unknown potential in volts.*

Procedure. Set up the circuit as in Fig. 2. Do not connect the standard cell or plug into the dc mains until an instructor has checked your circuit. The switch on the dc control box should be **off,** and the $100K$ rheostat should be set at *maximum* resistance. Prepare the solution by pipetting 5.0 ml of bromphenol blue indicator solution into a 100-ml volumetric flask. Make up to the mark with 0.3 N HCl. Note the exact concentration of stock HCl solution, and calculate the concentration of H^+ in your solution. This solution will be yellow in color.

Remove the cadmium electrode from the bottom of the cell, clean the cell with detergent if necessary, rinse several times with distilled water, and *thoroughly* rinse with the HCl solution prepared above. Reinsert the cadmium electrode *carefully* and fill with a small amount of the HCl solution so that the meniscus is on scale in the capillary part of the cell. Dry the bottom of the cell around the cadmium electrode, and watch for several minutes to see if any leaks are present. A slow leak can be best observed by a change in level of the solution in the capillary. If no leaks are present, fill the cell to the top of the capillary with HCl solution. During filling, bubbles may be trapped in the capillary section. These can be removed easily with a length of thin plastic tubing. Insert the glass cup and add enough HCl solution to cover the rim of the cup, then insert the Ag-AgCl electrode. Fill the outer jacket with water at about 22°C. Avoid air bubbles on the walls of the water jacket, as they will make readings of the capillary scale more difficult.

Do not allow the Ag-AgCl electrode to become dry. When not in use, store it in the vial in which it was issued.

Connect the cell into the circuit and standardize the potentiometer. The DPDT knife switch should be in position *a* which connects the battery circuit to terminal 1 and connects the E^- terminal to the standard cell.

Plug into the 110-v dc line and turn on the switch. **While current is being passed through the cell, be careful of shock from any exposed contacts.**

To adjust to the desired current (ca. 4 ma) turn the DPDT knife switch to position *b* and the step switch to 0.4. It is convenient not to alter the setting of the slide-wire from that used in standardization; this facilitates rapid standardization checks throughout the run. Carefully decrease the resistance of the variable resistor until zero galvanometer deflection is obtained. Do not decrease the resistor setting more

FIG. 2. Electrical circuit for the moving-boundary cell. For galvanometer control unit (GCU) and potentiometer, see Chap. XV.

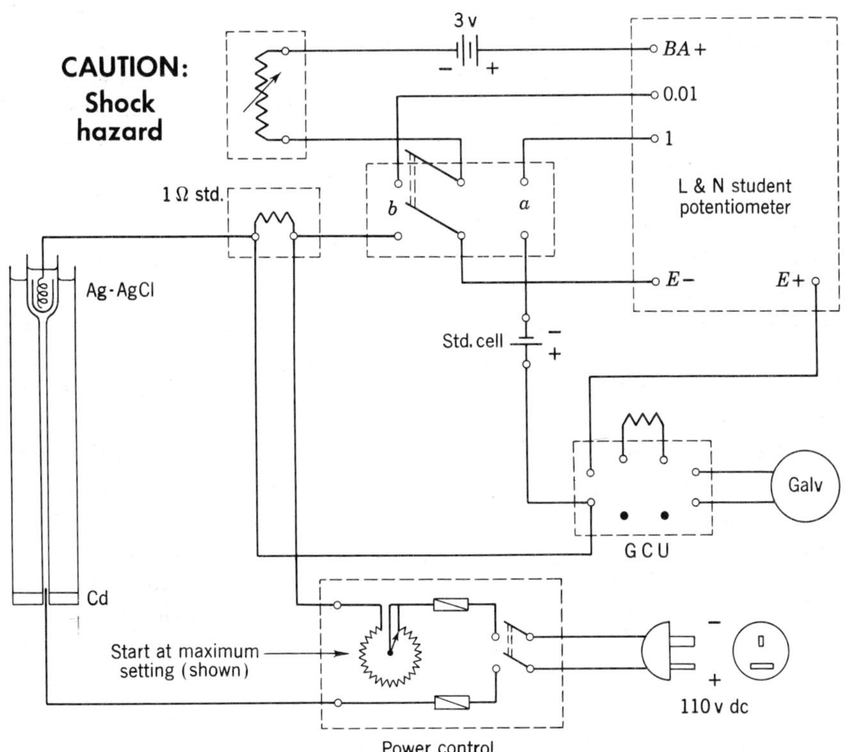

than halfway unless it is apparent that the galvanometer deflections are decreasing. It may be necessary to wait a few minutes before the cell resistance has increased enough to permit galvanometer balance to be achieved even at the maximum setting of the resistor.

The boundary should appear as a sharp line of demarcation between the yellow solution above and a pale blue solution below. A white background placed behind the jacket of the cell will make this boundary more clearly observable. When a satisfactory boundary is obtained and the current has the desired value, *continuously* maintain this current by manipulation of the rheostat and constant checking with the potentiometer. (Note that, if the current is adjusted only periodically, a "saw-tooth" variation will occur and give rise to a lower average current than that desired.) Occasionally restandardize the potentiometer against the standard cell. Record the time (to the nearest second) at which the boundary passes each 0.01-ml division on the pipette. Measure the temperature of the water in the jacket several times during the run. Terminate the run when the resistor reaches zero setting or the boundary goes off scale or after 40 min of taking data. Turn the dc switch off and pull out the plug.

Make a repeat run after rinsing and refilling the cell. To empty the cell, remove the Ag-AgCl electrode and glass cup, turn the cell upside down, then remove the Cd electrode, and let the cell drain.

When the experiment is finished, empty the cell and rinse thoroughly several times with distilled water, leaving the cell reasonably dry. Be sure to record the *complete* potentiometer setting and the precise value of the standard resistor. NOTE: If desired, this experiment can be performed without the use of an indicator. With good back-lighting there is a distinct, sharp boundary between the upper and lower solutions due to a difference in the indices of refraction. This can be seen best by moving the eye up and down until a reflection is seen from the boundary.

CALCULATIONS

Calculate the current i in amperes which was passed through the cell. Also plot the volume displacement of the boundary in milliliters vs. time in seconds. Draw the best straight line through these points and obtain the slope dV/dt. Using Eqs. (2) and (3), find T_H and T_{Cl} for the HCl concentration studied. Report the temperature range during the run.

DISCUSSION

Given the equivalent conductance Λ for 0.3 N HCl as 373 ohm^{-1} eqv^{-1} cm^2 at 25°C [4] and using your experimental transference numbers, calculate the ionic mobility for H^+ and Cl^- in 0.3 N HCl. Give the proper units for U_{H^+} and U_{Cl^-}.

In general, ion size and charge determine ionic mobilities, but U_{H^+} is abnormally large in aqueous solutions where H^+ is hydrated (conventionally written as H_3O^+). To account for this a special transport mechanism has been suggested[5] in which protons can *jump* from H_3O^+ to a neighboring H_2O solvent molecule:

$$\begin{matrix} & \text{H} & & & \text{H} & & & & \text{H} & & & \text{H} & \\ & | & \oplus & & | & & & & | & & & | & \oplus \\ \text{H—} & \text{O} & \text{—H} & & \text{O} & \text{—H} & \longrightarrow & \text{H—} & \text{O} & & \text{H—} & \text{O} & \text{—H} \end{matrix}$$

However, if the proton were to jump in random directions, the transport velocity would be slowed down as often as it would be speeded up. Can you suggest a reason to expect that these jumps will more often take place in the direction of the cathode?

APPARATUS

Complete potentiometer setup with high-sensitivity galvanometer (see Chap. XV); transference dc power-supply unit; transference cell (with jacket); small glass cup for top of cell; Ag-AgCl electrode; cadmium electrode with connector for attaching electrical leads; 20 electric leads with lugs; ring stand; large clamp and clamp holder; 100-ml volumetric flask; 5-ml pipette; 500- or 1000-ml beaker; 25°C thermometer (to fit jacket of cell); stopwatch or clock.

Emery paper to clean contacts; plastic "spaghetti." Solutions: 0.3 *N* HCl solution (150 ml), bromphenol blue indicator solution ($\sim$ 1 g liter^{-1}, 10 ml).

REFERENCES

1. J. R. Partington, in H. S. Taylor, "A Treatise on Physical Chemistry," vol. I, Van Nostrand, Princeton, N. J. (1931).
2. L. G. Longsworth, *J. Chem. Educ.,* **11,** 420 (1934); D. A. MacInnes and L. G. Longsworth, *Chem. Rev.,* **11,** 171 (1932).
3. H. S. Harned and B. B. Owen, "The Physical Chemistry of Electrolytic Solutions," 2d ed., p. 160, Reinhold, New York (1950).
4. B. B. Owen and F. H. Sweeton, *J. Am. Chem. Soc.,* **63,** 2811 (1941).
5. An excellent discussion and review of this topic are given by M. Eigen and L. De Maeyer in W. J. Hamer (ed.), "The Structure of Electrolytic Solutions," Wiley, New York (1959).

GENERAL READING

R. A. Robinson and R. H. Stokes, "Electrolyte Solutions," Academic Press, Inc., New York (1955).

H. S. Harned and B. B. Owen, *op cit.*

M. Spiro, Determination of Transference Numbers, in A. Weissberger (ed.), "Technique of Organic Chemistry," 3d ed., vol. I, part IV, chap. XLVI, Interscience, New York (1960).

Experiment 22. Conductance of Solutions

In this experiment we shall be concerned with electrical conduction through aqueous solutions. Although water is itself a very poor conductor of electricity, the presence of ionic species in solution increases the conductance considerably. The conductance of such electrolytic solutions depends on the concentration of the ions and also on the nature of the ions present (through their charges and mobilities), and conductance behavior as a function of concentration is different for strong and weak electrolytes. Both strong and weak electrolytes will be studied at a number of dilute concentrations, and from the data obtained the ionization constant for a weak electrolyte can be calculated.

THEORY

Electrolytic solutions obey Ohm's law just as metallic conductors do. Thus the current i passing through a given body of solution is proportional to the potential difference E; $E/i = R$, where R is the resistance of the body of solution in ohms. The *conductance* L is defined as the reciprocal of the resistance,

$$L = \frac{1}{R} \tag{1}$$

and is expressed in ohms^{-1}. The conductance of a homogeneous body of uniform cross section is proportional to the cross section A and inversely proportional to the length l:

$$L = \frac{\bar{L}A}{l} \quad \text{or} \quad \bar{L} = \frac{1}{R}\frac{l}{A} = \frac{k}{R} \tag{2}$$

where $\bar{L}$ is the *specific conductance* in ohm^{-1} cm^{-1}. The specific conductance is thus the reciprocal of the resistivity. The specific conductance of a solution in a cell of arbitrary design and dimensions can be obtained by first determining the cell constant k (the "effective" value of l/A) by measuring the resistance of a solution of known specific conductance. A standard solution that can be used for making this calibration is 0.02000 N potassium chloride, with $\bar{L}$ equal to 0.002768 ohm^{-1} cm^{-1} at 25°C.[1] Once the cell constant has been found, specific conductances can be calculated from the experimental resistances by using Eq. (2).

The specific conductance $\bar{L}$ depends on the equivalent concentrations and mobilities of the ions present. For a single electrolyte giving ions A^+ and B^- and having fractional ionization α at a solute concentration c in equivalents per liter, one obtains

$$\bar{L} = \frac{\alpha c \mathcal{F}}{1000}(U_{A^+} + U_{B^-}) \tag{3}$$

where the U's are the true ionic mobilities and $\mathcal{F}$ is the Faraday constant. Thus it is convenient to define a new quantity, the *equivalent conductance* Λ, by

$$\Lambda \equiv \frac{1000\bar{L}}{c} \tag{4}$$

Comparing Eqs. (3) and (4), we find that

$$\Lambda = \alpha \mathcal{F}(U_{A^+} + U_{B^-}) \tag{5}$$

This equivalent conductance is sometimes described as the actual conductance of that volume of solution which contains one equivalent weight of solute when placed between parallel electrodes 1 cm apart with a uniform electric field between them.

For a strong electrolyte, the fraction ionized is unity at all concentrations; thus Λ is roughly constant, varying to some extent owing to changes in mobilities with concentration but approaching a finite value Λ_0 at infinite dilution. From the effect of ion attraction on the mobilities, it can be shown theoretically[2] for strong electrolytes in dilute solution that

$$\Lambda = \Lambda_0(1 - \beta\sqrt{c}) \tag{6}$$

Using this relation, Λ_0 for strong electrolytes can be obtained experimentally from measurements of conductance as a function of concentration. At infinite dilution the ions act altogether independently, and it is then possible to express Λ_0 as the sum of the limiting conductances of the separate ions:

$$\Lambda_0 = \lambda_0^+ + \lambda_0^- \tag{7}$$

For a weakly ionized substance, Λ varies much more markedly with concentration because the degree of ionization α varies strongly with concentration. The equivalent conductance, however, must approach a constant finite value at infinite dilution, Λ_0, which again corresponds to the sum of the limiting ionic conductances. It is usually impractical to determine this limiting value from extrapolation of Λ values obtained with the weak electrolyte itself, since to obtain an approach to complete ionization the concentration must be made too small for effective measurement of conductance. However, Λ_0 for a weak electrolyte can be deduced from Λ_0 values obtained for *strong electrolytes* by the use of Eq. (7).

For sufficiently weak electrolytes, the ionic concentration is small and the effect of ion attraction on the mobilities is slight; thus we may assume the mobilities to be independent of concentration and obtain the approximate expression

$$\alpha \cong \frac{\Lambda}{\Lambda_0} \tag{8}$$

If one measures Λ for a weak electrolyte at a concentration c and calculates Λ_0 from the conductivity data for strong electrolytes as described above, it is possible to obtain the actual degree of ionization of the weak electrolyte at concentration c.

Equilibrium Constant for Weak Electrolyte. Knowing the concentration c of the weak electrolyte, say HAc, and its degree of ionization α at that concentration, the concentrations of H^+ and Ac^- ions and of un-ionized HAc can be calculated. Then the equilibrium constant in terms of concentrations K_c can be calculated from

$$K_c = \frac{(H^+)(Ac^-)}{(HAc)} = c\frac{\alpha^2}{1-\alpha} \tag{9}$$

This equilibrium constant K_c given by Eq. (9) using α values obtained from Eq. (8) differs from K_a, the equilibrium constant in terms of activities, by virtue of the omission of activity coefficients ($\gamma_\pm{}^2$) from the numerator of (9) and owing to the approximations inherent in (8). To an approximation which would be very rough at ordinary dilute concentrations but is fairly good at the very low ionic concentrations encountered in the dissociation of a weak electrolyte, the factors by which $\log K_c$ differs from $\log K_a$ are linear functions of the square root of the ionic strength.[3] We may here take the ionic strength to be αc. Thus, if $\log K_c$, as determined at a number of low concentrations, is plotted against $\sqrt{\alpha c}$, an extrapolation to $c = 0$ should give a fairly good value of $\log K_a$. However, reliable measurements at low concentrations are difficult to obtain.

METHOD

For determining ionic conductance by measuring the resistance of the solution in a conductivity cell, the use of dc circuitry is impractical, since the electrodes would quickly become "polarized"; that is, electrode reactions would take place which would set up an emf opposing the applied emf, leading to a spuriously high apparent cell resistance. Polarization can be prevented by (1) using a high (audio) frequency *alternating current,* so that the quantity of electricity carried during one half cycle is insufficient to produce any measurable polarization, and at the same time by (2) employing platinum electrodes covered with a colloidal deposit of "platinum black," having an extremely large surface area, to facilitate the adsorption of the tiny quantities of electrode reaction products produced in one-half cycle so that no measurable chemical emf is produced.

The resistance of a conductivity cell filled with an ionic solution can be measured accurately by use of a *Wheatstone-bridge* circuit employing high-frequency alternating current, where an audio oscillator is used as the source and where the detector is a telephone receiver or oscilloscope. A schematic diagram of an ac Wheatstone bridge and an analysis of the condition of balance are given in Chap. XV. In order for the resistance balance $R_1/R_2 = R_3/R_4$ to hold true, it is necessary that

$$\theta_1 = \theta_2 \qquad \text{and} \qquad \theta_3 = \theta_4 \tag{10}$$

where θ_i is the phase angle between the current and voltage in the ith arm of the bridge. The bridge arrangement to be used is shown in Fig. 1.

The arms R_3 and R_4 are the two parts of the slide-wire of a Student Potentiometer. There are two sets of connections to this slide-wire—L and H or L' and H'—which give R_3/R_4 equal to $A/(1000 - A)$ or $(4500 + A)/(5500 - A)$, respectively. These are the so-called short and long bridges and are shown schematically in Fig. 2*a* and *b*. The reading A is the number on the 0 to 100° scale of the slide-wire. Arm 1 contains the conductivity cell of resistance R, and arm 2 contains a

FIG. 1. Conductance bridge (long-bridge circuit shown).

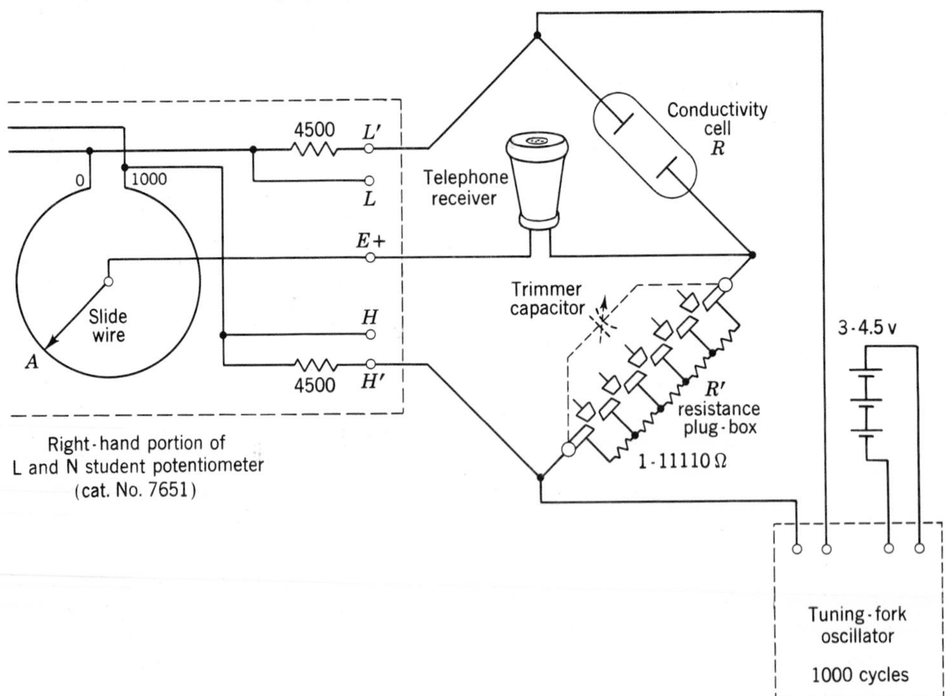

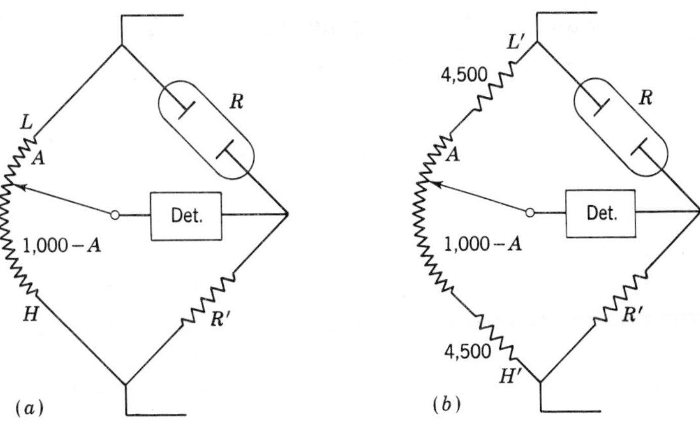

FIG. 2. (*a*) Short bridge: $R = R'[A/(1000 - A)]$
(*b*) Long bridge: $R = R'[(4500 + A)/(5500 - A)]$

precision plug box or decade resistor R'. Since the balance is always taken with A near 500, arms 3 and 4 are identical and $\theta_3 = \theta_4$ is assumed to hold. A trimmer capacitor may be placed across the plug box R' to balance the effective capacitance of the cell and make $\theta_1 = \theta_2$. Under the experimental conditions encountered here the reactances should be extremely small in comparison with the dc resistances. To a first approximation, a finite minimum signal in the detector may be taken to indicate the point of balance if a zero signal is not obtained. The capacitive reactance can then be effectively balanced with a trimmer capacitor if necessary, and a small adjustment then made to yield the final balance. In the present experiment a trimmer capacitor is seldom needed. In the case of a significant degree of polarization, very poor balance points are observed owing to large effective phase shifts resulting from severe distortion of the waveform.

EXPERIMENTAL

Set up the circuit as shown in Fig. 1, sandpapering all lugs before making connections. For short-bridge work, connect to terminals L and H on the potentiometer slide-wire. In this case the cell resistance R is given by

$$R = \frac{A}{1000 - A} R' \tag{11}$$

where A is the slide-wire reading and R' is the resistance of the resistance box. The short bridge is good for rapid, moderately precise work, but much greater accuracy can be obtained using the long-bridge setup. For long-bridge work, connect to terminals L' and H' on the potentiometer. In this case,

$$R = \frac{4500 + A}{5500 - A} R' \tag{12}$$

All possible measurements on solutions should be made with the long bridge. The short bridge is primarily of use in obtaining an approximate value of R. When this is known, the resistance box should be set to this value of R (or some round number within 5 per cent of R) and the long bridge used for a precise determination of the cell resistance.

In making connections to the resistance plug box, be sure that all connections are *tight*. Do not use terminals both as wire clamps and as binding posts for lugs at the same time. In using the plug box, remove plugs corresponding to the desired resistance. Each plug in place shorts out a resistance inside the box. Plugs not removed must be in tight; seat them with a strong twisting motion.

The ac source for the bridge may be a battery-operated tuning-fork oscillator which gives out a signal in the audio range (1000 cps). The power output from this oscillator can be varied by changing the voltage supplied by the batteries or by inserting a resistor in series with the bridge. The bridge should be operated with as low a power and for as short a time as possible to prevent polarization effects. Alternatively, a commercial electronic audio oscillator may be used.

Calibration Check. There may be a small calibration error in the slide-wire; that is, the position of the indicator may not correspond precisely to that of the contact on the slide-wire. This should be checked by replacing the cell in the bridge circuit with a second resistance box. Set both boxes to 1000 ohms and balance on the long bridge. If there is no error, the A reading should be exactly 500. To obtain a correction figure, make four readings of the balance point approaching zero or minimum hum twice from each side. Then reverse the position of the two plug boxes and take four more readings. Find the average of these values $\overline{A'}$. The correction term $(500 - \overline{A'})$ is to be *added* to all future long-bridge readings of A.

A satisfactory conductivity cell design is shown in Fig. 3. This cell is fragile and should be handled with care. The leads should be arranged to avoid placing any strain on the cell while it is mounted in the thermostat bath. The electrodes are sensitive to poisoning if very concentrated electrolytes are placed in the cell and to deterioration if allowed to become dry. After each emptying, the cell must be *immediately* rinsed or filled with water or solution. While the cell is in the bath, the filling arms must be stoppered by placing rubber policemen over the ends. If the cell is allowed to stand for any long time between runs, leave it filled with conductivity water rather than solution.

Draw liquid into the cell by sucking it in through the tapered tip as you would with a pipette. Empty the cell by allowing it to drain out the other end. The procedure for filling the cell with a new solution is to empty the cell, rinse it at least

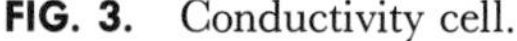

FIG. 3. Conductivity cell.

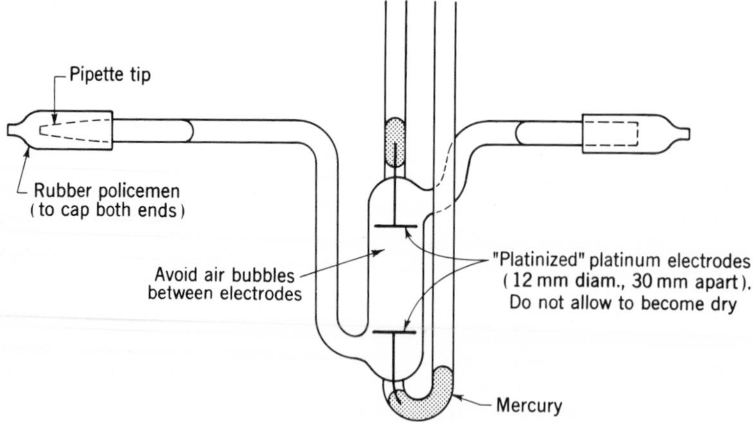

four times with aliquots of the desired solution using about enough to fill the cell one-fourth full, shake well on each rinsing, then fill the cell, being careful to avoid bubbles on the electrodes. Be careful to avoid loss of mercury from the contact arms.

Dilution Procedure. Clean thoroughly a 100-ml volumetric flask, a 250-ml wide-mouth flask, and a 25-ml pipette. Rinse these with conductivity water. Rinse the 250-ml flask with two or three *small* aliquots of the stock solution, and then take not more than 125 ml of the solution, noting the concentration given on the stock bottle.

Rinse the pipette with two or three small aliquots from the flask, and then pipette exactly 25.00 ml of the solution from the flask into the volumetric flask. Make up to the mark with conductivity water and mix thoroughly. Set this aside for the next measurement and dilution. Use the solution remaining in the 250-ml flask for rinsing and filling the conductivity cell. When the measurement of resistance of the cell containing that solution has been completed, discard the remaining solution from the 250-ml flask and rinse with two or three aliquots of the new solution from the volumetric flask. Decant the contents of the volumetric flask into the 250-ml flask, and rinse the volumetric flask with conductivity water.

Repeat the process described above as many times as necessary to obtain the dilutions needed. Care is important in this work, since dilution errors are cumulative.

Conductivity Water. Ordinary distilled water is not suitable for use in this experiment, since it has too high a conductance. Much of this conductivity results from dissolved CO_2 gas from the air, which can be removed by boiling distilled water and capping a full bottle while it is still hot. Even better conductivity water can be prepared by special distillation[4] or by passing distilled water through an ion-exchange resin to "deionize" it.

Procedure. Set up the bridge circuit and make the calibration check on the slide-wire. Then rinse and fill the cell with conductivity water, and measure its resistance on the short bridge. This value should be *at least* 200,000 ohms. If it is less, rinse the cell a few more times and repeat the measurement.

Record the value of R obtained. Fill the cell with 0.02000 N KCl solution and mount it in a 25°C thermostat bath. After making a short-bridge measurement to get the approximate value of R, adjust the resistance box and use the long bridge. Balance the bridge to minimum hum. If necessary, improve the balance with a trimmer capacitor placed across the resistance box; if excessive capacitance appears to be required, polarization is probably taking place and an instructor should be consulted. The final measurements on the solution being studied should consist of four readings, the balance point being approached twice from each side. The value of A on the slide-wire scale is recorded for each balance. There should be no appreciable drift in these values; if drift is observed, the cell is probably not in thermal equilibrium with the bath. Wait a few minutes and repeat the measurements. Be sure to record R' for the resistance box. The measurement on this KCl solution should be made with great care, since it determines the cell constant k and will affect all subsequent calculations.

If time permits, determine R of the cell for KCl dilutions of $\frac{1}{4}$, $\frac{1}{16}$, and $\frac{1}{64}$ and also make measurements on 0.02 N solution and three dilutions of HCl and/or KAc.

Measure R of the cell for acetic acid solutions at 0.05 N and dilutions of $\frac{1}{4}$, $\frac{1}{16}$, and $\frac{1}{64}$. For some HAc solutions (and the most dilute strong electrolyte solutions) it may be necessary to use two resistance boxes or else resort to short-bridge measurements.

At all times be sure that the thermostat bath is regulating properly; record the bath temperature.

At the end of the experiment, rinse the cell well, fill it with conductivity water, and return it with the filling arms stoppered.

CALCULATIONS

If the slide-wire calibration correction is appreciable, then all long-bridge readings should be corrected. From the result for the 0.02000 N KCl measurement, calculate the cell constant k, using $\bar{L} = 0.002768$ at 25°C.

Calculate the specific conductances $\bar{L}$ for all the solutions studied, using Eq. (2). If the conductance of the distilled water used was measurable, this should be subtracted from all the values of $\bar{L}$ obtained. Using Eq. (4), calculate equivalent conductances Λ for all solutions. The values of R, $\bar{L}$, and Λ for every solution measured should be appropriately tabulated, and the cell constant k should be given.

Those doing the strong electrolytes should plot Λ for each strong electrolyte against $\sqrt{c}$ and extrapolate to $c = 0$ to obtain Λ_0. In making the extrapolations, beware of increasingly large experimental uncertainty at the lowest concentrations and also of systematic errors due to conducting impurities or dilution errors at low concentrations. Combine these Λ_0's to obtain Λ_0 for acetic acid. For those not doing runs on strong electrolytes, the following data[6] may be used:

Solution	Λ_0 at 25°C	$d\Lambda_0/dT$
HCl	426.2	6.4
KCl	149.9	3.0
KAc	114.4	2.1

For each dilution of acetic acid, calculate α by Eq. (8) and then K_c by Eq. (9). Present in tabular form Λ, α, c, K_c for each dilution of acetic acid. Plot log K_c against $\sqrt{\alpha c}$. If an extrapolation to zero concentration is possible, make it and obtain a value for K_a. If the data do not appear to be sufficiently good to warrant an extrapolation, report an average or best value for K_c. Report the temperature at which the measurements were made.

APPARATUS

Wheatstone bridge or potentiometer slide-wire to be used as part of a bridge; oscillator (~1000 cycles, with power supply if needed); detector (telephone headset, tuning eye, or oscilloscope); precision resistance plug box or decade box; decade trimmer capacitor; conductivity cell, filled with conductivity water and capped off with clean rubber policemen; holder for mounting cell in bath; two leads to connect cell to bridge; 10 electrical leads with lugs; 100-ml volumetric flask; 25-ml pipette; two 100- or 250-ml beakers; two 125-ml erlenmeyer flasks; 500-ml glass-stoppered flask for storing conductivity water.

Constant-temperature bath set at 25°C; emery paper; conductivity water (1500 ml); *precisely* 0.02000 N KCl solution (300 ml); 0.02 N HCl solution (200 ml); 0.02 N potassium acetate solution (200 ml); 0.05 N acetic acid (250 ml).

REFERENCES

1. G. Jones and B. C. Bradshaw, *J. Am. Chem. Soc.*, **55,** 1780 (1933).
2. L. Onsager, *Physik. Z.*, **28,** 277 (1927); W. J. Moore, "Physical Chemistry," 2d ed., Prentice-Hall, Englewood Cliffs, N.J. (1955).
3. D. A. MacInnes, "The Principles of Electrochemistry," chap. 18, Reinhold, New York (1939).
4. T. Shedlovsky, Conductometry, in A. Weissberger (ed.), "Technique of Organic Chemistry," 2d ed., vol. I, part II, Interscience, New York (1949).
5. H. S. Harned and B. B. Owen, "The Physical Chemistry of Electrolytic Solutions," 2d ed., Appendix A, Reinhold, New York (1950).

GENERAL READING

R. A. Robinson and R. H. Stokes, "Electrolyte Solutions," Academic Press, Inc., New York (1955).
H. S. Harned and B. B. Owen, *op. cit.*
T. Shedlovsky, Conductometry, in A. Weissberger (ed.), *op. cit.*

Experiment 23. Temperature Dependence of EMF

In this experiment the following electrochemical cell is studied:

$$\mathrm{Cd}(s),\ \mathrm{Cd^{++}SO_4^{=}}(aq,\,c),\ \mathrm{Cd}(\mathrm{Hg},\,X_2) \qquad 1\ \mathrm{atm},\ T \tag{1}$$

The change in state accompanying the passage of 2 faradays of *positive* electricity from left to right through the cell is given by

$$\begin{array}{l} \text{Anode: } \mathrm{Cd}(s) = \mathrm{Cd^{++}}(aq,\,c) + 2e^- \\ \underline{\text{Cathode: } 2e^- + \mathrm{Cd^{++}}(aq,\,c) = \mathrm{Cd}(\mathrm{Hg},\,X_2)} \\ \text{Net: } \mathrm{Cd}(s) = \mathrm{Cd}(\mathrm{Hg},\,X_2) \qquad 1\ \mathrm{atm},\ T \end{array} \tag{2}$$

In the above, (s) refers to the pure crystalline solid and (Hg, X_2) represents a liquid (single-phase) cadmium amalgam in which the mole fraction of Cd is X_2.

From the emf of this cell and its temperature coefficient, the changes in free energy, entropy, and enthalpy for the above change in state are to be determined.

THEORY

When the cell operates reversibly at constant pressure and temperature, with no work being done except electrical work and expansion work,

$$\Delta G = -N\mathcal{E}\mathcal{F} \tag{3}$$

where ΔG is the increase in free energy of the system attending the change in state produced by the passage of N faradays of electricity through the cell, $\mathcal{F}$ is the Faraday constant, and $\mathcal{E}$ is the emf (electromotive force) of the cell.

From the Gibbs-Helmholtz equation, we have for a change in state at constant pressure and temperature

$$\left(\frac{\partial\,\Delta G}{\partial T}\right)_p = -\Delta S \tag{4}$$

Combining Eqs. (3) and (4), we find that

$$\Delta S = N\mathfrak{F}\left(\frac{\partial \mathcal{E}}{\partial T}\right)_p \tag{5}$$

Knowing both ΔG and ΔS, one can find ΔH by using

$$\Delta G = \Delta H - T\Delta S \tag{6}$$

METHOD

The emf of a cell is best determined by measurements with a potentiometer, since this method gives a close approach to reversible operation of the cell. The cell potential is opposed by a potential drop across the slide-wire of the potentiometer, and at balance only very small currents are drawn from the cell (depending on the sensitivity of the galvanometer used and the fineness of control possible in adjusting the slide-wire). The potentiometer circuit is described in Chap. XV.

EXPERIMENTAL

The cell consists of a small beaker with a top which will accommodate two electrodes as shown in Fig. 1. The *cadmium electrode* is made by plating cadmium onto a platinum wire which is sealed through the bottom of a small glass tube. Electrical contact is made to mercury contained in this tube. The *amalgam electrode* is made by placing a small quantity of the cadmium amalgam in the cup of a special J-shaped glass tube with a platinum wire sealed in to make electrical contact with mercury contained in the long arm of the tube.

Procedure. A cadmium-mercury amalgam containing 2 per cent Cd by weight will be used. This amalgam can be prepared as follows: Remove the oxide coating from a thin rod of pure Cd with dilute acid, rinse the rod thoroughly in distilled water, dry, and weigh. Then dissolve the rod in the proper (weighed) amount of triple-distilled mercury. Using a medicine dropper, fill the cup of the J electrode with this amalgam. Carefully insert this electrode into the cell, which previously

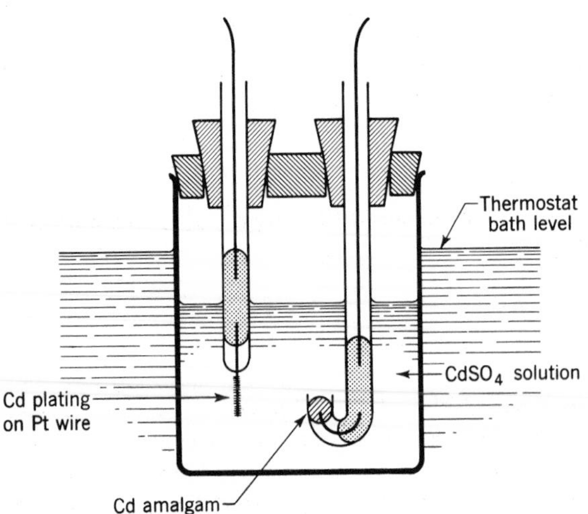

FIG. 1. Cadmium amalgam cell.

has been rinsed and filled with a 0.1 *M* $CdSO_4$ solution. The cell should be filled only half full to prevent contact of the solution with the cover.

The platinum wire of the other electrode is plated with a cadmium deposit by immersing the electrode in a beaker containing a 0.1 *M* solution of $CdSO_4$ and a pure cadmium rod. The electrode is connected to the negative terminal of a 1.5-v dry cell, and the cadmium rod is connected to the positive terminal. Current is passed through this plating bath until a heavy deposit of cadmium is visible on the electrode. This cadmium electrode is then transferred to the cell. Handle the electrode with care to avoid flaking off any of the cadmium deposit. It is advisable to keep the electrode wet at all times.

Mount the assembled cell in a thermostat bath. Assemble the potentiometer circuit and connect the cell. Consider the sign of ΔG for the change in state to decide on the proper connection. Have an instructor check your circuit.

After the cell has been in the thermostat bath for at least 10 min, measure the emf and repeat this measurement at least three times at 5-min intervals to verify that there is no systematic drift in the emf. The potentiometer circuit should be checked against the standard cell immediately before each reading. The emf should be determined as a function of temperature at four or more points in the range from 0 to 40°C. The same potentiometer must be used in making all these measurements.

CALCULATIONS

Plot the emf of the cell $\mathcal{E}$ vs. the absolute temperature T. Report the value of $\mathcal{E}$ and the slope $(\partial\mathcal{E}/\partial T)_p$ at 25.0°C (298.2°K) from the best smooth curve through your experimental points. Using Eqs. (3), (5), and (6), calculate ΔG, ΔS, and ΔH in calories per mole and give the change in state to which they apply.

From the known weight per cent Cd in the amalgam, compute the mole fraction X_2 of cadmium. Assuming for this concentration an activity coefficient of unity (so that the activity a_2 is equal to X_2), compute the standard free-energy change $\Delta G°$ for the change in state

$$\text{Cd}(s) = \text{Cd(Hg)}$$

by means of the equation

$$\Delta G = \Delta G° + RT \ln a \tag{7}$$

DISCUSSION

Explain why $\Delta G°$ is not equal to zero, as would be expected if the standard state were an "amalgam" with $X_2 = 1$.

APPARATUS

Complete potentiometer setup (see Chap. XV); cell (50-ml beaker or weighing bottle); platinum electrode; J electrode for holding amalgam; two leads for connections to cell; two beakers; battery jar; large ring stirrer; ring stand; large clamp and clamp holder.

Provision for electroplating cadmium from 0.1 *M* $CdSO_4$ onto platinum electrode; dilute

(3 per cent) cadmium amalgam (1 ml); eye dropper; mercury for making contact to electrodes; constant-temperature baths set at 15, 25, and 35°C; approximately 0.1 *M* $CdSO_4$ solution (150 ml); ice (2 lb).

GENERAL READING

F. E. Smith, *Phil. Mag.* (6), **19,** 250 (1910).
C. E. Teeter, Jr., *J. Am. Chem. Soc.,* **53,** 3927 (1931).
V. K. LaMer and W. G. Parks, *J. Am. Chem. Soc.,* **56,** 90 (1934).

Experiment 24. Activity Coefficients from Cell Measurements

We shall be concerned with the electrochemical cell

$$Ag(s) + AgCl(s),\ H^+Cl^-(aq,\ c),\ H_2(g,\ p\ \text{atm}) + Pt \tag{1}$$

Measurements of emf are to be made with this cell under reversible conditions at a number of concentrations c of HCl. From these measurements, relative values of activity coefficients at different concentrations can be derived. To obtain the activity coefficients on such a scale that the activity coefficient is unity for the reference state of zero concentration, an extrapolation procedure based on the Debye-Hückel limiting law is used. By this means, the standard electrode emf of the silver-silver chloride electrode is determined and activity coefficients are determined for all concentrations studied.

THEORY

The cell (1) may be considered as a combination of the two half-cells or "electrodes" described below.

Silver-Silver Chloride Electrode. This can be written

$$Ag(s) + AgCl(s),\ Cl^-(aq,\ c) \tag{2}$$

When 1 faraday of positive electricity passes reversibly from left to right through this electrode, the change in state is

$$Ag(s) + Cl^- = AgCl(s) + e^- \tag{3}$$

and the electrode emf (the electric potential of the solution with respect to the silver metal) is accordingly

$$\mathcal{E}_1 = \mathcal{E}_1{}^0 - \frac{RT}{\mathcal{F}} \ln \frac{1}{a_{Cl^-}} \tag{4}$$

where $\mathcal{E}_1{}^0$ is the standard electrode emf for the silver-silver chloride electrode, a_{Cl^-} is the activity of the chloride ion in the aqueous solution, and $\mathcal{F}$ is the Faraday constant.

Hydrogen Electrode. This can be written

$$Pt + H_2(g,\ p\ \text{atm}),\ H^+(aq,\ c) \tag{5}$$

With the reversible passage of 1 faraday the change in state is

$$\tfrac{1}{2}H_2(g) = H^+ + e^- \tag{6}$$

and the electrode emf is accordingly

$$\mathcal{E}_2 = \mathcal{E}_2{}^0 - \frac{RT}{\mathcal{F}} \ln \frac{a_{H^+}}{f_{H_2}{}^{1/2}} \tag{7}$$

where f_{H_2} is the fugacity of the hydrogen gas and a_{H^+} the activity of the aqueous hydrogen ion. By convention, the standard electrode emf for the hydrogen electrode is zero:

$$\mathcal{E}_2{}^0 = \mathcal{E}^0_{H_2/H^+} \equiv 0 \tag{8}$$

The Cell. Combining the hydrogen electrode with the silver-silver chloride electrode we obtain the cell (1). The over-all change in state is Eq. (3) minus Eq. (6):

$$H^+Cl^- + Ag(s) = AgCl(s) + \tfrac{1}{2}H_2(g) \tag{9}$$

The emf of the cell is given by Eq. (4) minus Eq. (7):

$$\mathcal{E} = \mathcal{E}_1 - \mathcal{E}_2 = \mathcal{E}^0 - \frac{RT}{\mathcal{F}} \ln \frac{f_{H_2}{}^{1/2}}{a_{H^+}a_{Cl^-}} \tag{10}$$

where

$$\mathcal{E}^0 = \mathcal{E}_1{}^0 - \mathcal{E}_2{}^0 = \mathcal{E}_1{}^0 \tag{11}$$

Activity Coefficients. Let us write

$$f_{H_2} = \gamma' p \qquad a_{H^+}a_{Cl^-} = \gamma_\pm{}^2 c^2 \tag{12}$$

where γ' is the activity coefficient for $H_2(g)$ and $\gamma_\pm$ is the mean activity coefficient for $H^+Cl^-(aq)$. Equation (10) can now be written

$$\mathcal{E} = \mathcal{E}^0 - \frac{2.303RT}{\mathcal{F}} \log \frac{p^{1/2}}{c^2} - \frac{2.303RT}{\mathcal{F}} \log \frac{\gamma'^{1/2}}{\gamma_\pm{}^2} \tag{13}$$

where p is in atmospheres and c is in moles per liter. From this equation it is clear that, if emf measurements are made on two or more cells which differ only in the concentrations c of HCl, the ratios of the corresponding activity coefficients $\gamma_\pm$ can be determined from the differences in emf. For the determination of the individual values of these activity coefficients, it is necessary to know the values of $\mathcal{E}^0$ and γ'. At 25°C, 1 atm, the activity coefficient γ' is 1.0006, which for the purpose of this experiment may be taken as unity. To determine $\mathcal{E}^0$, however, requires a procedure equivalent to determining the emf with the solute in its "reference state," at which the activity coefficient $\gamma_\pm$ is unity. However, the reference state for a solute in solution is the limiting state of zero concentration, which is inaccessible to direct experiment. However, the Debye-Hückel theory predicts the limiting behavior of $\gamma_\pm$ as the concentration approaches zero, and we can make use of this predicted behavior in devising an extrapolation procedure for the determination of $\mathcal{E}^0$. According to the Debye-Hückel limiting law,[1]

$$\log \gamma_\pm \cong -A\sqrt{\mu} \tag{14}$$

In the present case, the ionic strength μ is equal to the HCl concentration c. The value of the constant A given by the Debye-Hückel theory for a uni-univalent electrolyte in aqueous solution at 25°C is 0.509. While knowledge of this value may be helpful to the extrapolation, it is not necessary.

Let us rearrange Eq. (13) and set γ' equal to unity:

$$\mathcal{E}^0 = \mathcal{E} + \frac{2.303RT}{\mathcal{F}} \log \frac{p^{1/2}}{c^2} - \frac{2.303RT}{\mathcal{F}} \log \gamma_\pm^2 \tag{15}$$

Now define $\mathcal{E}^{0\prime}$ by

$$\mathcal{E}^{0\prime} \equiv \mathcal{E} + \frac{2.303RT}{\mathcal{F}} \log \frac{p^{1/2}}{c^2} + 2\frac{2.303RT}{\mathcal{F}} A\sqrt{c} \tag{16}$$

The value of $\mathcal{E}^{0\prime}$ should be close to that of $\mathcal{E}^0$ [depending on the validity of Eq. (14) as an approximation for $\log \gamma_\pm$]; in any case $\mathcal{E}^{0\prime}$ will approach $\mathcal{E}^0$ as the concentration approaches zero. A plot of $\mathcal{E}^{0\prime}$ vs. c should be approximately linear and have only a small slope, thus permitting a good extrapolation to zero concentration.[2]

Alternatively, one could define a quantity $\mathcal{E}^{0\prime\prime}$ by

$$\mathcal{E}^{0\prime\prime} \equiv \mathcal{E} + \frac{2.303RT}{\mathcal{F}} \log \frac{p^{1/2}}{c^2} \tag{17}$$

which would equal $\mathcal{E}^0$ at infinite dilution. If this quantity $\mathcal{E}^{0\prime\prime}$ is plotted against $\sqrt{c}$, we expect to obtain a curve which will give a limiting straight-line extrapolation to zero concentration.

In either case, the extrapolated intercept is the desired value of $\mathcal{E}^0$. Often it is best to make both extrapolations; with only a few points, use of $\mathcal{E}^{0\prime}$ is recommended.

With the value of $\mathcal{E}^0$ the activity coefficients for the various concentrations studied can be determined individually by use of Eq. (13). They can then be compared with those predicted by a more complete form of the Debye-Hückel equation, such as

$$\log \gamma_\pm = -0.509|z_+z_-|\frac{\sqrt{\mu}}{1 + B\sqrt{\mu}} \tag{18}$$

where B is approximately equal to unity.[1]

EXPERIMENTAL

The cell vessel consists of a small beaker with a stopper or cover with holes through which the hydrogen electrode assembly and the silver-silver chloride electrode assembly may be introduced. The assembled cell is shown in Fig. 1.

The hydrogen electrode consists of a mounted platinum gauze square contained within a glass sleeve having large side holes at about the level of the gauze and a side arm for admission of hydrogen near the top. The platinum gauze is "platinized," that is, coated with a deposit of platinum black by electrolytic deposition from a solution containing platinic chloride and a trace of lead acetate. This deposit should be removed with warm aqua regia and renewed if the electrode has been allowed to dry out or if there is evidence that the deposit has been "poisoned."

The silver-silver chloride electrode consists of a mounted platinum screen that has been heavily plated with silver from a cyanide bath, rinsed, aged in an acidified silver nitrate solution, rinsed, coated with a thin layer of silver chloride by anodizing in a dilute HCl solution (preferably no more than a few days before use), and kept in dilute HCl pending use. This is mounted in a glass sleeve with a small hole in the bottom to admit the cell solution and a small side hole near the top for passage of air; this sleeve protects the electrode from mechanical damage and also pre-

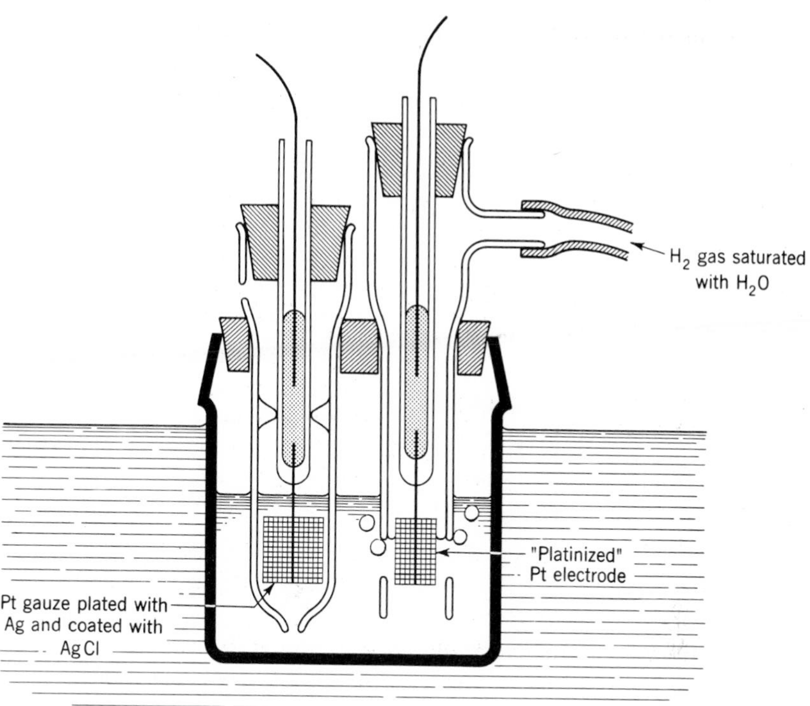

FIG. 1. Electrochemical cell with H_2 and Ag-AgCl electrodes.

vents the attainment of any significant concentration of dissolved H_2 in the solution in contact with the electrode.

Both electrode assemblies should be furnished ready for use. Care should be exercised to prevent the electrodes from becoming dry.

The use of hydrogen in any significant quantity is attended by explosion hazard. Hydrogen usage must be kept at the minimum necessary for the experiment, and wastage and leakage must be guarded against. **Smoking and the use of flames for any purpose cannot be permitted.**

The hydrogen to be used should be oxygen-free. Oxygen is most conveniently removed by passing tank hydrogen through a commercial catalytic purifier. The hydrogen should also be saturated with water vapor at room temperature (about 25°C) by bubbling it through water.

The partial pressure p of hydrogen at the electrode should be determined from the atmospheric pressure in the laboratory by subtracting the partial pressure of water vapor at 25°C and adding the mercury equivalent of the "water head" (the average difference in liquid levels inside and outside the hydrogen electrode shell).

Procedure. Fill the cell about half full with the appropriate HCl solution. Rinse the two electrodes in separate small portions of the same solution, and insert them. When the liquid level in the silver-silver chloride electrode shell has reached its equilibrium level, pass hydrogen through the cell at a moderate rate to sweep out the air and saturate the solution. After about 10 min, slow down the rate to a few bubbles per second and begin to make emf readings. Make at least four readings at 5-min intervals. These should show no significant drift.

Readings of emf are obtained with a potentiometer circuit (see Chap. XV). If a null galvanometer reading cannot be obtained with any setting of the potentiometer dial, reverse the leads and try again. The sign of the emf will depend on whether the null reading is obtained with the right-hand terminal of the cell ($Pt + H_2$) connected to the positive or to the negative terminal of the potentiometer.

Care should be exercised to prevent the cell from becoming polarized by accidental shorting or by passage of excessive currents during the potentiometer balancing.

Runs should be made with the following concentrations of HCl: 0.1, 0.05, 0.025, 0.0125, and 0.00625 *M*, obtained by successive volumetric dilution of 0.1 *M* HCl stock solution. Make up 200 ml of each solution.

CALCULATIONS

For each run calculate $\mathcal{E}^{0\prime}$ from Eq. (16) from the measured $\mathcal{E}$, the partial pressure p of H_2, and the concentration c of HCl. The value of $2.303RT/\mathcal{F}$ at 25°C is 0.05916 v and A is 0.509.

Plot $\mathcal{E}^{0\prime}$ vs. c and extrapolate to zero concentration to obtain $\mathcal{E}^0$ (which is equal to the standard electrode emf for the silver-silver chloride electrode). If you wish, also calculate $\mathcal{E}^{\circ\prime\prime}$ from Eq. (17), plot it vs. $\sqrt{c}$, and extrapolate to obtain another value of $\mathcal{E}^0$ as a check.

With this value of $\mathcal{E}^0$ calculate mean activity coefficients for all concentrations studied by use of Eq. (15). For each concentration, calculate also a theoretical mean activity coefficient by use of the Debye-Hückel equation in the form given in Eq. (18). Present your experimental and theoretical activity coefficients in tabular form.

APPARATUS

Complete potentiometer setup (see Chap. XV); 50-ml weighing bottle as cell; special three-hole stopper to fit cell and hold electrodes; two leads for connections to cell; hydrogen electrode and Ag-AgCl electrode; 200-ml volumetric flask; 100-ml pipette; 250-ml flasks; two 250-ml beakers; small gas bubbler; two pieces of gum-rubber tubing; large clamp and clamp holder.

Cylinder of hydrogen gas, regulator fitted with a Deoxo purifier to remove any oxygen and a flow reducer to limit flow to 5 $ft^3\ hr^{-1}$; large fritted-glass bubbler to saturate hydrogen with water vapor; constant-temperature bath set at 25°C; 0.1 *M* HCl solution (350 ml).

REFERENCES

1. W. J. Moore, "Physical Chemistry," 2d ed., Prentice-Hall, Englewood Cliffs, N.J. (1955); F. H. MacDougall, "Thermodynamics and Chemistry," 3d ed., Wiley, New York (1939).
2. H. S. Harned and R. W. Ehlers, *J. Am. Chem. Soc.*, **55,** 2179 (1933).

GENERAL READING

F. Daniels and R. A. Alberty, "Physical Chemistry," Wiley, New York (1955).
D. A. MacInnes, "The Principles of Electrochemistry," Reinhold, New York (1939).

Experiment 25. Electrochemical Cells with Liquid Junctions

An electrochemical cell often consists of a single liquid electrolyte and two different electrodes, as in Exps. 23 and 24. It is, however, possible to construct electrochemical cells in which there are two or more liquid electrolytes, and these electrolytes may either be physically separated by electrodes or else be in actual contact at a "liquid junction." The present experiment deals with cells with liquid junctions and with the effects of transference of ions across the liquid junctions. The cation transference number in aqueous HCl can be determined from measurements on such cells combined with data from the measurements made on a related chemical cell in Exp. 24.

THEORY

Experiment 24 dealt with a chemical cell, in which the change in state represents a chemical reaction:

$$\mathrm{Ag}(s) + \mathrm{H^+Cl^-}(aq, c) = \mathrm{AgCl}(s) + \tfrac{1}{2}\mathrm{H_2}(g, p \text{ atm})$$

Another important type of cell is the concentration cell, in which the change in state represents no over-all chemical change but only a physical change, namely, the transfer of a chemical substance from a solution of one concentration to one of another concentration. Such cells may be either "without transference" or "with transference," depending upon whether liquid junctions are absent or present. An example of a concentration cell without transference is

$$\mathrm{Ag}(s) + \mathrm{AgCl}(s), \mathrm{H^+Cl^-}(aq, c'), \mathrm{H_2}(g, p \text{ atm}) + \mathrm{Pt} \text{——} \mathrm{Pt} + \mathrm{H_2}(g, p \text{ atm}),$$
$$\mathrm{H^+Cl^-}(aq, c''), \mathrm{AgCl}(s) + \mathrm{Ag}(s) \qquad (1)$$

This cell consists of two opposed chemical cells of the kind used in Exp. 24, with different electrolyte concentrations, connected in series. The over-all change in state for this composite cell is

$$\mathrm{H^+Cl^-}(aq, c') = \mathrm{H^+Cl^-}(aq, c'') \qquad (2)$$

and the emf is given by

$$\mathcal{E} = -\frac{RT}{\mathfrak{F}} \ln \frac{a_\pm''^2}{a_\pm'^2} = -2\frac{RT}{\mathfrak{F}} \ln \frac{c''\gamma_\pm''}{c'\gamma_\pm'} \qquad (3)$$

where $\gamma_\pm'$ and $\gamma_\pm''$ are mean activity coefficients for the solutions of concentration c' and c'', respectively. We shall not concern ourselves further with cells of this type, the emf's of which can be predicted from measurements made on the chemical cell employed in Exp. 24.

Cell with Transference. Let us now consider a related concentration cell with transference:

$$\mathrm{Ag}(s) + \mathrm{AgCl}(s), \mathrm{M^+Cl^-}(aq, c'), \mathrm{M^+Cl^-}(aq, c''), \mathrm{AgCl}(s) + \mathrm{Ag}(s) \qquad (4)$$

This cell can be constructed from two half-cells of the type formulated in Eq. (24-2), one on each side of the central comma. The change in state and the emf for such half-cells are given by Eqs. (24-3) and (24-4). The central comma indicates that the two solutions are in direct contact and may even be permitted to interdiffuse at the boundary; in this case a liquid-junction potential $\mathcal{E}_L$ exists.

The emf of the cell (4) is

$$\mathcal{E} = \mathcal{E}' - \mathcal{E}'' + \mathcal{E}_L \tag{5}$$

where $\mathcal{E}'$ and $\mathcal{E}''$ are the left- and right-hand half-cell emf's. From Eq. (24-4) we obtain

$$\mathcal{E}' - \mathcal{E}'' = -\frac{RT}{\mathfrak{F}} \ln \frac{a''_-}{a'_-} = -\frac{RT}{\mathfrak{F}} \ln \frac{c''\gamma''_-}{c'\gamma'_-} \tag{6}$$

where γ'_- and γ''_- are anion activity coefficients. This expression corresponds to the change in state (for 1 faraday)

$$\mathrm{Cl}^-(aq, c') = \mathrm{Cl}^-(aq, c'') \tag{7}$$

For the complete cell the net change in state is that given in Eq. (7) *plus* the change taking place at the liquid junction, which is (for 1 faraday)

$$T_+\mathrm{M}^+(c') + (1 - T_+)\mathrm{Cl}^-(c'') = T_+\mathrm{M}^+(c'') + (1 - T_+)\mathrm{Cl}^-(c') \tag{8}$$

where T_+ is the cation transference number. The liquid-junction potential associated with the change in state in Eq. (8) is given by

$$\begin{aligned} \mathcal{E}_L &= -\frac{RT}{\mathfrak{F}} \ln \frac{(c''\gamma''_+)^{T_+}(c'\gamma'_-)^{(1-T_+)}}{(c'\gamma'_+)^{T_+}(c''\gamma''_-)^{(1-T_+)}} \\ &= -\frac{RT}{\mathfrak{F}} \ln \frac{c'\gamma'_-}{c''\gamma''_-} - 2T_+\frac{RT}{\mathfrak{F}} \ln \frac{c''\gamma''_\pm}{c'\gamma'_\pm} \end{aligned} \tag{9}$$

on the assumption that T_+ is independent of concentration. Thus, the over-all change in state for the cell (4) is

$$T_+\mathrm{M}^+\mathrm{Cl}^-(aq, c') = T_+\mathrm{M}^+\mathrm{Cl}^-(aq, c'') \tag{10}$$

and the over-all emf of the cell is

$$\mathcal{E} = -2T_+\frac{RT}{\mathfrak{F}} \ln \frac{c''\gamma''_\pm}{c'\gamma'_\pm} \tag{11}$$

It is evident that emf measurements on concentration cells of this kind, combined with measurements on the corresponding concentration cells without transference [cell (1) and Eq. (3)], can be used as a means of determining transference numbers.

Cell with a Salt Bridge. We shall now consider a similar cell which has a salt bridge:

$$\mathrm{Ag}(s) + \mathrm{AgCl}(s), \mathrm{M}^+\mathrm{Cl}^-(aq, c') \parallel \mathrm{M}^+\mathrm{Cl}^-(aq, c''), \mathrm{AgCl}(s) + \mathrm{Ag}(s) \tag{12}$$

The two half-cells involved here are identical with those in cell (4). However, the use of a double bar between the two half-cells indicates that the liquid-junction potential has been eliminated experimentally or corrected for theoretically. In either case, the two M^+Cl^- solutions are no longer in direct contact but are connected via a salt bridge (i.e., a tube containing a different electrolyte). Obviously, there are now two liquid junctions—one between the salt-bridge electrolyte and M^+Cl^- solution of concentration c' and the other between the salt bridge and the solution of concentration c''. The over-all junction potential will be the sum of liquid-junction potentials for these two junctions. In the following discussion, brief mention is made of a type of salt bridge for which the over-all junction potential can be calculated, but the primary emphasis is on a KCl salt bridge which is found experimentally to eliminate the junction potential.

A salt bridge involves a new and very different kind of liquid junction, namely, one between two *different* electrolytes at two different concentrations. Only under certain conditions is it possible to obtain a liquid junction between different electrolytes for which there is a reproducible and theoretically calculable junction potential. These necessary conditions often depend on the circumstances under which the junction is formed—whether by mechanical mixing, pure interdiffusion, etc. A favorable case is that of two electrolytes with the same equivalent concentration and having one ion in common; if the circumstances of forming the junction are such that the concentration of the common ion is uniform over the junction, the equation of Lewis and Sargent[1] is applicable:

$$\mathcal{E}_L = -\frac{RT}{\mathcal{F}} \ln \frac{\Lambda''}{\Lambda'} \tag{13}$$

where Λ' and Λ'' are the equivalent conductances of the left-hand and right-hand electrolytes.

The theory of a KCl salt bridge[2,3] is very much more complicated and is probably not altogether adequate to explain the performance of this salt bridge under ordinary conditions of use. Empirically, a saturated KCl salt bridge is found to eliminate the junction potential between two dilute electrolytes to within the precision of ordinary electrochemical measurements. The junction potential between the saturated KCl solution and a dilute solution is also presumably zero, or at least a constant independent of the composition and concentration of the dilute solution. Only a semiquantitative explanation of this effect will be offered here.

The use of KCl for salt bridges depends in large part on the fact that K^+ and Cl^- have almost the same mobilities in aqueous solution. The cation transference number for KCl solutions at 25°C has an almost constant value of 0.49 over the entire range of concentration from infinite dilution to saturation ($\sim$5 M). It will be noted that Eq. (9) predicts that $\mathcal{E}_L$ for a junction involving a single electrolyte vanishes when $T_+ = 0.5$, if it can be assumed that $\gamma_- = \gamma_\pm$.† This will be of importance in analyzing the junction between a dilute electrolyte and the saturated KCl, since the concentration gradient for KCl is much higher than that of the dilute electrolyte. Thus, as we traverse the junction starting from the dilute side, we find that the KCl concentration builds up to a greater value than the concen-

† This reasonable assumption is commonly made; indeed, it is doubtful whether the activity coefficient of an ion can be measured independently of an ion of the opposite sign. Potentials capable of being measured directly (unlike electrode potentials or liquid-junction potentials which involve indirect measurements) are independent of such assumptions; note that only mean activity coefficients occur in Eqs. (3) and (11).

tration of the other electrolyte before the other has decreased much. Within this region, then, we expect no very significant contribution to a junction potential, either from the dilute electrolyte (since its concentration has changed little) or from the KCl (since K^+ and Cl^- have substantially equal mobilities). Beyond this region, where nearly all the current is carried by the KCl, we expect no significant contribution from the KCl (same reason) or from the dilute electrolyte (since it does not carry enough of the current to exert a significant effect).

Thus there is a theoretical basis for the empirical fact that $\mathcal{E}_L$ is almost zero for a cell with a KCl salt bridge. The over-all emf of cell (12) is therefore simply $\mathcal{E}' - \mathcal{E}''$, which is given by Eq. (6). However, it would be a gross oversimplification to assume that the over-all change in state is just that given by Eq. (7); the actual change in state involves not only Cl^- but also M^+ and the ions of the salt bridge.

EXPERIMENTAL

This experiment will be performed with apparatus very similar to that used in Exp. 24. The entire experiment can be carried out with silver-silver chloride electrodes, in correspondence to the above discussion, or with hydrogen electrodes. In the latter case some of the above equations are not applicable as written; the appropriate equations can be derived by the student on the same principles.

Measurements should be made on: (I) concentration cells with a direct liquid junction between the two solutions and (II) concentration cells with a KCl salt bridge between the two solutions. Measurements on (III) concentration cells without liquid junction [cell (1)] need not be made if a set of measurements made on the related chemical cell of Exp. 24 are available. It is suggested that in each case the electrolytes be aqueous HCl at the following concentrations: (1) 0.1 and 0.025 *M*, (2) 0.1 and 0.00625 *M*, and (3) 0.025 and 0.00625 *M*. These solutions can be prepared by successive dilution of 0.1 *M* stock solution.

Each cell will consist of two 50-ml beakers, with appropriate stoppers, as used in Exp. 24. These beakers are to be clamped side by side in a constant-temperature bath regulated at 25.0°C. Each should contain one electrode. Connection between the two is made either with a liquid junction tube or with a salt-bridge tube.

In use, the liquid-junction tube (Fig. 1) is introduced into the two half-cells so that both tips are immersed, and the two solutions are drawn into the two arms by gentle suction so that they come into contact. Liquid is drawn further into the upper arm, which is then closed off. It is advisable to stop the suction briefly just short of contact in order to permit adjustment of the two beakers so that the liquid levels are the same within 1 mm. The purpose of this is to prevent siphoning of solution from one beaker to the other after the two solutions have been brought into contact. The rate of siphoning can be reduced by drawing down the tips to a reasonably fine bore, but not so fine as to make it difficult to draw the solutions into the arms. The tips should have as nearly as possible the same inside diameter. (It may be helpful to add a *small* amount of a colored indicator such as methyl red to one of the solutions to facilitate observation of movement of the boundary.)

The salt bridge (Fig. 2) is a tube of similar kind, but with extremely fine-bore tips, agar-filled tips, or ground-glass tips, etc.,[4] to prevent appreciable flow of the

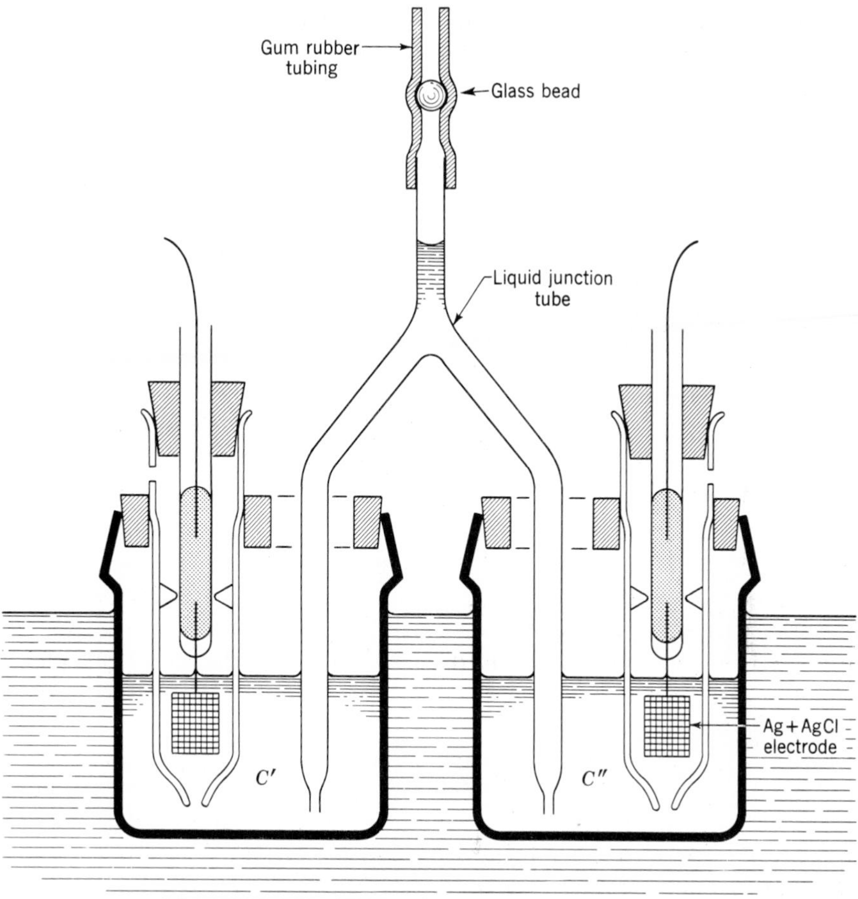

FIG. 1. Cell with transference, showing liquid junction tube.

saturated KCl solution into the test solutions. This is especially important if silver-silver chloride electrodes are being used. (In many cases it is impractical to fill this tube in the manner above described; the saturated KCl solution must be introduced from the top.) A simple and reasonably satisfactory salt bridge can be made using a liquid-junction tube having 1- to 2-mm tips, the inside surfaces of which are smeared with a trace of wax on the end of a wire. With one arm closed off with a rubber policeman, the other is filled by suction. A slender sliver of filter paper is introduced part way into the tip, and then a small ball of wax or plug of stopcock grease is pressed into the tip with the finger so as to seal off the tip to liquid flow except through the paper. This procedure is repeated for the other arm. All but a few millimeters of the protuding strips are then snipped off. The upper tube is then opened, and a few crystals of solid KCl are introduced and shaken into the two arms. Before reclosing the tube at the top, check to see if the rate of leakage of solution through the filter paper strips is just enough to keep them moist. The bridge should be stored with its two tips immersed in saturated KCl solution pending use. Just before use, the tips are washed with distilled water and then with

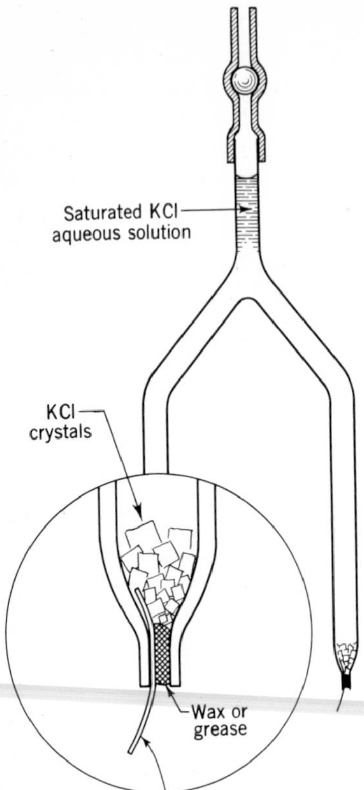

FIG. 2. Salt-bridge tube.

small aliquots of the solutions into which they are to be introduced. It is advisable (1) to have the two half-cells as nearly at the same liquid level as possible; (2) to avoid tipping the salt bridge, particularly when washing it and transferring it to the half-cells, and (3) to avoid any unnecessary agitation of the solutions in the half-cells.

CALCULATIONS

Using literature data for the emf of the corresponding chemical cell [Eq. (24-1)] as a function of concentration or your own data from Exp. 24, calculate emf's for the concentration cell without liquid junction [cell (1)] for the various concentrations employed in this experiment. Alternatively, calculate these emf's with Eq. (3) using literature data or your own data for the mean activity coefficient of HCl. Tabulate these emf's (III) with the ones (I, II) measured in this experiment.

Equations (3) and (6) predict that the emf for a cell without liquid junction (III) should have twice the magnitude of that for the same cell with the salt bridge (II) on the assumption that individual activity coefficients are equal to the mean activity coefficient. Determine the actual ratios of the emf's.

At each pair of concentrations calculate the cation transference number by use of Eqs. (3) and (11). Do you observe any significant variation of this transference number with concentration?

APPARATUS

Complete potentiometer setup (see Chap. XV); two 50-ml weighing bottles for half cells; two special three-hole stoppers to fit cells and hold electrodes; two leads for connections to cell; two hydrogen electrodes *or* two silver-silver chloride electrodes; liquid junction tube; salt bridge tube; 200-ml volumetric flask; 50-ml pipette; two 250-ml beakers; two large clamps and clamp holders; small gas bubbler (if hydrogen electrodes are used) with two pieces of gum-rubber tubing.

Constant-temperature bath regulated at 25.0°C; 0.1 *M* HCl solution (350 ml); cylinder of hydrogen gas (if H_2 is to be used) with regulator fitted with a Deoxo purifier to remove oxygen and a flow reducer to limit flow to 5 $ft^3\ hr^{-1}$.

REFERENCES

1. G. N. Lewis and L. W. Sargent, *J. Am. Chem. Soc.,* **31,** 363 (1909).
2. N. Bjerrum, *Z. Elektrochem.,* **17,** 389 (1911).
3. W. M. Clark, "The Determination of Hydrogen Ions," pp. 277–280, Williams & Wilkins, Baltimore (1928).
4. M. Dole, "The Glass Electrode," pp. 114–118, Wiley, New York (1941).

GENERAL READING

See list given in Exp. 24.

IX
CHEMICAL KINETICS

EXPERIMENTS

Experiment 26. Method of Initial Rates: Iodine Clock

The homogeneous reaction in aqueous solution

$$IO_3^- + 8I^- + 6H^+ \rightarrow 3I_3^- + 3H_2O \quad (1)$$

like virtually all reactions involving more than two or three reactant molecules, takes place not in a single molecular step but in several steps. The detailed system of steps is called the *reaction mechanism.* It is one of the principal aims of chemical kinetics to obtain information to aid in the elucidation of reaction mechanisms, which are fundamental to our understanding of chemistry.

THEORY

The several steps in a reaction are usually consecutive and tend to proceed at different speeds. Usually, when the over-all rate is slow enough to measure at all, it is because one of the steps tends to proceed so much more slowly than all the others that it effectively controls the over-all reaction rate and can be designated the *rate-controlling* step. A steady state is quickly reached in which the concentrations of the reaction intermediates are controlled by the intrinsic speeds of the reaction steps by which they are formed and consumed. A study of the rate of the over-all reaction yields information of a certain kind regarding the nature of the rate-controlling step and closely associated steps. Usually, however, rate studies supply only part of the information needed to formulate uniquely and completely the correct reaction mechanism.

When the mechanism is such that the steady state is quickly attained, the rate law for Eq. (1) can be written in the form

$$-\frac{d(IO_3^-)}{dt} = f[(IO_3^-), (I^-), (H^+), (I_3^-), (H_2O), \ldots] \qquad (2)$$

where parenthesized quantities are concentrations. In the general case the brackets might also contain concentrations of additional substances, referred to as catalysts, whose presence influences the reaction rate but which are not produced or consumed in the over-all reaction. The determination of the rate law requires that the rate be determined at a sufficiently large number of different combinations of the concentrations of the various species present to enable an expression to be formulated which accounts for the observations and gives good promise of predicting the rate reliably over the concentration ranges of interest. The rate law can be written to correspond in form to that predicted by a theory based on a particular type of mechanism, but basically it is an empirical expression.

The most frequently encountered type of rate law is of the form [again using the reaction of Eq. (1) as an example]

$$-\frac{d(IO_3^-)}{dt} = k(IO_3^-)^m(I^-)^n(H^+)^p \ldots \qquad (3)$$

where the exponents m, n, p, . . . are determined by experiment. Each exponent in Eq. (3) is the *order* of the reaction with respect to the corresponding species; thus, the reaction is said to be mth order with respect to IO_3^-, etc. The algebraic sum of the exponents, $m + n + p$ in this example, is the *over-all order* (or, commonly, simply the *order*) of the reaction. Reaction orders are usually, but not always, positive integers within experimental error.

The order of a reaction is determined by the reaction mechanism. It is related to, and is often (but not always) equal to, the number of reactant molecules in the rate-controlling step—the "molecularity" of the reaction. Consider the following proposed mechanism for the hypothetical reaction 3A + 2B = products:

a. A + 2B = 2C (fast, to equil., K_a)
b. A + C = products (slow, rate controlling, k_b)

The rate law predicted by this mechanism is

$$-\frac{d(A)}{dt} = \frac{3}{2}k_b(A)(C) = \frac{3}{2}k_b(A)K_a^{1/2}(A)^{1/2}(B) = k(A)^{3/2}(B)$$

The over-all reaction involves five reactant molecules, but it is by no means necessarily of fifth order. Indeed, the rate-controlling step in this proposed mechanism is bimolecular, and the over-all reaction order predicted by the mechanism is 5/2. It is also important to note that this mechanism is not the only one that would predict the above 5/2-order rate law for the given over-all reaction; thus experimental verification of the predicted rate law would by no means constitute proof of the validity of the above proposed mechanism.

It occasionally happens that the observed exponents deviate from integers or simple rational fractions by more than experimental error. A possible explanation is that two or more simultaneous mechanisms are in competition, in which case the observed order should lie between the extremes predicted by the individual mechanisms. A possible alternative explanation is that no single reaction step is effectively rate controlling.

We now turn our attention to the experimental problem of determining the exponents in the rate law. Except in first- and second-order reactions it is usually inconvenient to determine the exponents merely by determining the time behavior of a reacting system in which many or all reactant concentrations are allowed to change simultaneously and comparing the observed behavior with integrated rate expressions. A procedure is desirable which permits the dependences of the rate on the concentrations of the different reactants to be isolated from one another and determined one at a time. In one such procedure, all the species but the one to be studied are present at such high initial concentrations relative to that of the reactant studied that their concentrations may be assumed to remain approximately constant during the reaction; the apparent reaction order with respect to the species of interest is then obtained by comparing the progress of the reaction with that predicted by rate laws for first order, second order, and so on. This procedure would often have the disadvantage of placing the system outside the concentration range of interest and thus possibly complicating the reaction mechanism.

In another procedure, which we shall call the *initial rate method,* the reaction is run for a time small in comparison with the "half-life" of the reaction but large in comparison with the time required to attain a steady state, so that the actual value of the initial rate [the initial value of the derivative on the left side of Eq. (3)] can be estimated approximately. Enough different combinations of initial concentrations of the several reactants are employed to enable the exponents to be determined separately. For example, the exponent m is determined from two experiments which differ only in the IO_3^- concentration.

In the present experiment the rate law for the reaction shown in Eq. (1) will be studied by the initial rate method, at 25°C and at a pH of about 5. The initial concentrations of iodate ion, iodide ion, and hydrogen ion will be varied independently in separate experiments, and the time required for the consumption of a definite small amount of the iodate will be measured.

METHOD

The time required for a definite small amount of iodate to be consumed will here be measured by determining the time required for the iodine produced by the reaction (as I_3^-) to oxidize a definite amount of a reducing agent, arsenious acid, added at the beginning of the experiment. Under the conditions of the experiment arsenious acid does not react directly with iodate at a significant rate but reacts with iodine as quickly as it is formed. When the arsenious acid has been completely consumed, free iodine is liberated which produces a blue color with a small amount of soluble starch which is present. Since the blue color appears rather suddenly after a reproducible period of time, this series of reactions is commonly known as the "iodine clock reaction."

The reaction involving arsenious acid may be written, at a pH of about 5,

$$H_3AsO_3 + I_3^- + H_2O \rightarrow HAsO_4^= + 3I^- + 4H^+ \tag{4}$$

The over-all reaction, up to the time of the starch end point, can be written, from reactions (1) and (4),

$$IO_3^- + 3H_3AsO_3 \rightarrow I^- + 3HAsO_4^{=} + 6H^+ \tag{5}$$

Since with ordinary concentrations of the other reactants hydrogen ions are evidently produced in quantities large in comparison to those corresponding to pH 5, it is evident that buffers must be used to maintain constant hydrogen-ion concentration. As is apparent from the method used, the rate law will be determined under conditions of essentially zero concentration of I_3^-; the dependence of the rate on triiodide, which in fact has been shown to be very small,[1] will not be measured. Under these conditions, Eq. (3) is an appropriate expression for the rate.

A constant initial concentration of H_3AsO_3 is used in a series of reacting mixtures having varying initial concentrations of IO_3^-, I^-, and H^+. Since the amount of arsenious acid is the same in each run, the amount of iodate consumed up to the color change is constant, and related to the amount of arsenious acid by the stoichiometry of Eq. (5). The initial reaction rate in mole liter^{-1} sec^{-1} is thus approximately the amount consumed (per liter) divided by the time required for the blue end point to appear. From the initial rates of two reactions in which the initial concentration of only one reactant is varied and all other concentrations kept the same, it is possible to infer the exponent in the rate expression associated with the reactant which is varied. This is most conveniently done by taking logarithms of both sides of Eq. (3) and subtracting the expressions for the two runs.

EXPERIMENTAL

Solutions. Two acetate buffers, with hydrogen-ion concentrations differing by a factor of 2, will be made up by the student from stock solutions. Use will be made of the fact that at a given ionic strength the hydrogen-ion concentration is proportional to the ratio of acetic acid concentration to acetate ion concentration:

$$(H^+) = K\frac{(HAc)}{(Ac^-)}\frac{1}{\gamma_\pm^2} \tag{6}$$

where at 25°C, $K = 1.753 \times 10^{-5}$ mole liter^{-1}. The experiments will all be carried out at about the same ionic strength (0.16 ± 0.01), and accordingly the activity coefficient is approximately the same in all experiments, by the Debye-Hückel theory. It will also be seen that within wide limits the amount of buffer solution employed in a given total volume is inconsequential, provided the ionic strength of the resultant solution is always kept about the same. The solutions required are as follows:

Buffer A. Pipette 100 ml of 0.75 *M* NaAc solution, 100 ml of 0.22 *M* HAc solution, and about 20 ml of 0.2 per cent soluble starch solution into a 500-ml volumetric flask, and make up to the mark with distilled water [yields $(H^+) \cong 10^{-5}$ *M*].

Buffer B. Pipette 50 ml of 0.75 *M* NaAc solution, 100 ml of 0.22 *M* HAc solution, and about 10 ml of 0.2 per cent soluble starch solution into a 250-ml volumetric flask, and make up to the mark with distilled water [yields $(H^+) \cong 2 \times 10^{-5}$ *M*].

H_3AsO_3, 0.03 *M*. Should be made up from $NaAsO_2$ and brought to a pH of about 5 by addition of HAc.

KIO_3, 0.1 *M*.

KI, 0.2 *M*.

Suggested sets of initial volumes of reactant solutions, based on a final volume of 100 ml, are given in the table below.

Solution	Pipette sizes	Initial volumes of solutions, ml			
		I	II	III	IV
H_3AsO_3	5	5	5	5	5
IO_3^-	5	5	10	5	5
Buffer *A*	20, 25	65	60	40	
Buffer *B*	20, 25				65
I^-	25	25	25	50	25

Two or three runs should be made on each of the four sets. Two or more runs should also be made on a set with proportions chosen by the student in which the initial compositions of *two* reacting species differ from those in set I. In each case, the amount of buffer required is that needed to obtain a final volume of 100 ml.

It is convenient to use each pipette only for a single solution, in so far as possible, to minimize time spent in rinsing. The pipettes should be marked to avoid mistakes.

The buffer solutions and the iodide solution should be equilibrated to 25°C by clamping flasks containing them in a thermostat bath set at that temperature. Two vessels of convenient size (ca. 250 ml) and shape (beakers or erlenmeyer flasks), rinsed and drained essentially dry, should also be clamped in the bath. One of them should have a white-painted bottom surface (or have a piece of white cloth taped under the bottom) to aid in observing the blue end point unless other means are available to obtain a light background.

To make a run, pipette all the solutions *except* KI into one of the vessels and the KI solution into the other. Remove both vessels from the bath, and begin the reaction by pouring the iodide rapidly but quantitatively into the other solution, simultaneously starting the stopwatch. Pour the solution back and forth once or twice to complete the mixing, and place the vessel containing the final solution back into the bath. Stop the watch at the appearance of the first faint but definite blue color.

CALCULATIONS

The student should construct a table giving the actual initial concentrations of the reactants IO_3^-, I^-, and H^+. The H^+ concentrations should be calculated from the actual concentrations of NaAc and HAc in the stock solutions employed, with an activity coefficient calculated by use of the Debye-Hückel theory for the ionic strength ($\mu = 0.16$) of the reacting mixtures.

Using the known initial concentration of H_3AsO_3, calculate the initial rate for each run. From appropriate combinations of sets I, II, III, and IV calculate the exponents in the rate expression (3). Also calculate a value of the rate constant k from each run, and obtain an average value of k from all runs.

Write the rate expression, with the numerical values of the rate constant k and the experimentally obtained values of the exponents. Beside it write the temperature and ionic strength at which this expression was obtained.

Write another rate expression, in which those exponents which appear to be reasonably close (within experimental error) to integers are replaced by the integral values. Use this expression to calculate values for the initial rates of all sets studied, and compare them with the observed initial rates.

DISCUSSION

The kinetics of this reaction have been the subject of much study, and the mechanism is not yet completely elucidated with certainty. Following is an incomplete list of the mechanisms that have been proposed:

1. $IO_3^- + 2I^- + 2H^+ \xrightarrow{k} 2HOI + IO^-$ (slow)

   Followed by fast reactions (Dushman[1])

2. $IO_3^- + H^+ \overset{K}{\rightleftharpoons} HIO_3$ (fast, to equil.)

   $I^- + H^+ \overset{K'}{\rightleftharpoons} HI$ (fast, to equil.)

   $HIO_3 + HI \xrightarrow{k} HIO + HIO_2$ (slow)

   Followed by fast reactions (at low iodide concentrations; Abel and Hilferding[2])

3. $IO_3^- + I^- + 2H^+ \overset{K}{\rightleftharpoons} H_2I_2O_3$ (fast, to equil.)

   $H_2I_2O_3 \overset{K'}{\rightleftharpoons} I_2O_2 + H_2O$ (fast, to equil.)

   $I_2O_2 + I^- \xrightarrow{k} I_3O_2^-$ (slow)

   Followed by fast reactions (Bray and Liebhafsky[3])

4. $IO_3^- + I^- + 2H^+ \overset{K}{\rightleftharpoons} H_2I_2O_3$ (fast, to equil.)

   $H_2I_2O_3 \xrightarrow{k} HOI + HIO_2$ (slow)

   Followed by fast reactions (at low iodide concentrations; Bray and Liebhafsky[3])

5. $IO_3^- + H^+ \overset{K}{\rightleftharpoons} IO_2^+ + OH^-$ (fast, to equil.)

   $H^+ + OH^- \overset{1/K_w}{\rightleftharpoons} H_2O$ (fast, to equil.)

   $IO_2^+ + I^- \overset{K'}{\rightleftharpoons} IOIO$ (fast, to equil.)

   $IOIO + I^- \xrightarrow{k} I^+ + 2IO^-$ (slow)

   Followed by fast reactions (Morgan, Peard, and Cullis[4])

6. $IO_3^- + H^+ \overset{K}{\rightleftharpoons} IO_2^+ + OH^-$ (fast, to equil.)

   $H^+ + OH^- \overset{1/K_w}{\rightleftharpoons} H_2O$ (fast, to equil.)

   $IO_2^+ + I^- \overset{K'}{\rightleftharpoons} IOIO$ (fast, to equil.)

   $IOIO \xrightarrow{k} IO^+ + IO^-$ (slow)

   Followed by fast reactions (at low iodide concentrations; Morgan, Peard, and Cullis[4])

The student should discuss the above mechanisms in connection with his experimentally determined rate law.

The oxidation of iodide ion by chlorate ion ClO_3^- has also been studied.[5, 6] Although the reaction appears to be attended by complications which make it difficult to study, under certain conditions it can be carried out as an "iodine clock" experiment. (For the interested student, suggested concentration ranges for 20 to 25°C are ClO_3^-, 0.05 to 0.10 *M*; I^-, 0.025 to 0.10 *M*; H^+, 0.02 to 0.04 *M*. A sulfate-bisulfate buffer may be used.) The resulting rate law is not identical with that for the reaction with iodate, but appears to be compatible with mechanisms analogous to several of those given above.

APPARATUS

Three 200-ml beakers (bottom painted white); two 250-ml and one 100-ml beakers; two 5-, one 20-, two 25-, and one 50-ml pipettes; one 250- and one 500-ml volumetric flask; four 250-ml erlenmeyer flasks with four corks to fit; one 10-ml graduated cylinder; glass-marking pencil; stopwatch.

Constant-temperature bath (set at 25°C) with provision for mounting beakers and flasks; 0.75 *M* NaAc solution (300 ml); 0.22 *M* HAc solution (300 ml); 0.03 *M* H_3AsO_3 solution (150 ml); 0.1 *M* KIO_3 solution (150 ml); 0.2 *M* KI solution (500 ml); 0.2 per cent soluble starch solution, with trace of HgI_2 as preservative (75 ml).

REFERENCES

1. S. Dushman, *J. Phys. Chem.*, **8,** 453 (1904).
2. E. Abel and K. Hilferding, *Z. physik. Chem.*, **136A,** 186 (1928).
3. W. C. Bray, *J. Am. Chem. Soc.*, **52,** 3580 (1930).
4. K. J. Morgan, M. G. Peard, and C. F. Cullis, *J. Chem. Soc.*, **1951,** 1865.
5. W. C. Bray, *J. Phys. Chem.*, **7,** 92 (1903).
6. A. Skrabal and H. Schreiner, *Monatsh. Chem.*, **65,** 213 (1934).

GENERAL READING

W. J. Moore, "Physical Chemistry," 2d ed., chap. 17, Prentice-Hall, Englewood Cliffs, N.J. (1955).
F. H. MacDougall, "Physical Chemistry," chap. 15, Macmillan, New York (1952).
K. J. Laidler, "Chemical Kinetics," McGraw-Hill, New York (1950).

Experiment 27. Kinetics of a Hydrolysis Reaction

In the presence of hydrogen ions, diethyl acetal in aqueous solution hydrolyzes as follows, the reaction going substantially to completion:

$$CH_3CH(OC_2H_5)_2 + H_2O \xrightarrow{H^+} CH_3CHO + 2C_2H_5OH \qquad (1)$$

In this experiment the reaction will be shown to be first order with respect to acetal and with respect to hydrogen ion, the rate constant will be determined, and the temperature dependence of the rate constant will be used to calculate the activation energy for the reaction.

Other acetals, as well as numerous other organic compounds such as esters and epoxides, also undergo acid-catalyzed hydrolysis with similar kinetics.[1] Use has been made of kinetics measurements on reactions of this kind as a means of measuring hydrogen-ion concentration independently of hydrogen-ion activity.[2]

THEORY

A first-order reaction is ordinarily understood to be one in which the rate of disappearance of a single species is proportional to the concentration of that species in the reaction mixture. This terminology is often used even when, strictly speaking, the total reaction order is different from unity owing to the participation of additional species in the reaction which are themselves not consumed (i.e., catalysts—H^+ in the present instance) or the participation of substances which are present in such large amount that their concentrations do not undergo significant percentage change during the reaction (H_2O in the present instance). It would be more correct in such cases to state that the reaction is first order with respect to a given disappearing species.

The rate law for a first-order reaction may be expressed by the differential equation

$$-\frac{dc_A}{dt} = kc_A \tag{2}$$

where c_A is the instantaneous concentration of the disappearing reactant (here acetal) and k is the *specific reaction rate,* or simply *rate constant,* applicable to the specified conditions (temperature and in the present case hydrogen-ion concentration) which are constant throughout the course of the reaction. If the dependence of the rate of hydrolysis of acetal on hydrogen-ion concentration is known, it may be included in the expression for the rate law. In the present experiment it will be demonstrated that this dependence is first order, and we can write accordingly

$$-\frac{dc_A}{dt} = k'c_{H^+}c_A \tag{3}$$

where k' is another rate constant at the specified temperature, independent of the hydrogen-ion concentration.

If Eq. (2) is integrated with the initial condition $c = c_0$ at $t = 0$, we obtain

$$\ln\frac{c}{c_0} = -kt \qquad c = c_0e^{-kt} \tag{4}$$

A reaction may be shown to be first order by a variety of methods, some of which are:

1. The logarithm of the concentration c is plotted against time and the experimental points are shown to fit a straight line.

2. The time interval required for any definite fraction of the reactant to disappear is shown to be a constant, independent of when the interval is taken during the reaction. In the special case where the fraction is one-half, the time interval is called the "half-life" of the reactant.

3. The *rate* of the reaction is studied as a function of time. A well-known example is that of radioactive decay, where the rate of decay is given by a radiation intensity as measured, say, by a Geiger counter.

4. The *initial rate* of the reaction, $-(dc/dt)_{t=0}$, is determined at a number of initial concentrations c_0, and the initial rate is shown to be directly proportional to the initial concentration (see Exp. 26).

All the above methods require that the actual concentration or its instantaneous time derivative be known at least to within a multiplicative constant. However, there are methods useful for cases where only a linear function of the concentration

$$f = Ac + B \tag{5}$$

is available (A and B being unknown constants):

5. The reaction is allowed to go substantially to completion by waiting a very long time or by temperature change or catalysis, and a value of f_∞ is obtained. Then we can use the equation, derived from Eqs. (4) and (5),

$$\ln \frac{f - f_\infty}{f_0 - f_\infty} = -kt \tag{6}$$

in the manner of method 1 above.

6. *Guggenheim method.* In the present experiment we shall use a method[3] which eliminates the need for an f_∞ value. From Eqs. (4) and (5) we have

$$f(t) = Ac_0e^{-kt} + B$$

and at time $t + \Delta t$

$$f(t + \Delta t) = Ac_0e^{-k\,\Delta t}\,e^{-kt} + B$$

Taking the difference we obtain

$$\Delta f \equiv f(t + \Delta t) - f(t) = Ac_0(e^{-k\,\Delta t} - 1)e^{-kt} \tag{7}$$

Thus, *for constant* Δt, Δf varies exponentially in a way similar to c. If we plot its logarithm against t as in method 1, we should obtain a straight line, from the slope of which the rate constant can be obtained:

$$\ln \Delta f = 2.303 \log \Delta f = -kt + \text{const.} \tag{8}$$

The Guggenheim treatment and its results are in principle independent of the particular constant value chosen for Δt. The choice of a value for Δt depends on practical considerations: If it is too small, the scatter of points on the logarithmic plot will be too great, and if it is too large, the number of points that can be plotted becomes too small. For a clear demonstration of first-order kinetics and a good determination of the rate constant, the points plotted should cover at least one natural logarithmic cycle (one power of e). A good procedure would be to run the experiment over a total time sufficient to obtain about 1½ cycles (i.e., until increments between successive readings have decreased to about one-fifth of the initial value) and to take about one third of this total time for Δt.

This method may be seen to be very closely related to method 3 above. It uses two experimental readings separated by a constant time difference Δt to determine, not the actual rate itself, but rather a quantity which on the assumption of first-order kinetics must be directly proportional to the actual instantaneous rate. When the appropriate logarithmic plot gives a straight line, the assumption of first-order kinetics is confirmed. The method may be said to degenerate into method 3 in the limit of $\Delta t = 0$, and into method 5 in the limit $\Delta t = \infty$.

Dependence on Hydrogen-ion Concentration. In this experiment the rate constant k will be demonstrated to be proportional to the first power of the hydrogen-ion concentration. This suggests a mechanism which can be written

$$\begin{array}{ll} A + H_2O + H^+ = X^+ & \text{(fast equilibrium, } K^*) \\ X^+ \rightarrow H^+ + \text{products} & \text{(rate determining, } k_X) \end{array} \tag{9}$$

where A is acetal and X^+ is the activated complex ion. This predicts for the reaction rate

$$-\frac{dc_A}{dt} = k_Xc_{X^+} = k_XK^*c_{H^+}c_A \tag{10}$$

Comparison with Eqs. (2) and (3) gives

$$k = k' c_{H^+} = k_X K^* c_{H^+} \tag{11}$$

It is worthy of note that the rate constant is proportional to the *concentration*, rather than to the thermodynamic *activity*, of hydrogen ion. This was explained by Brönsted in terms of the transition-state theory.[4] It arises from the fact that the equilibrium constant K^* contains an activity coefficient for the ion X^+ in the numerator and one for the ion H^+ in the denominator while all other activity coefficients present are for uncharged species. For dilute solutions of given ionic strength the Debye-Hückel theory predicts that the activity coefficients of all univalent ions are very nearly equal, and those for H^+ and X^+ accordingly should cancel out. In the same order of approximation, the activity coefficients for uncharged species are unity. (In certain other cases activity coefficients do not cancel out, and the rate constants are there found to depend on the ionic strengths of the solutions.)

As a matter of convenience, acetate buffer solutions are to be used as a means of obtaining low but stable hydrogen-ion concentrations. The hydrogen-ion concentration in the reaction mixture can be calculated directly from the buffer composition and the acetic acid dissociation constant:

$$c_{H^+} = \frac{K}{\gamma_{\pm}^2} \frac{c_{HAc}}{c_{Ac^-}} \tag{12}$$

At 25°C, $K = 1.753 \times 10^{-5}$ mole liter^{-1}. Alternatively, the hydrogen-ion activity of the buffer can be determined with a pH meter, and the concentration calculated from

$$c_{H^+} = \frac{a_{H^+}}{\gamma_{H^+}} \tag{13}$$

Activity coefficients can be obtained with sufficient accuracy from the Debye-Hückel expression

$$\log \gamma_{H^+} = \log \gamma_{\pm} = -0.509 \frac{\sqrt{\mu}}{1 + \sqrt{\mu}} \tag{14}$$

where μ is the ionic strength (= NaAc concentration).

Dependence on Temperature. The Arrhenius activation energy E^* is related to the temperature variation of the rate constant by the equation

$$\frac{d \ln k'}{dT} = \frac{E^*}{RT^2} \tag{15}$$

If this is integrated with the assumption of constant E^*, we obtain

$$\ln k' = 2.303 \log k' = -\frac{E^*}{RT} + \text{const.} \tag{16}$$

which permits us to obtain E^* from the slope of a plot of the logarithm of the rate constant against the reciprocal of the absolute temperature. If the rate constant is available at only two temperatures, we can use the equation

$$\ln \frac{k_2'}{k_1'} = 2.303 \log \frac{k_2'}{k_1'} = \frac{E^*}{R} \frac{(T_2 - T_1)}{T_1 T_2} \tag{17}$$

Since in this experiment a buffer solution is being used at more than one temperature, we should examine the effect of possible temperature variation of the hydrogen-ion concentration in the buffer, since, in general, the dissociation constants of weak acids are functions of temperature. Failure to take this into account would have the effect of adding the heat of ionization of the weak acid to the activation energy. In the case of acetic acid the heat of ionization happens to be very small (-0.2 kcal) in comparison with the expected energy of activation, and this small quantity is partly offset by a very small correction ($+0.09$ kcal) for the temperature variation of the activity coefficient. Therefore with an acetate buffer the effect of temperature on hydrogen-ion concentration can be neglected for the present experiment.

METHOD

As a measurable physical quantity which may be taken as a linear function of the concentration of the disappearing reactant, the *total volume* V of a given quantity of the reaction mixture might be used. To a good approximation, the volume is a linear function of the numbers of moles N_i of the component species i present:

$$V = \sum_i N_i \bar{V}_i$$

since the partial molal volumes $\bar{V}_i$ are approximately constant for both solvent and solutes in a dilute solution. In turn the numbers of moles N_i are linear functions of the concentration of the disappearing reactant. Similarly we might use the electrical conductance of the reacting mixture in the event that the species concerned are ionic, or the optical density for a given wavelength of light if the species have absorption bands.

In the present experiment we shall make use of the total volume of the solution as measured with a dilatometer, which is a vessel to which a graduated capillary of small diameter is attached so that small changes in the volume of the contained liquid can be measured by movement of the meniscus of the liquid in the capillary. The capillary need not be graduated to correspond to the total volume of solution; it is sufficient that the graduations give the volume above any fixed reference point in the capillary in any arbitrary units. The capillary reading h is then a linear function of the total volume and thus, by the above argument, is also a linear function of the concentration of the disappearing reactant.

EXPERIMENTAL

The dilatometer is shown in Fig. 1. It must be handled with great care, as it is very fragile. Special care should be exercised in cleaning it and in putting it into and taking it out of its holder.

Thermostat baths at 20.0, 25.0, and 30.0°C are required, with temperature regulation of ± 0.002°C, as the volume changes produced even by small temperature changes are of the same order of magnitude as those produced by the reaction being studied. A Beckmann thermometer or its equivalent should be used for a careful and frequent monitoring of the bath regulation.

Materials. The acetal should be of high purity, dry, and free of acidic substances. If necessary the commercially available product may be refluxed over calcium oxide and fractionated.

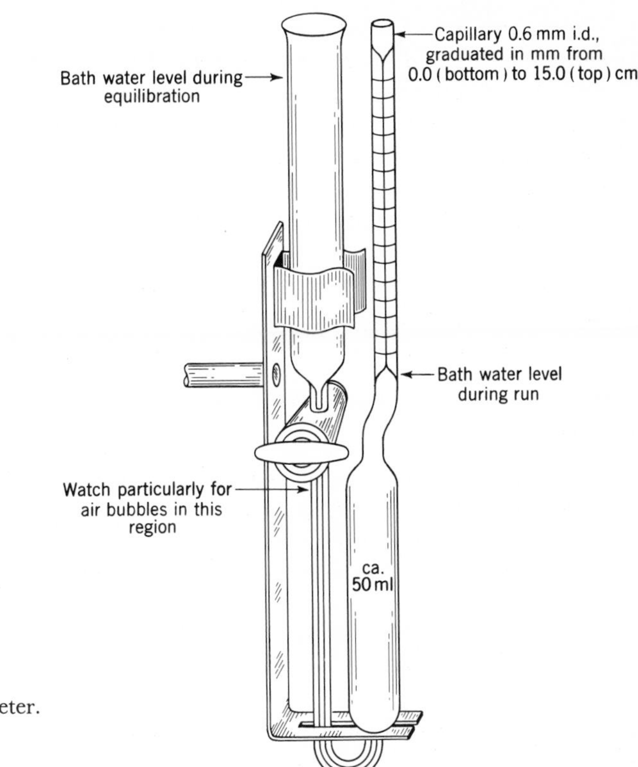

FIG. 1. Dilatometer.

Water used in the preparation of the stock solutions and water to be used for making up the final buffer solutions should be as free of dissolved gases as possible. Boiled distilled water may be used.

The following buffer solutions will be needed and should be made up volumetrically from the stock solutions provided (0.1 *M* NaAc, 1.5 *M* HAc):

I. 0.02 *M* in NaAc and 0.3 *M* in HAc ($c_{H^+} \cong 3.4 \times 10^{-4}$ *M*; pH $\cong$ 3.5)

II. 0.02 *M* in NaAc and 0.6 *M* in HAc ($c_{H^+} \cong 6.7 \times 10^{-4}$ *M*; pH $\cong$ 3.2)

To save time 250 ml of each of these solutions should be made up at the beginning of the period. At least 15 min before it will be needed, 100 ml of each solution in a volumetric flask should be placed in the thermostat bath to equilibrate. At the same time, a clean, dry 250-ml flask should be clamped in the bath for later use in preparing the reaction mixture. Flasks and solutions should be brought close to bath temperature before being placed in a bath if someone else is performing a run in the same bath.

Cleaning the Dilatometer. The dilatometer should be very carefully cleaned. First, the stopcock plug should be removed and set aside for thorough cleaning. After the stopcock barrel has been scrubbed out with a test-tube brush and detergent solution and any excess stopcock grease from the stopcock leads cleaned out with a pipe cleaner, the two ends of the barrel may be plugged with corks. To facilitate further cleaning and rinsing, a one-hole rubber stopper equipped with a short length of tubing is affixed to the mouth of the dilatometer and connected to a water aspirator with pressure tubing. With the aspirator on, the end of the capillary is dipped into a battery jar or lipless beaker containing a detergent solution (see Fig. 2) until the dilatometer is partly filled. It should then be carefully shaken for a few minutes. By the same technique it is repeatedly and very thoroughly rinsed with distilled water and dried by sucking air through it. It need not be rigorously dry except in the capillary tube and in the stopcock barrel and leads. The latter can be dried with the help of a towel and pipe cleaner. The stopcock plug should be scrubbed with detergent, and its bore should be cleaned with a pipe cleaner. It should be rinsed and dried thoroughly, carefully greased as described in Chap. XVII, and reinserted into the barrel. The dilatometer can then be installed in its holder and placed in the bath to equilibrate.

Between and after runs it is not necessary to clean the dilatometer so thoroughly or to regrease the stopcock. The used solution should be removed by suction, and the dilatometer then thoroughly rinsed and dried.

Procedure. Make up the reacting mixture by pouring 100 ml of buffer solution into the clean dry 250-ml flask, and then pipetting in 2 ml of acetal. The mixture should be swirled in the bath until the acetal has completely dissolved.

With the stopcock of the dilatometer closed, introduce a sufficient quantity of the reacting mixture. After all air bubbles have risen to the surface, the dilatometer can be mounted higher in the bath (so that the entire capillary is above the water surface) and the stopcock can be opened to admit the solution into the bulb. When the bulb is partly filled, the one-hole stopper with affixed tube should be attached and suction applied by mouth so as to reverse the flow; the purpose of this is to dislodge any air bubbles which may be trapped in the tube below the stop-

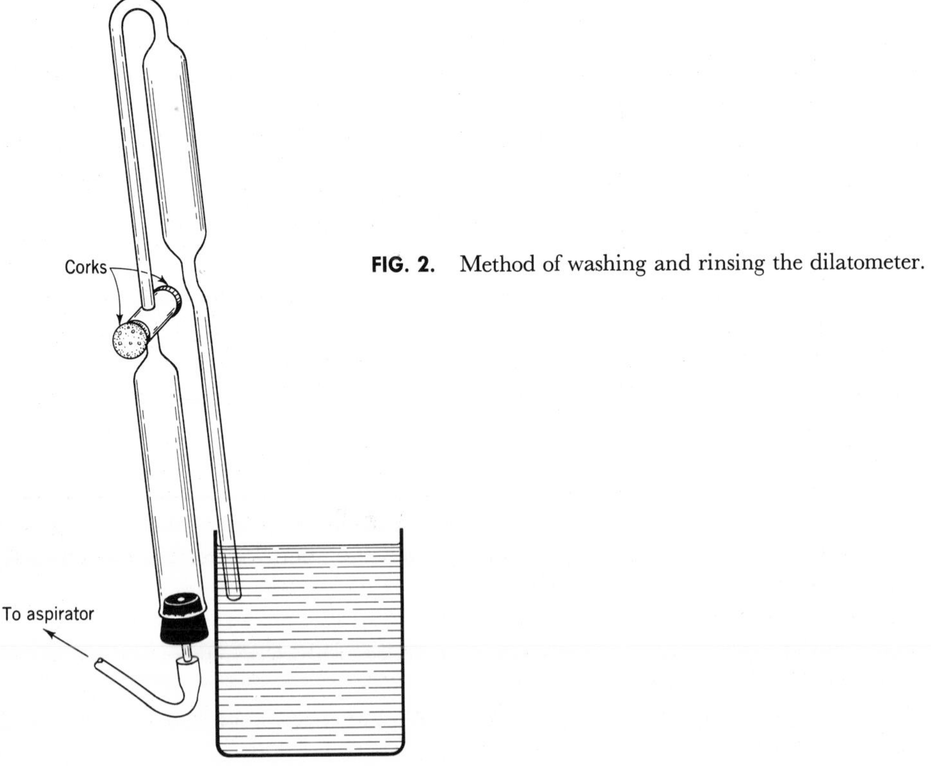

FIG. 2. Method of washing and rinsing the dilatometer.

cock. After a few repetitions of this suction, close the stopcock and raise the dilatometer from the bath for a few seconds to permit inspection for the presence of air bubbles; if there are none, the solution may be allowed to fill the bulb completely. The rate of filling should be reduced drastically toward the end in order that it can be cut off suddenly as soon as the meniscus is on scale in the capillary. It is inadvisable to draw the meniscus down in the capillary by suction unless absolutely necessary, for drainage from the capillary wall is likely to form liquid plugs which drain slowly and unreliably during the run.

Readings of the position of the meniscus (estimated to one-tenth of the smallest scale division) should be made at 30-sec intervals, starting as soon as possible after the stopcock has been closed. They should be continued until differences between successive readings are averaging about one-fifth of the differences observed near the beginning of the run (discounting the first half dozen readings). The bath temperature should be frequently read to 0.001° and recorded.

Runs should be made under the following sets of conditions:

1. Buffer solution I ($c_{H^+} \cong 3.4 \times 10^{-4}\ M$) at 25.0°C
2. Buffer solution II ($c_{H^+} \cong 6.7 \times 10^{-4}\ M$) at 25.0°C
3. Buffer solution II ($c_{H^+} \cong 6.7 \times 10^{-4}\ M$) at 20.0°C
4. Buffer solution I ($c_{H^+} \cong 3.4 \times 10^{-4}\ M$) at 30.0°C

If time is limited, it is advisable to perform runs 2 and 3 or 1 and 4 in order to determine the activation energy E^* from data obtained at constant hydrogen-ion concentration.

CALCULATIONS

For each run a table should be constructed with the following entries: t, $h(t)$, Δh, and log Δh, where $\Delta h = h(t + \Delta t) - h(t)$; Δt should be chosen in accord with the discussion of the Guggenheim method. A plot of log Δh against t is then constructed, and the best straight line drawn through the points. Semilog paper (one decimal cycle) is convenient. The plot is likely to show some initial curvature, which should be disregarded in drawing the straight line; it is presumably due to drift toward temperature equilibrium following the filling operation. The rate constant k is calculated from the slope of the line.

If the plotted points tend to show a slight systematic oscillation about the line, a periodic variation in bath temperature due to thermoregulator cycling is probably responsible; if possible, compare the period of the oscillation with that of the thermoregulator cycling. Draw your line so as to even out these fluctuations.

The hydrogen-ion concentrations should be calculated by use of either Eq. (12) or (13). If Eq. (12) is used, the changes in Ac^- and HAc concentrations due to the small ionization of the acetic acid should not be neglected; they may be taken account of in a second approximation, the magnitude of the ionization having been estimated in a first approximation using the concentration values calculated directly from those for the stock solutions.

The results of runs 1 and 2 should be used to demonstrate that the reaction is first order with respect to hydrogen ion, and a value of k' should be calculated at 25°C.

The activation energy E^* should be calculated from the variation of k' with temperature.

APPARATUS

Dilatometer; special clamp for mounting dilatometer; one-hole rubber stopper to fit top of dilatometer, with short length of glass tubing affixed; magnifier (optional); clock or stopwatch; two clamps; three clamp holders; one 100- and two 250-ml volumetric flasks; 250-ml erlenmeyer flask; 2-, 50-, and 100-ml pipettes; battery jar; glass-stoppered bottle for storing acetal; medium length (~2 ft) of gum-rubber tubing; corks to fit stopcock barrel.

Constant-temperature baths set at 20, 25, and 30°C with Beckmann thermometers mounted in each; water aspirator, equipped with rubber hose; stopcock grease; pipe cleaners; acetone for rinsing; reagent-grade acetal (15 ml); 0.1 *M* sodium acetate (200 ml); 1.5 *M* acetic acid (300 ml).

REFERENCES

1. J. N. Brönsted and W. F. K. Wynne-Jones, *Trans. Faraday Soc.*, **25,** 59 (1929).
2. M. Kilpatrick, Jr., and E. F. Chase, *J. Am. Chem. Soc.*, **53,** 1732 (1931).
3. E. A. Guggenheim, *Phil. Mag.*, **2** (7), 538 (1926).
4. W. J. Moore, "Physical Chemistry," 2d ed., Prentice-Hall, Englewood Cliffs, N.J. (1955).

GENERAL READING

A. A. Frost and R. G. Pearson, "Kinetics and Mechanism," Wiley, New York (1953).

Experiment 28. Gas-phase Kinetics

Although a vast majority of important chemical reactions occur primarily in liquid solution, the study of simple gas-phase reactions is very important in developing a theoretical understanding of chemical kinetics. A detailed molecular explanation of rate processes in liquid solution is extremely difficult. At the present time reaction mechanisms are much better understood for gas-phase reactions; even so, this problem is by no means simple. This experiment will deal with the unimolecular decomposition of an organic compound in the vapor state. The compound suggested for study is cyclopentene, but several other compounds are also suitable.[1]

THEORY

A discussion of bimolecular reactions (which usually give rise to second-order kinetics) can be based quite naturally on collision theory or on transition-state theory.[1,2] We shall assume a general knowledge of these treatments as background for the discussion of unimolecular reactions (which usually give rise to first-order kinetics). The crucial question is: How does a molecule acquire the necessary energy to undergo a spontaneous unimolecular decomposition? If the "activation" occurs via a collision, one could normally expect second-order kinetics. However, Lindemann pointed out that this would not be true if the time between collisions is short compared with the average lifetime of an activated molecule.

Let us consider a simple unimolecular decomposition† in the gas phase

$$A \rightarrow B + C$$

The proposed reaction mechanism will consist of three steps: (1) collisional activation, (2) collisional deactivation, and (3) spontaneous decomposition of the activated molecule. Thus,

$$A + A \rightarrow A + A^* \qquad k_1 \tag{1}$$

$$A^* + A \rightarrow A + A \qquad k_2 \tag{2}$$

$$A^* \rightarrow B + C \qquad k_A \tag{3}$$

where A* is an activated A molecule with a definite internal energy ϵ which is greater than a certain critical value ϵ^* necessary for reaction to occur, k_1 and k_2 are second-order rate constants, and k_A is a first-order rate constant. The over-all rate of reaction is given by

$$+\frac{d(B)}{dt} = +\frac{d(C)}{dt} = -\frac{d(A)}{dt} = k_A(A^*) \tag{4}$$

where parentheses indicate concentrations of the species. As discussed below, the value of k_A will depend on the particular value of ϵ involved. If the concentration of A* is small, one can make the steady-state approximation, $d(A^*)/dt = 0$ and obtain

$$+\frac{d(A^*)}{dt} = k_1(A)^2 - k_2(A^*)(A) - k_A(A^*) = 0 \tag{5}$$

Solving Eq. (5) for (A*) and substituting the resulting expression into Eq. (4) give

$$-\frac{d(A)}{dt} = \frac{k_1 k_A (A)^2}{k_A + k_2(A)} \tag{6}$$

High-pressure Limit. At high concentrations deactivation is much more probable than decomposition, since the collision frequency is high, and deactivation should occur at the first collision suffered by A*. Thus at high pressure, $k_2(A) \gg k_A$ and the reaction becomes first order:

$$-\frac{1}{(A)}\frac{d(A)}{dt} = \frac{k_1}{k_2}k_A \tag{7}$$

Also

$$\frac{k_1}{k_2} = \frac{(A^*)}{(A)} \cong f_A \tag{8}$$

where f_A is the fraction of A molecules in an activated state, with some internal energy ϵ. Obviously f_A depends on the value of ϵ, as does k_A. Thus,

$$-\frac{1}{(A)}\frac{d(A)}{dt} = \int_{\epsilon^*}^{\infty} k_A(\epsilon) f_A(\epsilon)\, d\epsilon = k_\infty \tag{9}$$

where k_∞, the value of the integral, corresponds to the experimental first-order rate constant k_{exp} determined at high pressures.

† In the following treatment several details and difficulties will be overlooked; more advanced developments are given by Benson[1] and Trotman-Dickenson.[3]

Rice and Ramsperger[4] and Kassel[5] have given an expression for k_A as a function of ϵ:

$$k_A(\epsilon) = 0 \qquad \text{for } \epsilon < \epsilon^*$$
$$= \nu\left(\frac{\epsilon - \epsilon^*}{\epsilon}\right)^{n-1} \qquad \text{for } \epsilon \geqslant \epsilon^* \tag{10}$$

Equation (10) is based on a model in which the molecule contains a total internal energy ϵ distributed among n weakly coupled harmonic oscillators. One of these oscillators is localized in a weak bond which will break when energy ϵ^* is concentrated in it; the other $n - 1$ oscillators are assumed to act as a reservoir of freely available energy. The probability that an energy at least as large as ϵ^* is localized in one oscillator is given by $(1 - \epsilon^*/\epsilon)^{n-1}$, and ν is the frequency of energy transfer among the various oscillators in the molecule. For such a model, one would expect ν to be of about the same order of magnitude as molecular vibrational frequencies—namely, 10^{13} sec^{-1}. [A more realistic and sophisticated molecular model has been proposed by N. B. Slater[1, 3] which gives results very similar to those based on Eq. (10) and which also predicts a value for ν of about 10^{13} sec^{-1}.]

To get a rough approximation for $f_A(\epsilon)$ we can use a classical model in which the normal modes of vibration of the molecule A are represented by n classical harmonic oscillators. With this drastic assumption, one can use Boltzmann statistics to obtain[6]

$$f_A(\epsilon) = \frac{1}{(n-1)!kT}\left(\frac{\epsilon}{kT}\right)^{n-1} e^{-\epsilon/kT} \tag{11}$$

When Eqs. (10) and (11) are substituted into Eq. (9) we find that

$$k_\infty = \frac{\nu}{(n-1)!} e^{-\epsilon^*/kT} \int_0^\infty x^{n-1} e^{-x}\, dx \tag{12}$$

where $x = (\epsilon - \epsilon^*)/kT$. The definite integral is the gamma function $\Gamma(n) = (n - 1)!$ Thus,

$$k_\infty = \nu e^{-\epsilon^*/kT} = \nu e^{-E^*/RT} \tag{13}$$

where $E^* = N_0\epsilon^*$. Equation (13) can be compared directly with the empirical Arrhenius equation which is used to obtain the experimental activation energy:

$$k = Ae^{-E_{act}/RT} \tag{14}$$

The temperature-independent factor A has now been given a physical significance and an estimated magnitude.

The theory presented above can be improved by using a quantum mechanical model for the oscillations of the activated complex; this will permit a consideration of the effect of possible structural changes in the activated complex. The final result from this more sophisticated model[7] is

$$k = \nu^* e^{\Delta S^*/R} e^{-\Delta H^*/RT} \tag{15}$$

where ν^* is an average frequency of the vibrational modes in the activated complex and ΔS^* and ΔH^* are the entropy and enthalpy changes for forming the activated complex (transition state) from a normal species. Comparing Eqs. (14) and (15) one can identify A with $\nu^* e^{\Delta S^*/R}$, but ν^* is not well known, since it depends on the properties of an activated molecule (which are themselves not well known). Perhaps the best thing that can be done at present is to assign ν^* a value of about 10^{13} sec^{-1} (the usual value of A in many reactions). Then, when the experimental value of A is less than 10^{12} or greater than 10^{14}, we can look for a possible explanation in terms of a value of ΔS^* which differs appreciably from zero.†

Low-pressure Limit. We now wish to comment on the behavior of Eq. (6) at low concentrations where the collision frequency is so low that deactivation will be very slow compared with decomposition. At low pressures, $k_2(\mathrm{A}) \ll k_A$ and we find second-order kinetics:

$$-\frac{1}{(\mathrm{A})}\frac{d(\mathrm{A})}{dt} = k_1(\mathrm{A}) \tag{16}$$

A detailed treatment of the change with pressure of the apparent first-order rate constant is quite complicated,[2, 3] but we can easily see that

$$k_1(\mathrm{A}) \ll \frac{k_1 k_A}{k_2} \cong k_\infty \tag{17}$$

Thus at low initial pressures the "first-order rate constant" k_{exp} should decrease as the pressure is decreased (i.e., the half time for the reaction at constant temperature is independent of pressure at high pressure but rises as the pressure approaches zero). For reactions where $A \gg 10^{13}$ sec^{-1}, this change has been observed to occur, but normally (i.e., where $A \sim 10^{13}$) the change will occur at very low pressure and is not observed experimentally.

Chain Mechanisms.[8] The fact that first-order kinetics are observed for a gas-phase reaction does not prove that the unimolecular mechanism described above must be involved. Indeed, very many organic decompositions which experimentally are first order have complicated free-radical chain mechanisms.

As an example, let us consider a simple *hypothetical* chain mechanism for the dehydrogenation of a hydrocarbon:

$$\begin{aligned} \mathrm{M}_a &\rightarrow \mathrm{H} + \mathrm{R} && k_1 \\ \mathrm{H} + \mathrm{M}_a &\rightarrow \mathrm{H}_2 + \mathrm{R} && k_2 \\ \mathrm{R} &\rightarrow \mathrm{H} + \mathrm{M}_b && k_3 \\ \mathrm{H} + \mathrm{R} &\rightarrow \mathrm{M}_c && k_4 \end{aligned} \tag{18}$$

where the M's are stable molecules and R is a free radical. The chain is initiated by the first step, propagated by many repetitions of the second and third steps (to form the stable products H_2 and M_b), and terminated by the last step. By writing the equations for $d(\mathrm{H})/dt$ and $d(\mathrm{R})/dt$ and making the steady-state assumption that (H) and (R) are constant, one can obtain

$$(\mathrm{H}) = \left(\frac{k_1 k_3}{k_2 k_4}\right)^{1/2} \qquad (\mathrm{R}) = \left(\frac{k_1 k_2}{k_3 k_4}\right)^{1/2}(\mathrm{M}_a) \tag{19}$$

Now the rate of disappearance of M_a is given by

$$\begin{aligned} -\frac{d(\mathrm{M}_a)}{dt} &= k_1(\mathrm{M}_a) + k_2(\mathrm{H})(\mathrm{M}_a) \\ &= \left[k_1 + \left(\frac{k_1 k_2 k_3}{k_4}\right)^{1/2}\right](\mathrm{M}_a) \end{aligned} \tag{20}$$

† Transition-state theory gives the same result as Eq. (15) except that ν^* is replaced by a universal factor $kT/h (= 6 \times 10^{12}$ sec^{-1} at 300°K). Although this would appear to resolve the uncertainty as to the value of ν^* (and thus allow better calculation of ΔS^* from A values), the theory involves several assumptions which are open to question on physical grounds.[7]

and we see that the over-all rate is first order. [When the chain is long, $k_2 \gg k_4$ and $k_3 \gg k_1$, so that k_1 is negligible compared with $k_1k_2k_3/k_4$ in Eq. (20).]

The presence of a chain reaction can usually be detected by adding small quantities of an inhibitor such as nitric oxide or propylene, which will markedly reduce the rate by reacting with the radicals and greatly shortening the chain length.[9] Another technique is to add small amounts of a compound which is known to provide relatively large concentrations of free radicals and see if the over-all rate is increased. A detailed treatment of chain mechanisms will not be given here, but it should be pointed out that the over-all rate law is often very complex and the apparent order of the reaction often changes considerably with pressure. To obtain a complete picture of the kinetics may require measurements over the range from a few millimeters of Hg to above 10 atm.

Wall Effects. In the above discussion we have assumed that the reaction is homogeneous (i.e., no catalytic reaction at the walls of the reaction bulb). The fact that the data give first-order kinetics is not a proof that wall effects are absent. This point can be checked by packing a reaction bulb with glass spheres or thin-wall tubes and repeating the measurements under conditions where the surface-to-volume ratio is increased by a factor of 10 to 100. (This will not be done in this experiment, but the system chosen for study should be free from serious wall effects or it may not be possible to discuss the experimental results in terms of the theory of unimolecular reactions.)

METHOD[10]

The three basic experimental features of gas-phase kinetic studies are temperature control, time measurement, and the determination of concentrations. Of these, the principal problem is that of following the composition changes in the system. Perhaps the most generally applicable technique is the chemical analysis of aliquots; however, continuous methods are much more convenient. By far the easiest method is to follow the change in total pressure. This technique will be used in the present experiment. Obviously, the pressure method is possible only for a reaction which is accompanied by a change in the number of moles of gas. Also, the stoichiometry of the reaction should be straightforward and well understood so that pressure changes can be directly related to extent of reaction.

For the simple apparatus design shown in Fig. 1 both the reactant and the products must be sufficiently volatile to avoid condensation in the manometer, which is much cooler than the reaction flask. (Heating wire may be wound around the connecting tubing between the furnace and the manometer to permit warming this section to about 50°C if necessary.) Also there should be no chemical reaction between the vapors and glass, stopcock grease, or mercury. The furnace should be capable of operating at temperatures up to 500°C, and the temperature should remain constant to within less than 1°C during a run. A large, well-insulated furnace has the disadvantage of heating up very slowly, but it will maintain a reasonably constant temperature without regulation. The Pyrex reaction bulb should be mounted in the center of the furnace. A large bulb (about 1000 ml) with a well to hold the thermocouple junction is preferable. However, a small bulb (as small as 100 ml) can be used, and the thermocouple can be wound around the outside of the bulb and then covered with aluminum foil. A two-junction chromel-alumel thermocouple, with the reference junction immersed in an ice bath,

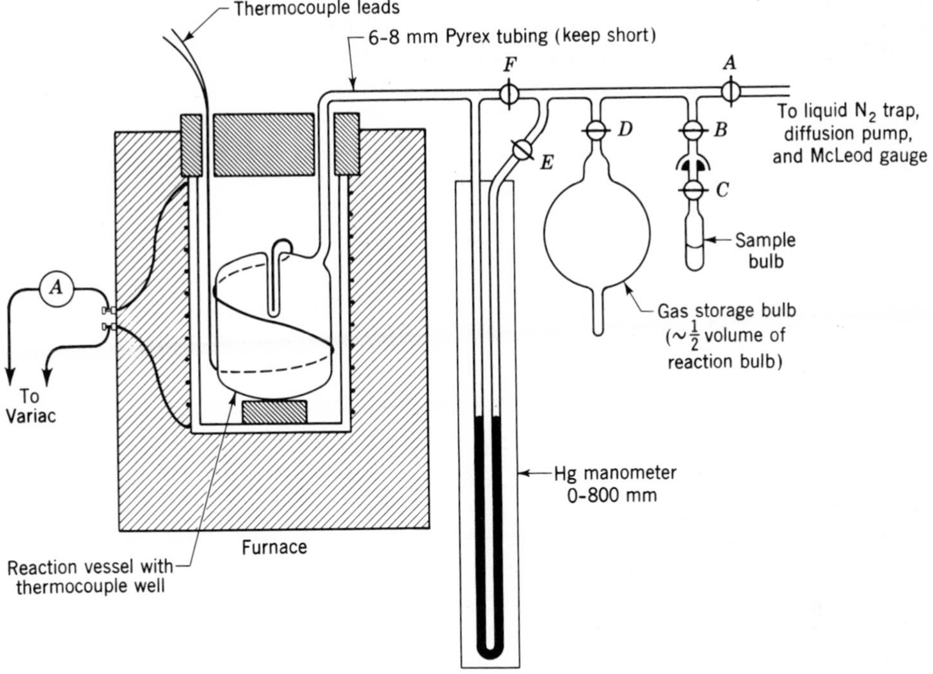

FIG. 1. Apparatus for high-temperature gas-phase kinetics experiment.

is used to measure temperatures (see Chap. XVI). The connecting tubing between the reaction bulb and the mercury in the manometer should be short and of as small bore as feasible. The rate of the reaction should be slow enough so that the time for filling the reaction bulb and for the gas to warm up to the furnace temperature is small compared with the length of the run. Since this initial period is about 30 to 60 sec, the temperature should be chosen to give a half-life of at least 30 min.

We must finally derive an expression for the rate law in terms of the total pressure of the system. As an example, consider the gas-phase decomposition $A \rightarrow B + C$, and assume that the ideal-gas law holds for all species. Let the initial total pressure be p^0; this will also be the partial pressure of species A at zero time ($p_A{}^0$). At some arbitrary time t, $p_B = p_C = p_A{}^0 - p_A$, and since $p = p_A + p_B + p_C$,

$$p_A = 2p^0 - p \tag{21}$$

For a first-order reaction $\ln (A)^0/(A) = kt$; therefore

$$\ln p^0 - \ln (2p^0 - p) = \ln \frac{p^0}{2p^0 - p} = kt \tag{22}$$

Thus a plot of $\ln (2p^0 - p)$ vs. t should be a straight line. For a moderately fast reaction it is often difficult to make a direct measurement of p^0. It is then best to back-extrapolate the early pressure data to zero time to obtain a value of p^0. Another possibility is to allow the reaction to go to completion (assuming there is no back reaction) and measure p^∞, which is equal to $2p^0$ for the particular reaction under consideration. This method is usually not so reliable, since side reactions which have little effect on the early stages of the reaction may influence the final pressure. (The experimental value of p^∞ is often found to be slightly less than the expected value.) Another approach is to use the Guggenheim method as in Exp. 27; this eliminates the need for a p^0 value.

In deriving Eq. (22) the dead-space volume V_D in the manometer and connecting tube has not been considered. Since V_D changes during the reaction (change of the mercury level in the manometer), $p^0/(2p^0 - p)$ in Eq. (22) must be multiplied by a correction factor for very precise work.[11] With $V_D \sim 20$ ml and $V_B \sim 1000$ ml, this correction factor varies linearly with pressure from 1.00 to $\sim$0.98 during the entire run and can be neglected.

Once the order of the reaction is established by a plot of $\ln (2p^0 - p)$ vs. t, there is a rapid method of evaluating specific rate constants which utilizes the time for the reaction to proceed to a given fraction reacted. The half time and third time for a first-order reaction are given by

$$\begin{aligned} kt_{1/2} &= \ln 2 = 0.691 \\ kt_{1/3} &= \ln 1.5 = 0.406 \end{aligned} \tag{23}$$

For the reaction $A \rightarrow B + C$, $t_{1/2}$ is the time required for the total pressure p to reach $3p^0/2$ and $t_{1/3}$ is the time required to reach $4p^0/3$. Either (or both) times can be used to obtain k; it is also possible to check that the pressure data are consistent with first-order kinetics by calculating $t_{1/2}/t_{1/3}$. This ratio should be 1.70 for a first-order reaction; it is 1.50 and 2.00 for zero-order and second-order, respectively.

EXPERIMENTAL

The reaction suggested for study is the decomposition of cyclopentene† to cyclopentadiene and hydrogen:

$$\begin{array}{c} H_2C\text{—}CH \\ | \quad\;\; \| \\ H_2C \quad CH \\ \diagdown \; \diagup \\ C \\ H_2 \end{array} \longrightarrow \begin{array}{c} HC\text{—}CH \\ \| \quad\;\; \| \\ HC \quad CH \\ \diagdown \; \diagup \\ C \\ H_2 \end{array} + H_2 \tag{24}$$

This reaction is quite clean cut, and at least 95 per cent of the products are accounted for by Eq. (24). Vanas and Walters[14] have studied the reaction in the gas phase and find that p^∞/p^0 is about 1.9, which indicates the occurrence of some side reactions. However, they carried out a careful chemical analysis of the products and showed that the partial pressures of cyclopentadiene and hydrogen are equal to each other and to the increase in total pressure Δp over at least the first half of the reaction. With the exception of the last stages of the decomposition, this reaction is very well suited to the pressure method. In addition, it has been shown that the reaction is homogeneous and does not involve a chain mechanism.

The rate of reaction should be studied at a single temperature for several different initial pressures in the range 50 to 200 mm. A furnace temperature of about 510°C will give a convenient half-life ($\sim$30 min). Ordinarily it is only

† Cyclopentene can be obtained in very high purity as an NBS Standard Hydrocarbon Sample or obtained from the Special Products Division of the Phillip's Petroleum Co. Cyclohexene, a more readily available compound, is also suitable for study under the same conditions; however, the stoichiometry is much more complicated[12] and there are some unresolved questions about the kinetics.[13]

necessary to follow the reaction until Δp exceeds $0.5p^0$. However, data should be taken on one of the runs until Δp is at least $0.75p^0$. (If possible, let this reaction mixture stand overnight and obtain a value of p^∞.) If NO gas is available, add about 2 to 3 per cent of NO to the cyclopentene for one of the runs and check for any indication of inhibition; consult the instructor regarding any necessary changes in the procedure. If more than one day is available for experimental work, raise the temperature of the furnace by about 10°C and make several more runs.

Procedure. The furnace should be turned on the day before measurements are to be made so that it will achieve a steady temperature. Set the power supply to a predetermined voltage which is appropriate for the desired reaction temperature. The heating current should be measured with a series ammeter and recorded periodically. At the start of the experiment, place the reference thermocouple junction in a Dewar flask filled with ice and distilled water (see Chap. XVI) and connect the thermocouple to a potentiometer circuit (see Chap. XV). Measure the thermocouple emf and check to see if the furnace is at the proper temperature. If the temperature shows appreciable long-term drift (greater than $\pm 0.5°\ hr^{-1}$) adjustment of the heater current will be necessary. On making any change in voltage setting, be careful to note the time response of the furnace as an aid in making later adjustments.

While the temperature stability of the furnace is being checked, evacuate the system (all stopcocks shown in Fig. 1 should be open *except* B and C) with a diffusion pump until the pressure is 10^{-4} mm Hg or lower. Then close stopcocks E and F and check for leaks in the reaction bulb or manometer. Next close stopcock D, slowly freeze the cyclopentene with liquid nitrogen, and then open stopcocks B and C in order to pump off any air. Close C, remove the liquid nitrogen, and allow the solid to melt so that it will liberate any dissolved gases. Repeat this process at least once more, and then allow the cyclopentene to warm to room temperature. Close stopcock A and open D and C to permit the storage bulb to be filled with vapor (the vapor pressure at 25°C is about 350 mm).

To start a run, **slowly** open stopcock F and watch the manometer. When the pressure has reached about 95 per cent of the desired value for p^0, close F and start a stopwatch. Record pressure and time readings every minute during the early stages of the reaction and every few minutes thereafter until the end of the run.

Analysis of Products. It is possible to design an apparatus which will permit the efficient removal of the entire reaction mixture for analysis. With the apparatus shown in Fig. 1, a qualitative analysis of the products can be made if desired. Analytical details are given by Vanas and Walters.[14]

CALCULATIONS

Plot the pressure reading for each run vs. time and extrapolate to zero time to obtain a value for p^0. For each run determine $t_{1/3}$ and $t_{1/2}$ and check their ratio with that expected for first-order kinetics. Use Eqs. (23) to calculate k, in units of seconds^{-1}, for each of these times. Plot your data from the longest run in the form log $(2p^0 - p)$ vs. t in seconds, draw the best straight line through the points (weighting the early points most heavily), and determine the specific rate constant k as indicated from Eq. (22).

Tabulate T, p^0, $t_{1/3}$, and k for each run, and list your best over-all value of k

for each temperature studied. If data were obtained at two different temperatures, use the integrated form of Eq. (14) to calculate a value of the activation energy. Compare your result with the literature value[14] of 58.8 kcal $mole^{-1}$, which is based on a linear plot of ln k vs. $1/T$ for data over the range 485 to 545°C.

DISCUSSION

How well do your data fit first-order kinetics?

Calculate the frequency factor ν and discuss its value in terms of the theory of unimolecular decompositions.

APPARATUS

Gas kinetics apparatus as shown in Fig. 1, including vacuum line, sample bulb, gas storage bulb, manometer, Pyrex reaction bulb; high-temperature furnace; variable-voltage power supply; ammeter for measuring heater current; two-junction chromel-alumel thermocouple; 1-qt Dewar; millivolt-range potentiometer setup (see Chap. XV); thermocouple calibration table; stopwatch.

Cyclopentene (or cyclohexene); ice (3 lb); liquid nitrogen (2 liters); cylinder of NO gas, with needle valve and pressure tubing (optional).

REFERENCES

1. S. W. Benson, "Foundations of Chemical Kinetics," chaps. X and XI, McGraw-Hill, New York (1960).
2. Any standard physical chemistry text, such as W. J. Moore, "Physical Chemistry," 2d ed., chap. 17, Prentice-Hall, Englewood Cliffs, N. J. (1955).
3. A. F. Trotman-Dickenson, "Gas Kinetics," secs. 2.3, 2.4, 3.2, Butterworth, London (1955).
4. H. C. Ramsperger, *Chem. Revs.,* **10,** 27 (1932).
5. L. S. Kassel, "Kinetics of Homogeneous Gas Reactions," chap. 5, Reinhold (ACS Monograph), New York (1932).
6. S. W. Benson, *op. cit.,* pp. 222–223.
7. *Ibid.,* pp. 250–252.
8. E. W. R. Steacie, "Atomic and Free Radical Reactions," pp. 82–86, Reinhold (ACS Monograph), New York (1946).
9. A. F. Trotman-Dickenson, *op. cit.,* pp. 153–160.
10. A. Farkas and H. W. Melville, "Experimental Methods in Gas Reactions," Macmillan, London (1939).
11. A. O. Allen, *J. Am. Chem. Soc.,* **56,** 2053 (1934).
12. L. Küchler, *Trans. Faraday Soc.,* **35,** 874 (1939).
13. D. Rowley and H. Steiner, *Discussions Faraday Soc.,* **10,** 198 (1951).
14. D. W. Vanas and W. D. Walters, *J. Am. Chem. Soc.,* **70,** 4035 (1948).

GENERAL READING

A. A. Frost and R. G. Pearson, "Kinetics and Mechanism," especially pp. 67–72, Wiley, New York (1953).

R. N. Pease, "Equilibrium and Kinetics of Gas Reactions," Princeton University Press, Princeton, N. J. (1942).

Experiment 29. Kinetics of the Decomposition of Benzenediazonium Ion

In an acidic aqueous solution, benzenediazonium ion ($C_6H_5N_2^+$) will decompose[1] to form nitrogen and phenol:

$$C_6H_5N_2^+ + H_2O \rightarrow C_6H_5OH + N_2(g) + H^+ \tag{1}$$

In this experiment you are to follow the course of the above reaction by a spectrophotometric measurement of the unreacted diazonium ion.[2] The reaction order with respect to $C_6H_5N_2^+$, the rate constant k, and the activation energy for the reaction are to be determined.

THEORY

The rate of reaction (1), $-d(C_6H_5N_2^+)/dt$, can be written in terms of the concentrations of the reacting species as

$$\frac{-d(C_6H_5N_2^+)}{dt} = k'(C_6H_5N_2^+)^n(H_2O)^m \tag{2}$$

As written above, the reaction would be nth-order with respect to $C_6H_5N_2^+$, mth-order with respect to water, and would have an over-all order of $n + m$. The reaction is not acid-catalyzed, although very high acid concentrations (say 12 N HCl) seem to slightly increase the rate.[1] Thus the effect of changes in the H^+ concentration due to reaction (1) can be completely neglected. Since the present experiment will be performed in a dilute aqueous solution, the concentration of water, (H_2O), will be very nearly constant throughout the reaction. Thus the factor $(H_2O)^m$ can be absorbed into the rate constant and Eq. (2) can be rewritten as

$$\frac{-dc}{dt} = kc^n \tag{3}$$

where c represents the instantaneous concentration ($C_6H_5N_2^+$).

Equation (3) can readily be integrated to give

$$c = c_0e^{-kt} \qquad \text{for } n = 1 \tag{4a}$$

$$c^{1-n} - c_0^{1-n} = (n - 1)kt \qquad \text{for } n \neq 1 \tag{4b}$$

where c_0 is the concentration at $t = 0$. In other words, if the reaction is first-order, a plot of log c vs. t should give a straight line of slope $-k/2.303$ and intercept log c_0. If the reaction is nth-order where n (which need not be an integer) is not equal to unity, a plot of c^{1-n} vs. t should give a straight line of slope $(n - 1)k$ and intercept c_0^{1-n}. By making such plots for various trial values of n and determining which gives the best straight-line dependence over a wide range of concentration, one can obtain the order n of the reaction† and then determine the appropriate rate constant k_n.

†Other methods of determining the reaction order are discussed in Exps. 26 and 27.

If the value of a rate constant is measured at several different temperatures, it is almost always found that the temperature dependence can be represented by

$$k = \mathcal{A}e^{-E^*/RT} \tag{5}$$

where the factor $\mathcal{A}$ is independent of temperature. The Arrhenius activation energy E^* can be easily determined by plotting log k vs. $1/T$. This should give a straight line of slope $-E^*/2.303R$.

METHOD

Any physical variable giving an accurate measure of the extent to which a reaction has gone toward completion can be used to obtain rate data. In this experiment, we shall monitor the concentration of unreacted diazonium ion by measuring the absorption of ultraviolet light by the solution.

According to the Beer-Lambert law,[3] the intensity of light I transmitted by an absorbing medium is given by

$$I = I_0 e^{-c\epsilon' d} \tag{6}$$

where c is the concentration of absorbing molecules, d is the path length, I_0 is the intensity of incident light, and ϵ' is an extinction coefficient. The absorbancy A, defined as log (I_0/I), thus gives a direct measure of the concentration:

$$A \equiv \log \frac{I_0}{I} = \frac{c\epsilon' d}{2.303} = c\epsilon d \tag{7}$$

where ϵ is the *absorptivity*. When the concentration is expressed in moles per liter, ϵ is called the molar absorptivity. For first-order reactions, the quantity ϵd will cancel out of Eq. (4*a*) and k can be obtained directly from a plot of log A vs. t. However, for orders different from first order, ϵd does not cancel out of Eq. (4*b*). In such cases, ϵd must be evaluated by measuring the absorbancy of a solution of known concentration in order to permit k to be calculated in concentration units.

For a brief description of spectrophotometers and their use in determining the absorbancy, see Exp. 40.

EXPERIMENTAL

Kinetic runs are to be made at 25, 30, and 40°C. Well-regulated thermostat baths operating at about these temperatures will be required. The actual temperatures of each of these baths should be measured with a good thermometer and recorded.

The concentration of benzenediazonium ion can be determined by the absorbancy at wavelengths between 295 and 325 mμ. Below 295 mμ products of the reaction produce interfering absorption, and above 325 mμ the extinction coefficient is too small to permit effective measurement of changes in the benzenediazonium ion concentration.[4] The absorbancy will be measured using a spectrophotometer such as a Beckman Model DU; detailed instructions for operating this instrument will be provided in the laboratory. A wavelength of 305 mμ should be used, with a slit width of 0.3 mm. For $A < 1$, use the "1" scale; when $A > 1$, use the ".1" scale. Make two absorbancy readings on each sample.

The diazonium salt which should be used in this experiment is benzenediazonium fluoborate ($C_6H_5N_2BF_4$, M.W. 191.9). The great majority of diazonium salts are notoriously unstable solids and can decompose with explosive violence. The fluoborates are by far the safest to use and are not known to explode; however, reasonable caution should be used in preparing the compound. Since even benzenediazonium fluoborate will decompose slowly, it should not be prepared too far in advance, and it must be stored in a refrigerator. A simple high-yield procedure for its preparation has been given by Dunker, Starkey, and Jenkins.[5] Recrystallization of the product from 5 per cent fluoboric acid yields white needle-like crystals which can be dried by vacuum pumping at 1 mm for several hours.†

The diazonium salt should be available at the beginning of the experiment. Remove a *small* quantity from the refrigerator and warm it rapidly to room temperature. Prepare approximately 10^{-3} M solutions by placing an accurately weighed 15- to 20-mg sample of the salt into each of three 100-ml volumetric flasks, and then make up to the mark with a 0.2 M HCl solution. Label the flasks and be sure to record the exact weight of salt placed in each flask. Return the unused diazonium salt to the refrigerator at once. Be careful not to waste it.

Using a hypodermic syringe, withdraw a sample of about 5 ml of each solution *as soon as possible* after it is made up. Chill these samples by placing them in test tubes which are set in crushed ice, then put them aside for absorbancy measurements (to be made as soon as conveniently possible). These measurements will provide a value for ϵd in case it is needed later on.

Suspend one of the volumetric flasks in each of the three constant-temperature baths. Allow about 20 min for the solutions to achieve thermal equilibrium. After thermal equilibrium has been attained, you may begin taking samples for spectrophotometric analysis.

When you take a sample, use the following procedure: Withdraw about 1 ml of the solution with the hypodermic syringe and use this to rinse out the syringe. Then quickly withdraw a 5-ml sample and place it in a labeled test tube set in crushed ice for chilling. Record the time of discharge into the test tube. After the sample is chilled (3 to 5 min) use about 1 ml of it to rinse out the spectrophotometer cell. Fill the cell with the remaining sample and measure its absorbancy, using the 0.2 M HCl solution as a blank. These cells are fragile and expensive; handle them with care.

The reason for chilling the sample is to slow down the reaction rate so that a negligible amount of reactant will decompose between the time you chill the sample and the time you make the absorbancy measurement. Since it is impossible to eliminate completely errors due to reaction after withdrawal and cooling, it is important to try to perform the sample removal and chilling procedure in as reproducible a fashion as possible. This will lead to a partial cancellation of such errors.

†After storage at 0°C in a vacuum desiccator for several weeks, these crystals tend to stick together. After six months there is clear evidence of decomposition; fortunately, the main impurity is phenol (2 to 3 per cent) which does not interfere much with rate studies in aqueous solution.[2] By a very careful purification, it is possible to obtain a benzenediazonium fluoborate sample which can be stored at 0°C for several months without any signs of decomposition. The sample is dissolved in acetone, and then chloroform is added until a few crystals are formed. When the solution is then chilled to −20°C for 30 min, the compound will crystallize out in the form of tiny white needles. After three such recrystallizations, the sample can again be dried by pumping, and can be stored in a vacuum desiccator.

Take as many measurements as you reasonably can without rushing. Since the runs at the higher temperatures will proceed more rapidly, it will be necessary to take samples from them at more frequent intervals. A suggested interval might be once every 25 min for the 25° bath, every 15 min for the 30° bath, and every 10 min for the 40° bath.

At the end of the experiment, wash the cells thoroughly with distilled water and dry them very carefully. Store in a safe place.

CALCULATIONS

Using all the data points from any single run, prepare rough plots of the following: (1) $A^{1/2}$ vs. t (order ½), (2) $\log A$ vs. t (order 1), (3) A^{-1} vs. t (order 2), and (4) any additional plots you feel to be necessary in order to establish the order of the reaction.

Having determined the order of the reaction, make an accurate graph of the appropriate plot for each of the runs and determine the value of k (in concentration units) for each temperature. These plots may be of A values rather than c values. The value of the slope can then be corrected, if necessary, to give k in concentration units by utilizing the known ϵd value. Finally, plot $\log k$ vs. $1/T$ and determine E^*.

Report your results for the order of reaction, $k(T_1)$, $k(T_2)$, $k(T_3)$, and E^*. Give correct *units* for each quantity. Use second as the unit of time, mole per liter as the unit of concentration, and kilocalorie as the unit of energy.

DISCUSSION

From your results, calculate the extent of reaction that would occur in a sample of the initial solution after 30 min at 0°C. Does this indicate that varying lengths of time between the chilling of a sample and its absorbancy measurement would introduce serious or negligible errors in your data?

APPARATUS

Spectrophotometer, such as a Beckman Model DU; two or more Corex sample cells; constant-temperature baths set at 25, 30, and 40°C; lens tissue; three 100-ml volumetric flasks; clock or stopwatch; hypodermic syringe; about 20 test tubes; plastic pail or large battery jar; beaker.

Benzenediazonium fluoborate (75 mg), stored in a refrigerator; 0.2 M hydrochloric acid (400 ml); crushed ice.

REFERENCES

1. E. A. Moelwyn-Hughes and P. Johnson, *Trans. Faraday Soc.*, **36,** 948 (1940); M. L. Crossley, R. H. Kienle, and C. H. Benbrook, *J. Am. Chem. Soc.*, **62,** 1400 (1940).
2. J. E. Sheets and C. G. Swain, *J. Am. Chem. Soc.*, to be published (1967).
3. M. G. Mellon, "Analytical Absorption Spectroscopy," Wiley, New York (1950); W. J. Moore, "Physical Chemistry," 3d ed., p. 820, Prentice-Hall, Englewood Cliffs, N.J. (1962).
4. A. Wohl, *Bull. soc. chim. française*, **6,** 1319 (1939).
5. M. F. W. Dunker, E. B. Starkey, and G. L. Jenkins, *J. Am. Chem. Soc.*, **58,** 2308 (1936).

GENERAL READING

W. West, Spectroscopy and Spectrophotometry, in A. Weissberger (ed.), "Techniques of Organic Chemistry," 2d ed., vol. I, part II, chap. XXI, Interscience, New York (1949).

R. Livingston, Fundamental Operations and Measurements in Obtaining Rate Data, in A. Weissberger (ed.), "Techniques of Organic Chemistry," vol. VIII, part I, chap. III, Interscience, New York (1961).

Experiment 30. Kinetics of a Fast Reaction

Although conventional kinetic methods have proved very useful in studying a wide range of chemical reactions, special techniques are needed for investigating fast reactions (i.e., reactions with half-lives less than a few seconds). Such techniques may also provide a way to elucidate the rapid steps of reaction mechanisms for which only the slow rate-controlling step can be investigated by classical methods. In recent years, a wide variety of new methods have been developed for fast reactions in solution.[1,2] The earliest of these are the various flow methods (both continuous and stop-flow) which are suitable for reactions with $\sim 1 \text{ sec} > t_{1/2} > 10^{-3}$ sec.[3] For half-lives below 10^{-3} sec, it is necessary to use methods which avoid the mixing of reactants, and several sophisticated techniques (such as relaxation methods) are now available for studying very fast reactions with $t_{1/2}$ values as short as 10^{-9} sec.[1,2]

In this experiment, the simplest fast-reaction technique—the continuous-flow method—will be used to study the kinetics of the formation of the ferric thiocyanate complex $FeSCN^{2+}$.

THEORY

For the fast reaction between ferric and thiocyanate ions in an acid solution of constant pH, the observed behavior is consistent with the simple mechanism[4]

$$Fe^{3+} + SCN^- \underset{k_r}{\overset{k_f}{\rightleftharpoons}} FeSCN^{2+} \tag{1}$$

where k_f is the bimolecular forward rate constant and k_r is the unimolecular reverse rate constant.† The rate law resulting from mechanism (1) is

$$\frac{d(FeSCN^{2+})}{dt} = k_f(Fe^{3+})(SCN^-) - k_r(FeSCN^{2+}) \tag{2}$$

Let us recall that the equilibrium constant K is related to the rate constants by

$$K = \frac{k_f}{k_r} = \frac{(FeSCN^{2+})_\infty}{(Fe^{3+})_\infty(SCN^-)_\infty} \tag{3}$$

where the subscript ∞ denotes the equilibrium ($t = \infty$) value. Let us also note that

†In fact, the detailed mechanism is more complex since both a direct and a base-catalyzed path exist.[4] The value of k_f as used in mechanism (1) is found to be dependent on the H^+ concentration: $k_f = k_1 + k_2/(H^+)$. Since this experiment is restricted to a single value of (H^+), the more general mechanism is omitted.

$$(\mathrm{FeSCN^{2+}}) + (\mathrm{SCN^-}) = (\mathrm{FeSCN^{2+}})_\infty + (\mathrm{SCN^-})_\infty \tag{4}$$

at any time t. Using these relations, we can rewrite Eq. (2) in the form

$$\frac{d(\mathrm{FeSCN^{2+}})}{dt} = k_f(\mathrm{Fe^{3+}})[(\mathrm{FeSCN^{2+}})_\infty + (\mathrm{SCN^-})_\infty] - k_f[(\mathrm{Fe^{3+}}) + K^{-1}](\mathrm{FeSCN^{2+}}) \tag{5}$$

In order to simplify the integration of Eq. (5), let us choose the experimental conditions such that $(\mathrm{Fe^{3+}}) \gg (\mathrm{SCN^-})$. This will allow us to assume that $(\mathrm{Fe^{3+}})$ is essentially constant during the course of the reaction. If, in addition, the initial conditions are chosen so that $(\mathrm{FeSCN^{2+}}) = 0$ at $t = 0$, we find

$$\ln \frac{(\mathrm{FeSCN^{2+}})_\infty - (\mathrm{FeSCN^{2+}})}{(\mathrm{FeSCN^{2+}})_\infty} = -\,[(\mathrm{Fe^{3+}}) + K^{-1}]k_f t \tag{6}$$

This is an approximate solution which becomes exact only when $(\mathrm{Fe^{3+}})$ is constant [you can check Eq. (6) by direct differentiation]. In actual practice, $(\mathrm{Fe^{3+}})_0$ will be chosen to be ten times larger than $(\mathrm{SCN^-})_0$, so that $(\mathrm{Fe^{3+}})$ will vary by about 10 per cent during the reaction.†

If a plot of $\ln\,[(\mathrm{FeSCN^{2+}})_\infty - (\mathrm{FeSCN^{2+}})]$ vs. t is linear, then the first-order dependence on $(\mathrm{SCN^-})$ and $(\mathrm{FeSCN^{2+}})$ is confirmed. The rate dependence on $(\mathrm{Fe^{3+}})$ has been established as first order[4] and will not be tested in this experiment.

METHOD

The continuous-flow method[3,5] is a simple and straightforward technique. Two reactant solutions are forced under pressure into a T-shaped mixing chamber, and then the reacting mixture flows down a long capillary tube. It is important that the solutions mix well and rapidly ($\sim 10^{-3}$ sec). When the mixing time is much shorter than the half-life of the reaction, a steady state is set up such that various positions along the capillary tube correspond to different reaction times. A quantitative correlation between the reaction time t and the distance x from the mixing chamber to a given point along the tube can be achieved by measuring the time interval $\Delta\tau$ needed for a known volume ΔV of solution to flow through the tube. Assuming a constant cross-sectional area $\mathcal{A}$ for the capillary, the average linear flow velocity $\bar{u}$ is given by $\bar{u} = \Delta V/(\mathcal{A}\,\Delta\tau)$. Thus, on the average, the reaction time is related to x by

$$t = x\,\frac{\mathcal{A}\,\Delta\tau}{\Delta V} \tag{7}$$

It is important that the flow of the reacting solution should be as close to "mass flow" as possible, so that all the fluid arriving at a small volume element located at some fixed point along the tube will have traveled for the same length of time after leaving the mixing chamber. Laminar flow is undesirable since it is fast near the center of the capillary and quite slow near the walls (see Exp. 5). Since turbulent flow is much closer to mass flow, we wish to use flow rates that are greater than $1000\ \eta/\rho r$

†With this choice of an initial ferric concentration which is much larger than the thiocyanate concentration, any formation of $\mathrm{Fe(SCN)_2^+}$ species can be neglected. Also we shall work at a low pH value so that the hydrolysis of ferric ions can be neglected.

[the minimum value for turbulent flow; see Eq. (5-11)]. Deviations from mass flow will blur the time value appropriate to a given distance x. Fortunately, the resulting error in the rate constant is no more than 2 to 3 per cent for turbulent flow; but it may be as high as 10 per cent for streamline flow.[3,5]

In this experiment, the reaction is to be followed with a Beckman Model DU spectrophotometer. The response of this instrument is rather slow, several seconds being required to make an absorbancy reading. Since the reaction to be studied is rapid (half-life of less than 1 sec), it is not possible to follow the progress of the reaction directly as in Exp. 29. However, the continuous-flow method is a very appropriate way† to study fast reactions with a slowly responding instrument. The design described in the experimental section is based directly on that first used by Dalziel; excellent detailed descriptions of his equipment are available in the literature.[3,5]

The complex $FeSCN^{2+}$ has an absorption maximum near 450 mμ, whereas neither Fe^{3+} nor SCN^{-} absorbs in that region.[6] Therefore,

$$(A_\infty - A) = \epsilon d[(FeSCN^{2+})_\infty - (FeSCN^{2+})] \tag{8}$$

where A is the absorbancy, ϵ is the extinction coefficient, and d is the optical path length. From Eqs. (6) and (8) we see that a plot of log $(A_\infty - A)$ vs. t should give a straight line of slope $-k_f[(Fe^{3+}) + K^{-1}]/2.303$. Note that A_∞ values obtained at different points along the tube may not all agree with each other, since there may be variations in the capillary tube and its placement with respect to the light beam. Also note that errors in $(A_\infty - A)$ caused by a drift in the zero setting of the spectrophotometer could cause appreciable errors in the rate constant. Readings corresponding to a large per cent reaction are most sensitive since the $(A_\infty - A)$ values are then small.

Finally, we must remember that there will be a salt effect[7] on the rate of this reaction: both the rate constant k_f and the equilibrium constant K are functions of the ionic strength μ. An (approximately constant) ionic strength of 0.40 will be chosen here to facilitate comparison with previous work.[4]

EXPERIMENTAL

A sketch of the complete assembled apparatus is shown in Fig. 1, and more detailed drawings of the capillary support frame are given in Fig. 2. There are two important differences between this design and that of Dalziel:[5] (1) the carboys of reactant solutions are mounted in a stationary thermostat bath and are connected to the movable capillary support frame by rubber pressure tubing, and (2) the mixing chamber is machined from a block of Lucite instead of being fabricated from glass. A detailed drawing of this mixing chamber is given in Fig. 3.

In order to assemble the apparatus, remove the phototube housing from a Beckman Model DU spectrophotometer and replace the cell holder unit (sample chamber) with the special housing in which the capillary support frame slides back and forth. Make sure that the alignment is correct (so that the capillary support

†The principal disadvantage of this method is the fact that large quantities of solution are required. Although the present chemicals are cheap and easily obtained, this would be a serious limitation in studying reactions involving rare or costly reactants. In those cases, one would need to use a stop-flow method with a more rapidly responding photometric system.[3]

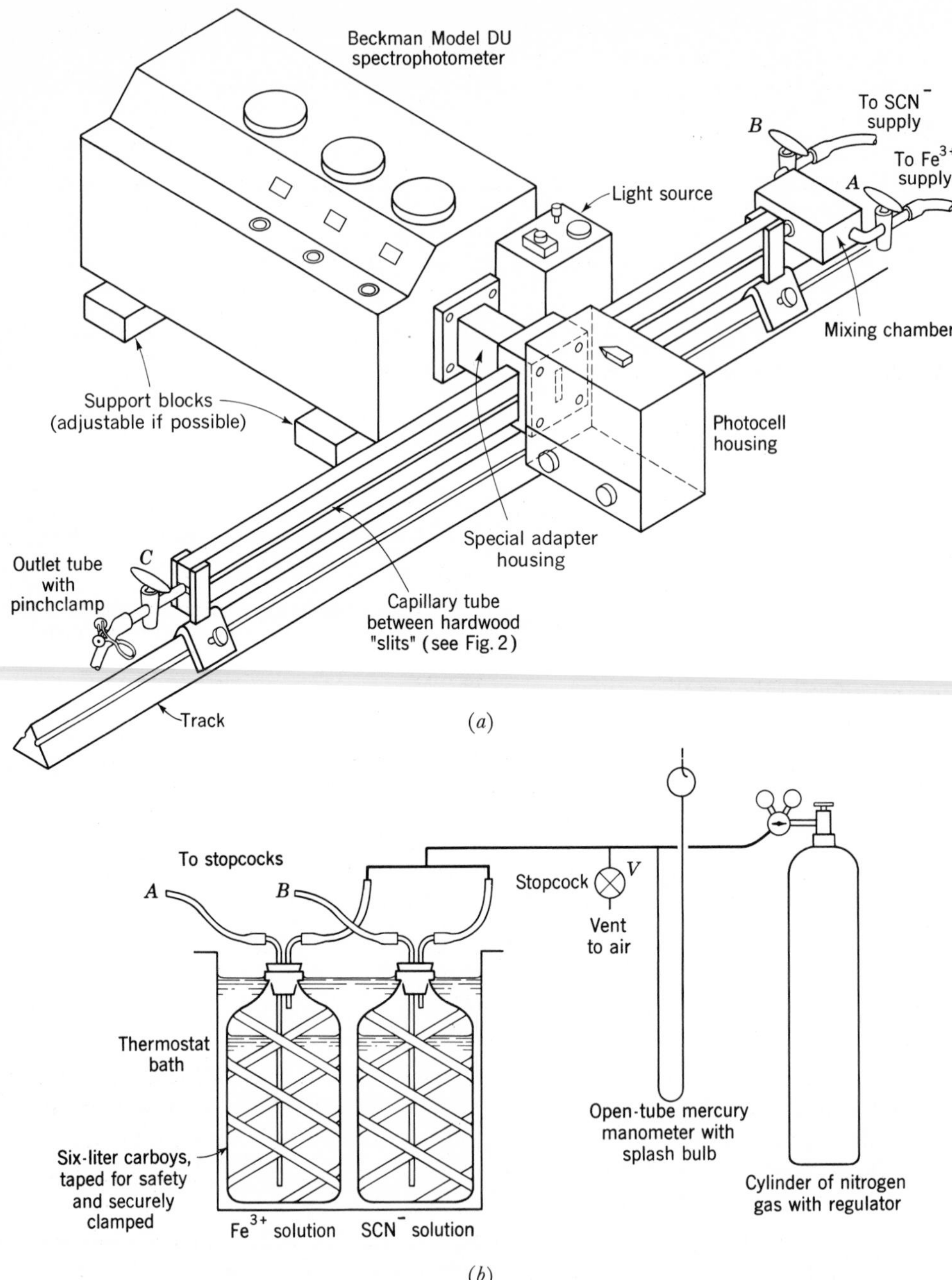

FIG. 1. Flow-kinetics apparatus: (*a*) spectrophotometer setup; (*b*) schematic diagram of system for driving reactant solutions.

frame moves smoothly) before you bolt this housing to the spectrophotometer. It is convenient to have the spectrophotometer sitting on a base with adjustable legs to facilitate this alignment. Finally, bolt the phototube housing onto the rear of this special adapter housing.

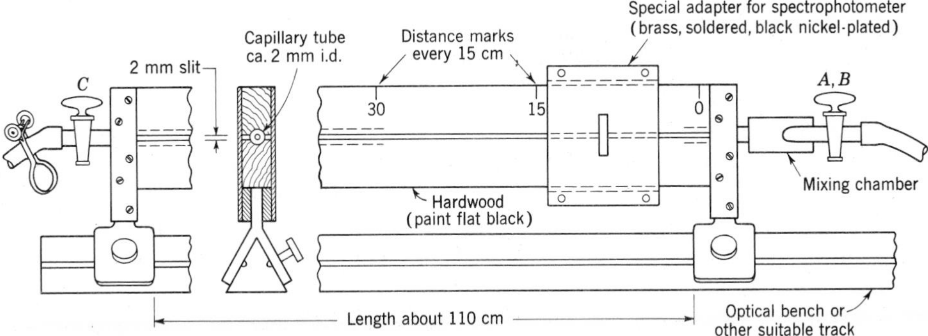

FIG. 2. Detail of reaction capillary tube and support frame.

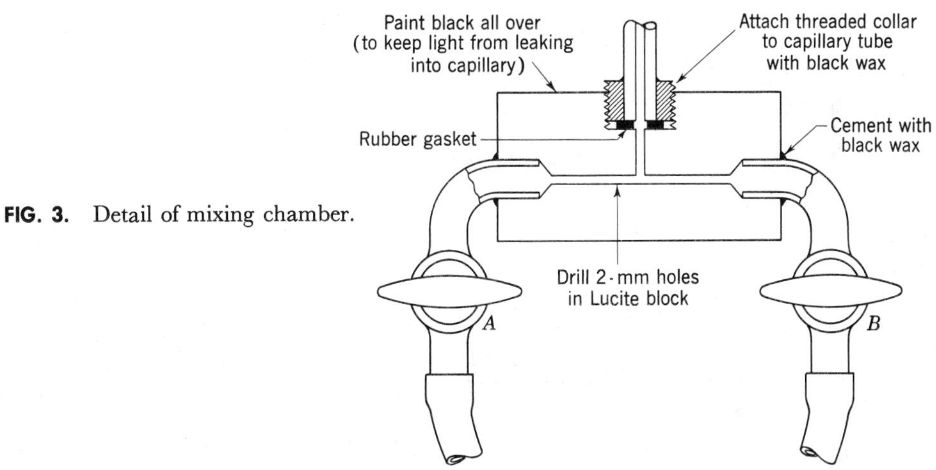

FIG. 3. Detail of mixing chamber.

Next, fill the two carboys† with the appropriate solutions. Solution A should be 0.02 *M* in $Fe(NO_3)_3$, 0.2 *M* in $HClO_4$ and 0.14 *M* in $NaClO_4$; solution B should be 0.002 *M* in NaSCN, 0.2 *M* in $HClO_4$ and 0.14 *M* in $NaClO_4$. Be careful in handling these solutions; perchloric acid will give you dishpan hands. Now mount the carboys in the thermostat bath and connect them by a long piece of flexible pressure tubing to the appropriate stopcocks which are sealed into the mixing chamber. Again, test that the capillary frame will move smoothly back and forth through its housing. Do not force it. If there is any difficulty, ask an instructor to check the alignment. Proper alignment is crucial. Along the top of the capillary support frame, there should be a series of fiducial marks (say six or seven) which can be lined up with a reference mark on the special housing. This enables one to set the spectro-

†Before being used in this experiment, each carboy should be pressure tested to verify that there are no flaws which would make it unsafe. It is recommended that the empty carboy be placed behind a protective barrier and subjected to an internal gas pressure of 2 atm.

photometer at reproducible points along the capillary which are at known distances x away from the mixing chamber.

To complete the setup, connect the reagent carboys to each other via a T tube which leads to an open-tube mercury manometer and a regulated supply of a suitable driver gas (such as air or N_2).

It is important that stray light should not reach the capillary tube, since it may be reflected down the walls of the tube and be detected by the spectrophotometer. The support frame around the capillary is designed to reduce such stray light by providing a deep narrow slit-like aperture; but one must still avoid horizontal light leaks. It may be worthwhile to cover both ends of the entire support frame with blackout cloths. (Do not cover the source housing on the Model DU, as it gets hot.)

Success in this experiment depends on good technique; the procedure should be followed carefully. Before beginning the measurements, you should look over Exp. 40 and read the Beckman DU spectrophotometer instruction manual for detailed information on operating this instrument.

Procedure. Turn on the spectrophotometer and allow at least 20 min for it to warm up prior to use. The wavelength setting should be 455 mμ throughout the entire experiment. With both reagent stopcocks A and B and the vent stopcock V closed, slowly increase the gas pressure on the reagent solutions until the manometer indicates about 500 mm Hg pressure above 1 atm. With the outlet stopcock C *open,* now open and close the reagent stopcocks A and B (one at a time) several times to make sure that both solutions are flowing smoothly and to remove any air bubbles from the system. Use a beaker to catch the outflow from the capillary tube.† Then set the capillary frame at the first fiducial mark (one nearest to the mixing chamber) and carry out the three following steps:

1. Open stopcock A and allow the Fe^{3+} solution to flow for a sufficient time to remove from the capillary tube any solution containing $FeSCN^{2+}$ species (until the outflow is clear). Then close stopcock A and the outlet stopcock C. In accordance with the spectrophotometer operating instructions, zero the instrument with this Fe^{3+} solution (i.e., adjust the dark current, slit width, and sensitivity controls so that the instrument reads 100 per cent transmission or $A = 0$).

2. To begin a run, open the outlet stopcock C and then turn both stopcocks A and B to their fully open positions. Catch the outflow of solution from the capillary in a beaker until the flow becomes stable (as indicated by a constant manometer reading, usually before 100 ml of solution is collected). Then *quickly* switch the outlet tube from the beaker to a 250-ml volumetric flask and simultaneously start a stopwatch. When this flask is full, stop the watch and record the elapsed time ($\sim$50 sec). Return the outlet tube to the beaker. While one student is carrying out the above flow-rate measurement, his partner should determine the absorbancy A of the reaction mixture and record that value together with the distance x from the mixing chamber. Work quickly to avoid any unnecessary waste of the reagent solutions.

3. When both the flow and absorbancy measurements are complete, close the outlet stopcock C and then as soon as possible close both stopcocks A and B. This is a crucial step in the procedure; if A and B are left open, solution may siphon from one carboy to the other. After about two minutes, determine the absorbancy again

†As an optional step, you can record the time required for a given volume (say 250 ml) of each separate solution to flow through the capillary tube. The times for solutions A and B should agree within a few per cent.

to obtain A_∞ (the infinite time value). Verify that this value does not change after one more minute.

For the next run, move the capillary support frame so as to line up the second fiducial mark and repeat steps 1 to 3 at this new distance setting. Be careful in moving the capillary support frame.

Make two runs at each of the six or seven positions along the capillary tube. Use special care in making the absorbancy readings at large values of x (corresponding to large per cent reaction and a small $A_\infty - A$ value). If time permits, you should also take data at a different driving pressure. Either increase or decrease the gas pressure depending on whether you need more data at low per cent reaction or at high, but it may not be safe to exceed about 700 mm overpressure.

During the course of the experiment, more of solution A will be used up than solution B if the Fe^{3+} solution is always used in step 1 to make the zero adjustment of the spectrophotometer at each distance setting. The resulting change in the liquid level for solution A relative to that for solution B may change the relative flow rates of these solutions. This can be avoided by alternating the use of solutions A and B for making the zero adjustments (or, if necessary, corrected by merely running enough of solution B out through the capillary periodically to equalize the levels).

Before leaving the laboratory, record the concentrations of the reactant solutions, the temperature of the thermostat bath, the radius of the capillary tube, and the distances x corresponding to the various fiducial marks along the capillary support frame.

CALCULATIONS

Using Eq. (7), calculate the reaction time t corresponding to each run; tabulate these times together with the appropriate $(A_\infty - A)$ and $\log(A_\infty - A)$ values. Plot $\log(A_\infty - A)$ vs. t, and determine the slope of the best straight line through the data points. From the value of this slope, calculate the rate constant k_f. The literature value[4] of K is 146 ± 5 liters mole^{-1} at 25°C and an ionic strength of 0.40, and you should take the (Fe^{3+}) value to be an average of the initial value ($t = 0$, but *after* mixing of the two solutions) and the equilibrium value ($t = \infty$, as calculated with K). Also report the back-reaction rate constant k_r. Give the proper units for each rate constant.

DISCUSSION

What fraction of the Fe^{3+} in solution A is hydrolyzed to $Fe(OH)^{2+}$ if the hydrolysis constant K_h is known[4] to be 2×10^{-3}? What are the principal sources of error in this experiment? How fast a reaction do you think could be measured with this apparatus? What is the limiting design factor in this method?

APPARATUS

Beckman Model DU spectrophotometer; 6-v battery and battery charger (or regulated dc power supply); adjustable support for spectrophotometer (optional); movable capillary support frame with mixing chamber and special housing attached; set of four retaining bolts for mounting housing on the spectrophotometer; two carboys (~6 liters) for reactant solutions; open-tube mercury manometer; cylinder of nitrogen gas with pressure regulator (or source of regulated compressed air); pressure tubing and hose clamps; stopcock for venting the carboys; gum-rubber tubing for outlet of capillary; a 250-ml volumetric flask; a beaker (~500 ml); stopwatch; black-out cloths (optional).

Constant-temperature bath (set at 25°C) with provision for mounting carboys; solution *A* which is 0.0200 *M* in $Fe(NO_3)_3$, 0.20 *M* in $HClO_4$ and 0.14 *M* in $NaClO_4$ (5 liters); solution *B* which is 0.00200 *M* in NaSCN, 0.20 *M* in $HClO_4$ and 0.14 *M* in $NaClO_4$ (5 liters).

REFERENCES

1. E. F. Caldin, "Fast Reactions in Solution," Wiley, New York (1964); *Discussions Faraday Soc.,* vol. 17 (1954).
2. S. L. Friess, E. S. Lewis, and A. Weissberger (eds.), "Investigation of Rates and Mechanisms of Reactions," 2d ed., vol. VIII, part II of "Techniques of Organic Chemistry," Interscience, New York (1963).
3. *Ibid.,* chap. XIV, "Rapid Reactions" by F. J. Roughton and B. Chance, esp. pp. 704–748.
4. J. F. Below, Jr., R. E. Connick, and C. P. Coppel, *J. Am. Chem. Soc.,* **80,** 2961 (1958).
5. K. Dalziel, *Biochem. J.,* **55,** 79 (1953).
6. H. S. Frank and R. L. Oswalt, *J. Am. Chem. Soc.,* **69,** 1321 (1947).
7. W. J. Moore, "Physical Chemistry," 3d ed., pp. 368–369, Prentice-Hall, Englewood Cliffs, N.J. (1962); D. F. Eggers, Jr., N. W. Gregory, G. D. Halsey, Jr., and B. S. Rabinovitch, "Physical Chemistry," pp. 481–484, Wiley, New York (1964).

X

SURFACE PHENOMENA

EXPERIMENTS

Experiment 31. Surface Tension of Solutions

The capillary-rise method is used to study the change in surface tension as a function of concentration for aqueous solutions of *n*-butanol and sodium chloride. The data are interpreted in terms of the surface concentration using the Gibbs isotherm.

THEORY

If a body of material is homogeneous, the value of any *extensive* property is directly proportional to the quantity of matter contained in the body:

$$Q = \bar{Q}_V V = \bar{Q}_m m = \bar{Q}_N N \tag{1}$$

where Q is the extensive quantity; V, m, and N are, respectively, the volume, mass, and number of moles of the substance involved. $\bar{Q}_V$, $\bar{Q}_m$, and $\bar{Q}_N$ are, respectively, the specific values of Q per unit volume, per unit mass, and per mole and have *intensive* magnitudes.

It is known, however, that the values of extensive properties of bodies often thought of as homogeneous are not always independent of the surface area. In fact, liquid bodies with surfaces are in general not entirely homogeneous, for the value of a given intensive quantity (say $\bar{Q}_V$) in the region of the surface may at equilibrium deviate from the value that this quantity has in the bulk of the solution ($\bar{Q}_V$). We can write

$$Q = \int_V Q_V \, dV = \bar{Q}_V V + \int_\tau (Q_V - \bar{Q}_V) \, dV \tag{2}$$

where the second integral needs to be taken only over a region τ in the neighborhood of the surface, within which Q_V is different from $\bar{Q}_V$, the *bulk* value which prevails through the body except near the surface. We can replace the volume element dV in the second integral by $dA\,dx$, where dA is an element of surface area and dx an element of distance inward from the surface of the body. The integration over dA extends over the surface of the body, and that over dx extends to a distance τ inside the body beyond which Q_V is substantially equal to $\bar{Q}_V$. If $(Q_V - \bar{Q}_V)$ is independent of position on the surface of the body, the integration over dA can be carried out at once, and we have

$$Q = \bar{Q}_V V + \bar{Q}_A A \tag{3}$$

where we have introduced a new quantity, called a specific surface quantity,

$$\bar{Q}_A \equiv \int_\tau (Q_V - \bar{Q}_V) \, dx \tag{4}$$

This quantity represents the *excess*, per unit area of surface, of the quantity Q over what Q would be for a perfectly homogeneous body of the same magnitude with $Q_V = \bar{Q}_V$ throughout; see Fig. 1. In some cases $\bar{Q}_A$ may be negative, corresponding to a deficiency rather than an excess.

If the body has surfaces of several different kinds (like a crystal with different kinds of crystal faces or a liquid with part of its surface in contact with the air and the remainder of its surface in contact with solid or other liquid phases), the parenthesized quantity in Eq. (2) is independent of surface positional coordinates only within the boundaries of each kind of surface. Each kind of surface will have in general a different $\bar{Q}_A$, and we write in such a case

$$Q = \bar{Q}_V V + \sum_i \bar{Q}_{A_i} A_i \tag{5}$$

Surface Concentration. When the extensive quantity concerned is the number N of moles of solute, the corresponding specific bulk property is $\bar{N}_V \equiv c$, the bulk concentration (concentration in the interior of the solution). The corresponding specific surface quantity $\bar{N}_A \equiv u$ is called *surface concentration* and represents

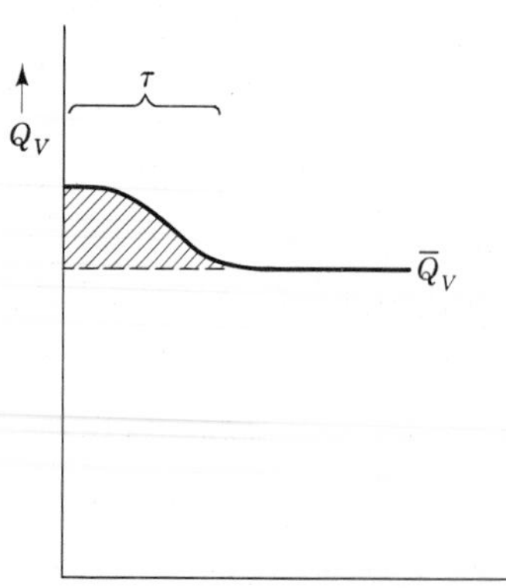

FIG. 1. Schematic plot of Q_V vs. x. The shaded area is equal to $\bar{Q}_A$.

excess of solute per unit area of the surface over what would be present if the internal (bulk) concentration prevailed all the way to the surface. It may be expressed in moles per square centimeter.

Surface Free Energy or Surface Tension. Under conditions of constant temperature and pressure the equilibrium state sought by any system is that of lowest free energy G, and the maximum work (other than expansion work) done by the system in any change of state under these conditions is equal to the free-energy decrease, $-\Delta G$. A body of liquid with a free surface will tend to assume the shape which gives it the lowest possible free energy at the given temperature and pressure prevailing.

The free energy of a system containing variable surface areas can be written, from Eq. (5), as follows:

$$G = G_0 + \sum_i \gamma_i A_i \tag{6}$$

where $\overline{G}_{A_i} \equiv \gamma_i$ is the specific surface free energy or *surface tension* of surface i, which may be a free surface (exposed to air or vapor or vacuum) or an interface with another liquid or solid. In the event that the surface is an interface, this quantity is called *interfacial tension.* For a stable free liquid surface it clearly must be positive. The surface tension γ_i is equal to the expenditure of work required to increase the net area of surface i by one unit of area, say 1 cm^2; if the increase in surface area is accomplished by moving a 1-cm line segment in a direction perpendicular to itself, γ_i is equal to the force, or "tension," in dynes opposing the moving of the line segment. Accordingly, it is usually expressed in units of dynes per centimeter (= ergs per square centimeter).

The variation of surface tension with temperature will not be discussed here, except to remark that surface tension decreases with temperature and that the rate of decrease is large enough to require that the temperature of measurement of surface tension be kept constant, to the order of 0.1°C, by means of a thermostat.

The Gibbs Isotherm. It is found that the surface tensions of solutions are in general different from those of the corresponding pure solvents. It has also been found that solutes whose addition results in a decrease in surface tension tend to concentrate slightly in the neighborhood of the surface (positive surface concentration); those whose addition results in an increase in surface tension tend to become less concentrated in the neighborhood of the surface (negative surface concentration). The migration of solute either toward or away from the surface is always such as to make the surface tension of the solution (and thus the free energy of the system) lower than it would be if the concentration of solute were uniform throughout (surface concentration equal to zero). Equilibrium is reached when the tendency for free-energy decrease due to lowering surface tension is balanced by an opposing tendency for free-energy increase due to increasing nonuniformity of solute concentration near the surface.

Let us imagine a body of solution of volume V, surface area A, bulk concentration c, and bulk osmotic pressure Π at constant temperature T and external pressure p. For arbitrary changes dA and dV in the area and volume† of the solution, the free-energy change can be written

$$dG = \gamma\, dA - \Pi\, dV \tag{7}$$

† The volume change may be thought of as resulting from the motion of a piston, containing a semipermeable membrane, against the osmotic pressure Π.

This is an exact differential; from the well-known reciprocity relation[1] we find that

$$-\left(\frac{\partial \gamma}{\partial V}\right)_A = \left(\frac{\partial \Pi}{\partial A}\right)_V \tag{8}$$

This can be rewritten

$$-\frac{d\gamma}{dc}\left(\frac{\partial c}{\partial V}\right)_A = \frac{d\Pi}{dc}\left(\frac{\partial c}{\partial A}\right)_V \tag{9}$$

where the presence of total derivatives is justified, since at constant pressure and temperature both the osmotic pressure and the surface tension are determined completely by the concentration.

Now we can write for the total number of moles of solute $N = cV + uA$ and rearrange this to give

$$c = \frac{N - uA}{V} \tag{10}$$

Differentiating, we obtain

$$\left(\frac{\partial c}{\partial V}\right)_A = -\frac{c}{V} \qquad \left(\frac{\partial c}{\partial A}\right)_V = -\frac{u}{V} \tag{11}$$

For a perfect solute

$$\Pi = \frac{N}{V}RT = cRT$$

and

$$\frac{d\Pi}{dc} = RT \tag{12}$$

We finally obtain, on combining Eqs. (9), (11), and (12),

$$\frac{u}{c} = -\frac{1}{RT}\frac{d\gamma}{dc} \tag{13}$$

This equation was first derived by Willard Gibbs and is called the *Gibbs isotherm.* We can also write it in the form†

$$u = -\frac{1}{RT}\frac{d\gamma}{d\ln c} = -\frac{1}{2.3RT}\frac{d\gamma}{d\log c} \tag{14}$$

Surface-active Substances: Surface Adsorption. Many organic solutes in aqueous solution, particularly polar molecules and molecules containing both polar and nonpolar groupings, considerably reduce the surface tension of water. Such solutes tend to accumulate strongly at the surface where, in many cases, they form a unimolecular film of adsorbed molecules.

Usually the film is substantially complete and can accept no more solute molecules when the bulk concentration attains some small value, and hence the surface concentration undergoes little change when the bulk concentration is increased further over a wide range (see Fig. 2). From Eq. (14) we can therefore

† Equation (14) has been derived for a perfect solute and for real solutions applies only at low concentrations. In general, $d\gamma = -uRT\,d\ln a$, where a is the activity of the solute. Activity coefficients for *n*-butanol in aqueous solution at 0°C (which to fairly good approximation can be used at 25°C) are:[2] 0.1 *M*, 0.943; 0.2 *M*, 0.916; 0.4 *M*, 0.882; 0.6 *M*, 0.856; 0.8 *M*, 0.838; and 1.0 *M*, 0.823.

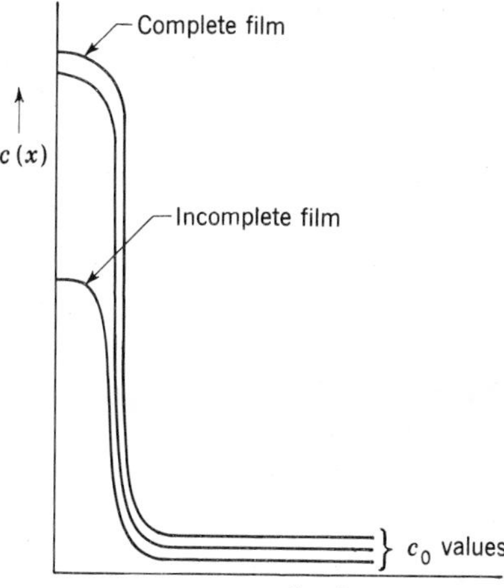

FIG. 2. Variation of the solute concentration near a free surface for the case of positive surface adsorption. The bulk concentration is represented by c_0, and x is the distance measured inward from the surface.

expect that over this range a plot of the surface tension of the solution against the logarithm of the bulk concentration should be linear. It will deviate from linearity both at low and at high concentrations, in both cases yielding a slope of smaller absolute magnitude.

Solutions of Electrolytes. In solutions of certain electrolytes, among them NaCl and KCl, we find that the surface tension *increases* with concentration, indicating a *negative* surface concentration. This is a result of interionic electrostatic attraction, which tends to make the ions draw together and away from the surface. Measurements have shown that in dilute solution the surface tension increases linearly with concentration; thus we see from Eq. (13) that the surface concentration must be directly proportional to the bulk concentration. In actual practice the surface tension often drops initially at low concentrations and then rises linearly; the initial drop is presumably due to impurities and can be eliminated by careful work.

The ratio u/c has dimensions of length and is a measure of the "effective thickness" of the region at the surface in which the actual concentration is significantly less than the bulk concentration. Indeed, we may consider a very crude picture in which the actual concentration $c(x)$ may be supposed to be zero from the surface inward to a distance x_0 and to be equal to the bulk concentration c_0 from that distance inward. It will easily be seen from Eq. (4) that

$$x_0 = \frac{u}{c_0} \tag{15}$$

This distance, by the above argument, is independent of bulk concentration.

A model of a liquid surface in which there is no negative or positive surface concentration would have the solute uniformly distributed right out to the surface. In electrolyte solutions an ion tends to be surrounded by ions of the opposite charge, but at the surface there are ions which are not uniformly surrounded. There is, therefore, an unbalanced electrostatic force tending to draw these surface ions into the body of the solution. In Fig. 3*a* a more nearly correct model is shown, in which the ions have largely drawn away from the surface. The shaded area above the curve labeled c_0 in Fig. 3*b* represents the negative of the surface concentration; the

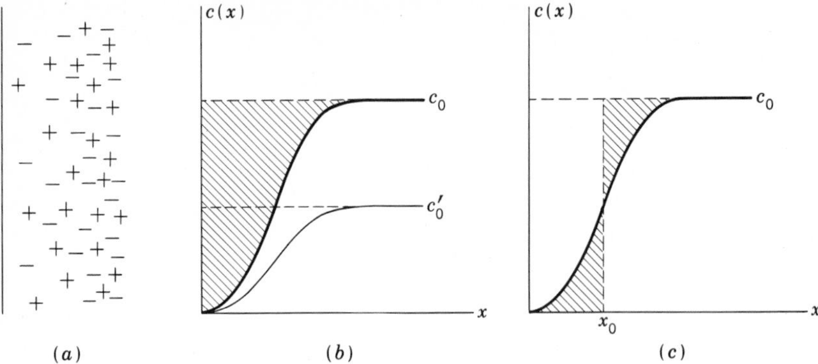

FIG. 3. Variation of ionic solute concentration near a free surface: (*a*) schematic diagram of the distribution of ions, showing negative surface adsorption; (*b*) concentration vs. distance for two different bulk concentrations (the shaded area is equal to $-u$ for a solution of bulk concentration c_0); (*c*) the "equivalent empty-layer thickness" x_0 chosen such that the two shaded areas will be equal.

dotted curve corresponds to a different bulk concentration c_0' and shows the proportionality of surface concentration to bulk concentration. Figure 3*c* shows the significance of the "equivalent empty-layer thickness" x_0. The two shaded areas are equal.

METHOD

There are many experimental techniques for measuring the surface tension of liquids. In the *ring method* one determines the force necessary to pull a metal ring free from the surface of a liquid. The DuNouy tensiometer, in which the ring is hung from the beam of a torsion balance, is often used, but it cannot be easily thermostatted. In calculating the surface tension, it is necessary to apply a correction factor which takes into account the shape of the liquid held up by the ring. In the *drop-weight method* one determines the weight of a drop which falls from a tube of known radius. Again, a correction factor is needed because the drop that actually falls does not represent all the liquid that was supported by surface tension. In the *bubble-pressure method* one determines the maximum gas pressure obtained in forming a gas bubble at the end of a tube of known radius immersed in the liquid. Detailed descriptions of these and other methods may be found elsewhere.[3]

Capillary Rise. In the absence of external forces a body of liquid tends to assume a shape of minimum area. It is normally prevented from assuming spherical shape by the force of gravity, as well as by contact with other objects. When a liquid is in contact with a solid surface, there exists a specific surface free energy for the interface, or interfacial tension γ_{12}. A solid surface itself has a surface tension γ_2, which is often large in comparison with the surface tensions of liquids. Let a liquid with surface tension γ_1 be in contact with a solid with surface tension γ_2, with which it has an interfacial tension γ_{12}. Under what circumstances will a liquid film freely spread over the solid surface and "wet" it? This will happen if in creating liquid-solid interface and an equal area of liquid surface at the expense of an equal area of solid surface the free energy of the entire system decreases:

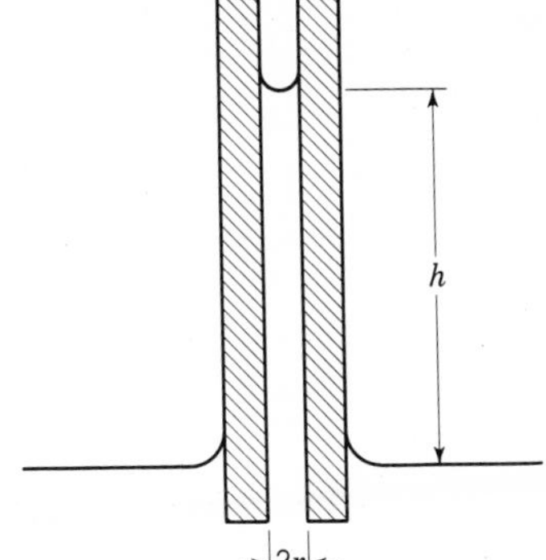

FIG. 4. Capillary rise h in a tube of radius r.

$$\gamma_1 + \gamma_{12} - \gamma_2 < 0 \tag{16}$$

If we have a vertical capillary tube which dips into a liquid, a film of the liquid will tend to run up the capillary wall if condition (16) is obeyed. Then, in order to reduce the surface of the liquid, the meniscus will tend to rise in the tube. It will rise until the force of gravity on the liquid in the capillary above the outside surface, $\pi r^2(h + r/3)\rho g$, exactly counterbalances the tension at the circumference, which is $2\pi r\gamma_1$. In these expressions ρ is the density of the liquid, g is the acceleration of gravity, h is the height of the liquid above the outside surface, r is the radius of the cylindrical capillary, and $r/3$ is a correction for the amount of liquid above the bottom of the meniscus, assuming it to be hemispherical (see Fig. 4). Thus we obtain

$$\gamma_1 = \frac{1}{2}\left(h + \frac{r}{3}\right) r\rho g \tag{17}$$

If Eq. (16) is not obeyed, but if instead

$$\gamma_1 \cos\theta + \gamma_{12} - \gamma_2 = 0 \tag{18}$$

for some value of θ, the liquid will not tend to spread indefinitely on the solid surface but will tend instead to give a *contact angle* θ (see Fig. 5). This may be the case

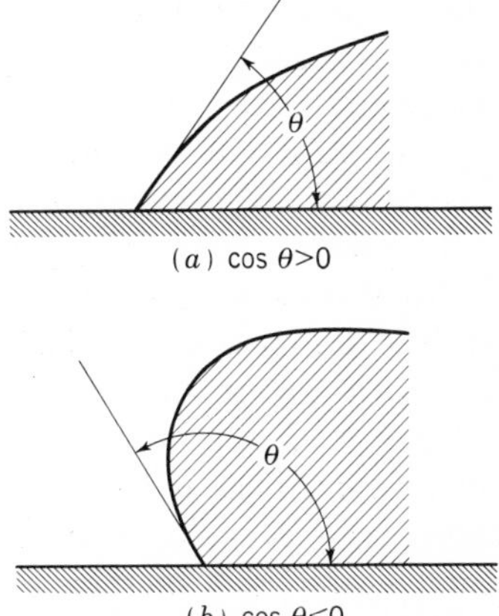

FIG. 5. Contact angle between a liquid and solid surface: (*a*) $\cos\theta > 0$ (e.g., water on a glass surface which is not completely clean); (*b*) $\cos\theta < 0$ (e.g., Hg on glass or water on paraffin).

with aqueous solutions or water on glass surfaces that are not entirely clean. We shall then have, instead of Eq. (17),

$$\gamma_1 \cos\theta = \frac{1}{2}\left(h + \frac{r}{3}\right) r\rho g \tag{19}$$

However, in practice, there is usually some "hysteresis"; that is, the contact angle finally attained is somewhat variable, depending on whether the liquid has been advancing over the solid surface or receding from it. Thus two different capillary rise heights are to be expected. If the *same* height is obtained regardless of whether the liquid was allowed to rise from below or fall from above in the capillary, it may be assumed that Eqs. (16) and (17) are almost certainly valid. This is nearly always true of aqueous solutions in carefully cleaned glass capillary tubes.

EXPERIMENTAL

If the capillary tube has not been recently cleaned, it should be soaked in hot nitric acid for several minutes and rinsed copiously with distilled water. A clean

FIG. 6. Apparatus for measuring surface tension by the method of capillary rise.

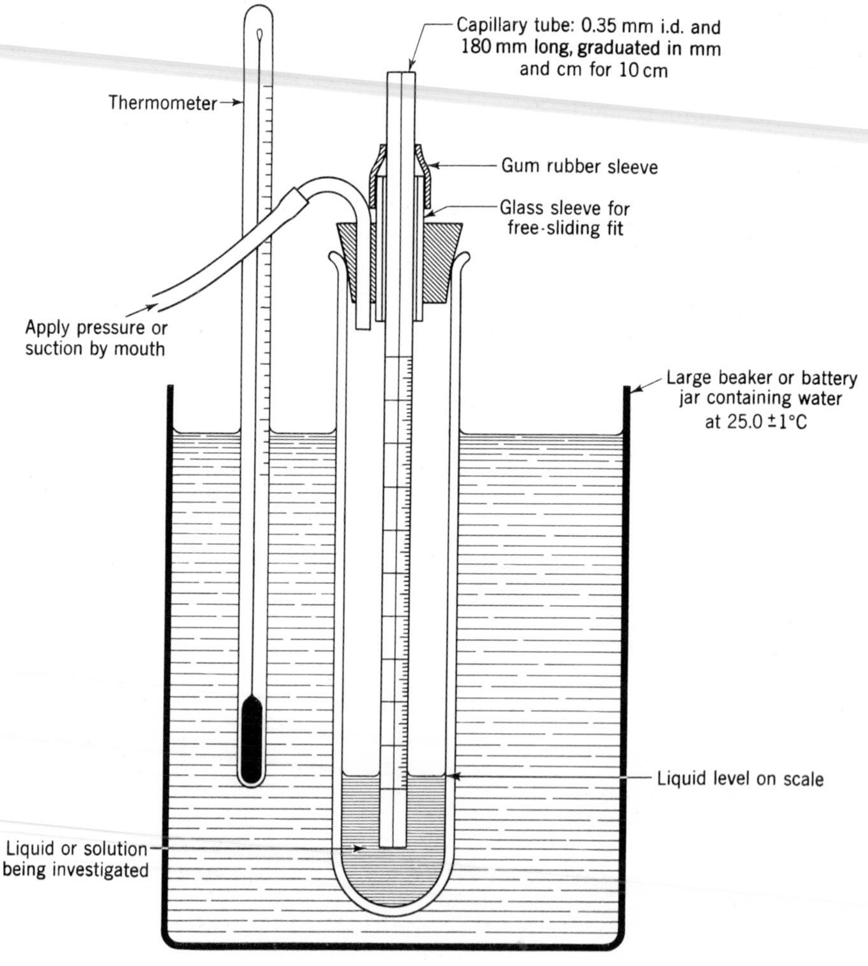

capillary is essential to obtaining good results. When not in use, the capillary should be stored by immersing it in a tall flask of distilled water. Assemble the apparatus as shown in Fig. 6. Adjust the capillary tube upward or downward until the outside liquid level is at or slightly above the zero position on the scale.

Determine the height h of capillary rise for pure water at 25.0°C. Take at least four readings, alternately allowing the meniscus to approach its final position from above and below. Also be sure to read the position of the outside level. If there is not good agreement among these readings, reclean the capillary and repeat the measurements.

Repeat the above procedure with 0.8 M n-butanol solution, dilute to precisely three-quarters the concentration and repeat, and so on until eight concentrations have been used (the last being 0.11 M). Rinse the apparatus and capillary with one or two small aliquots of fresh solution at each concentration change.

If time permits, repeat the above procedure with NaCl solutions. Use solutions of concentrations approximately 4, 3, 2, and 1 M.

CALCULATIONS

From the data obtained for pure water, calculate the capillary radius r and use it in calculating the surface tension of each solution studied. Use Eq. (17) for these calculations. For the butanol solutions one may assume that the density is equal to that of pure water; however, for NaCl solutions it is necessary to use values of ρ obtained by interpolation in Table 1. At 25.0°C for pure water, the surface tension is 72.0 dyne cm^{-1} and the density is 0.9970 g cm^{-3}.

For the runs on n-butanol solutions, plot the surface tension of the solution γ vs. the logarithm of the bulk concentration c and determine the slope. The surface concentration (in moles per square centimeter) can be calculated from Eq. (14). Express this surface concentration in molecules per square angstrom, and obtain the "effective cross-sectional area" per molecule of adsorbed butanol in square angstroms.

TABLE 1. Density of NaCl Solutions at 25°C[a]

% by wt.	NaCl, g liter^{-1}	Moles liter^{-1}	Density, g cm^{-3}
0	0.0	0	0.997
1	10.05	0.1719	1.004
2	20.25	0.3464	1.011
4	41.07	0.7027	1.026
6	62.48	1.069	1.040
8	84.47	1.445	1.055
10	107.1	1.832	1.070
12	130.3	2.229	1.085
14	154.1	2.636	1.100
16	178.6	3.056	1.115
18	203.7	3.485	1.131
20	229.6	3.928	1.147
22	256.1	4.382	1.163
24	283.3	4:847	1.179
26	311.3	5.326	1.196

[a] Calculated from data given in "Handbook of Chemistry and Physics," 40th ed., Chemical Rubber Publishing Co., Cleveland (1958).

For the runs on NaCl solutions, plot γ vs. the bulk concentration c expressed in moles per cubic centimeter. As seen by Eq. (13) the ratio u/c can be determined from the slope of the straight line obtained. Calculate the "effective empty layer thickness" x_0 in angstroms for NaCl. Since the laws of ideal solutions do not hold at the NaCl concentrations studied, the results obtained with NaCl have only qualitative significance and the value of x_0 obtained represents only a rough order of magnitude.

APPARATUS

One (or two) graduated capillary tubes (cleaned with concentrated HNO_3, rinsed thoroughly with distilled water, and stored in distilled water); ring stand; battery jar; test tube, with two-hole stopper assembly, to hold capillary; 0 to 30°C thermometer; one large clamp and one thermometer clamp; two clamp holders; 20-in. length of gum-rubber tubing; 200-ml volumetric flask; 50-ml pipette; 250-ml beakers.

Water aspirator with attached clean gum-rubber tube; 0.8 M aqueous solution of n-butanol (250 ml); 4 M solution of NaCl (400 ml).

REFERENCES

1. P. S. Epstein, "Textbook of Thermodynamics," Wiley, New York (1937).
2. W. D. Harkins and R. W. Wampler, *J. Am. Chem. Soc.,* **53,** 850 (1931).
3. W. D. Harkins, Determination of Surface and Interfacial Tension, in Weissberger (ed.), "Technique of Organic Chemistry," 2d ed., vol. I, part I, chap. IX, Interscience, New York (1949).

GENERAL READING

N. K. Adams, "The Physics and Chemistry of Surfaces," 3d ed., Oxford, London (1941).
J. J. Bikerman, "Surface Chemistry," 2d ed., Academic Press, Inc., New York (1958).

Experiment 32. Adsorption from Solution

In this experiment and in Exp. 33 we shall be concerned with the adsorption of molecules from the gas phase or from solution onto the surface of a solid. The term *adsorption* is used to describe the fact that there is a greater concentration of the adsorbed molecules at the surface of the solid than in the gas phase or in the bulk solution. In general one uses solid adsorbents of small particle size and often with surface imperfections such as cracks and holes which serve to increase the surface area per unit mass greatly over the apparent geometrical area. Such small, porous particles may have specific areas in the range from 10 to 1000 $m^2\ g^{-1}$. Some examples of adsorbents commonly used in experiments of this kind are charcoal, silica gel (SiO_2), alumina (Al_2O_3), zeolites, and molecular sieves. The adsorption from aqueous solutions of acetic acid on charcoal will be investigated in the present experiment.

THEORY

The type of interaction between the adsorbed molecule and the solid surface varies over a wide range from weak nonpolar van der Waals' forces to strong chemical bonding. Examples of adsorption where ionic or covalent bonding occurs are the adsorption of chloride ions on silver chloride (ionic) or of oxygen gas on metals where oxygen-metal bonds are formed (covalent). In these cases the process is called *chemisorption,* and it is generally characterized by high heats of adsorption (from 10 to 100 kcal per mole of gas adsorbed). Chemisorption is highly specific in nature and depends on the chemical properties of both the surface molecules and the adsorbed molecules. Adsorption arising from the weaker van der Waals' and dipole forces is not so specific in character and can take place in any system at low or moderate temperatures. This type of adsorption is called *physical adsorption* and is usually associated with low heats of adsorption (less than about 10 kcal mole^{-1}). Physical adsorption forces are similar to those which cause condensation of gases into liquids or solids. When an adsorbing molecule approaches the surface of the solid, there is an interaction between that molecule and the molecule in the surface which tends to concentrate the adsorbing molecules on the surface in much the same way that a gas molecule is condensed onto the surface of bulk liquid. Another respect in which physical adsorption is similar to liquid condensation is the fact that molar heats of adsorption are of the same order of magnitude as molar heats of vaporization.

Isotherms. The amount adsorbed per gram of solid depends on the specific area of the solid, the equilibrium solute concentration in the solution (or pressure in the case of adsorption from the gas phase), the temperature, and the nature of the molecules involved. From measurements at constant temperature, one can obtain a plot of N, the number of moles adsorbed per gram of solid, vs. c, the equilibrium solute concentration. This is called an *adsorption isotherm.*

In principle one can apply the Gibbs isotherm, Eq. (31-13), to the problem of adsorption at the solid-solution interface.[1] In this case, the surface concentration u will equal N/A (where A is the specific area of the solid) and $d\gamma/dc$ will refer to the change in interfacial tension with solute concentration. Although most solutes affect the solid-liquid interfacial tension in qualitatively the same way as they affect the surface tension at the air-liquid interface, very little is known quantitatively about $d\gamma/dc$ as a function of concentration. Thus, while it can be generally predicted that a solute which lowers the surface tension of water will be adsorbed on a solid surface from aqueous solution, Eq. (31-13) is not useful for even a semi-quantitative calculation of the extent of such adsorption.

Often it is possible to represent experimental results over a limited range by an empirical isotherm suggested by Freundlich:[2]

$$N = Kc^a \tag{1}$$

where K and a are constants which have no physical significance but can be evaluated by a plot of log N vs. log c. However, Eq. (1) fails to predict the behavior usually observed at low and at high concentrations. At low concentrations, N is often directly proportional to c; at high concentrations N usually approaches a constant limiting value which is independent of c.

Much effort has been devoted to developing a theory of adsorption which would explain the observed experimental facts. In some simple systems a theory derived by Langmuir can be applied. This theory is restricted to cases where only one layer of molecules can be adsorbed at the surface. In physical adsorption from the gas phase there is often a formation of many adsorbed layers at higher pressures, as in the case of nitrogen gas adsorbed on charcoal or silica gel at 77°K (see Exp. 33). In the case of chemisorption from the gas phase or adsorption from solution monolayer adsorption is usually observed. Monolayer adsorption is distinguished by the fact that the amount adsorbed reaches a maximum value at moderate concentrations (corresponding to complete coverage of the surface of the adsorbent by a layer one molecule thick) and remains constant with further increase in concentration. The Langmuir isotherm can be derived from either kinetic or equilibrium arguments[2, 3] and is most commonly applied to the chemisorption of gases. We shall give a form appropriate to adsorption from solution:

$$\theta = \frac{kc}{1 + kc} \tag{2}$$

where θ is the fraction of the solid surface covered by adsorbed molecules and k is a constant at constant temperature. Now $\theta = N/N_m$, where N is the number of moles adsorbed per gram of solid at an equilibrium solute concentration c and N_m is the number of moles per gram required to form a monolayer. Making this substitution and rearranging Eq. (2), we obtain

$$\frac{c}{N} = \frac{c}{N_m} + \frac{1}{kN_m} \tag{3}$$

If the Langmuir isotherm is an adequate description of the adsorption process, then a plot of c/N vs. c will yield a straight line with slope $1/N_m$. If the area σ occupied by an adsorbed molecule on the surface is known, the specific area A (in square meters per gram) is given by

$$A = N_m N_0 \sigma \times 10^{-20} \tag{4}$$

where N_0 is Avogadro's number and σ is given in square angstroms.

If adsorption isotherms are determined at several different temperatures, one would predict that the slopes of the c/N vs. c plots should all be the same if the number of adsorption sites (that is, N_m) is independent of temperature, which is usually true. However, the intercepts should change with temperature, since k is a function of temperature. The thermodynamic theory of adsorption from solution is quite complicated, and we shall merely state that one can write

$$\left(\frac{\partial \ln c}{\partial T}\right)_{p,\theta} = \frac{\Delta H}{RT^2} \tag{5}$$

where ΔH is a differential heat for the adsorption process at a constant pressure p and a constant coverage θ. This process involves not only the adsorption of solute molecules but also the displacement of solvent molecules; this complicates the interpretation of ΔH. From Eq. (3) one can see that $(1/kN_m)$ equals $(c_{0.5}/N_m)$, where $c_{0.5}$ is the equilibrium concentration at a coverage $\theta = 0.5$ (that is, $N = \frac{1}{2}N_m$). Thus at 1 atm,

$$\frac{d \ln (1/kN_m)}{dT} = \left(\frac{\partial \ln c}{\partial T}\right)_{\theta=0.5} = \frac{\Delta H}{RT^2} \tag{6}$$

Generally ΔH in Eq. (6) is positive, which means that the extent of adsorption is greater at lower temperatures.

For the adsorption from dilute aqueous solutions of acetic acid on charcoal, the conditions for monolayer adsorption appear to be satisfied. Also, neither acetic acid nor water is appreciably soluble in charcoal, so that bulk *absorption* can be neglected.

EXPERIMENTAL

Clean and dry seven 250-ml erlenmeyer flasks. These should either have glass-stoppered tops or be fitted with rubber stoppers. Place approximately 1 g of charcoal (weighed accurately to the nearest milligram) in six of these flasks. To each flask, add 100 ml of acetic acid solution measured accurately with a pipette. Suggested initial concentrations are 0.15, 0.12, 0.09, 0.06, 0.03, and 0.015 M, which can be made by diluting a stock solution of approximately 0.15 M acid. To the flask containing no charcoal, add 100 ml of 0.03 M acid; this sample will serve as a control. After the seven samples have been tightly stoppered, they should be shaken periodically for a period of 30 min and then allowed to stand in a thermostat bath at 25°C. Allow at least 1 hr for equilibrium and preferably several hours or overnight.

Filter all the samples through fine filter paper. Discard the first 10 ml of the filtrate as a precaution against adsorption of the acid by the filter paper. [Alternatively, remove two 25-ml aliquots with a pipette. Use a glass-wool filter (see Exp. 15) to prevent withdrawing any solid particles. First draw up about 10 ml in the pipette and discard this portion. Then draw up somewhat more than 25 ml, remove the filter, and adjust the liquid level to the mark.] Titrate two 25-ml aliquots with 0.1 N standardized sodium hydroxide solution using phenolphthalein as an indicator. For the titration of the 0.03 and 0.015 M samples use a 10-ml burette. Both in preparing the samples and in making the titrations use a careful analytical technique.

It is advisable to wash the charcoal adsorbent with distilled water several times to remove any impurities, then dry it in an oven at 120°C prior to use. If this has not been done, prepare an extra sample containing 1 g of charcoal and 100 ml of distilled water. Stopper and shake periodically for 30 min; then filter and titrate two 25-ml aliquots as above.

If sufficient time is available, prepare a parallel set of seven samples which are allowed to equilibrate overnight in a refrigerator at about 10°C. Filter (or withdraw aliquots) rapidly so as to prevent the temperature from changing substantially before the sample of solution is removed.

CALCULATIONS

Calculate the final concentration of acetic acid for each sample. The value for the control solution should agree with its initial value. If the sample of charcoal in pure water was studied, it should show no acidity.

From the values of the initial and final concentrations of acetic acid in 100 ml of solution calculate the number of moles present before and after adsorption and obtain the number of moles adsorbed by difference. Compute N, the number of moles of acid adsorbed per gram of charcoal. Plot an isotherm of N vs. the equilibrium (final) concentration c in moles per liter.

As suggested by Eq. (3), plot c/N vs. c. Draw the best straight line through these points, and calculate N_m from the slope. On the assumption that the adsorption area of acetic acid is 21 A^2, calculate the area per gram of charcoal from Eq. (4).

If data were also obtained at a lower temperature, plot the isotherm (N vs. c) and the Langmuir equation (c/N vs. c) for this temperature on the same graphs as the 25°C data. How do the slopes and intercepts of the two Langmuir plots compare? Assuming that ΔH in Eq. (6) is independent of temperature, calculate a value for it.

APPARATUS

Seven 250-ml erlenmeyer flasks, glass-stoppered or with rubber stoppers; three funnels; funnel holder (or three rings, with clamps and stands); fine porosity filter paper; three 250-ml beakers; stirring rod; one 10- and one 50-ml burette; burette stand and holder; several 100-ml titration flasks; a 5-, 10-, 25-, 50-, and 100-ml pipette; spatula; watch glass.

Activated charcoal (acid-free, 10 g); 0.15 M acetic acid (600 ml); 0.1 M sodium hydroxide (150 ml); phenolphthalein indicator; constant-temperature bath, set at 25°C; access to a refrigerator (optional). NOTE: if isotherms are to be measured at two temperatures, most of the equipment and chemicals should be doubled.

REFERENCES

1. S. Glasstone, "The Elements of Physical Chemistry," p. 554, Van Nostrand, Princeton, N. J. (1946).
2. W. J. Moore, "Physical Chemistry," 2d ed., pp. 515–518, Prentice-Hall, Englewood Cliffs, N. J. (1955).
3. G. S. Rushbrooke, "Introduction to Statistical Mechanics," pp. 211–214, Oxford, New York (1949).

GENERAL READING

H. G. Cassidy, "Adsorption and Chromatography," pp. 68–79, Interscience, New York (1951).

Experiment 33. Physical Adsorption of Gases

A brief, general description of adsorption on the surface of a solid is given in Exp. 32, which deals primarily with monolayer adsorption from solution. The present experiment is concerned with the multilayer physical adsorption of a gas (the *adsorbate*) on a high-area solid (the *adsorbent*). Since such adsorption is caused by forces very similar to those which cause the condensation of a gas to a bulk liquid, appreciable adsorption only occurs at temperatures near the boiling point of the absorbate. The adsorption of N_2 gas on a high-area solid will be studied at 77.4°K (the boiling point of liquid nitrogen), and the surface area of the solid will be obtained.

THEORY

We shall be concerned here with the adsorption isotherm, i.e., the amount adsorbed as a function of the equilibrium gas pressure at a constant temperature. For physical adsorption (sometimes referred to as van der Waals' adsorption) five distinct types of isotherms have been observed;[1] we shall discuss the theory for the most common type, a typical example of which is shown in Fig. 1. It has unfortunately become standard practice to express the amount adsorbed by v, the volume of gas in cubic centimeters at STP (standard pressure and temperature: $p = 1$ atm, $T = 273.2°K$) rather than in moles. If the adsorbed volume required to cover the entire surface with a complete *monolayer* is denoted by v_m, one can describe the isotherm in terms of the coverage θ:

$$\theta = \frac{v}{v_m} \tag{1}$$

As shown in Fig. 1, adsorption increases rapidly at high pressures and several layers of adsorbate are present even at a relative pressure $p/p_0 = 0.8$. The pressure p_0 is the saturation pressure of the gas (i.e., the vapor pressure of the liquid at that temperature). When $p/p_0 = 1.0$, bulk condensation will occur to form a liquid film on the surface ($\theta \rightarrow \infty$). One can also see from Fig. 1 that there is no clear, sharp indication of the formation of a first layer; indeed, the second and higher layers usually begin to form before the first layer is complete. Clearly we cannot obtain a good value of v_m from the adsorption isotherm without the aid of a theory which will explain the shape of the isotherm.

Brunauer, Emmett, and Teller[2] were the first to propose a theory for multilayer adsorption. Since the behavior of adsorbed molecules is even more difficult to describe in detail than that of molecules in the liquid state, the BET theory contains some rather drastic assumptions. In spite of this, it is still the most useful theory of physical adsorption available to date. The BET theory gives a correct semiquantitative description of the shape of the isotherm and provides a good means of evaluating v_m (which is then used to obtain the surface area of the solid).

The usual form of the BET isotherm is derived for the case of a free (exposed) surface, where there is no limit on the number of adsorbed layers which may form.

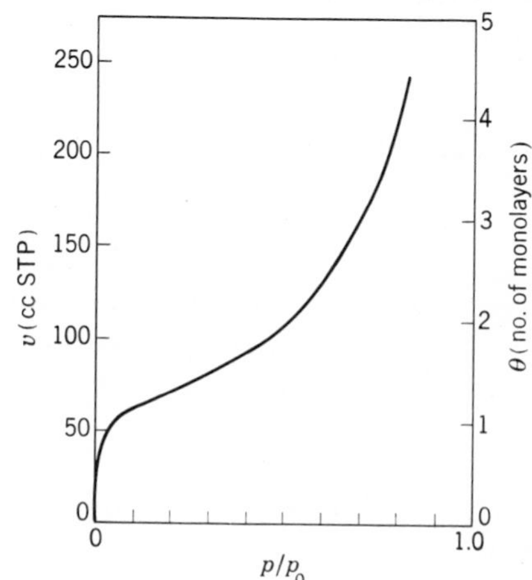

FIG. 1. A typical isotherm for the physical adsorption of nitrogen on a high-area solid at 77°K.

Such an assumption is clearly not good for a very porous adsorbent, such as one with deep cracks having a width of a few monolayer thicknesses, since the surface of these cracks can hold only a few layers even when the cracks are filled. Fortunately, the BET theory is most reliable at low relative pressures (0.05 to 0.3) where only a few complete layers have formed, and it can be applied successfully to the calculation of v_m even for porous solids.

The original derivation of the BET equation[1, 2] was an extension and generalization of Langmuir's treatment of monolayer adsorption. This derivation is based on kinetic considerations—in particular on the fact that, at equilibrium, the rate of condensation of gas molecules to form each adsorbed layer is equal to the rate of evaporation of molecules from that layer. In order to obtain an expression for θ as a function of p (the isotherm) it is necessary to make several simplifying assumptions. The physical nature of these assumptions in the BET theory can be seen most clearly from a different derivation based on statistical mechanics.[3] Neither derivation will be presented here, but we shall discuss the physical model on which the BET equation is based. A detailed review of this model has been given by Hill;[4] the important assumptions are as follows.

1. The surface of the solid adsorbent is uniform; i.e., all "sites" for adsorption of a gas molecule in the first layer are equivalent.

2. Adsorbed molecules in the first layer are localized; i.e., they are confined to sites and cannot move freely over the surface.

3. Each adsorbed molecule in the first layer provides a site for adsorption of a gas molecule in a second layer, each one in the second layer provides a site for adsorption in a third, with no limitation on the number of layers.

4. There is no interaction between molecules in a given layer. Thus, the adsorbed gas is viewed as many independent stacks of molecules built up on the surface sites.

5. All molecules in the second and higher layers are assumed to be like those in the bulk liquid. In particular, the energy of these molecules is taken to be the same as the energy of a molecule in the liquid. Molecules in the first layer have a different energy owing to the direct interaction with the surface.

In brief, the statistical derivation is based on equilibrium considerations—in particular on finding that distribution of the heights of the stacks which will make the free energy a minimum.

The BET isotherm obtained from either derivation is

$$\theta = \frac{n}{S} = \frac{cx}{(1 - x)[1 + (c - 1)x]} \tag{2}$$

where S is the number of sites, n is the number of adsorbed molecules, x is the relative pressure (p/p_0), and c is a dimensionless constant greater than unity and dependent only on the temperature. Note that θ equals zero when $x = 0$ and approaches infinity as x approaches unity, in agreement with Fig. 1. Making use of Eq. (1), we can rearrange Eq. (2) to the usual form of the BET equation:

$$\frac{x}{v(1 - x)} = \frac{1}{v_m c} + \frac{(c - 1)x}{v_m c} \tag{3}$$

Thus a plot of $[x/v(1 - x)]$ vs. x should be a straight line; in practice, deviations from a linear plot are often observed below $x = 0.05$ or above $x = 0.3$. From the slope s and the intercept I, both v_m and c can be evaluated:

$$v_m = \frac{1}{s + I} \qquad c = 1 + \frac{s}{I} \tag{4}$$

The volume adsorbed (in cubic centimeters STP) is related to N, the number of moles adsorbed, by

$$v = NRT_0 \tag{5}$$

where $T_0 = 273.2°\text{K}$ and $R = 82.05\ \text{cm}^3$ atm. The total area of the solid is

$$A = N_0 N_m \sigma \tag{6}$$

where N_0 is Avogadro's number and σ is the cross-sectional area of an adsorbed molecule.

Although we shall not be concerned experimentally with measuring heats of adsorption, it is appropriate to comment that ΔH for the physical adsorption of a gas is always negative, since the process of adsorption results in a decrease in entropy. The *isosteric heat of adsorption* (the heat of adsorption at constant coverage θ) can be obtained by application of the Clausius-Clapeyron equation if isotherms are determined at several different temperatures; the thermodynamics of adsorption has been fully discussed by Hill.[5]

METHOD

Adsorption from the gas phase can be measured by either gravimetric or volumetric techniques. In the gravimetric method, first developed by McBain and Bakr, the weight of adsorbed gas is measured by observing the stretching of a helical spring from which the adsorbent is hung (see Fig. 2). In the volumetric method, the amount of adsorption is inferred from pV measurements which are made on the gas before and after adsorption takes place. An excellent review of the many apparatus designs in common use has been given by Joy;[6] we shall consider only a conventional volumetric apparatus similar to one which has been very completely described by Barr and Anhorn.[7] This apparatus is shown in Fig. 3. The central feature in this design is a gas burette connected to a manometer which can be adjusted to maintain a constant volume in the arm containing the gas.

The gas burette shown in Fig. 3 is constructed from two 50-ml bulbs, large-bore capillary tubing, and a stopcock (F). Fiducial marks are engraved above the top bulb, between the bulbs, and below the bottom bulb. Before the burette is attached to the vacuum system, the volume between fiducial marks (V_1 and V_2) can be accurately measured by weighing the mercury required to fill each bulb. More elegant designs[6] achieve greater flexibility in operation by using five or six bulbs, but two are sufficient for the purpose of evaluating V_3, the volume of the tubing between the top of the gas burette and the zero level in the manometer. This is accomplished by measuring the pressure p of gas with both bulbs in use, then filling the lower bulb with mercury and determining the new pressure value p'. From the perfect-gas law

$$V_3 = \frac{pV_1 - (p' - p)V_2}{p' - p} \tag{7}$$

When an isotherm is being determined, the temperature of the gas in the burette

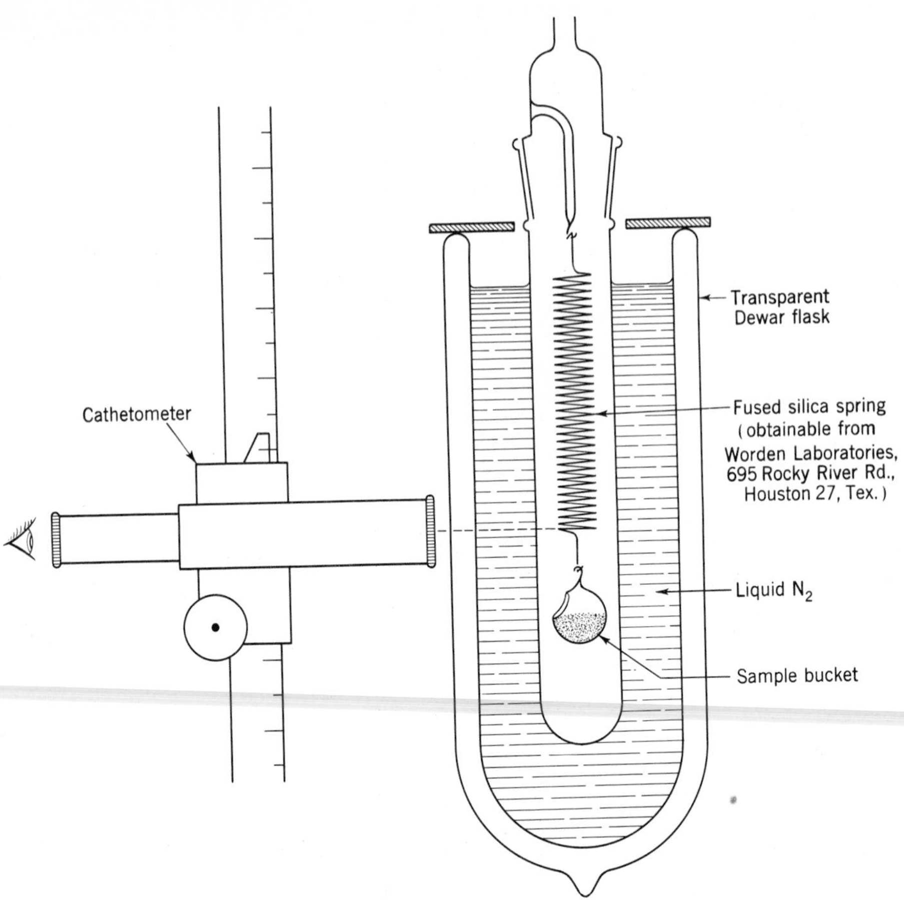

FIG. 2. Gravimetric adsorption apparatus.

system must be known and should remain constant. Although a water jacket is often used, an air jacket is sufficient for the present experiment.

Adsorbent. For the apparatus described here, a sample of a high-area solid adsorbent which has a total surface area of 150 to 250 m² should be used. Of the adsorbents most commonly used (charcoal, silica, alumina), silica is recommended as an excellent choice. The sample bulb should be small enough so that it is almost completely filled with the powder. Figure 4 shows a type of bulb which can easily be filled; a loose plug of Pyrex wool in the capillary will prevent loss of powder during filling and later during degassing. The exact weight of the sample should be determined before the bulb is attached to the system. After it is attached to the vacuum line, the sample must be degassed (i.e., pumped on to remove any physically adsorbed substances, principally water). This can be done by mounting a small electric tube furnace around the sample bulb and heating to 200 to 250°C for several hours. Before heating, stopcock *A* should be opened to pump out all the air (stopcock *B* remains closed); this must be done cautiously to avoid forming a tight plug of powder in the capillary tube (gentle tapping will help also). After this initial degassing, a shorter degassing period will suffice between adsorption runs.

Adsorbate Gas. For physical adsorption, any pure gas which does not react with the solid adsorbent can be used. However, for quantitative area measure-

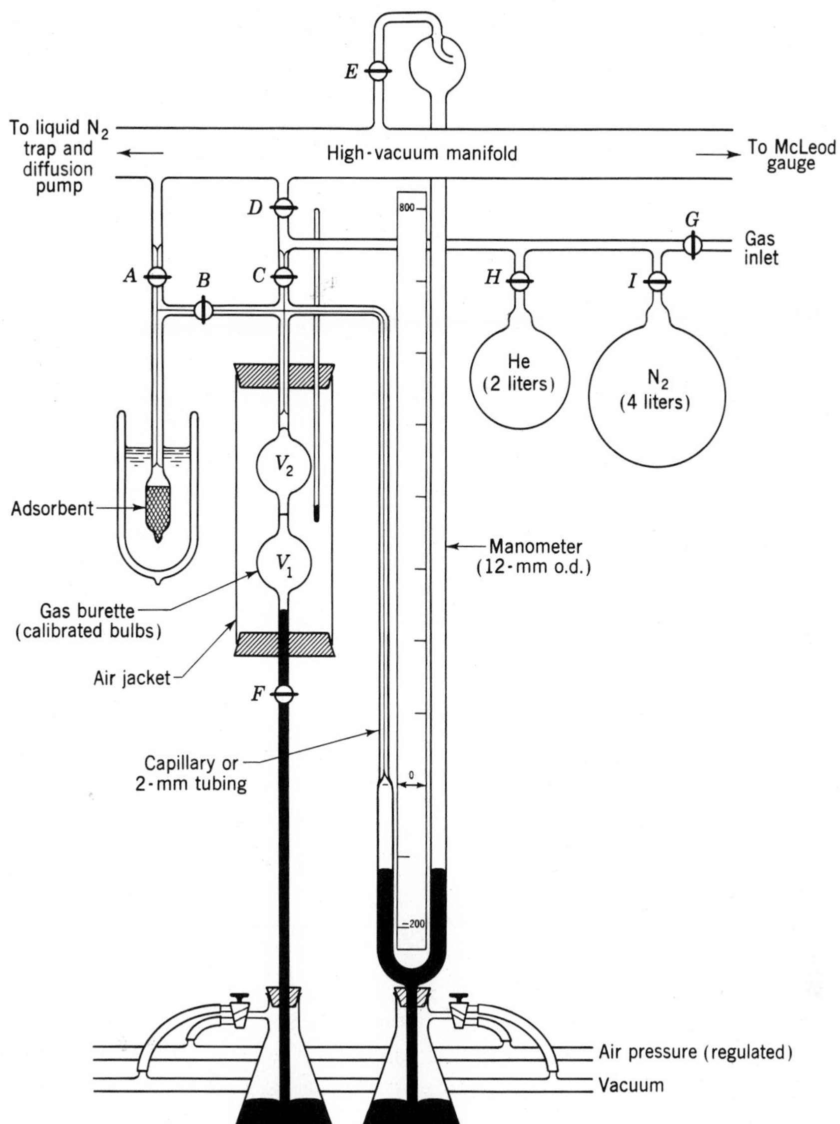

FIG. 3. Apparatus for measuring adsorption isotherms by the volumetric method.

ments, a molecule of known adsorption area is required. Nitrogen gas is a very common choice and will be used in this experiment.

Liquid nitrogen is the most convenient constant-temperature bath for isotherm measurements with N_2 gas. For high-precision work, the temperature of this bath should be measured with a thermocouple so that an accurate value of p_0 can be obtained, or p_0 should be measured directly with a separate nitrogen vapor-pressure manometer.[6, 7] For this experiment, it is adequate to assume that p_0 is equal to the atmospheric pressure in the room.

We can now develop the necessary equations for calculating the amount adsorbed from the pV data obtained during a run. Let us denote the known volume of the gas burette by V_B ($= V_1 + V_2 + V_3$ or $V_2 + V_3$ as the case may be)

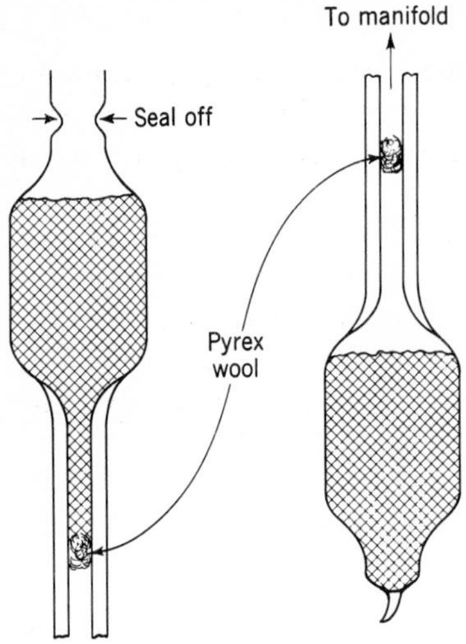

FIG. 4. Detail drawing of the sample bulb, showing method of filling.

and its temperature by T_B. Since the sample bulb is not completely filled by the solid adsorbent, we must also consider the so-called dead-space volume occupied by gas. Let us denote this volume by V_s and consider it to be at a single temperature T_s. If the burette is filled with gas at an initial pressure $p_1{}^0$ and then stopcock B is opened, the pressure will drop to a new equilibrium value p_1. The number of moles adsorbed is

$$N_1 = \frac{p_1{}^0 V_B}{RT_B} - \left(\frac{p_1 V_B}{RT_B} + \frac{p_1 V_s}{RT_s}\right) \tag{8}$$

where the V's are in cubic centimeters and p's are in atmospheres. Equation (8) can be rewritten in terms of v_1 (the amount adsorbed in cubic centimeters STP) by using Eq. (5):

$$v_1 = p_1{}^0 V_B^* - p_1(V_B^* + V_s^*) \tag{9}$$

where the p's are now in millimeters of Hg and

$$V_B^* = \frac{273.2 V_B}{760 T_B} \qquad V_s^* = \frac{273.2 V_s}{760 T_s} \tag{10}$$

The value of V_B^* can be calculated from V_B and T_B, which are known. V_s^* is constant but unknown; however, it can be determined if a run is made using helium gas. Since He is not significantly adsorbed at liquid-nitrogen temperature, $v_1 = 0$ and V_s^* can be calculated from Eq. (9).

If N_2 gas is admitted to the bulb, adsorption does occur and Eq. (9) yields a value of v_1, the "volume" adsorbed at the equilibrium pressure p_1. Now stopcock B is closed and more N_2 gas is added to the burette to achieve a new initial pressure $p_2{}^0$. When B is opened, more adsorption will occur and the pressure will change to an equilibrium value p_2. The total volume adsorbed at p_2 is

$$v_2 = [p_1{}^0 V_B^* + (p_2{}^0 - p_1)V_B^*] - p_2(V_B^* + V_s^*) \tag{11}$$

The generalization of Eq. (11) for v_j, the volume adsorbed at p_j after j additions of gas to the burette, is obvious; for example,

$$v_3 = [p_1{}^0 V_B^* + (p_2{}^0 - p_1)V_B^* + (p_3{}^0 - p_2)V_B^*] - p_3(V_B^* + V_s^*)$$

Note that the bracket contains an expression for the *total* amount of gas added to the system and the second term represents the amount remaining in the gas phase at equilibrium. Since the effect of errors is cumulative in this method, care should be exercised in measuring all pressures.

Normally the entire gas burette is used ($V_B = V_1 + V_2 + V_3$), but on occasion it may be convenient to obtain two points on the isotherm from a single filling of the burette; this can be accomplished after the first point is obtained, by raising the mercury level so as to fill bulb V_1. Equation (11) is still applicable, but the value of the last term is changed, since V_B now equals $V_2 + V_3$ (in that term only) and a new equilibrium pressure must be used.

EXPERIMENTAL

Details of the operation of the vacuum system (Fig. 3) should be reviewed carefully in consultation with an instructor before beginning the experiment. In the following it is assumed that both the helium and nitrogen storage bulbs have already been filled to a pressure slightly over 1 atm, the diffusion pump is operating, and the sample has been degassed.

Stopcocks *B*, *C*, *D*, *E*, and, of course, *G* should be closed and the pressure determined with the McLeod gauge; it should be 10^{-5} mm or less. Now set the mercury level exactly at the lower mark in the gas burette and close stopcock *F*. Also raise the mercury in the manometer to approximately the zero level. After closing stopcock *A* and opening *C*, *D*, and *E*, read the McLeod gauge again and also verify that the mercury level is the same in both arms of the manometer.

Slowly raise a narrow-mouth Dewar flask filled with liquid nitrogen into place, and clamp it so that the sample bulb is completely immersed. Then plug the mouth of the Dewar loosely with glass wool or a piece of clean towel to retard condensation of oxygen from the air. (Liquid O_2 dissolved in the liquid N_2 would raise the temperature of the bath.)

Close stopcocks *D* and *E*, and **very slowly** turn the stopcock on the helium storage bulb while watching the manometer. As soon as the mercury levels begin to move, cease turning the stopcock and let the gas slowly fill the gas burette to a pressure of about 300 mm. When this pressure is reached, immediately close the stopcock on the helium storage bulb and then close *C*. Adjust the mercury level in the manometer so that the left arm is exactly at the zero level. Wait a few minutes for equilibrium to be achieved, readjust to the zero level if necessary, and record the pressure. Now carefully raise the mercury level in the gas burette to the center mark (i.e., fill bulb V_1 with Hg) and again adjust the manometer to the zero level. After a short wait, record the new pressure. Using the known values of V_1 and V_2 (given by the instructor), one can now calculate V_3 from Eq. (7).

Next open stopcock *B* slowly and allow He to enter the sample bulb. Wait for at least 3 min, then reset the manometer to the zero level and read the pressure. After several minutes more, readjust this level (if necessary) and read the pressure again. When the pressure is constant, record its value and also record T_B, the ambient temperature at the gas burette. The quantity V_s^* can be calculated from these data using Eq. (9) with $v_1 = 0$. Note that, in calculating V_B^* from Eq. (10), the appropriate value of V_B is $V_2 + V_3$.

Slowly open stopcock A and pump off the He gas. Lower the Dewar flask and allow the sample to warm up to room temperature. Open stopcocks C and D and continue pumping for at least 15 min. During this time, reset the Hg level in the gas burette to the lower mark and lower the mercury in the manometer to approximately the zero level. (Do the two arms still read the same? Open stopcock E and see if there is any change.) Now close stopcocks A and B and replace the liquid-nitrogen Dewar around the sample bulb. If time is limited and values of V_3 and V_s^* have been provided, this helium run may be omitted and the following procedure is then carried out directly after first cooling the sample.

Procedure for Measuring the N_2 Isotherm. Close stopcocks D and E, and fill the gas burette with N_2 gas to a pressure of about 300 mm. Follow the procedure given above in filling the burette and measuring the pressure. Record this pressure p_1^0. *Slowly* open stopcock B and allow N_2 to enter the sample bulb. Again follow the procedure given previously for obtaining the new equilibrium pressure p_1. In the case of N_2, a longer period may be necessary to achieve equilibrium, since adsorption is now taking place. The volume adsorbed v_1 can be calculated from Eq. (9). [In this case V_B in Eq. (10) is $V_1 + V_2 + V_3$.]

Now close stopcock B and add enough N_2 gas to the burette to bring the pressure up to about 100 mm. Record this pressure p_2^0; then open B and obtain the next equilibrium pressure p_2. The volume v_2 is calculated from Eq. (11). Continue to repeat this process so as to obtain about seven points in the pressure range from 0 to about 250 mm. Each time start with an initial pressure p_j^0 somewhat greater (say 15 to 25 per cent) than the desired equilibrium pressure p_j. If time permits, obtain additional points somewhat more widely spaced over the range 250 to 650 mm. At all times be sure that the liquid-nitrogen level completely covers the sample bulb.

Several times during the period, record the barometric pressure and T_B, the temperature at the gas burette.

CALCULATIONS

From your helium data and the known values of V_1 and V_2, calculate V_3 from Eq. (7). If the temperature at the gas burette has been fairly constant throughout the experiment, use the average value as T_B in Eq. (10) and calculate values of V_B^* when $V_B = V_1 + V_2 + V_3$ and when $V_B = V_2 + V_3$. These values can then be used in all further calculations. If T_B has varied by more than $\pm 0.5°C$, appropriate changes in V_B^* should be made where necessary. Now use Eq. (9) to calculate V_s^*.

For each equilibrium point on the isotherm, calculate a value of v, the volume adsorbed at pressure p. If the barometric pressure has been almost constant, its average value may be taken as p_0, the vapor pressure of nitrogen at the bath temperature. For each isotherm point, calculate $x = p/p_0$.

Plot the isotherm (v vs. x) at 77°K and compare it qualitatively with the one shown in Fig. 1. Finally, calculate $x/v(1 - x)$ for each point and plot that quantity vs. x; see Eq. (3). Draw the best straight line through the points between $x = 0.05$ and 0.3, and determine the slope and intercept of this line. From Eq. (4) calculate v_m and c for the sample studied.

Using Eqs. (5) and (6) and the known weight w of the adsorbent sample, calculate the *specific area* $\bar{A}$ in square meters per gram of solid. The cross-sectional area for an adsorbed N_2 molecule may be taken as 15.8 A^2.

DISCUSSION

What factors can you think of that would tend to make the BET theory less reliable above $\theta = 0.3$, below $\theta = 0.05$?

APPARATUS

Adsorption apparatus (Fig. 3), containing high-area sample, attached to high-vacuum line equipped with McLeod gauge, diffusion pumps, and liquid-nitrogen trap (see Chap. XVII); high-purity helium and nitrogen gas; small electric tube furnace; narrow-mouth taped Dewar flask and clamp for mounting; glass wool or clean towel; 0 to 30°C thermometer; stopcock grease.

REFERENCES

1. J. W. Williams, R. A. Alberty, and E. O. Kraemer, The Colloidal State and Surface Chemistry, in H. S. Taylor and S. Glasstone (eds.), "A Treatise on Physical Chemistry," 3d ed., vol. II, pp. 594–611, chap V, Van Nostrand, Princeton, N.J. (1951).
2. S. Brunauer, P. H. Emmett, and E. Teller, *J. Am. Chem. Soc.,* **60,** 309 (1938).
3. T. L. Hill, *J. Chem. Phys.,* **14,** 263 (1946) and **17,** 772 (1949).
4. T. L. Hill, Theory of Physical Adsorption, in "Advances in Catalysis," vol. IV, pp. 225–242, Academic Press, Inc., New York (1952).
5. *Ibid.,* pp. 242–255.
6. A. S. Joy, *Vacuum,* **3,** 254 (1953).
7. W. E. Barr and V. J. Anhorn, *Instruments,* **20,** 454, 542 (1947).

GENERAL READING

S. Brunauer, "Physical Adsorption," chaps. I-IV, Princeton University Press, Princeton, N.J. (1945).

XI

MACROMOLECULES

EXPERIMENTS

Experiment 34. Osmotic Pressure

Macromolecules are very large molecules with molecular weights ranging in order of magnitude from 1000 to 1,000,000 or more. They are with a few exceptions organic molecules, and many examples such as cellulose and starch exist in nature. Macromolecules can also be made synthetically. These are often called (high) polymers because structurally they are formed by the linking together of monomer units to form chains of considerable length.

From measurements of the osmotic pressure of dilute solutions of a polymer, the number average molecular weight of the polymer will be obtained.

THEORY

When a liquid solution of a solute B in a solvent A is separated from pure solvent A by a membrane that is permeable to A alone and both phases are at the same temperature and under the same pressure, the solvent molecules A will pass through the membrane into the solution. This can be prevented by applying a pressure to the solution which is greater, by a definite amount Π, than the pressure on the solvent. This *osmotic pressure* Π can be related to the vapor pressure of A, since at equilibrium the chemical potential of A in solution, μ_A, must equal the chemical potential of pure A, $\mu_A{}^0$. If the partial molal volume of solvent $\bar{V}_A$ is taken as being independent of pressure, the result of equating chemical potentials is[1]

$$\Pi \bar{V}_A = RT \ln \frac{p_A{}^0}{p_A} \tag{1}$$

Approximating $\bar{V}_A$ by $\tilde{V}_A$, the molal volume of pure A, and assuming Raoult's law, we obtain

$$\Pi\, \tilde{V}_A \cong -RT \ln X_A = -RT \ln (1 - X_B) \tag{2}$$

where X_A and X_B are the mole fractions of A and B in the solution. For *dilute* solutions, ln $(1 - X_B)$ can be replaced by $-X_B$ to give

$$\Pi = \frac{RT}{\tilde{V}_A} X_B \cong \frac{N_B RT}{V_A} \cong \frac{N_B RT}{V} \tag{3}$$

where V_A, the volume of solvent containing N_B moles of solute, is approximately equal to the total volume of the solution V.

In general, the observed osmotic pressures do not obey the ideal-solution law of Eq. (3). Owing to the large size of high-polymer molecules, interactions are important even in dilute solutions, but these can be taken into account fairly well by including an osmotic second virial coefficient:[2]

$$\Pi = \frac{N_B RT}{V}\left(1 + \frac{BN_B}{V}\right) \tag{4}$$

This equation can be written as

$$\frac{\Pi}{C_2} = \frac{RT}{M}(1 + \beta C_2) \tag{5}$$

where M is the molecular weight of the solute, C_2 is the concentration of solute in grams per unit volume of solution ($= MN_B/V$), and β equals B/M. Thus by plotting Π/C_2 vs. C_2, it is possible to determine both M and β.

Osmotic pressure is the one colligative property of solutions which is suitable for determining very high molecular weights, since Π is of the order of several millimeters of Hg even for very dilute solutions. The other colligative properties—freezing-point depression, boiling-point elevation, and vapor-pressure lowering—show effects which are too small for accurate measurement; typical values for dilute high-polymer solutions would be 5×10^{-4}°C, 10^{-4}°C, and 10^{-4} mm Hg, respectively.

Number-average Molecular Weight. When a polymer sample is polydisperse (i.e., there is a distribution of molecules with different weights), a determination of molecular weight must give some kind of average value. When a colligative property is involved, the average is a *number-average* molecular weight $\bar{M}_n$, since the effect depends only on the number of molecules per unit volume and is independent of their size or shape. This is easily seen for the case of osmotic pressure by comparing Eqs. (4) and (5). Molecular-weight determinations based on properties other than the colligative properties will give different kinds of average molecular weights. One common method involves light scattering,[3] which yields a *weight-average* molecular weight $\bar{M}_w$. Both $\bar{M}_n$ and $\bar{M}_w$ are defined and discussed in Exp. 35 along with the *viscosity-average* molecular weight $\bar{M}_v$. It should be noted that $\bar{M}_w$ will always be greater than $\bar{M}_n$ for a polydisperse polymer sample. (For a monodisperse polymer, $\bar{M}_n = \bar{M}_w = \bar{M}_v$.)

METHOD

Several methods of osmotic-pressure measurement are discussed by Wagner.[4] In the dynamic-equilibrium method, flow of solvent through the membrane can

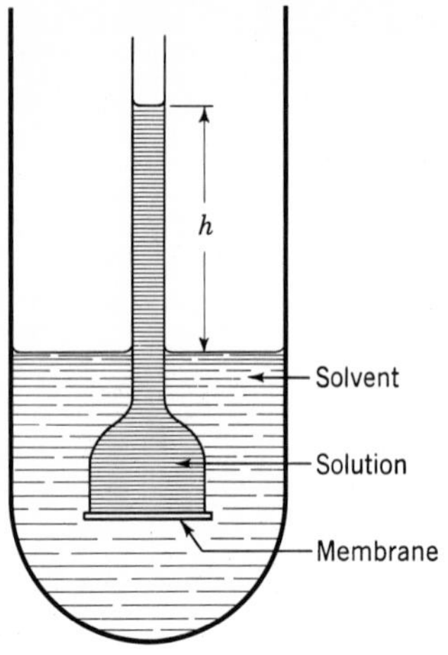

FIG. 1. A simple osmometer; h is the internal head uncorrected for capillary rise.

be prevented by applying an external gas pressure to the solution; the equilibrium pressure which is necessary to obtain zero flow will equal the osmotic pressure. Although this method is rapid, it involves a complex cell which must be leaktight. Described below are two other methods which are frequently used. In both techniques, the osmotic pressure is determined from the internal head of solution in a capillary tube on the solution side of the membrane (see Fig. 1).

Static Method. In the static method, solvent is allowed to diffuse through the membrane until there is no further change in the internal head. It is necessary to correct this head for the effect of surface tension (capillary rise) and to calculate the equilibrium concentration of the solution which will differ from the initial concentration due to passage of solvent through the membrane. The disadvantage of this method is that it is slow, equilibrium usually requiring several days. However, no attention is needed during this time.

Half-sum Method. Fuoss and Mead[4, 5] have proposed a rapid method which involves constant attention for about an hour. With the solution and solvent in thermal equilibrium, the internal head is adjusted initially to be close to the expected equilibrium value. To illustrate this method let us assume that the initial head is slightly above the equilibrium value. Frequent readings are made to follow the decrease in this head with time (curve A in Fig. 2). After sufficient time has elapsed to indicate an approximate asymptotic value, the head is adjusted to be roughly as far below this asymptote as it was initially above. Now readings are made to follow the increase with time (curve B in Fig. 2). By calculating one-half

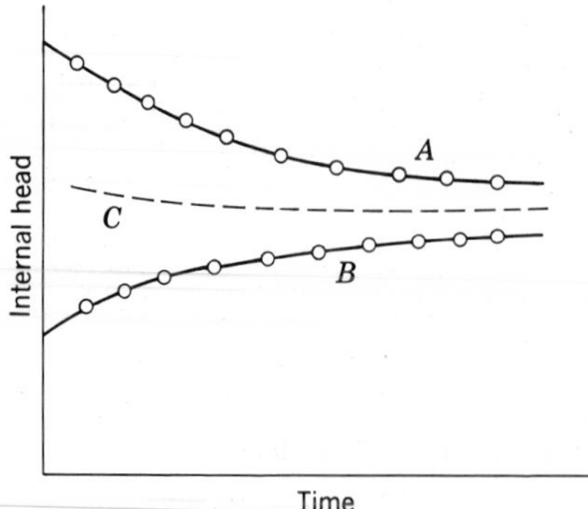

FIG. 2. Fuoss-Mead method of half sums. Circles indicate the experimental points; the dashed line C indicates the average of curves A and B.

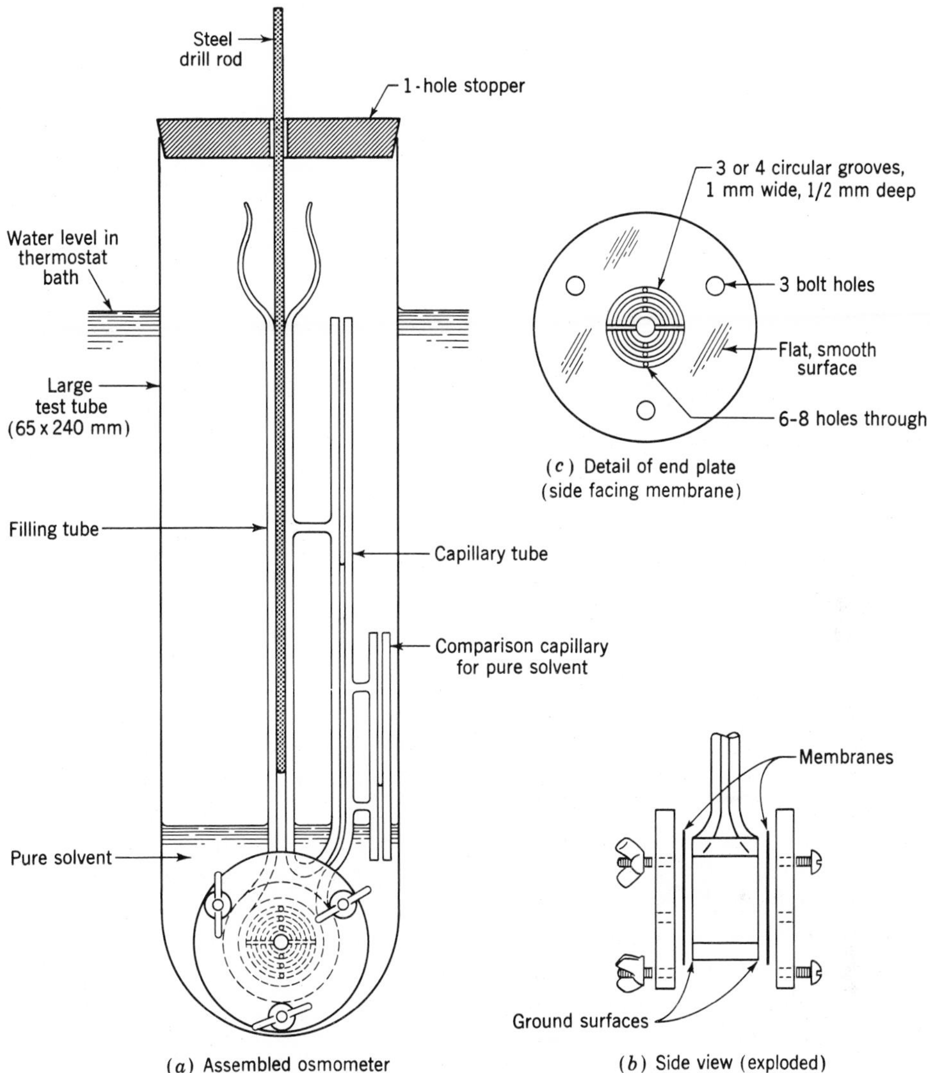

FIG. 3. Zimm-Meyerson osmometer: (*a*) the completely assembled apparatus; (*b*) side view of the cell; (*c*) detail view of one of the end plates.

the sum of the ordinates of curves *A* and *B* at several values of the time, one can obtain curve *C* which converges rapidly to a constant value. Since only a little solvent flows out of the solution during measurements along curve *A* and approximately the same amount of solvent flows into the solution during measurements along curve *B*, the equilibrium concentration may be assumed to be equal to the initial concentration. Correction for the effect of capillary rise is still necessary.

Osmometer. Of many designs which have been used, two are especially simple to construct and operate. The Schulz-Wagner osmometer[4] is of an excellent design but is limited to static measurements. A simplified version of this cell, suitable for student use, has been described also.[6]

The osmometer suggested for this experiment is based on the design of Zimm and Myerson[7] and is shown in Fig. 3. This osmometer consists of a small, heavy-wall cylindrical cell with a 2-mm i.d. capillary filling tube and a 0.5-mm i.d. measuring capillary sealed into its side. The open ends of the cell are ground flat and smooth, so that the two membranes, which are held in place by perforated metal plates, also serve as gaskets. The end plates, machine screws, and wing nuts should be stainless steel (or brass is satisfactory if only organic liquids are to be used). The holes and grooves in the end plates may be replaced, for simplicity, by several drill holes if a disk of filter paper is used to support each membrane. Attached to the measuring capillary is a short length of capillary with the same inside diameter. This is immersed in the solvent to provide a correction for capillary rise.

Once the cell is filled with solution, a steel drill rod which fits the filling tube as closely as possible is inserted. By raising or lowering this steel rod, one can adjust the position of the meniscus in the measuring capillary. Thus measurements can be made using the half-sum method or using the static method where the level is set initially at the expected value in order to save time.

When volatile solvents are used, a small pool of mercury in the flared top of the filling tube will prevent evaporation around the metal rod. Also, a close-fitting one-hole stopper in the outer test tube which holds the pure solvent will retard evaporation of solvent and reduce absorption of water from the atmosphere if a water-soluble solvent is being used.

Membranes. Of the many materials used for membranes the most convenient one is cellulose in the form of nonwaterproofed cellophane sheet (du Pont No. 300 or 600). Cellophane is a good membrane for methyl ethyl ketone, the solvent to be used in this experiment, and can be prepared in a range of porosities by treatment with strong basic solutions.[4, 6] To condition a membrane in water for use with an organic solvent, it is necessary to wash it, successively, with 25, 50, 75, and 100 per cent aqueous alcohol (or acetone) solutions and then displace the alcohol (or acetone) by similar washings with the desired organic solvent. Membranes should be stored in the solvent and never allowed to dry out.

EXPERIMENTAL

Polystyrene is a suitable polymer for investigation in methyl ethyl ketone (MEK) solvent. It is necessary to have a reasonably high molecular weight fraction to avoid diffusion of solute molecules through the membrane. If such solute diffusion occurs, the osmotic pressure will change with time.

An initial weight concentration of polymer which will produce about an 8-cm internal head is desirable. If an approximate value of the molecular weight is known, this concentration can be estimated from Eq. (3). Make up 50 ml of this solution in a volumetric flask. Pipette 25 ml of this solution into a clean 50-ml volumetric flask, and make up to the mark with solvent. Repeat this dilution procedure at least twice to obtain solutions which are one-quarter and one-eighth of the initial concentration. If these solutions are allowed to stand for a considerable time before the osmometer is filled, be sure to seal them carefully to avoid evaporation of solvent and subsequent change of concentration.

Assemble the osmometer by placing a round cellophane membrane (conditioned for and stored in MEK) on each of the metal end plates and bolting these plates carefully about the cell as shown in Fig. 3*c*. The membranes should *never* be allowed to dry out. After the osmometer is assembled, place it in the large test tube containing pure solvent.

It may be desirable to test the osmometer for leaks along the seal between the ground-glass edges of the cell and the metal end plates. This leak test can be accomplished by filling the osmometer with pure solvent and inserting the steel drill rod into the filling tube so as to create an internal head (liquid level in the measuring capillary above that in the comparison capillary). If the osmometer is leak-tight, the level in the capillary should change only very slowly owing to diffusion through the membrane. If the level changes rapidly, a leak along the gasket is indicated and the cell should be taken apart, inspected for flaws, reassembled, and retested.

In order to fill and empty the cell it is convenient to use a hypodermic syringe with a long, stainless-steel needle which can be inserted down the filling tube all the way to the bottom of the cell. After the osmometer has been leak-tested, rinse it several times with small quantities of solution and then fill it with the solution to about halfway up the filling tube. Be sure that there are no air bubbles in the cell; bubbles can be removed by gentle tapping or by removing some of the solution and refilling. Insert the steel drill rod into the filling tube so as to adjust the level in the capillary to approximately the expected level. Immediately rinse the syringe and needle with pure solvent to prevent any deposit of polymer from evaporation of residual solution.

The osmometer should be mounted in a thermostat bath at 25°C which is regulated to within ±0.01°C or better. A glass-walled thermostat tank is best, since it will permit the test tube to be well immersed and enable the capillary levels to be observed through the glass wall. If such a bath is not available, immerse the test tube to the level of the solvent inside and read the capillary levels over the edge of the bath. The level of the liquid in the two capillaries should be read using a cathetometer. This instrument consists of a telescope mounted on a vertical bar engraved with a millimeter scale. The telescope is moved up or down until the liquid level is in the center of the field and the position on the bar is recorded. A more complete description is given in Chap. XVIII. The internal head Δh is the difference between the height of solution in the measuring capillary and the height of solvent in the comparison capillary $h - h_{comp.}$ Determine the internal head for at least four concentrations of polymer.

Either the static method or the half-sum method described previously may be used. If the static method is employed, it is necessary to know the volume of the cell and the cross-sectional area of the measuring capillary in order to compute the equilibrium concentration. Since this correction is small, these dimensions need not be known to high precision. The volume of the cell can be obtained by carefully filling it with solvent using a calibrated syringe. To measure the area of the capillary, introduce a slug of mercury and measure its length. Then transfer the mercury to a weighing bottle and weigh. Using the known density of mercury, one can calculate the cross-sectional area.

CALCULATIONS

For each solution, calculate the initial concentration in grams of solute per milliliter of solution. If the half-sum method was used, make the appropriate plots of internal head Δh vs. time as shown in Fig. 2 to obtain the equilibrium head.

If the static method was used, correct the initial concentration for diffusion of solvent to obtain the equilibrium concentration C_2. Calculate the osmotic pressure Π, in dynes per square centimeter, for each solution from

$$\Pi = (\Delta h)\rho g \tag{6}$$

where the solution density ρ is taken to be the same as the density of pure solvent and g is the acceleration due to gravity.

Tabulate your values for Δh, Π, C_2, and Π/C_2. Plot Π/C_2 vs. C_2, and draw the best straight line through the experimental points. (It is possible that the experimental points may show a slight curvature; in this case, draw the straight line which is tangent to the curve at zero concentration.) From the intercept and slope of this line, calculate the number-average molecular weight $\bar{M}_n$ and the osmotic second virial coefficient β using Eq. (5).

APPARATUS

One or more osmometers (complete with end plates, bolts, large test tube, drill rod, and stopper); membranes, conditioned for use in methyl ethyl ketone; four 50-ml glass-stoppered volumetric flasks; 25-ml pipette; several beakers; 25-ml hypodermic syringe with long needle; constant-temperature bath (preferably with glass walls) set at 25°C; large clamp for mounting the osmometer; cathetometer; stopwatch; mercury (optional).

High-molecular-weight polystyrene powder; reagent-grade methyl ethyl ketone (500 ml).

REFERENCES

1. W. J. Moore, "Physical Chemistry," 2d ed., p. 134, Prentice-Hall, Englewood Cliffs, N.J. (1955).
2. P. J. Flory, "Principles of Polymer Chemistry," pp. 279–282, 530–539, Cornell University Press, Ithaca, N.Y. (1953).
3. *Ibid.,* pp. 283–303.
4. R. H. Wagner, Determination of Osmotic Pressure, in A. Weissberger (ed.), "Technique of Organic Chemistry," 2d ed., vol. I, part I, chap. XI, Interscience, New York (1949).
5. R. M. Fuoss and D. J. Mead, *J. Phys. Chem.,* **47,** 59 (1943).
6. F. Daniels, J. H. Mathews, J. W. Williams, P. Bender, and R. A. Alberty, "Experimental Physical Chemistry," 5th ed., p. 220, McGraw-Hill, New York (1956).
7. B. H. Zimm and I. Myerson, *J. Am. Chem. Soc.,* **68,** 911 (1946).

GENERAL READING

S. Glasstone, "Textbook of Physical Chemistry," 2d ed., pp. 651–673, Van Nostrand, Princeton, N.J. (1946).

Experiment 35. Intrinsic Viscosity: Chain Linkage in Polyvinyl Alcohol

While the basic chemical structure of a synthetic high polymer is usually well understood, many physical properties depend on such characteristics as chain length, degree of chain branching, and molecular weight, which are not easy to specify exactly in terms of a molecular formula. Moreover, the macromolecules in a given sample are seldom uniform in chain length or molecular weight (which for a linear polymer is proportional to chain length); thus, the nature of the distribution of molecular weights is another important characteristic.

A polymer whose molecules are all of the same molecular weight is said to be *monodisperse;* a polymer in which the molecular weights vary from molecule to molecule is said to be *polydisperse.* Specimens that are approximately monodisperse can be prepared in some cases by fractionating a polydisperse polymer; this fractionation is frequently done on the basis of solubility in various solvent mixtures.

This experiment is concerned with the linear polymer polyvinyl alcohol (PVOH), $\text{-}(\text{CH}_2\text{—CHOH}\text{-})_{\bar{n}}$, which is prepared by hydrolysis of the polyvinyl acetate (PVAc) obtained from the direct polymerization of the monomer vinyl acetate, $CH_2{=}CH{-}OOCCH_3$. As ordinarily prepared polyvinyl alcohol shows a negligible amount of branching of the chains. It is somewhat unusual among synthetic high polymers in that it is soluble in water.

A characteristic of interest in connection with PVOH and PVAc is the consistency of orientation of monomer units along the chain. In the formula given above it is assumed that all monomer units go together "head to tail." However, occasionally a monomer unit will join onto the chain in a "head-to-head" fashion, yielding a chain of the form

$$(\text{CH}_2\text{—CHX})_{\bar{n}}\text{CH}_2\text{—CHX—}\underbrace{\text{CHX—CH}_2}\text{—CH}_2\text{—CHX}(\text{CH}_2\text{—CHX})_{\bar{n}}\cdots$$

head-to-head linkage ↑ (between CHX—CHX); reversed monomer unit (CHX—CH₂ underbraced)

where X is Ac or OH. The frequency of head-to-head linkage depends on the relative rates of the normal growth-step reaction α

$$\underset{\rightarrow}{\text{R}}\cdot + \text{M} \xrightarrow{k_\alpha} \underset{\rightarrow}{\text{R}}\text{—}\underset{\rightarrow}{\text{M}}\cdot \qquad (1\alpha)$$

and the abnormal reaction β

$$\underset{\rightarrow}{\text{R}}\cdot + \text{M} \xrightarrow{k_\beta} \underset{\rightarrow}{\text{R}}\text{—}\underset{\leftarrow}{\text{M}}\cdot \qquad (1\beta)$$

(where $\underset{\rightarrow}{\text{R}}\cdot$ is the growing polymer radical, the arrow representing the predominant monomer orientation). The rates, in turn, must depend on the activation energies:

$$\frac{k_\beta}{k_\alpha} \propto \frac{e^{-E_\beta^*/RT}}{e^{-E_\alpha^*/RT}} = e^{-(E_\beta^* - E_\alpha^*)/RT}$$

Presumably the activation energy for the normal reaction is the lower one, in accord with the finding of Flory and Leutner[1, 2] that the frequency of head-to-head linkages in PVAc increases with increasing polymerization temperature.

In this experiment, the method of Flory and Leutner will be used to determine the fraction of head-to-head attachments in a single sample of PVOH. The method depends on the fact that in PVOH a head-to-head linkage is a 1,2-glycol structure, and 1,2-glycols can be specifically and quantitatively cleaved by periodic acid or periodate ion. Treatment of PVOH with periodate should therefore break the chain into a number of fragments, bringing about a corresponding decrease in the effective molecular weight. All that is required is a measurement of the molecular weight of a specimen of PVOH before and after treatment with periodate.

METHOD[3]

For the determination of very high molecular weights, freezing-point depressions, boiling-point elevations, and vapor-pressure lowerings are too small for accurate measurement. Osmotic pressures are of a convenient order of magnitude, but measurements are time consuming. The technique to be used in this experiment depends on the determination of the intrinsic viscosity of the polymer. However, molecular-weight determinations from osmotic pressures are valuable in calibrating the viscosity method.

The coefficient of viscosity η of a fluid is defined in Exp. 5. It is conveniently measured, in the case of liquids, by determination of the time of flow of a given volume V of the liquid through a vertical capillary tube under the influence of gravity. For a virtually incompressible fluid such as a liquid, this flow is governed by Poiseuille's law in the form

$$\frac{dV}{dt} = \frac{\pi r^4(p_1 - p_2)}{8\eta L}$$

where dV/dt is the rate of liquid flow through a cylindrical tube of radius r and length L and $(p_1 - p_2)$ is the difference in pressure between the two ends of the tube. In practice a viscosimeter of a type similar to that shown in Fig. 1 is used. Since $(p_1 - p_2)$ is proportional to the density ρ, it can be shown that for a given total volume of liquid

$$\frac{\eta}{\rho} = Bt \tag{2}$$

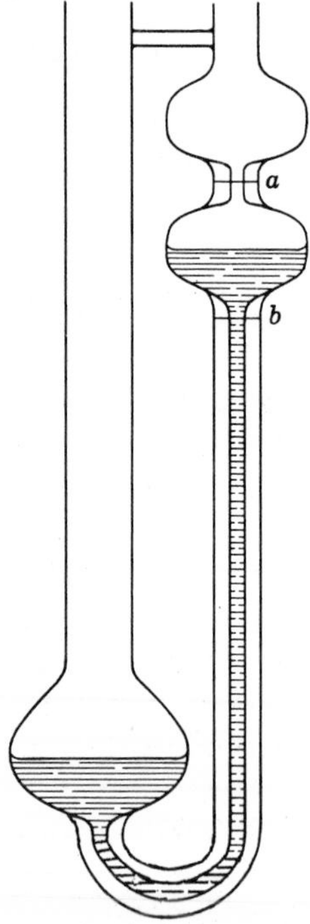

FIG. 1. Ostwald viscosimeter.

where t is the time required for the upper meniscus to fall from the upper to the lower fiducial mark (a to b) and B is an apparatus constant which must be determined through calibration with a liquid of known viscosity (e.g., water). The derivation of this equation is similar to that given for Eq. (5-10). For high-precision work, it may be necessary to consider a kinetic-energy correction to Eq. (2). As in Eq. (5-16), we can write

$$\frac{\eta}{\rho} = Bt - \frac{V}{8\pi Lt}$$

but the correction term is usually less than 1 per cent of Bt and may be neglected in this experiment.

THEORY

Einstein showed that the viscosity η of a fluid in which small rigid spheres are dilutely and uniformly suspended is related to the viscosity η_0 of the pure fluid (solvent) by the expression[4]

$$\frac{\eta}{\eta_0} - 1 = \frac{5}{2}\frac{v}{V} \tag{3}$$

where v is the volume occupied by all the spheres and V the total volume. The left-hand side of Eq. (3) is called the *specific viscosity* η_{sp}. For nonspherical particles the numerical coefficient of v/V is greater than $5/2$ but should be a constant for any given shape provided the rates of shear are sufficiently low to avoid preferential orientation of the particles.

The *intrinsic viscosity,* denoted by $[\eta]$, is defined as the ratio of the specific viscosity to the weight concentration of solute, in the limit of zero concentration:

$$[\eta] \equiv \lim_{c\to 0} \frac{\eta_{sp}}{c} = \lim_{c\to 0}\left(\frac{1}{c}\ln\frac{\eta}{\eta_0}\right) \tag{4}$$

where c is usually defined as the concentration in grams of solute per 100 ml of solution. Both η_{sp}/c and $(1/c)(\ln \eta/\eta_0)$ show a reasonably linear concentration dependence at low concentrations. A plot of $(1/c)(\ln \eta/\eta_0)$ vs. c usually has a small negative slope, while a plot of η_{sp}/c vs. c has a positive and larger slope.[3] Careful work demands that either or both of these quantities be extrapolated to zero concentration, although $(1/c)(\ln \eta/\eta_0)$ for a single dilute solution will give a fair approximation to $[\eta]$.

If the internal density of the spherical particles (polymer molecules) is independent of their size (i.e., the volume of the molecule is proportional to its molecular weight), the intrinsic viscosity should be independent of the size of the particles, and hence of no value in indicating the molecular weight. This, however, is not the case; to see why, we must look into the nature of a polymer macromolecule as it exists in solution.

Statistically Coiled Molecules. A high polymer such as PVOH contains many single bonds, around which rotation is possible. If the configurations around successive carbon atoms are independent and unrelated, it will be seen that two parts of the polymer chain more than a few carbon atoms apart are essentially uncorrelated in regard to direction in space. The molecule is then "statistically coiled" and resembles a loose tangle of yarn:

Simple statistical treatments[2] show that the mean distance between the two ends of the chain, and indeed also the effective mean diameter d of the coiled molecule regarded as a rough sphere, should be proportional to the square root of the chain length and thus to the square root of the molecular weight:

$$d \propto M^{1/2}$$

The volume v_m occupied by a molecule should then vary as $M^{3/2}$. The number of molecules in a given weight of polymer varies inversely with the molecular weight; hence the total volume of the spheres is

$$v \propto \frac{cV}{M} M^{3/2} = cVM^{1/2}$$

Therefore,

$$[\eta] = KM^{1/2} \tag{5}$$

where K is a constant. This treatment is much simplified; it ignores, among other things, the problem of "excluded volume"; that is, the chain cannot coil altogether randomly because it is subject to the restriction that no two parts of the chain may be at the same point in space at the same time. This restriction becomes more and more important the higher the molecular weight. Even more serious is the effect of solvent; the above treatment tacitly assumes a "poor solvent" which would barely get the polymer into solution. A "good solvent," by solvating the polymer, makes the size of the statistical coil increase faster with chain length than it otherwise would, owing to enhancement of the excluded volume effect. Accordingly, instead of Eq. (5) we might write

$$[\eta] = KM^{a} \tag{6}$$

where K and a are empirical parameters characteristic both of the polymer itself and of the solvent. The exponent a varies from about 0.5, for well-coiled polymer molecules in a poor solvent, to as much as 1.7, for a rigidly extended "rodlike" polymer molecule.

Flory and Leutner,[1] working with monodisperse specimens of PVOH differing from one another in molecular weight over a wide range (obtained by fractionating polydisperse commercial PVOH), established a correlation between the molecular weight, as determined from osmotic pressure measurements, and the intrinsic viscosity. They found that for PVOH in aqueous solution at 25°C,

$$[\eta] = 2.0 \times 10^{-4} M^{0.76} \tag{7}$$

Equation (7) also holds for a polydisperse sample of PVOH, but the molecular weight in this case is $\bar{M}_v$, the "viscosity average" molecular weight defined below.

Number-average and Viscosity-average Molecular Weight. For a polydisperse polymer, any determination of molecular weight must yield an average of some sort. When a colligative property such as osmotic pressure is used, the average is a "number average":

$$\bar{M}_n = \frac{\int_0^\infty MP(M)\,dM}{\int_0^\infty P(M)\,dM} \tag{8}$$

where $P(M)$ is the molecular-weight distribution function; that is, $P(M)\,dM$ is proportional to the number of molecules with molecular weights between M and $M + dM$. However, the average obtained from intrinsic viscosity is not the same kind of average. It is called the "viscosity average" and is given by

$$(\bar{M}_v)^a = \frac{\int_0^\infty M^{1+a}P(M)\,dM}{\int_0^\infty MP(M)\,dM} \tag{9}$$

For a monodisperse polymer, $\bar{M}_v = \bar{M}_n = M$, but for a polydisperse polymer the two kinds of averages are not equal but are related by a constant factor which depends on the distribution function $P(M)$ and the parameter a. A commonly encountered distribution function, and one that is likely to be valid for PVOH, is one that arises if the probability of a chain-termination reaction during the polymerization is constant with time and independent of the chain length already achieved. It is also the most likely function for the product resulting from cleavage with periodate if the head-to-head structures can be assumed to be randomly distributed along the PVOH chains. This distribution function is

$$P(M) = \frac{1}{\bar{M}_n}\, e^{-M/\bar{M}_n} \tag{10}$$

When this function is used as the weighting function in evaluating averages, it can be shown[3, 5] that

$$\frac{\bar{M}_v}{\bar{M}_n} = [(1 + a)\Gamma(1 + a)]^{1/a}$$

where Γ is the "gamma function." For $a = 0.76$ (the value given above for polyvinyl alcohol),

$$\frac{\bar{M}_v}{\bar{M}_n} = 1.89 \tag{11}$$

If a much exceeds 0.5, $\bar{M}_v$ is much closer to a "weight-average" molecular weight,

$$\bar{M}_w = \frac{\int_0^\infty M^2P(M)\,dM}{\int_0^\infty MP(M)\,dM} \tag{12}$$

than it is to the number average $\bar{M}_n$. In fact, when $a = 1$, $\bar{M}_v$ and $\bar{M}_w$ are identical, and with the distribution assumed in Eq. (10) their ratio to $\bar{M}_n$ is 2.

Determination of Frequency of Head-to-head Occurrences. We wish to calculate the fraction of linkages which are head to head (that is, the ratio of "backward" monomer units to total monomer units), on the assumption that degradation arises exclusively from cleavage of 1,2-glycol structures and that all such structures are cleaved. Let us denote this ratio by Δ. It is equal to the *increase* in the number of molecules in the system, divided by the total number of monomer units represented by all molecules present in the system. Since these numbers are in inverse proportion to the respective molecular weights,

$$\Delta = \frac{1/\bar{M}_n' - 1/\bar{M}_n}{1/M_0} \tag{13}$$

where $\bar{M}_n$ and $\bar{M}_n'$ are number-average molecular weights before and after degradation, respectively, and M_0 is the monomer weight, equal to 44. Thus,

$$\Delta = 44\left(\frac{1}{\bar{M}_n'} - \frac{1}{\bar{M}_n}\right) \tag{14}$$

Making use of Eq. (11) we can write

$$\Delta = 83\left(\frac{1}{\bar{M}_v'} - \frac{1}{\bar{M}_v}\right) \tag{15}$$

which permits viscosity averages to be used directly.

EXPERIMENTAL

Clean the viscosimeter thoroughly with cleaning solution, rinse copiously with distilled water (use a water aspirator to draw large amounts of distilled water through the capillary), and dry with acetone and air. Immerse in a 25° thermostat bath to equilibrate. Place a small flask of distilled water in a 25°C bath to equilibrate. Equilibration of water or solutions to bath temperature, in the amounts used here, should be complete in about 10 min.

If a stock solution of the polymer is not available, it should be prepared as follows: Weigh out accurately in a weighing bottle or on a watch glass 4.0 to 4.5 g of the dry polymer. Transfer to a 250-ml beaker. Fill three-fourths full with distilled water, and stir, with gentle warming, until the polymer is dissolved. Cool, and transfer quantitatively to a 250-ml volumetric flask, avoiding foam as much as possible by letting the solution run down the side of the flask. Make up to the mark with distilled water, and mix gently (to avoid foam) but thoroughly. If the solution appears contaminated with insoluble material that would possibly interfere with the viscosity measurements, filter it through Pyrex wool. Wash all glassware *very thoroughly* with water as soon as possible after use. (Since making up this solution may take considerable time, it is suggested that the calibration of the viscosimeter with water be carried out concurrently.)

Pipette 50 ml of the stock solution into a 100-ml volumetric flask, and make up to the mark with distilled water, observing the above precautions to prevent foaming. Mix, and place in the bath to equilibrate. In this and other dilutions, rinse the pipette *very thoroughly* with water and dry with acetone and air.

To cleave the polymer, pipette 50 ml of the stock solution into a 250-ml flask and add up to 25 ml of distilled water and 0.25 g of solid KIO_4. Warm the flask to about 70°C, and stir until all the salt is dissolved. Then clamp the flask in a thermostat bath and stir until the solution is at 25°C. Transfer quantitatively to a 100-ml volumetric flask, and make up to the mark with distilled water. Mix, and place in the bath to equilibrate. (This operation can be carried out while viscosity measurements are being made on the uncleaved polymer.)

To obtain the second concentration of each material, dilute the solution with an equal volume of distilled water. Place in the bath to equilibrate.

If time permits, the densities of the solutions should be measured with a Westphal balance. Otherwise, the densities may be taken equal to that of the pure solvent without introducing appreciable error.

The recommended procedure for measuring the viscosity is as follows:

1. Pipette the required quantity of solution (or water) into the viscosimeter. Immediately rinse the pipette copiously with water, and dry it with acetone and air before using again.
2. The viscosimeter should be mounted vertically in a constant-temperature bath so that both fiducial marks are visible and below the water level. If a glass-walled thermostat bath which will allow readings to be made with the viscosimeter in the bath is not available, fill a large beaker or battery jar with water from the bath and set it on a dry towel for thermal insulation. The water will have to be changed frequently. The temperature should be maintained within ±0.05° of 25°C during a run.
3. By mouth suction through a rubber tube, draw the solution up to a point well above the upper fiducial mark. Release the suction and measure the flow time between the upper and lower marks with a stopwatch. Obtain two or more additional runs with the same filling of the viscosimeter. Three runs agreeing within about 1 per cent should suffice.
4. Rinse the viscosimeter *very thoroughly* with distilled water, then dry with acetone and air. Be sure to remove *all* polymer with water before introducing acetone.

If time permits, carry out a third dilution (to half of the second concentration) on each of the two materials, and determine the viscosities.

CALCULATIONS

At 25°C, the density of water is 0.9970 g cm^{-3} and the coefficient of viscosity η_0 is 0.8937 centipoise. Using your time of flow for pure water, determine the apparatus constant B in Eq. (2).

For each of the polymer solutions studied, calculate the viscosity η and the concentration c in grams of polymer per 100 ml of solution. Then calculate η_{sp}/c and $(1/c)(\ln \eta/\eta_0)$. Plot both η_{sp}/c and $(1/c)(\ln \eta/\eta_0)$ vs. c and extrapolate linearly to $c = 0$ to obtain $[\eta]$ for the original and for the degraded polymer.

Calculate $\bar{M}_v$ and $\bar{M}_n$ for both the original polymer and the degraded polymer, then obtain a value for Δ. Report these figures together with the polymerization temperature for the sample studied. Discuss the relationship between Δ and the rate constants k_α and k_β.

APPARATUS

Ostwald viscosimeter; two 100- and two 250-ml volumetric flasks; a 10- and a 50-ml pipette; 250-ml glass-stoppered flask; one 100- and two 250-ml beakers; stirring rod; bunsen burner; tripod stand and wire gauze; 0 to 100°C thermometer; length of gum-rubber tubing. If polymer stock solution is to be prepared by student: weighing bottle; funnel; Pyrex wool.

Glass-walled thermostat bath at 25°C or substitute; polyvinyl alcohol (M.W. ~ 60,000, 5 g of solid or 200 ml of 18 g liter^{-1} solution); KIO_4 (1 g); chromic acid cleaning solution (50 ml); Westphal balance, if needed.

REFERENCES

1. P. J. Flory and F. S. Leutner, *J. Polymer Sci.*, **3**, 880 (1948); **5**, 267 (1950).
2. P. J. Flory, "Principles of Polymer Chemistry," Cornell University Press, Ithaca, N.Y. (1953).
3. T. E. McGoury and H. Mark, Determination of Viscosity and Viscometry of Dilute Polymer Solutions, in A. Weissberger (ed.), "Technique of Organic Chemistry," 2d ed., vol. I, parts I and III, chaps. VIII and VIII Supplement, Interscience, New York (1949).
4. A. Einstein, "Investigations on the Theory of the Brownian Movement," chap. III, Dover, New York (1956).
5. J. R. Schaefgen and P. J. Flory, *J. Am. Chem. Soc.*, **70**, 2709 (1948).

GENERAL READING

F. W. Billmeyer, Jr., "Textbook of Polymer Chemistry," Interscience, New York (1957).

Experiment 36. Helix-Coil Transition in Polypeptides

Polymer molecules in solution can be found in many different geometric conformations, and there exist a variety of experimental methods (e.g., viscosity, light scattering, optical rotation) for obtaining information about these conformations.[1] In this experiment, the measurement of optical rotation will be used to study a special type of conformational change which occurs in many polypeptides.

The two important kinds of conformation of a polypeptide chain are the helix and the random coil. In the helical form the amide hydrogen of each "amide group"

```
          H   R
           \ /
  —N—C—C—
    |  ||
    H  O
```

is internally hydrogen-bonded to the carbonyl oxygen of the third following amide group along the chain. Thus, this form involves a quite rigid, rodlike structure (see Fig. 1). Under different conditions, the polypeptide molecule may be in the form of a statistically random coil (see Exp. 35). The stable form of the polypeptide will depend on several factors—the nature of the peptide groups, the solvent, and the temperature. For example, poly-γ-benzyl-*l*-glutamate† (PBG)

†Note that the usual chemical description of polypeptides is in terms of amino-acid residues, as in the PBG formula shown, rather than in terms of amide groups, which are more convenient for the present discussion.

$$-\!\!\left(\mathrm{NH{-}CH{-}\overset{\overset{\displaystyle O}{\|}}{C}}\right)_{\!N}$$
$$\mathrm{CH_2}$$
$$\mathrm{CH_2}$$
$$\mathrm{C_6H_5{-}CH_2{-}O{-}C{=}O}$$

has a helical conformation when dissolved in ethylene dichloride at 25°C, but it is in the random-coil form when dissolved in dichloroacetic acid at the same temperature. This difference is quite reasonable since a hydrogen-bonding solvent like dichloroacetic acid can form strong hydrogen bonds with the amide groups and thus disrupt the internal hydrogen bonds which are necessary for the helical form. For a mixed solvent of dichloroacetic acid and ethylene dichloride, PBG can be made to transform from the random coil to the helix by raising the temperature over a fairly narrow range. It is this rapid reversible transition which will be investigated here.

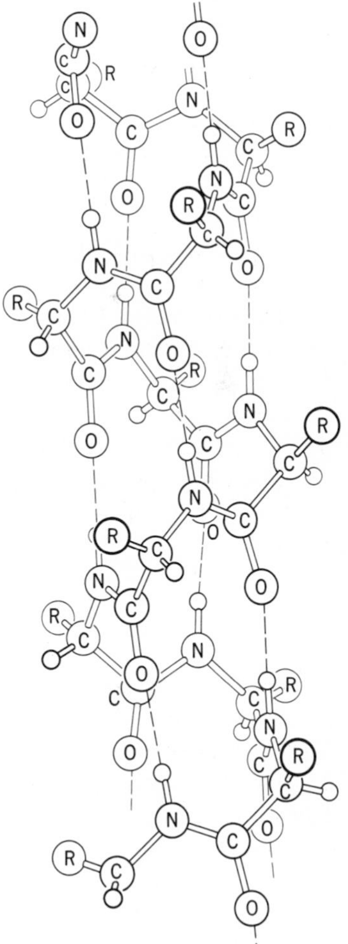

FIG. 1. The Pauling-Corey alpha helix. In addition to the right-handed helix shown, a left-handed one is also possible (with the same *l*-amino acids). In proteins the right-handed helix is regarded as the more probable. [*Reprinted by permission from L. Pauling, "The Nature of the Chemical Bond," p*. 500, *Cornell University Press, Ithaca, N.Y.* (1960).]

As we shall see below, the solvent plays a crucial role in determining which form is stable at low temperatures. When the helix is stable at low temperatures, the transition to the random coil at high temperatures is called a "normal" transition. For the case where the random coil is the more stable form at low temperatures, the transition is called an "inverted" transition.

THEORY

We wish to present here a very simplified and approximate statistical-mechanical theory of the helix-coil transition. The treatment is closely related to that given by Davidson.[2] Let us consider the change

$$\text{coil} \cdot N\text{S} = \text{helix} + N\text{S} \tag{1}$$

where the polymer molecules each consist of N segments (monomer units) and are dissolved in a solvent S which can hydrogen-bond to the amide groups when the chain is in the random-coil form. We shall (for convenience) artificially simplify the physical model of internal hydrogen bonding in the helix by assuming that the hydrogen bond formed by each amide group is with the *next* amide group along the chain (see Fig. 2) rather than the third following amide group as in the actual helix. We can then assume that the chain segments are independent of each other. Let z_1 be the molecular partition function of a segment in the *random-coil form* with a solvent molecule S hydrogen-bonded to it, and z_2 be the product of the partition function of a segment in the *helical form* times the partition function of a "free" solvent molecule S. We will then define a parameter s by

$$z_2 = sz_1 \tag{2}$$

Note that s is a ratio of partition functions and many of the contributions to z_1 and z_2 (e.g., vibrational terms) will cancel out. The principal contributions to s will involve differences between the helix and random-coil form, and we may guess that s can be represented in the general form[2]

FIG. 2. Hypothetical model of an internally hydrogen-bonded chain, with the simplification that *adjacent* "amide groups" are connected by hydrogen bonds. Note the distinction between the *amino-acid residue* and the *"amide group"*; the latter is the more convenient unit of structure for the present discussion.

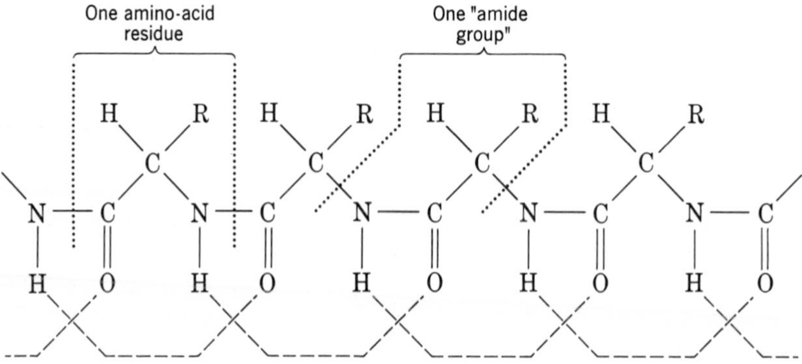

$$s = s_0 e^{-\epsilon/kT} \tag{3}$$

where ϵ is the energy change per segment and s_0 is related to the entropy change per segment for the change in state (1).

First-order Transition Model. To simplify the model even further, let us assume for the time being that a given polymer molecule is either completely in the helical form or completely in the random-coil form. This assumption will lead to a first-order transition between these two forms. The partition function for a random-coil molecule z_c is then given by

$$z_c = z_1{}^N \tag{4}$$

while that for a helical molecule z_h will be

$$z_h = z_2{}^N = s^N z_1{}^N \tag{5}$$

if one neglects end effects (e.g., at the beginning of the chain the first carbonyl oxygen is not involved in an internal hydrogen bond).

At constant pressure, the two forms will be in equilibrium with each other at some temperature T^* at which $\Delta G = 0$ for the change in state (1). Since ΔV will be quite small for change (1), we can take $\Delta A \cong 0$ and $\tilde{A}_c = \tilde{A}_h$ at T^*, where $\tilde{A}$ is the Helmholtz free energy per mole of polymer. For independent polymer molecules, we have[3]

$$\tilde{A} = -kT \ln z^{N_0} = -RT \ln z \tag{6}$$

where N_0 is Avogadro's number and z is the partition function for a single polymer molecule. Thus, one finds that $z_h = z_c$ (or $s = 1$) at T^*. With the use of Eq. (3), the value of T^* can be related to the parameters ϵ and s_0:

$$\frac{\epsilon}{kT^*} = \ln s_0 \tag{7}$$

For an inert (non-hydrogen-bonding) solvent, one observes experimentally a "normal" transition: the helix, which is stable at low temperatures, is transformed at higher temperatures into the random coil. This case is represented by our model when $\epsilon < 0$ and $s_0 < 1$. Since the solvent is inert, random-coil segments are essentially unbonded, whereas helical segments have internal hydrogen bonds and thus a lower energy ($\epsilon_h - \epsilon_c < 0$). In the random-coil polymer molecule, considerable rotation can occur about the single bonds in the chain skeleton, but the helical form has a rather rigid structure. Therefore, there is a decrease in the entropy per segment on changing from the relatively free rotational configurations of the flexible random coil to the more rotationally restricted helix (and thus $s_0 < 1$). From Eqs. (3) to (6), it follows that $s > 1$ at low temperatures ($T < T^*$) and thus $\tilde{A}_h < \tilde{A}_c$ and the helix is the more stable form. At high temperatures ($T > T^*$), $s \cong s_0 < 1$ and the random coil is the more stable form.

For an active (hydrogen-bonding) solvent, one observes experimentally an "inverted" transition: the random coil is stable at low temperatures and changes into the helix when the solution is heated. This case is represented by our model when $\epsilon > 0$ and $s_0 > 1$. Here the solvent plays a dominant role since a solvent molecule is strongly hydrogen-bonded to each random-coil segment. In terms of energy, there is little difference between polymers with random-coil segments and with helical segments since there is comparable hydrogen bonding in both forms. It is now almost impossible to predict the sign of ϵ, but it is certainly quite reasonable to find that the energy change associated with (1) may be positive ($\epsilon_h - \epsilon_c > 0$). Although a helical segment will still have a lower entropy than a random-coil segment due to the rigidity of the helix, the solvated random coil is now less flexible than previously. More importantly, the free solvent molecules will have a higher entropy than solvent molecules which are bonded to the random coil (cf. "iceberg effect"[4]). Thus the entropy change associated with (1) is positive because of the release of S molecules (and therefore $s_0 > 1$). From Eqs. (3) to (6), we see that at low temperatures $s < 1$ and the random coil will be stable in this inverted case.

Recalling that ΔV is small so that $\Delta G \cong \Delta A$, we can make use of Eqs. (4) to (6) to obtain

$$\Delta\tilde{S} = -\left(\frac{\partial \Delta\tilde{G}}{\partial T}\right)_p \cong R\frac{\partial}{\partial T}\left(T\ln\frac{z_h}{z_c}\right) = NR\ln s_0 \tag{8}$$

The entropy change *per mole of monomer*, ΔS_m, is then given by

$$\frac{\Delta\tilde{S}}{N} \equiv \Delta S_m = R\ln s_0 \tag{9}$$

Since $\Delta\tilde{G} = 0$ for the first-order transition at p and T^*, we have for the enthalpy change *per mole of monomer*

$$\Delta H_m = T^*\,\Delta S_m = RT^*\ln s_0 = N_0\epsilon \tag{10}$$

The first-order theory presented above is related to the treatment of Baur and Nosanow,[5] who used a similar but perhaps physically less realistic model to derive the same results [i.e., Eqs. (7), (9), and (10)].†

Cooperative Transition Model. It is an experimental fact that the helix-coil transition is *not* a first-order transition. In order to account for this fact, one must adopt a more realistic model by eliminating the assumption that an entire polymer molecule is all in a given form. Indeed, a polymer molecule can have some sections which are helical and others which are randomly coiled. The formation of a helical region will be a cooperative process. Since segment (i.e., amide group) n is hydrogen-bonded to segment $n + 3$, $n + 1$ to $n + 4$, $n + 2$ to $n + 5$, etc., it is difficult to initiate this ordered internal bonding; but once a single hydrogen-bond link is made, the next ones along the chain are much easier to achieve (a sort of "zipper" effect).

No attempt will be made here to develop the details of such a cooperative model. Readers with a sufficient background in statistical mechanics should refer to Davidson's presentation[2] or to the original papers in the literature.[6] The crucial idea is to introduce a "nucleation" parameter σ which is independent of temperature and very small in magnitude. It is then assumed that the partition function z_2 is changed to the value σz_2 for the *initial* segment of a helical section (i.e., the internally bonded segment directly adjacent to a solvent-bonded segment). Physically,

†In addition, Baur and Nosanow showed for the inverted case that the helical form will be stable only between T^* and another much higher transition temperature T', where the helix reverts to the random-coil form. (For PBG, it is estimated[5] that $T' \cong 700°$K.) This is physically reasonable in terms of our model: at very high temperatures, all hydrogen bonds (internal or with solvent) will be broken and the random coil will predominate owing to its higher entropy.

this means that it is difficult to initiate a new helical section. For such a model, it can be shown[2,6] that X_h, the mole fraction of the segments in helical sections, will undergo a very rapid but *continuous* change from $X_h \cong 0$ when $s < 1$ to $X_h \cong 1$ when $s > 1$. Thus, a rapid cooperative transition occurs in the vicinity of a critical temperature T^* (the value of T for which $s = 1$). It is the fact that σ is very small which ensures a sharp transition region (see Fig. 3). If σ is set equal to 1, the result is $X_h = s/(1 + s)$, which corresponds to a very gradual transition.[2] If σ is set equal to 0, the transition becomes first-order. For high-molecular weight PBG, a value of $\sigma \cong 10^{-4}$ seems to be appropriate to obtain a fairly good quantitative fit to the experimental data.[2] It should be noted that the transition is sharpest (and the model most successful) when polypeptides with $N \sim 1000$ or more are used.

METHOD

Since the helical form of a polypeptide is rigid and rodlike, its solutions are more viscous than corresponding solutions of the random-coil form, and the transition can be detected by measuring the intrinsic viscosity (see Exp. 35). However, the highly ordered structure of the helical form causes it to have an optical rotatory power markedly different from that of a random coil. Indeed, use of optical rotation for following the transition gives better results than does intrinsic viscosity since the optical rotation is directly related to the fraction X_h of segments in the helical form, whereas the hydrodynamic properties of the polymer molecule change substantially at the first appearance of random-coil regions in the helix (in effect, causing the otherwise straight rod to bend randomly in one or several places).

The polarimeter and its operation are described in Chap. XVIII. Although not stressed there, it is obviously necessary to use a polarimeter in which the temperature of the sample tube can be well controlled. The specific rotation $[\alpha]^t$ as determined with the sodium D doublet at t°C is defined by Eq. (XVIII-9), and we note here that for a solution containing two solutes (helix and random coil) one can show that

$$[\alpha]^t = X_h[\alpha]_h{}^t + X_c[\alpha]_c{}^t \tag{11}$$

where $[\alpha]_h{}^t$ and $[\alpha]_c{}^t$ are the specific rotations of helix and random-coil form. In a

FIG. 3. Percentage of polypeptide in helix form, as a function of the parameter s, for $\sigma = 0$ and $\sigma = 10^{-2}$.

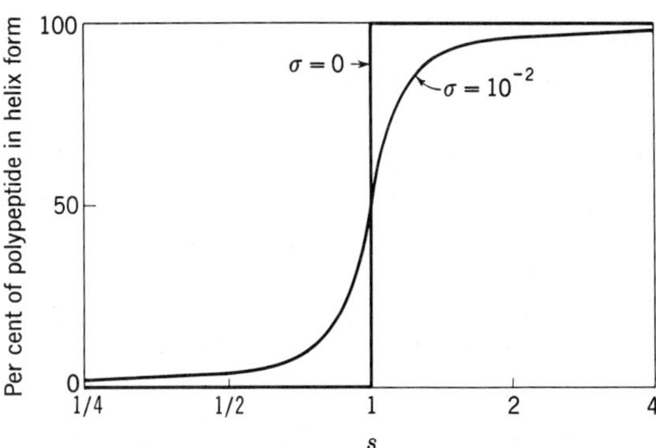

narrow range of temperature near T^*, $[\alpha]_h{}^t$ and $[\alpha]_c{}^t$ will be essentially constant. Thus measurements of $[\alpha]^t$ will determine the mole fraction X_h as a function of T.

EXPERIMENTAL

A solution of poly-γ-benzyl-*l*-glutamate (PBG) in a mixed solvent of dichloroacetic acid (DCA) and ethylene dichloride, 76 volume per cent in DCA, will be used. The dichloroacetic acid should be purified by vacuum distillation; the ethylene dichloride may be purified by conventional distillation in air. Mix the proper volumes of the two liquids to make about 150 to 200 ml of the desired solvent. In order to prepare approximately 100 ml of a 2.5 weight per cent polymer solution, weigh accurately a sample of about 3.8 g of PBG and dissolve it in about 150 g of solvent (also accurately weighed). The resulting solution is very viscous; it must be mixed well and then allowed to stand for two or three days until any small undissolved particles have settled and the solution is clear. During this period, the solution should be placed in a polyethylene bottle and stored in a refrigerator. The remaining solvent should also be stored for future density determinations.

Since the solution is difficult to prepare, it is recommended that it be made available to the student. **Warning: The solvent is extremely corrosive.**

Detailed instructions for using the polarimeter and the temperature-regulating bath will be provided in the laboratory. After determining the path lengths of the cells to be used, fill a cell with pure solvent and zero-adjust the instrument. Next, rinse and fill a cell with the polymer solution.†

After mounting the solution cell in the polarimeter, it should not be necessary to move this cell during the rest of the experiment. Provisions must be made for measuring the temperature of the sample without obscuring the light path. Begin measurements with the temperature at about 10°C and read the optical rotation α at reasonably spaced temperature intervals until about 50°C is reached. The exact temperature intervals to be used are at your discretion, but should be close enough to follow the essential features of the variation of optical rotation; small intervals (perhaps 1 or 2°) should be used when the optical rotation is changing rapidly with temperature (near 30°), and larger intervals may be used when the changes with temperature are small. Be sure to allow sufficient time for thermal equilibration between readings.

In order to calculate $[\alpha]^t$, the density of the solutions must be known at each temperature. The density of the solution is close enough to that of the solvent so that they can be assumed to be identical. The density of the solvent should be determined with a pycnometer for at least three different temperatures in the range 10 to 50°C. The volume of the pycnometer should first be determined by weighing it empty and also filled with distilled water at a known temperature. Since the density of water as a function of temperature is well known, the volume of the pycnometer can be determined. This procedure (see Exp. 12) is then repeated using the solvent, and since the volume of the pycnometer is now known the density can be calculated. The solvent density should be plotted against temperature and the best straight line drawn through the points obtained.

†A difficulty in filling these cells is the problem of avoiding any air bubbles which might obscure part of the light path. Since the solution is viscous, this can be a tedious job and may require some time. If possible, it is wise to fill the cells about an hour before use and allow them to stand.

Record the composition of the solution and the molecular weight (or N value) of the polymer used.

CALCULATIONS

For each data point, calculate the *specific rotation* at temperature t from

$$[\alpha]^t = 100\frac{\alpha}{Lp\rho} \tag{12}$$

where α is the observed rotation in degrees, L is the path length of the cell in decimeters, p is the weight per cent of solute in the solution, and ρ is the density of the solution. These density values are interpolated from the ρ-vs.-T plot for the solvent.

Construct a plot of $[\alpha]^t$ vs. temperature, and determine the limiting (asymptotic) values of the rotation: $[\alpha]_h$ from the high-temperature plateau, $[\alpha]_c$ from the low-temperature plateau. If it is assumed that these represent *temperature-independent* specific rotations for the helix and random-coil forms, respectively, Eq. (11) gives for X_h:

$$X_h = \frac{[\alpha]^t - [\alpha]_c}{[\alpha]_h - [\alpha]_c} \tag{13}$$

Using this equation, you can add to your plot a scale of X_h values so that the plot will also represent X_h vs. T. Determine and report the "transition" temperature T^* at which $X_h = 0.5$.

DISCUSSION

If one *arbitrarily* defined an equilibrium constant by $K = X_h/X_c$ and used the data in this experiment together with the van't Hoff equation $d \ln K/d(1/T) = -\Delta\tilde{H}^0/R$ to determine the value of $\Delta\tilde{H}^0$, to what (if anything) would such an enthalpy change refer?

APPARATUS

Polarimeter, with one or more optical cells (complete with windows, caps, and Teflon or Neoprene washers); constant-temperature control for range 10 to 50°C; pycnometer; 25-ml pipette for filling the pycnometer and a small pipette for filling the cell; rubber bulb for pipetting; 0 to 50°C thermometer; 250-ml beaker; gum-rubber tubing; lint-free tissues for wiping cell windows; 100-ml polyethylene bottles for PBG solution and excess solvent.

Poly-γ-benzyl-*l*-glutamate (M.W. 250,000; 4 g of solid or 100 ml of 2.5 weight per cent solution); ethylene dichloride–dichloroacetic acid solvent (76 volume per cent DCA) stored in polyethylene bottle; wash acetone.

REFERENCES

1. M. A. Stahmann (ed.), "Polyamino Acids, Polypeptides and Proteins," University of Wisconsin Press, Madison, Wis. (1962).
2. N. Davidson, "Statistical Mechanics," pp. 378–393, McGraw-Hill, New York (1962).
3. W. J. Moore, "Physical Chemistry," 3d ed., chap. 15, Prentice-Hall, Englewood Cliffs, N.J. (1962).

4. H. S. Frank and W-Y. Wen, *Discussions Faraday Soc.,* **24,** 133 (1957); G. Nemethy and H. A. Scheraga, *J. Chem. Phys.,* **36,** 3382, 3401 (1962).
5. M. E. Baur and L. H. Nosanow, *J. Chem. Phys.,* **38,** 578 (1963).
6. B. H. Zimm and J. K. Bragg, *J. Chem. Phys.,* **31,** 526 (1959); B. Zimm, P. Doty, and K. Iso, *Proc. Natl. Acad. Sci.,* **45,** 160A (1959).

GENERAL READING

P. Doty, J. H. Bradbury, and A. M. Holtzer, *J. Am. Chem. Soc.,* **78,** 947 (1956); P. Doty and J. T. Yang, *J. Am. Chem. Soc.,* **78,** 498 (1956).

C. H. Bamford, A. Elliott, and W. E. Handy, "Synthetic Polypeptides," Academic Press, New York (1956).

XII

ELECTRIC AND MAGNETIC PROPERTIES

EXPERIMENTS

Experiment 37. Dipole Moment of Polar Molecules in Solution

When a substance is placed in an electric field, such as exists between the plates of a charged condenser, it becomes to some extent electrically polarized. The polarization results at least in part from a displacement of electron clouds relative to atomic nuclei; polarization resulting from this cause is termed *electronic polarization.* For molecular substances *atomic polarization* may also be present owing to a distortion of the molecular skeleton. Taken together these two kinds of polarization are called *distortion polarization.* Finally, when molecules possessing permanent dipoles are present in a liquid or gas, application of an electric field produces a small preferential orientation of the dipoles in the field direction, leading to *orientation polarization.*

It is the orientation polarization which is of primary interest in the present experiment, which is concerned with the determination of the magnitude of the *permanent dipole moment* μ of disubstituted benzene molecules in benzene solution. This is accomplished experimentally through measurements of the *dielectric constant* ϵ, given by

$$\epsilon = \frac{C}{C_0} \tag{1}$$

where C is the capacitance of a condenser when the *dielectric medium* is the solution or gas in question and C_0 is the capacitance of the same condenser when the medium is a vacuum.[1]

THEORY

An electric dipole[2] consists of two point charges, $-q$ and $+q$, with a separation represented by a vector $\mathbf{r}$, the positive sense of which is from $-q$ to $+q$. The electric dipole moment is defined by

$$\mathbf{m} = q\mathbf{r} \tag{2}$$

A molecule possesses a dipole moment whenever the center of gravity of negative charge does not coincide with the center of positive charge. In an electric field, all molecules have an induced dipole moment (which is aligned approximately parallel to the field direction) owing to distortion polarization. In addition, *polar molecules* have a *permanent dipole moment* (i.e., a dipole moment which exists independently of any applied field) of constant magnitude μ and a direction which is fixed relative to the molecular skeleton.

The *resultant* (vector sum) electric moment of the medium, per unit volume, is known as the *polarization* **P**.[3] For an isotropic medium **P** is parallel to the electric field intensity **E**, and to a first approximation it is proportional to **E** in magnitude. For a pure substance **P** is given by

$$\mathbf{P} = \overline{\mathbf{m}}\frac{N_0}{\tilde{V}} = \overline{\mathbf{m}}\frac{N_0\rho}{M} \tag{3}$$

where $\overline{\mathbf{m}}$ is the average dipole moment of each molecule, N_0 is Avogadro's number, $\tilde{V}$ is the molar volume, M is the molecular weight, and ρ is the density.

The moment of a polarized dielectric is equivalent to a moment that would result from electric charges of opposite sign on opposite surfaces of the dielectric. In a condenser these "polarization charges" induce equal and opposite charges in the metal plates that are in contact with them. These induced charges are in addition to the charges that would be present at the same applied potential for the condenser with a vacuum between the plates. Accordingly, the capacitance is increased by the presence of a polarizable medium. Thus the dielectric constant ϵ [see Eq. (1)] is greater than unity. By electrostatic theory it can be shown[3] that

$$\epsilon\mathbf{E} = \mathbf{E} + 4\pi\mathbf{P} \tag{4}$$

The average dipole moment $\overline{\mathbf{m}}$ for an atom or molecule in the medium is given by

$$\overline{\mathbf{m}} = \alpha\mathbf{F} \tag{5}$$

where **F** is the *local* electric field intensity and α is the polarizability (which is independent of field intensity if the field is not so intense that saturation is incipient). To a good approximation **F** may be taken as the electric field intensity at the center of a spherical cavity in the dielectric, within which the atom or molecule is contained. Thus **F** is the resultant of **E** and an additional contribution due to the polarization charges on the surface of the spherical cavity; electrostatic theory[4] gives

$$\mathbf{F} = \mathbf{E} + \frac{4\pi}{3}\mathbf{P} \tag{6}$$

Combining this with Eq. (4) we obtain

$$\mathbf{F} = \frac{\epsilon + 2}{\epsilon - 1}\frac{4\pi}{3}\mathbf{P} \tag{7}$$

and using Eqs. (3) and (5) we obtain for a pure substance

$$\frac{\epsilon - 1}{\epsilon + 2}\frac{M}{\rho} = \frac{4\pi}{3}N_0\alpha \equiv P_M \tag{8}$$

This is the *Clausius-Mosotti* equation. The quantity P_M is called the *molar polarization* and has the dimensions of volume per mole.

If the molecules have no permanent dipole moment, only distortion polarization takes place. The corresponding polarizability is denoted by α_0. If each molecule has a permanent dipole moment of magnitude μ, there is a tendency for the moment to become oriented parallel to the field direction, but this tendency is almost completely counteracted by thermal motion which tends to make the orientation random. The component of the moment in the field direction is $\mu \cos\theta$, where θ is the angle between the dipole orientation and the field direction. The potential energy V of the dipole in a local field of intensity $\mathbf{F}$ is $-(\mu\cos\theta)F$, which is small in comparison with kT under ordinary experimental conditions. By use of the Boltzmann distribution, the average component of the permanent moment in the field direction is found to be

$$\begin{aligned}\overline{m}_\mu &= [\mu\cos\theta e^{-V/kT}]_{\text{av}} = [\mu\cos\theta e^{\mu F\cos\theta/kT}]_{\text{av}}\\ &\cong \mu\left[\cos\theta\left(1 + \frac{\mu F\cos\theta}{kT}\right)\right]_{\text{av}}\end{aligned}$$

where the average is taken over all orientations in space. The average of $\cos\theta$ vanishes, but the average of its square is ⅓; accordingly, as found by Debye,

$$\overline{m}_\mu = \frac{\mu^2}{3kT}F \tag{9}$$

Thus the total polarizability is given by

$$\alpha = \alpha_0 + \frac{\mu^2}{3kT} \tag{10}$$

and the molar polarization can be written

$$\begin{aligned}P_M &= \frac{\epsilon - 1}{\epsilon + 2}\frac{M}{\rho} = \frac{4\pi}{3}N_0\left(\alpha_0 + \frac{\mu^2}{3kT}\right)\\ &= P_d + P_\mu \end{aligned}\tag{11}$$

where P_d and P_μ are, respectively, the distortion and orientation contributions to the molar polarization:

$$P_d = \frac{4\pi}{3}N_0\alpha_0 \qquad P_\mu = \frac{4\pi}{3}N_0\frac{\mu^2}{3kT} \tag{12}$$

Immediately it is clear that a plot of P_M vs. $1/T$ utilizing measurements of ϵ as a function of temperature will yield both α_0 and μ. This technique is readily applicable to gases, as in Exp. 38. In principle it is applicable to liquids and solutions also but is seldom convenient owing largely to the small temperature range accessible between the melting point and boiling point.

In the foregoing derivation a static (dc) electric field was assumed. The equations apply also to alternating (ac) fields, provided the frequency is low enough to enable the molecules possessing permanent dipoles to orient themselves in response to the changing electric field. Above some frequency in the upper rf or far-infrared range the permanent dipoles can no longer follow the field, and the orientation term in Eq. (11) disappears. At infrared and visible frequencies the dielectric constant cannot be measured by the use of a condenser. However, it is known from electromagnetic theory that in the absence of high magnetic polarizability (which does not exist at these frequencies for any ordinary materials)

$$\epsilon = n^2$$

where n is the *index of refraction.* We then obtain from Eq. (11) the relation of Lorentz and Lorenz:

$$P_d = R_M = \frac{n^2 - 1}{n^2 + 2}\frac{M}{\rho} = \frac{4\pi}{3}N_0\alpha_0 \tag{13}$$

where R_M is known as the *mole refraction.* Thus the distortion polarizability α_0 can in principle be obtained from a measurement of the refractive index at some wavelength in the far infrared where the distortion polarization is virtually complete. However, it is not experimentally convenient to measure the index of refraction in the infrared range. The index of refraction n_D measured with the visible sodium D line can usually be used instead: Although the atomic contribution to the distortion polarization is absent in the visible, and the electronic contribution is not in all cases at its dc value, these variations in the distortion polarization are small and usually negligible in comparison with the orientation polarization. The measurement of n_D can be made conveniently in an Abbe or other type of refractometer (see Chap. XVIII). Thus, P_d can be measured independently from P_M, and P_μ can be determined by difference. By this means μ can be determined from measurements made at a single temperature.

Measurements in Solution. We are here concerned with a dilute solution containing a polar solute 2 in a nonpolar solvent 1. The molar polarization can be written

$$P_M = X_1P_{1M} + X_2P_{2M} = \frac{\epsilon - 1}{\epsilon + 2}\frac{(M_1X_1 + M_2X_2)}{\rho} \tag{14}$$

where the X's are mole fractions, M's are molecular weights, and ϵ and ρ (without subscripts) pertain to the solution. Since a nonpolar solvent has only distortion polarization, which is not greatly affected by interactions between molecules, we can take P_{1M} to have the same value in solution as in the pure solvent:

$$P_{1M} = \frac{\epsilon_1 - 1}{\epsilon_1 + 2}\frac{M_1}{\rho_1} \tag{15}$$

We can then get P_{2M} from

$$P_{2M} = \frac{1}{X_2}(P_M - P_{1M}X_1) \tag{16}$$

obtained by rearrangement of Eq. (14).

Values of P_{2M} calculated using Eq. (16) are found to vary with X_2, generally increasing as X_2 decreases. This effect arises from strong solute-solute interactions due to the permanent dipoles. This difficulty can be eliminated by extrapolating P_{2M} to infinite dilution ($X_2 = 0$) to obtain $P_{2M}{}^0$. Although this could be done by plotting P_{2M} for each of a series of solutions against X_2, it is easier and more accurate to follow the procedure of Hedestrand,[5] which is given below.

Let us assume a linear dependence of ϵ and ρ on the mole fraction X_2:

$$\epsilon = \epsilon_1 + aX_2 \tag{17}$$

$$\rho = \rho_1 + bX_2 \tag{18}$$

On writing out Eq. (16) explicitly and using Eqs. (15), (17), and (18), it is possible to rearrange terms and obtain the *limiting* expression

$$P_{2M}{}^0 = \frac{3M_1 a}{(\epsilon_1 + 2)^2 \rho_1} + \frac{\epsilon_1 - 1}{(\epsilon_1 + 2)\rho_1}\left(M_2 - \frac{M_1 b}{\rho_1}\right) \tag{19}$$

Thus measurements on solutions of the *slope* of ϵ vs. X_2 and the *slope* of ρ vs. X_2 enable us to calculate the limiting molar polarization of the solute in solution. If we assume that the molar distortion polarization in an infinitely dilute solution is equal to that in the pure solute, then

$$P_{2d}{}^0 = R_{2M} = \frac{n_2{}^2 - 1}{n_2{}^2 + 2}\frac{M_2}{\rho_2} \tag{20}$$

where n_2 is the index of refraction and ρ_2 is the density measured for the solute in the pure state. From these two expressions, we can obtain the molar orientation polarization of the solute at infinite dilution:

$$P_{2\mu}{}^0 = P_{2M}{}^0 - P_{2d}{}^0 = \frac{4\pi}{3}N_0\frac{\mu^2}{3kT} \tag{21}$$

On substituting the numerical values of the physical constants, we obtain

$$\mu = 0.0128(P_{2\mu}{}^0 T)^{1/2} \times 10^{-18} \text{ esu cm} \tag{22}$$

where $P_{2\mu}{}^0$ is given in cubic centimeters per mole and T is given in degrees Kelvin. The units 10^{-18} esu cm in which dipole moments are conventionally given are called *debyes*.

An alternative expression for $P_{2\mu}{}^0$ has been given by Smith,[6] who improved a method of calculation first suggested by Guggenheim.[7] This expression presupposes knowledge of the index of refraction n of the *solution*, and assumes that

$$n^2 = n_1{}^2 + cX_2 \tag{23}$$

where c, like a and b, is a constant determined by experiment. It follows[6] that

$$P_{2\mu}{}^0 = \frac{3M_1}{\rho_1}\left[\frac{a}{(\epsilon_1 + 2)^2} - \frac{c}{(n_1{}^2 + 2)^2}\right] \tag{24}$$

This expression is an approximate one which holds when $\epsilon_1 - n_1{}^2$ is small (as in the case of benzene, where it is 0.03) and M_2 and b are not too large. It is a useful form when the index of refraction n_2 of the pure solute is inconvenient to determine; this is often the case when the pure solute is solid. Note also that Eq. (24) does not require a knowledge of the densities of the solutions.

Solvent Effects. The values of P_{2M}^0 obtained from dilute solution measurements differ somewhat from P_M values obtained from the pure solute in the form of a gas. This effect is due to solvent-solute interactions in which polar solute molecules induce a local polarization in the nonpolar solvent. As a result μ as determined in solution is often smaller than μ for the same substance in the form of a gas, although it may be larger in other cases. Usually the two values agree within about 10 per cent. A discussion of solvent effects is given by LeFèvre.[4]

METHOD

Heterodyne-beat Method. There are several methods[8] of measuring the dielectric cell capacitance C which is needed for determining ϵ. Resonance methods and bridge techniques for measuring reactance are especially suitable for work on liquids or solutions having high electrical conductance. For solutions with low conductance, very accurate work can be done using the heterodyne-beat method, a block diagram of which is shown in Fig. 1.

A crystal-controlled oscillator generates a constant-frequency signal f_0, which is usually about 1 Mc. The frequency f of the variable oscillator depends on the values of L and C in the "tank" circuit:

$$f = \frac{1}{2\pi\sqrt{LC}} \tag{25}$$

The inductance L is fixed, while C is the sum of several capacities: C_X (the cell capacitance), C_P (the capacitance of a variable precision air capacitor), C_T (the capacitance of a course tuning capacitor), and C_S (stray capacitances from leads, etc.). The mixer combines these two rf signals to give an audio beat frequency $f - f_0$. Several circuits are available for the necessary electronic components;[9] a commercial beat-frequency oscillator, made by General Radio Company, can be easily adapted by providing a means of connecting the external cell and precision air capacitors.

The detector may be a pair of earphones or "magic tuning eye" to indicate a zero beat frequency ($f = f_0$). Alternatively an oscilloscope can be used with the beat frequency $f - f_0$ applied to the vertical plates of the cathode-ray tube and a fixed audio frequency f_a applied to the horizontal plates. This fixed frequency f_a may be 60-cycle line frequency or the output of an audio oscillator (in which case

FIG. 1. A block diagram of the heterodyne-beat apparatus for measuring the capacitance of a dielectric cell (C_X). C_P is a variable precision air capacitor, and C_T is a coarse tuning capacitor.

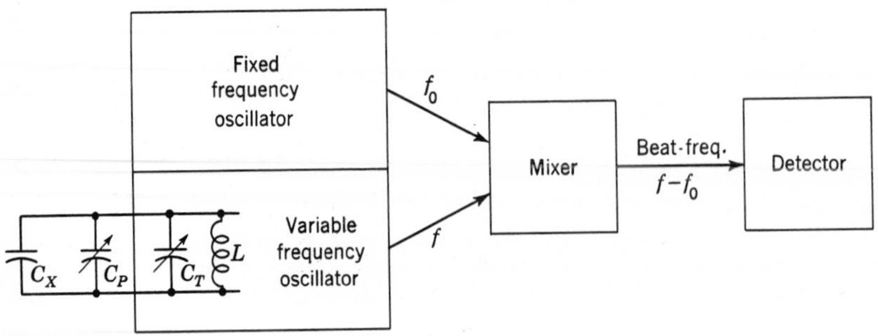

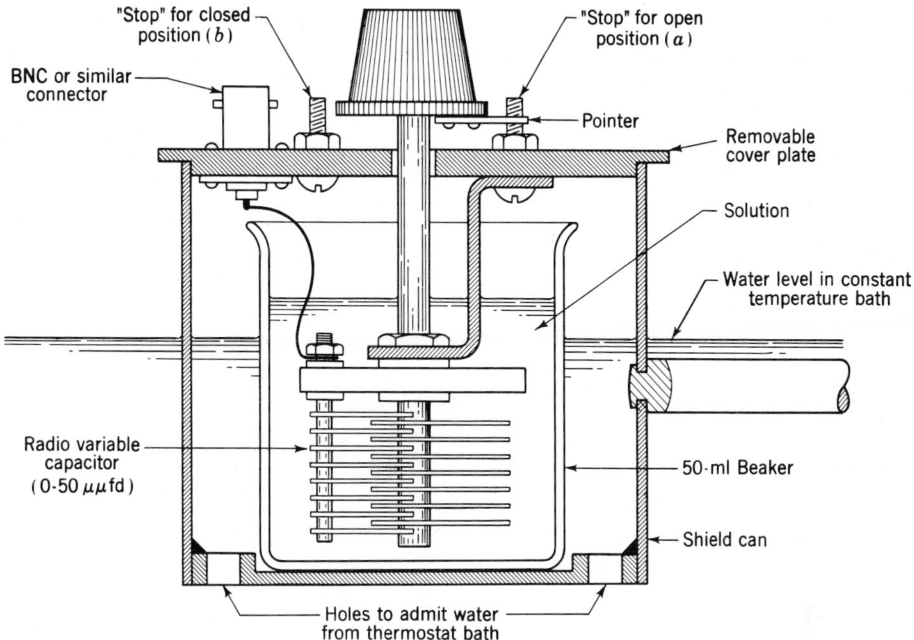

FIG. 2. Variable-capacitance dielectric cell for solutions.

the coarse tuning capacitor T may be eliminated). Either f_a or $f - f_0$ is adjusted initially to give a simple Lissajous figure as an indication of balance. In any case, it is desired to maintain a balance which indicates a constant beat frequency and thus a constant f; from Eq. (25) we see that this implies constant C. Changes in the cell capacitance C_X can be determined by reading the changes in C_P that are needed to restore balance.

If f_0 is not subject to appreciable drift, very high precision is possible, since changes in beat frequency of much less than 1 cycle are easily detected. From Eq. (25) we find that $|\Delta C/C| = 2|\Delta f/f|$ and with f about 10^6 cycles one can detect a change in capacitance of a few parts per million.

To avoid the problem of determining the stray capacitance from leads and also to reduce the influence of any drift in f_0, it is desirable to use a cell with a variable capacitance rather than one with fixed plates.† In this case, one measures the difference in capacitance between the minimum a and maximum b settings of the cell capacitor. Such a difference is not affected by the capacitance of the electrical leads and is affected only by that drift in f_0 which may occur in the short time interval between readings. The dielectric constant of a liquid or solution is now given by

$$\epsilon = \frac{\Delta C(\text{liq})}{\Delta C(\text{air})} \tag{26}$$

where ΔC is the difference $(C_b - C_a)$ for the cell. It is possible to use air rather than vacuum readings, since the dielectric constant of air is very close to unity.

A suitable cell can be made from a small radio condenser of about 40 to 50 $\mu\mu$f as shown in Fig. 2. The condenser, with a long shaft, is mounted on a circular

† For high-precision work with a very stable oscillator, a fixed-plate capacitor cell is best, since it eliminates any error due to lack of reproducibility in setting a variable capacitor. However, in this case one must determine the lead capacitance from measurements on a material of known dielectric constant.

insulating plate. Means should be provided for reproducible positioning in the minimum a and maximum b positions. This assembly fits into the top of a grounded brass shield which holds a lipless beaker.

EXPERIMENTAL

Detailed instructions for the operation of the equipment to be used should be provided by the instructor. In general, oscillators should be allowed to warm up for at least 1 hr to achieve stable, drift-free operation.

With the cell capacitor and cell beaker clean and dry, assemble the cell and mount it in the constant temperature bath. Set the capacitor at the minimum a position and set the precision air capacitor at a high value (approximately 250 $\mu\mu$f). If a zero-beat detector is used, adjust the coarse tuning capacitor to obtain a zero beat. When an oscilloscope and audio oscillator are used to detect the balance, adjust either the audio frequency f_a or a coarse tuning capacitor to obtain a simple, stable Lissajous figure (preferably a circle). Now record the reading of the precision air capacitor. Change the cell capacitor setting to the maximum b and restore balance (zero beat, or the same Lissajous figure) by varying the precision air capacitor. Record the new reading. Since the beat frequency is maintained constant, the sum of the cell capacitance and precision capacitance must be constant. Therefore, ΔC(air) is equal to the difference between the two readings of the precision capacitor.

Rinse the cell beaker and variable capacitor with the pure solvent or the solution to be measured, fill the cell beaker to a level which will completely immerse the capacitor, and reassemble the cell. Determine ΔC(liq) in the same manner as above. Handle the capacitor with care; damage to the plates can change ΔC.

Measurements should be made on pure benzene and on dilute solutions of *o*- and *m*-dichlorobenzene. Make up 50 or 100 ml of each solution as follows. Weigh a dry, clean volumetric flask; add an appropriate amount of solute; and weigh again. Now carefully make up to the mark with benzene and reweigh. Suggested concentrations are 1, 2, 3, and 4 mole per cent of solute. The densities can be calculated from these weighings.

CALCULATIONS

For each solution studied, calculate ϵ [Eq. (26)], ρ, and X_2. Plot ϵ and ρ vs. the mole fraction of solute X_2, and draw the best straight lines through your points; see Eqs. (17) and (18). Obtain the slopes a and b; the intercepts should agree with the pure solvent results. Using Eq. (19), calculate $P_{2M}{}^0$, the molar polarization at infinite dilution.

Estimate $P_{2d}{}^0$ from Eq. (20) using the literature value of the refractive index of the solute n_2, and obtain $P_{2\mu}{}^0$. Calculate the dipole moment, in debyes, from Eq. (22). This procedure should be carried out for each solute studied.

DISCUSSION

Compare your experimental results with the values computed from a vector addition of carbon-chlorine bond moments obtained from the dipole moment of monochlorobenzene (1.55 debyes). If they do not agree, suggest possible physical reasons for the disagreement.

APPARATUS

Heterodyne beat-frequency oscillator (such as General Radio 1304B) comprising fixed and variable high-frequency oscillators and a mixer; beat detector (such as "magic eye" as null detector or source of stable audio frequency and oscilloscope for displaying a Lissajous figure); coarse tuning capacitor (unnecessary if a stable variable-frequency audio oscillator is employed); dielectric cell and cell holder; low-capacitance double-shielded lead for connection to cell; precision air capacitor (0 to 300 $\mu\mu$f, such as General Radio 722D); five 50- or 100-ml volumetric flasks; a 5-ml Mohr pipette; acetone wash bottle; rubber pipette bulb.

Benzene (analytical reagent grade, 0.5 to 1 liter); *o*- and *m*-dichlorobenzene (10 to 20 ml each); acetone for rinsing.

REFERENCES

1. F. Bitter, "Currents, Fields and Particles," pp. 36*ff.*, Technology Press, Cambridge, Mass. (1956).
2. *Ibid.,* p. 57.
3. *Ibid.,* pp. 110ff.
4. R. J. W. LeFèvre, "Dipole Moments," 3d ed., pp. 7–10 and chap. III, Methuen, London (1953).
5. G. Hedestrand, *Z. physik. Chem.,* **B2,** 428 (1929).
6. J. W. Smith, *Trans. Faraday Soc.,* **46,** 394 (1950).
7. E. A. Guggenheim, *Trans. Faraday Soc.,* **45,** 714 (1949).
8. C. P. Smyth, Determination of Dipole Moments, in A. Weissberger (ed.), "Technique of Organic Chemistry," 3d ed., vol. I, part III, chap. XXXIX, pp. 2599ff., Interscience, New York (1960).
9. J.-Y. Chien, *J. Chem. Educ.,* **24,** 494 (1947).

GENERAL READING

P. Debye, "Polar Molecules," Reinhold, New York (1929), reprinted by Dover, New York (1945).
R. J. W. LeFèvre, *op. cit.*

Experiment 38. Dipole Moment of Polar Molecules in the Gas Phase

In Exp. 37, it is shown that the permanent dipole moment of polar molecules can be determined from measurements of the dielectric constant. In that experiment measurements are made at a single temperature on solutions of a polar solute in a nonpolar solvent; the orientation polarization of the solute is obtained by extrapolating the molar polarization to infinite dilution and subtracting a calculated value of the distortion polarization. The present experiment is concerned with measurements at more than one temperature on a pure substance in the gaseous state; here distortion and orientation polarization can be separated by their different temperature dependences.[1]

The gas to be studied in this experiment is hydrogen chloride, which has a large dipole moment and also a low enough boiling point ($-83.7°$C) to permit making measurements down to Dry Ice temperature ($-78.5°$C). Other suitable gases with large dipole moments but possessing somewhat higher boiling points include hydrogen sulfide, ammonia, methyl chloride, and sulfur dioxide.

THEORY

As in Exp. 37 we shall use the Clausius-Mosotti equation. We shall assume that the dielectric constant of the gas is very close to unity and that deviations from the perfect-gas law are small in comparison with the experimental uncertainties. Thus, Eq. (34-11) can be written

$$\frac{4\pi}{3} N_0 \left(\alpha_0 + \frac{\mu^2}{3kT} \right) = P_M = \frac{\epsilon - 1}{3} \frac{M}{\rho} = \frac{C - C_0}{3C_0} \frac{RT}{p} \tag{1}$$

where P_M is the *molar polarization*, ϵ is the dielectric constant (ratio of the capacitance C of a condenser with the gas between the plates to that C_0 in vacuum), α_0 is the distortion polarizability, and μ is the permanent dipole moment of the gas molecule. A plot of P_M vs. $1/T$ should give a straight line; μ can be calculated from the slope and α_0 from the intercept.

METHOD

The heterodyne-beat method, described in Exp. 37, should be used. The same electronic components are employed as before, but a different cell design is required.[2]

A capacitance cell for gases is shown in Fig. 1. It is designed to satisfy the following criteria: (1) the capacitance C_0 should be large enough (preferably 500 $\mu\mu$f or more) to permit reasonable precision in the measurement of the relatively small capacity changes expected, (2) solid dielectrics should make a negligible contribution to the cell capacitance (or at least a known contribution which can be corrected for), (3) the outer plate of the condenser or a suitable shield should be grounded and all sources of stray capacitance should be minimized, and (4) the cell should be vacuumtight, insensitive to vibration, thermally stable over the temperature range employed (-78.5 to 100°C), and resistant to chemical attack by the gas being studied. The cell shown is an assembly of concentric cylindrical plates of thin stainless steel (separated by very small glass spacers) mounted in a Pyrex bulb. Doubtless many other suitable designs can be formulated.

The cell should be fixed in position and connected to a vacuum and gas-handling system as shown in Fig. 2. It should be mounted so that a Dewar flask or a steam jacket can be affixed without disturbing it or its electrical leads. The high-frequency lead between the cell and the beat-frequency oscillator should be a double-shielded, low-capacity coaxial cable, as short as conveniently possible. This cable should be detachable from the cell for the purpose of determining C_0.

Since the changes in dielectric constant are very small, the greatest care must be exercised in the design and operation of the equipment. The beat-frequency oscillator must have good stability, and the detection of the constant beat frequency should be as sensitive as possible. If a stable audio-frequency source is available, the comparison of the beat frequency with this fixed frequency by means of a Lissajous figure on an oscilloscope is the best technique (see Exp. 37). If there is frequency drift due to variations in the ac line voltage, a regulated power supply or constant-voltage transformer (such as a Sola) should be used. If there is frequency drift due to temperature variations, it may be necessary to provide air thermostatting of the beat-frequency oscillator. Variable stray capacities must also be avoided, and electrical leads should not be moved more than absolutely necessary after measurements of ΔC have begun.

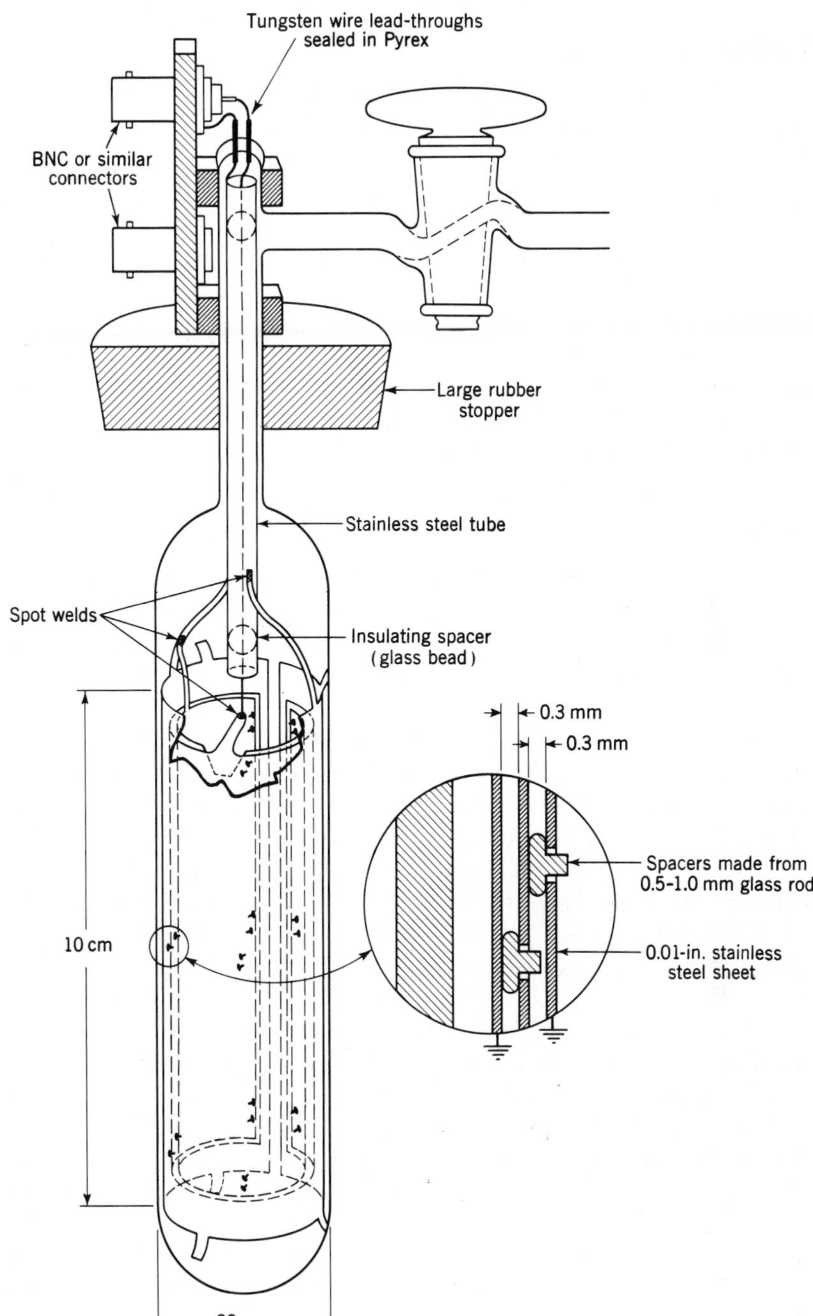

FIG. 1. Capacitance cell for gases. The detail view shows the small glass spacers in position between the stainless-steel sheets.

In order to measure accurately both the large C_0 value and the small $\Delta C(= C - C_0)$ value, a precision air capacitor with both a high and a low range is very desirable. With the precision capacitor connected in parallel with the cell and set on the high scale (say 100 to 1000 $\mu\mu$f range), C_0 is measured by discon-

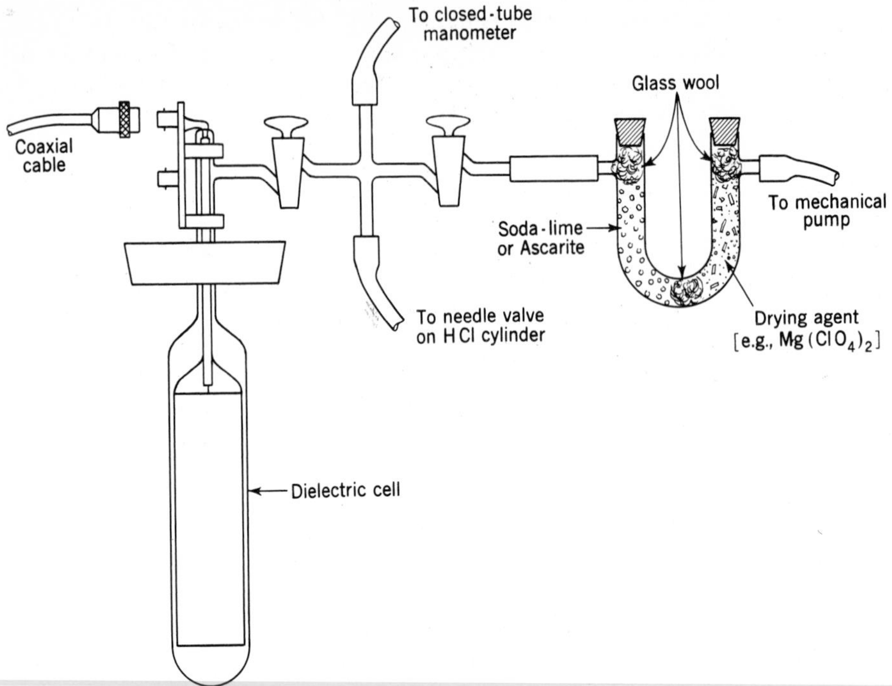

FIG. 2. Gas-handling system for filling dielectric cell.

necting the cable from the cell. Although it is possible to measure ΔC directly from the change in capacitance of a parallel precision air capacitor (method used in Exp. 37), the precision of the ΔC measurement can be improved by a factor of 10 to 100 by using the arrangement shown in Fig. 3. In this arrangement a large fixed capacitor C_1 (2000 to 3000 $\mu\mu$f) is mounted in parallel with the precision air capacitor C_P (used on low scale, say 10 to 100 $\mu\mu$f), and this combination is placed in *series* with the cell C. For such a circuit, ΔC is given by[2]

$$\Delta C = \frac{(C_L + C)^2}{(C_1 + C_P)^2 + (C_1 + C_P + C_L + C)\,\Delta C_P}\,\Delta C_P \tag{2}$$

FIG. 3. Special arrangement of capacitors for measuring very small changes in the capacitance C of a dielectric cell. C_T is a coarse tuning capacitor; C_1 is a known fixed capacitor (2000 to 3000 $\mu\mu$f); C_P is a precision air capacitor. Grounded shielding is shown by dashed lines.

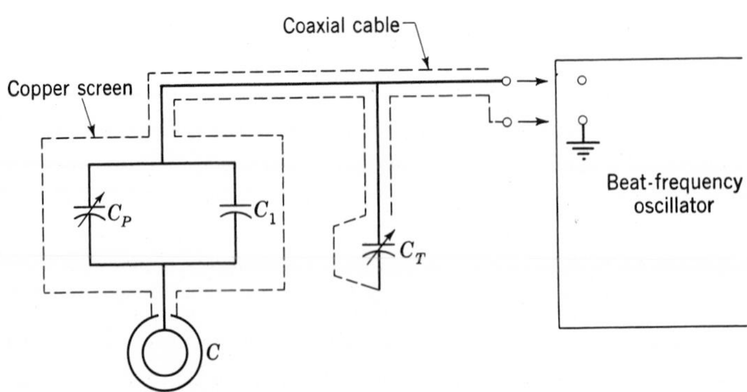

where ΔC_P is the change in C_P which is necessary to balance a change ΔC in the cell capacitance. Since neither side of the parallel combination of C_1 and C_P is at ground potential, a grounded shielding screen is needed. There is a leakage capacitance C_L ($\sim$100 $\mu\mu$f) between these capacitors and the grounded screen.

EXPERIMENTAL

Turn on the vacuum pump and the electronic equipment: these should be left on throughout the experiment. At least 1 hr should be allowed for the oscillators to warm up. Specific instructions for operation of the electronic equipment may be given by the instructor.

Evacuate the cell and flush out the line from the HCl cylinder by admitting HCl to a few centimeters pressure and pumping it out; this should be repeated once or twice. Test for leaks by evacuating the system, closing off the pump line, and checking the manometer occasionally for half an hour or more.

When the beat-frequency oscillator has warmed up, measure C_0, the vacuum capacity of the cell. For this purpose the precision air capacitor should be on the *high scale* and should be connected in *parallel* with the cell. With the coaxial lead disconnected from the cell connector and attached to the blank connector mounted beside it, set the precision air capacitor to a high value, well in excess of the expected cell capacitance. Vary the coarse tuning condenser to give the required condition of frequency balance (i.e., zero beat or else a constant beat as shown by comparison with a *stable* audio comparison frequency through use of a Lissajous figure on an oscilloscope). Make any required fine adjustment with the precision air capacitor to achieve the best balance, and record the setting. Reconnect the coaxial lead to the cell, and obtain a balance by adjusting the precision air capacitor. Record the new reading. The difference between these two readings is $C_0 + \delta$, where δ is any fixed contribution to the capacity due to any solid dielectrics (e.g., glass) in the cell. For the cell shown in Fig. 1, δ may be assumed to be negligible; for other cells it may be necessary to use a calculated value of δ.

One must now insert the fixed capacitor C_1 and change the circuit connections in accordance with Fig. 3. The precision air capacitor should be on *low scale* and set near the center of the range. It is very important that the copper-screen shield be well grounded. The coaxial lead to the cell should be in a position which will not later be disturbed. Adjust the coarse tuning capacitor to achieve a balance (zero beat or Lissajous figure) as before. Set the precision air capacitor off balance and restore balance four times, twice from each side. Examine the readings for evidence of backlash and drift.

Test the electrostatic shielding of the cell by holding a metal plate next to it (or bringing a silvered Dewar flask into position around it) and rebalancing. A significant change in the capacitance indicates stray capacity.

Position a Dewar flask containing a previously prepared Dry Ice-acetone mixture (see Chap. XVI) so that the cell bulb is completely immersed. This must be done with caution to avoid foaming. To hasten thermal equilibration of the internal components of the cell, admit air or HCl to a few centimeters pressure; after a steady pressure is shown by the manometer, quickly reevacuate the cell. Obtain four precision air capacitor readings as before, and compare them with the room-temperature readings. A small variation of C_0 with temperature may be expected owing to thermal expansion of the metal plates and glass components; the magnitude of this variation will depend on the cell construction. If it is large enough to affect the results significantly, C_0 should be determined at each of the desired temperatures.

Now close off the pump and admit HCl gas to about 1 atm pressure. After attainment of equilibrium read the pressure precisely and close off the cell. Again take and average four balance readings on the precision air condenser. Reevacuate the cell and obtain a new vacuum value, averaging four readings as before. If there is evidence of significant drift or erratic behavior, one or two additional gas readings, alternated with vacuum readings, should be taken. If feasible, the temperature of the Dry Ice-acetone mixture should be measured with a thermocouple (e.g., copper-constantan, Chap. XVI), the junction being taped to the bulb.

The Dewar flask should be removed, and the bulb dried. Another Dewar flask, containing an ice-water mixture and a ring stirrer, is fixed in place so that the bulb is completely immersed. Again admit a small amount of HCl or air to facilitate heat transfer. After allowing reasonable time for equilibration, repeat the above procedure for taking vacuum and gas capacitance readings and manometer readings. The temperature of the bath should be checked with a thermometer or a thermocouple.

Finally the Dewar flask is replaced by a steam jacket (see Exp. 1), and the procedure is repeated. If the temperature is not measured directly with a thermocouple, it can be taken as the boiling point of water at the ambient atmospheric pressure; the barometer reading should be corrected for mercury expansion (see Chap. XVIII).

At the end of the experiment pump the HCl out of the cell and admit air to atmospheric pressure.

If time permits, a reading at a fourth temperature may be taken. With care a reading in the range 150 to 200°C can be taken with a stirred oil bath; careful attention is required to maintain a constant temperature. Alternatively, an intermediate temperature can be obtained with refluxing acetone (normal boiling point = 56.5°C). Acetone vapor is introduced into the top of the steam jacket. The effluent is led into a condenser connected below the steam jacket. The condensate may be conducted via a U tube (serving as a vapor trap) back to the boiling flask or simply caught in a receiving flask.

At each temperature, the ΔC value can be calculated from ΔC_P, the difference between the average precision air capacitor readings obtained with the cell evacuated and filled with gas, by using Eq. (2). However, if the values of C_1 and C_L are not precisely known, one can obtain ΔC values by means of a calibration plot. Such a calibration will require an additional precision variable capacitor which is inserted in place of the cell. One is then able to make *known* changes ΔC in this precision capacitor, determine the corresponding ΔC_P values, and make a calibration plot of ΔC vs. ΔC_P.

CALCULATIONS

For each temperature studied, list the pressure used and the experimental value of ΔC_P along with the calculated values of $\Delta C (= C - C_0)$ and polarization P_M (in cubic centimeters per mole). Plot P_M vs. $1/T$ and draw the best straight line through the experimental points. From the slope calculate μ with Eq. (1) and express it in debyes (1 debye = 10^{-18} esu-cm). Also calculate α from the intercept at $1/T = 0$, and express it in cubic angstroms per molecule.

DISCUSSION

In the HCl molecule the nuclei are 1.29 A apart. Assuming that the molecule consists of an H^+ and a Cl^- ion, both spherically symmetrical, separated by that distance, what would be the expected permanent dipole moment? (The electronic charge e is 4.80×10^{-10} esu.) Would you expect an appreciable moment for an HCl molecule if the bond were completely covalent? What do you conclude from your measured dipole moment regarding the charge distribution in the molecule and the nature of the bond?

APPARATUS

Gas capacitance cell (see text and Fig. 1); beat-frequency oscillator and accessories (see Exp. 37); double-shielded coaxial cable; closed-tube manometer; mechanical vacuum pump; small cylinder of anhydrous HCl, equipped with a needle valve; four-way glass tube junction or two Y tubes; two stopcocks or pinch clamps; two 1-qt Dewar flasks; steam jacket and steam generator (see Exp. 1); three long and one or more short lengths of rubber pressure tubing; U tube with stoppers.

Magnesium perchlorate; Ascarite; glass wool; ice; Dry Ice; acetone.

REFERENCES

1. C. P. Smyth, Determination of Dipole Moments, in A. Weissberger (ed.), "Technique of Organic Chemistry," 3d ed., vol. I, part III, chap. XXXIX, pp. 2599ff., Interscience, New York (1960).
2. K. B. McAlpine and C. P. Smyth, *J. Am. Chem. Soc.*, **55**, 453 (1933); E. W. Greene and J. W. Williams, *Phys. Rev.*, **42**, 119 (1932).

GENERAL READING

See titles listed at the end of Exp. 37.

Experiment 39. Magnetic Susceptibility

When an object is placed in a magnetic field, in general a magnetic moment is induced in it. This phenomenon is analogous to the induction of an electric moment in an object by an electric field (see Exp. 37) but differs from it in that an induced magnetic moment may have either direction in relation to the applied field. If the induced moment is parallel to the external field (as in the electric case), the material is called *paramagnetic* or *ferromagnetic,* depending on whether the field due to the induced moment is small or large in comparison with the external field. If the moment is antiparallel to the external field, the material is called *diamagnetic;* the moment in this case is always small. This experiment will deal only with paramagnetic and diamagnetic substances in solution.

THEORY

If **I** is the magnetization (magnetic moment per unit volume, analogous to the electric polarization **P**) induced by the field **H**, the volume magnetic susceptibility χ is defined by the equation

$$\mathbf{I} = \chi \mathbf{H} \tag{1}$$

For a paramagnetic substance χ is positive, and for a diamagnetic substance it is negative; it is a dimensionless number, ordinarily very small in comparison with unity (except in the case of ferromagnetism) and essentially independent of **H** for fields readily available in the laboratory.

Magnetic susceptibilities are usually given in the literature on a weight or molar basis. Thus, while the volume susceptibility χ is induced moment per unit volume per unit applied field and is dimensionless, the weight susceptibility

$$\chi_g = \frac{\chi}{\rho} \tag{2}$$

(where ρ is the density) is induced moment per unit weight per unit applied field and typically has units of cubic centimeters per gram. The molal susceptibility

$$\chi_M = M\chi_g = \frac{M}{\rho}\chi \tag{3}$$

(where M is the molecular weight) is induced moment per mole per unit applied field and typically has units of cubic centimeters per mole.

Diamagnetism. Nearly all known substances are diamagnetic. Diamagnetism results from the precession of the electronic orbits in atoms which occur when a magnetic field is present. Volume diamagnetic susceptibilities are generally very small in magnitude compared with volume paramagnetic susceptibilities for pure substances. In paramagnetic substances the observed susceptibility is the resultant of a paramagnetic contribution and a very much smaller diamagnetic contribution. In an estimation of the paramagnetism this diamagnetic contribution is often neglected, but in the case of aqueous solutions a correction should be made for the diamagnetic susceptibility of the water owing to the relatively large amount of it present.

Paramagnetism. The most important source of paramagnetism is the magnetic moment which is associated with the spin of the electron. The electron has two spin states, having spin magnetic quantum numbers $-\frac{1}{2}$ and $+\frac{1}{2}$, with the principal component of magnetic moment respectively parallel and antiparallel to the magnetic field direction. Spin paramagnetism (or in some cases ferromagnetism) exists in a substance if the atoms, molecules, or ions in it contain unequal numbers of electrons in the two possible spin states. This condition obviously exists when the atom, molecule, or ion contains an odd number of electrons (as in Fe^{3+}, Cu^{2+}, $(C_6H_5)_3C\cdot$ and other free radicals, etc.). It may also exist when the number of electrons is even, if a degenerate electronic level (such as a d or f atomic subshell) is only partially filled. For example, the ferrous ion Fe^{2+} has six electrons outside the argon shell. The available orbitals of lowest energy are the five degenerate (i.e., equal energy) $3d$ orbitals. Each of these may contain two electrons with their spins opposed (one with spin $+\frac{1}{2}$, the other with spin $-\frac{1}{2}$, in accord with the Pauli exclusion principle) or a single electron with either spin. No spin paramagnetism would occur if the six outer electrons of Fe^{2+} occupied three of the five $3d$ orbitals in pairs so that all spin magnetic moments cancelled. However, this would be contrary to a principle known as *Hund's first rule,* which states that, when several electronic orbitals of equal or very nearly equal energy are incompletely filled, the electrons tend to occupy as many as possible of the orbitals singly rather than in pairs, the electrons in singly occupied orbitals all having the same spin. In Fe^{2+} this rule predicts that one $3d$ orbital will contain a pair of electrons with spins opposed and the other four orbitals will each contain a single electron, the four spins being the same. Thus many ferrous salts are paramagnetic. In molecular oxygen O_2, two molecular orbitals of equal energy each contain a single electron in accordance with Hund's first rule; consequently, oxygen gas is paramagnetic.

An atom, molecule, or ion containing one or more unpaired electrons with the same spin has a permanent magnetic moment μ. In the absence of orbital contributions to the moment (see below), μ is completely determined by the number of unpaired electrons n:

$$\mu = \sqrt{n(n+2)}\mu_B \tag{4}$$

where μ_B, the "Bohr magneton," is given by

$$\mu_B = \frac{eh}{4\pi mc} = 0.927 \times 10^{-20} \text{ erg gauss}^{-1} \tag{5}$$

Thus, for example, the "spin-only" magnetic moment of Fe^{2+} is

$$\mu = \sqrt{4 \times 6}\,\mu_B = 4.90 \text{ Bohr magnetons}$$

Orbital magnetic moments may also contribute to paramagnetism. An electron in an orbital with one or more units of angular momentum behaves like an electric current in a circular loop of wire and produces a magnetic moment. When all orbitals in a subshell (e.g., all five $3d$ orbitals) are equally filled (with one electron each as in Fe^{3+} or two electrons each as in Cu^{+}), the orbital moments cancel one another and there is no orbital contribution to the observed moment. In other cases (e.g., Fe^{2+}) an orbital contribution may arise, although usually it is "quenched" to a large extent by interactions with neighboring molecules or ions and does not contribute more than a few tenths of a Bohr magneton to the total moment. (Important exceptions are certain rare-earth ions, since quenching occurs to a much smaller extent for $4f$ orbitals than for $3d$ orbitals.) Atomic nuclei often possess spin magnetic moments, but these are so small as to have a negligible effect on magnetic susceptibility. They are important, however, in nuclear magnetic resonance spectroscopy.

In the absence of an applied field, the atomic moments in a paramagnetic substance orient themselves essentially at random owing to thermal motion and there is no net observable moment. In the presence of a magnetic field the atomic moments tend to line up with the field, but the degree of net alignment is slight because of the disorienting effect of thermal motion. It is possible to show[1] that the paramagnetic contribution to the molal susceptibility is $N_0\mu^2/3kT$, where N_0 is Avogadro's number, k is the Boltzmann constant, and T is the absolute temperature. The total molal susceptibility can be written

$$\chi_M = N_0\alpha + \frac{N_0\mu^2}{3kT} \tag{6}$$

where α is the small (negative) diamagnetism per molecule. We can write this in the form

$$\chi_M = N_0\alpha + \frac{C}{T} \tag{7}$$

where C is called the *Curie constant* for the substance concerned. If C is determined by experiment, the magnetic moment of the atom, molecule, or ion is obtained from it with the equation

$$\mu = \left(\frac{3kC}{N_0}\right)^{1/2} \tag{8}$$

Expressing this result in units of Bohr magnetons, we obtain

$$\mu = 2.824\sqrt{C} \tag{9}$$

where C is in cgs units.

Atomic Magnetism and Bond Type. The present experiment is largely concerned with complex ions of transition-group metals, such as hexahydrated or ammoniated ferrous or ferric ions and ferro- or ferricyanides. Here each metal ion is surrounded by a number of negative or neutral groups called *ligands*. This number is six in the cases cited and in other common cases may be four or eight.

Pauling[2] has proposed a criterion for distinguishing between essentially ionic and essentially covalent bonding between the metal ion and its ligands. Where the number of unpaired electrons in the complex as deduced from the measured susceptibility is the same as that expected for the free (gaseous) metal ion, the bonding with the ligands is considered to be ionic (i.e., due to Coulomb attraction as in $[Fe^{III}F_6]^{3-}$ or due to electrostatic polarization of neutral ligands by the central ion as in $[Co^{III}(H_2O)_6]^{3+}$). Where the number of unpaired electrons found in the complex is considerably less than the free metal ion value (as in most complexes with cyanides, ammonia, carbon monoxide, etc.), the bonding is considered to be covalent. It is assumed that the electrons are paired owing to the necessity of accommodating, in the atomic orbitals, some additional electrons donated by the ligands for forming electron-pair bonds. Thus, in $[Co^{III}(NH_3)_6]^{3+}$ the six electrons outside the argon shell of Co^{3+} are augmented by six electron pairs from the ligands, giving 18 electrons. Of these, 12 electrons (or six pairs) are shared with the ligands to form six octahedral covalent bonds, using two $3d$, one $4s$, and three $4p$ orbitals of cobalt. The other 6 electrons are paired in the remaining three $3d$ orbitals. Since all electrons are paired with spins opposed, salts of this complex are diamagnetic.

Another theory, due largely to van Vleck,[3] holds that the phenomena explained by Pauling in terms of essentially covalent bonding are better explained by assuming that the fivefold degenerate $3d$ level is split into two or more levels of different energy by perturbations due to the ligands, the energy differences between the levels being greater than can be overcome by the electron-unpairing tendency of Hund's first rule. (Thus, in $[Co^{III}(NH_3)_6]^{3+}$ the $3d$ level is split into a lower level with three orbitals and an upper one with two; the six outer electrons of Co^{3+} fill the lower three with paired spins, and the complex has no permanent magnetic moment.) In this theory there is no clear-cut distinction between ionic and covalent bonds based on magnetic properties alone; it is generally believed that in metal ion complexes of both types the bonds are partially ionic and partially covalent in character while in complexes of neutral metal atoms (such as the metal carbonyls) the bonds are primarily covalent with perhaps a small ionic character. This "crystal field" or "ligand field" theory has gained wide acceptance.

METHOD

Most methods for the determination of a magnetic susceptibility depend upon measuring the force resulting from the interaction between a magnetic field gradient and the magnetic moment induced in the sample by the magnetic field. The x component of this force, per unit volume of the sample, is

$$\mathbf{f}_x = \mathbf{I}\frac{\partial \mathbf{H}}{\partial x} = \chi \mathbf{H}\frac{\partial \mathbf{H}}{\partial x} \tag{10}$$

This force is such as to tend to draw the sample into the strongest part of the field if the sample is paramagnetic (χ positive) or repel it into the weakest part if the sample is diamagnetic (χ negative). The work done by the system when a volume dV of the sample is carried from a point of field strength H_1 to a point of field strength H_2 is (assuming for simplicity that H varies only as a function of x)

$$\begin{aligned} dw &= dV \int f_x\, dx = dV\chi \int H \frac{dH}{dx}\, dx = dV\chi \int_{H_1}^{H_2} H\, dH \\ &= \tfrac{1}{2}\chi(H_2^2 - H_1^2)\, dV \end{aligned} \tag{11}$$

The Gouy Balance.[4] In the Gouy balance (Fig. 1) a long tube, divided into two regions by a septum, is suspended from one side of an analytical balance so as to hang vertically in a magnetic field. The septum is in the strongest part of the field and the two ends of the tube are in regions of essentially zero field strength. The part of the tube above the septum is filled with the sample to be investigated, and the part below is empty.

In addition to the downward gravitational force acting on the tube, a force is exerted by the magnetic field. Let us calculate the work done in lowering the tube, with cross-sectional area A, by an amount Δx. This is equivalent to bringing a volume $A\,\Delta x$ of the specimen from a region of zero field strength to a region of field strength H. Thus, ignoring gravitational work,

$$w = \tfrac{1}{2}\chi H^2 A\,\Delta x = f\,\Delta x$$

Therefore the downward force on the tube due to its interaction with the magnetic field is†

$$f = \tfrac{1}{2}\chi H^2 A \tag{12}$$

In making a measurement, the "apparent weight" W is determined in the absence of a field and then with a field present, and the difference is equated to f:

$$(W_{\text{field}} - W_{\text{no field}}) = f = \tfrac{1}{2}\chi H^2 A \tag{13}$$

The weight W in each case is a *force* (in dynes) obtained by multiplying the mass of

† In case the top of the tube is not at zero field strength, we should write

$$f = \tfrac{1}{2}\chi(H_{\max}^2 - H_{\min}^2)A$$

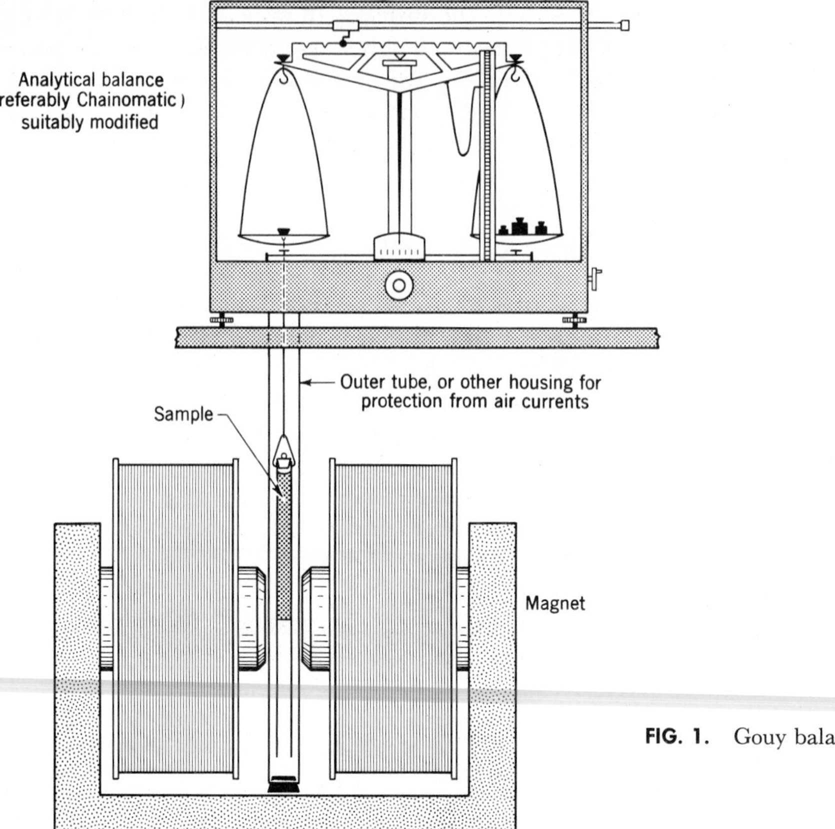

FIG. 1. Gouy balance.

the weights used (in grams) by the acceleration of gravity (in centimeters per second squared).

The magnet should provide a field of at least 4000 gauss and preferably 6000 or more. The field should be reasonably homogeneous over a region considerably larger than the diameter of the tube. For a sample tube up to 15 mm in diameter, a magnet with gap of 1 in. and a pole diameter of at least 3 in. is convenient.

For obtaining the weights in the presence and absence of a field it is most convenient to have an electromagnet, the field of which can easily be turned on and off. Such a magnet, with a regulated power supply, has the disadvantage of being rather expensive. A permanent magnet is usually less expensive, but special arrangements for making the no-field measurements are required. If the magnet is mounted on rails or on a pivot, it can be rolled or swung in and out of its normal position. If the magnet is stationary, the Gouy tube can be hung at two different levels (Fig. 2). If the latter method is to be used, the septum should be in the strongest part of the field in the lower position and in essentially zero field in the upper position. The sample tube should be long enough so that in either position the bottom end is in an essentially zero field region *below* the strong part of the field.

A conventional analytical balance (preferably a Chainomatic type) is mounted on a sturdy table over the magnet as shown in Fig. 1. The Gouy tube is supported by a nonmagnetic wire or thread which passes through a hole drilled in the base of the balance. If an electromagnet is used, the left-hand pan may be dispensed with and the wire attached directly to the stirrup. If, instead, a permanent magnet is used with the scheme shown in Fig. 2, a hole must be drilled in the pan so that the wire can pass through it to a hook which is attached to the stirrup for the no-field weighing or allowed to rest on the pan for the in-field weighing. The Gouy tube should be protected against air currents. Provision should also be made for mounting a thermometer near the Gouy tube.

EXPERIMENTAL

The procedure to be used in operating the Gouy balance will necessarily depend on the details of construction and cannot be given here with any completeness; a set of instructions should be compiled by the instructor and posted near the apparatus. The balance should be operated in the normal manner; the beam must be off the knife-edges when the Gouy tube is being mounted, demounted, or changed in position. It is important to **remove your watch** when working near the magnet and to keep steel and iron tools or instruments out of the way.

In order to determine the "apparatus constant" $H^2A/2$ which appears in Eq. (13), measurements are made on a material of known susceptibility. For this purpose, a common standard is an aqueous solution of nickel chloride, about 30 per cent $NiCl_2$ by weight. Prepare 100 ml of such a solution with an accurately known weight fraction of $NiCl_2$ in air-free distilled water. When this solution is weighed on the Gouy balance, record the ambient temperature.

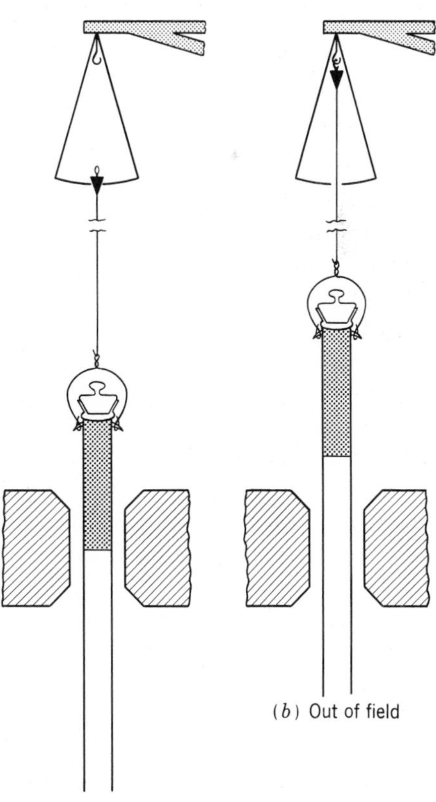

FIG. 2. Positioning of Gouy tube for (*a*) in-field and (*b*) out-of-field weighings when a permanent magnet is used.

Solutions of the following salts† in air-free distilled water should be studied. In each case, the concentration ($\sim$0.5 M) must be precisely known. If possible, prepare the solutions in advance since some of these salts dissolve quite slowly.

$Mn^{II}SO_4$, manganous sulfate
$KMn^{VII}O_4$, potassium permanganate (NOTE: this is soluble only to about 0.4 M)
$[Fe^{II}(H_2O)_6](NH_4)_2(SO_4)_2$, ferrous ammonium sulfate
$K_4[Fe^{II}(CN)_6]$, potassium ferrocyanide
$K_3[Fe^{III}(CN)_6]$, potassium ferricyanide

The first two compounds illustrate the effect of two different oxidation states of a single element, manganese. The next three demonstrate the different effects of essentially ionic bonding and essentially covalent (or strong crystal-field) bonding.

It is important to know the densities of all solutions. A satisfactory procedure is to weigh the Gouy tube empty and then filled with water to a fiducial mark near the top. From the known density of water at this temperature, the volume is calculated. The tube is then filled with the solution to be studied up to the same fiducial mark and weighed. (All these weighings are in the absence of a magnetic field.) Alternatively, the density of each solution can be determined with a Westphal balance or a good hydrometer.

CALCULATIONS

Calibration. The *weight* susceptibility of an aqueous nickel chloride solution is given by Selwood[5] as

$$\chi_g = \left[\frac{10{,}030p}{T} - 0.720(1-p)\right] \times 10^{-6} \qquad \mathrm{cm^3\,g^{-1}} \tag{14}$$

where p is the weight fraction of $NiCl_2$ and T is the absolute temperature. The second term in the brackets is the correction for the diamagnetism of the water used as solvent. This expression assumes that the solution is free of dissolved atmospheric oxygen.

From the χ_g given by this expression and the density of the $NiCl_2$ solution, the volume susceptibility χ can be calculated [Eq. (2)]. With this and the measured weight difference, determine and report the apparatus constant $H^2A/2$ appearing in Eq. (13).

Measurements on Unknown Solutions. The weight susceptibility of a solution is related to the molal susceptibility by

† Magnetic measurements may be made on powdered crystalline salts rather than on aqueous solutions. The volume susceptibilities are very much larger (an attractive feature if a strong magnet is not available), but the molal susceptibilities are not so easily interpretable in terms of atomic moments, owing to interaction effects in the crystalline state. In place of Eq. (7), we write (neglecting the diamagnetic term)

$$\chi_M = \frac{C}{T + \Delta}$$

This is called the *Curie-Weiss law.* The constant Δ may be positive or negative and for most compounds is less than 75° in magnitude. To obtain a value of the Curie constant from which an atomic moment can be calculated, it is necessary to measure χ_M at more than one temperature. When the reciprocal of χ_M is plotted against absolute temperature, the reciprocal of the slope is the Curie constant C. The density ρ required in the calculations is not the crystal density, but an effective powder density determined in the manner described for solutions.

$$\chi_g = \frac{\chi_M\,(\text{solute})}{M} p - 0.720 \times 10^{-6}(1 - p) \tag{15}$$

where p is again the weight fraction of solute. If the concentration c of the solute in moles per liter is known, we can write the volume susceptibility directly in the form

$$\chi = \frac{c\chi_M}{1000} - 0.720 \times 10^{-6}\left(\rho - \frac{cM}{1000}\right) \tag{16}$$

From the experimental weight difference, χ is determined by use of Eq. (13) and the known apparatus constant $H^2A/2$. From Eq. (16) the solute molal susceptibility χ_M is obtained.

If the material is paramagnetic (χ_M positive), the small negative diamagnetic term $N_0\alpha$ can be neglected in Eq. (7) and the constant C can be determined. The atomic moment μ can then be calculated from Eq. (9). With neglect of any orbital contribution, the number of unpaired electrons can be found approximately with Eq. (4). For each paramagnetic substance studied, calculate the number of unpaired electrons and comment on the type of bonding involved in the complexes.

APPARATUS

Gouy balance (comprising a magnet, power supply if needed, suitably modified analytical balance); glass-stoppered Gouy tube; several 100-ml volumetric flasks and glass-stoppered 200-ml flasks; 0 to 30°C thermometer; Westphal balance or hydrometer (optional).

$NiCl_2$ (40 g); $MnSO_4$ (10 g); $KMnO_4$ (10 g); $K_4Fe(CN)_6$ (25 g); $K_3Fe(CN)_6$ (20 g); $Fe(NH_4)_2(SO_4)_2 \cdot 6H_2O$ (20 g); or a solution of each salt of an accurately known concentration (100 ml).

REFERENCES

1. W. J. Moore, "Physical Chemistry," 2d ed., pp. 317–318, 322, Prentice-Hall, Englewood Cliffs, N. J. (1955).
2. L. Pauling, "The Nature of the Chemical Bond," pp. 161ff., Cornell University Press, Ithaca, N. Y. (1960).
3. J. H. van Vleck, *J. Chem. Phys.*, **3**, 807 (1935).
4. P. W. Selwood, "Magnetochemistry," 2d ed., pp. 3ff., Interscience, New York (1956).
5. *Ibid.*, p. 26.

GENERAL READING

L. E. Orgel, "An Introduction to Transition-Metal Chemistry: Ligand-Field Theory," Methuen, London (1960).

E. C. Stoner, "Magnetism," Methuen, London (1948).

L. F. Bates, "Modern Magnetism," 3d ed., Cambridge, New York (1951).

J. H. van Vleck, "Electric and Magnetic Susceptibilities," Oxford, New York (1944).

L. Michaelis, Determination of Magnetic Susceptibility, in A. Weissberger (ed.), "Technique of Organic Chemistry," 2d ed., vol. I, part II, chap. XXIX, Interscience, New York (1949).

XIII SPECTRA AND MOLECULAR STRUCTURE

EXPERIMENTS

Experiment 40. Absorption Spectrum of a Conjugated Dye

Absorption bands in the visible region of the spectrum correspond to transitions from the ground state of a molecule to an excited electronic state which is 40 to 70 kcal above the ground state. In many substances, the lowest excited electronic state is more than 70 kcal above the ground state and no visible spectrum is observed. Those compounds which are colored (i.e., absorb in the visible) generally have some weakly bound or delocalized electrons such as the odd electron in a free radical or the π electrons in a conjugated organic molecule. In this experiment we are concerned with the determination of the visible absorption spectrum of several symmetrical polymethine dyes and with the interpretation of these spectra using the "free-electron" model.

THEORY

The visible bands for polymethine dyes arise from electronic transitions involving the π electrons along the polymethine chain. The wavelength of these bands depends on the spacing of the electronic energy levels. Bond orbital and molecular orbital calculations have been made for these dyes,[1] but the predicted wavelengths are in poor agreement with those observed. We shall present here the simple free-electron model first proposed by Kuhn;[2] this model contains some drastic assumptions but has proved reasonably successful for molecules like a conjugated dye.

As an example, consider a dilute solution of 1,1′-diethyl-4,4′-carbocyanine iodide (kryptocyanine):

```
                      H  H  H
Et—N:         C=C—C=C—C         N+—Et   I−
   \          /          \\       //
     C=C                    C—C
     H  H                   H  H

                      H  H  H
Et—+N         C—C=C—C=C         :N—Et   I−
   \\         //          \        /
     C—C                     C=C
     H  H                    H  H
```

The cation can "resonate" between the two limiting structures above; that is, the wave function for the ion has equal contributions from both states. Thus all the bonds along this chain can be considered equivalent, with bond order 1.5 (similar to the C—C bonds in benzene). Each carbon atom in the chain and each nitrogen at the end is involved in bonding with three atoms by three localized bonds (the so-called σ bonds). The extra valence electrons on the carbon atoms in the chain and the three remaining electrons on the two nitrogens form a mobile cloud of π electrons along the chain (above and below the plane of the chain). We shall assume that the potential energy is constant along the chain and that it rises sharply to infinity at the ends; i.e., the π electron system is replaced by free electrons moving in a one-dimensional box of length L. The quantum mechanical solution for the energy levels of this model[3] is

$$E_n = \frac{h^2 n^2}{8mL^2} \qquad n = 1, 2, 3, \ldots \tag{1}$$

where m is the mass of an electron and h is Planck's constant.

Since the Pauli exclusion principle limits the number of electrons in any given energy level to two (these two have opposite spins: $+\frac{1}{2}$, $-\frac{1}{2}$), the ground state of a molecule with N π electrons will have the $N/2$ lowest levels filled and all higher levels empty. When the molecule (or ion in this case) absorbs light, this is associated with a one electron jump from the highest filled level ($n_1 = N/2$) to the lowest empty level ($n_2 = N/2 + 1$). The energy change for this transition is

$$\Delta E = \frac{h^2}{8mL^2}(n_2{}^2 - n_1{}^2) = \frac{h^2}{8mL^2}(N + 1) \tag{2}$$

Since $\Delta E = h\nu = hc/\lambda$, where c is the speed of light and λ is the wavelength in centimeters,

$$\lambda = \frac{8mc}{h} \frac{L^2}{N + 1} \tag{3}$$

Let us denote the number of carbon atoms in a polymethine chain by p; then $N = p + 3$. Kuhn assumed that L was the length of the chain between nitrogen atoms plus one bond distance on each side; thus, $L = (p + 3)l$, where l is the bond length between atoms along the chain. Therefore,

$$\lambda = \frac{8mcl^2}{h} \frac{(p + 3)^2}{p + 4} \tag{4}$$

Putting $l = 1.39 \times 10^{-8}$ cm (the bond length in benzene, a molecule with similar bonding) and converting λ from centimeters to millimicrons (1 mμ = 10^{-7} cm), we find that

$$\lambda \text{ (in m}\mu) = 63.7 \frac{(p + 3)^2}{p + 4} \tag{5}$$

If there are easily polarizable groups at the ends of the chain (such as benzene rings), the potential energy of the π electrons in the chain does not rise so sharply at the ends. In effect this lengthens the path L, and we can write

$$\lambda \text{ (in m}\mu) = 63.7 \frac{(p + 3 + \alpha)^2}{p + 4} \tag{6}$$

where α should be a constant for a series of dyes of a given type. If such a series is studied experimentally, this empirical parameter α may be adjusted to achieve the best fit to the data; in any event, α should lie between 0 and 1.[2]

In order to compare the results of this model with the more sophisticated bond or molecular orbital calculations let us use Eq. (5), which assumes that $\alpha = 0$, to calculate the wavelength λ for kryptocyanine (in which $p = 9$) and compare that value with those given by Herzfeld and Sklar:[1,2]

Free electron	$\lambda = 707$ mμ
Bond orbital (case 1)	$\lambda = 3900$
Bond orbital (case 2)	$\lambda = 2900$
Molecular orbital	$\lambda = 2700$

Note that only the free-electron model predicts an absorption band in the visible in agreement with observation. While the orbital calculations are poor for polymethine dyes, they are in principle a superior approach and have given excellent results for unsaturated hydrocarbons.

METHOD

Although there are many different spectrophotometers currently available, the Beckman Model DU (shown schematically in Fig. 1) is perhaps the best for student use. A general description of spectrophotometers will be given in terms of this instrument, but the principles involved are applicable to any other design.

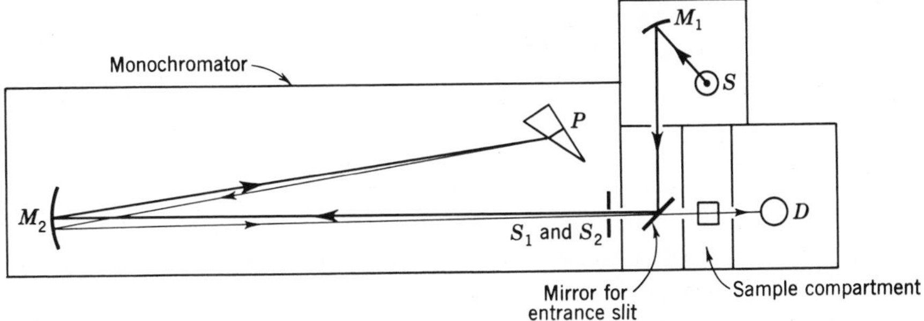

FIG. 1. Schematic diagram of a Beckman Model DU Spectrophotometer.

The source S is a battery-operated tungsten lamp which provides a "white" light for operation in the visible. (The tungsten lamp can be replaced by a hydrogen discharge tube for work in the near ultraviolet.) A condensing mirror M_1 sends a beam of light from this source through the entrance slit S_1 into the monochromator. This beam is reflected to a quartz prism by the collimating mirror M_2. The prism P is a Littrow type; the light undergoes refraction on entering the front surface, is reflected from a silvered back surface, and undergoes a second refraction on leaving the prism. (Some instruments achieve dispersion of the light by means of a diffraction grating instead of a prism.) When the prism is rotated, a narrow band which is almost monochromatic at any desired wavelength can be passed through the exit slit S_2. A sample cell,† with plane parallel windows, is mounted between the slit and the detector D. The intensity of light incident on the sample cell can be controlled by varying the slit width. The narrowest possible slit width is best, since this gives the most nearly monochromatic beam. All the light which is transmitted by the sample falls on the detector (a photomultiplier tube or some type of barrier layer cell). The photocurrent is then amplified and used to indicate the intensity of this transmitted light.

It is now necessary to define several terms commonly used in spectrophotometry. Absorption spectra are often characterized by the *per cent transmittance* at a given wavelength; this is defined by

$$\%T = 100\frac{I}{I_0} \tag{7}$$

where I is the intensity of light transmitted by the sample and I_0 is the intensity of light incident on the sample. When the sample is in solution and a cell must be used, I is taken to be the intensity of light transmitted by the cell when it contains solution while I_0 is taken to be the intensity of light transmitted by the cell filled with pure solvent. Another way of describing spectra is in terms of the *absorbancy* A where

$$A = \log\frac{I_0}{I} \tag{8}$$

[Until recently, the quantity log (I_0/I) was often called the *optical density*.] A completely transparent sample would have $\%T = 100$ or $A = 0$, while a completely opaque sample would have $\%T = 0$ or $A = \infty$.

† For measurements in the visible, inexpensive Pyrex cells are very satisfactory. Corex cells can be used in the near ultraviolet, although quartz cells are necessary for most ultraviolet studies.

The absorbancy A is related to the path length d of the sample and the concentration c of absorbing molecules by the Beer-Lambert law,[4]

$$A = \epsilon cd \tag{9}$$

where the proportionality constant ϵ is called the *absorptivity* or *extinction coefficient*. When the concentration is expressed in moles per liter, ϵ is the molar absorptivity. The quantity ϵ is a property of the absorbing material which varies with wavelength in a characteristic manner; its value depends only slightly on the solvent used and on the temperature.

For quantitative measurements, it is important to calibrate the cells so that a correction can be made for any small difference in path length between the solution cell and the solvent cell. For analytical applications, one must check the validity of Beer's law, since slight deviations are often observed and a calibration of absorbancy vs. concentration is then required. Such quantitative techniques are described elsewhere[4] and will not be necessary for conducting the present experiment.

EXPERIMENTAL

Instructions for operating the spectrophotometer will be made available in the laboratory. Turn on the instrument as instructed, and allow it to warm up for at least 20 minutes prior to use. For most instruments, such a warm-up period is necessary to achieve stable, drift-free operation.

Several polymethine dyes should be studied, preferably a series of dyes of a given type with varying chain length. In addition to the 1,1′-diethyl-4,4′-carbocyanine iodides mentioned previously, 1,1′-diethyl-2,2′-carbocyanine iodides and 3,3′-diethyl thiacarbocyanine iodides are suitable. Other possible compounds can be found in the literature.[5]

Choose any one of the available dyes, and prepare 10 ml of a solution using methyl alcohol as the solvent. The concentration should be approximately 10^{-3} M. (If the solutions are to be kept for a long time, they should be stored in dark glass bottles to prevent slow decomposition by daylight.)

Follow the spectrophotometer operating instructions carefully, and obtain the spectrum of this initial solution. Take absorbancy readings at widely spaced intervals throughout the visible region (400 to 750 mμ) until the absorption band is located. Then take readings at much closer intervals throughout the band. Dilute the initial solution and redetermine the spectrum. Repeat this procedure until a spectrum is obtained with an absorbancy reading of about 1 at the peak (per cent T about 10). The band shape will change with concentration, since these dyes dimerize. At the final concentration used, the monomer band (higher wavelength band) will be much more prominent than the dimer band, which will disappear or remain as a shoulder on the low-wavelength side of the main peak. If the spectrophotometer cell holder will accommodate more than two cells, several concentrations can be studied simultaneously.

Make up solutions (10 ml) of the other dyes at approximately the same molar concentration that gave the best results previously. Obtain their spectra in the same way.

CALCULATIONS

Carefully plot all spectra (A vs. λ) and determine λ_{max}, the wavelength at the peak, for each.

Using Eq. (6), calculate λ from the free-electron model. If a series of dyes of a single type has been studied, choose α to give the best fit for one of the series and use this value for all others in the series.

Report your experimental values of λ_{max} together with the theoretical results.

APPARATUS

Spectrophotometer, such as a Beckman Model DU; four Pyrex sample cells; lens tissue; 6-v battery and battery charger (or regulated dc power supply); several 10-ml volumetric flasks; wash bottle.

Reagent-grade methyl alcohol (150 ml); several polymethine dyes, preferably a series such as 1,1′-diethyl-4,4′-cyanine iodide, -carbocyanine iodide, and -dicarbocyanine iodide or 1,1′-diethyl-2,2′-cyanine iodide, -carbocyanine iodide, and -dicarbocyanine iodide (a few milligrams of each is sufficient). (Gallard-Schlesinger Chemical Mfg. Corp., 1001 Franklin St., Garden City, N.Y., is a possible supplier.)

REFERENCES

1. K. F. Herzfeld and A. L. Sklar, *Rev. Mod. Phys.,* **14,** 294 (1942).
2. H. Kuhn, *J. Chem. Phys.,* **17,** 1198 (1949).
3. W. J. Moore, "Physical Chemistry," 2d ed., pp. 277–278, Prentice-Hall, Englewood Cliffs, N.J. (1955); or any introductory book in quantum mechanics.
4. M. G. Mellon, "Analytical Absorption Spectroscopy," Wiley, New York (1950); D. F. Boltz, "Selected Topics in Modern Instrumental Analysis," chap. 4, Prentice-Hall, Englewood Cliffs, N.J. (1952).
5. L. G. S. Brooker, *Rev. Mod. Phys.,* **14,** 275 (1942); N. I. Fisher and F. M. Hamer, *Proc. Roy. Soc.,* Ser. A, **154,** 703 (1936).

GENERAL READING

T. R. P. Gibb, "Optical Methods of Chemical Analysis," chap. II, McGraw-Hill, New York (1942).

W. West, Spectroscopy and Spectrophotometry, in A. Weissberger (ed.), "Technique of Organic Chemistry," 2d ed., vol. I, part II, chap. XXI, Interscience, New York (1949).

Experiment 41. Infrared Spectroscopy: Vibrational Spectrum of SO_2

The infrared region of the spectrum extends from the long-wavelength end of the visible region at 1 μ out to the microwave region at about 1000 μ, 1 micron (μ) being equal to 10^{-4} cm. Although considerable work is now being done in the far infrared (wavelengths greater than 50 μ), the region between 2 and 25 μ has received the greatest attention because the vibrational frequencies of most molecules lie in this region. It is common practice to specify infrared frequencies in wavenumber units (cm^{-1}); thus the 2 to 25 μ region extends from 5000 down to 400 cm^{-1}.

THEORY

Almost all infrared work makes use of absorption techniques where radiation from a source emitting all infrared frequencies is passed through a sample of the material to be studied. When the frequency of this radiation is the same as a vibrational frequency of the molecule, the molecule may be vibrationally excited; this results in loss of energy from the radiation and gives rise to an absorption band. The spectrum of a molecule generally consists of several such bands arising from different vibrational motions of the molecule.

Associated with each vibrational energy level there are also closely spaced rotational energy levels. In general, transitions occur from a particular rotational level (quantum number J) in a given vibrational state (quantum number v) to a different rotational level (quantum number J') in an excited vibrational state (quantum number v'). The appearance of this rotational fine structure will depend on the resolution of the spectrometer used, as shown schematically in Fig. 1. Rotation-vibration spectra are discussed in Exp. 42 for the case of diatomic molecules and will not be considered here.

In this experiment we shall be concerned with the infrared bands of SO_2 gas under low or medium resolution, i.e., with only the vibrational spectrum. Electron diffraction studies show that SO_2 is a symmetrical, nonlinear molecule.[1] For a nonlinear molecule containing n atoms there are $3n$-6 vibrational degrees of freedom. Thus, SO_2 has three basic patterns of vibration called "normal modes." These are shown in Fig. 2. All vibrations of the molecule may be expressed as linear combinations of these normal modes.

The frequencies of the normal modes of vibration are called *fundamentals*. For

FIG. 1. Schematic infrared band contours at (*a*) low, (*b*) and (*c*) medium, and (*d*) high resolution. For the band shown in (*b*) there is no *Q* band ($\Delta J = 0$ transitions are forbidden); the bands shown in (*c*) and (*d*) have *Q* branches.

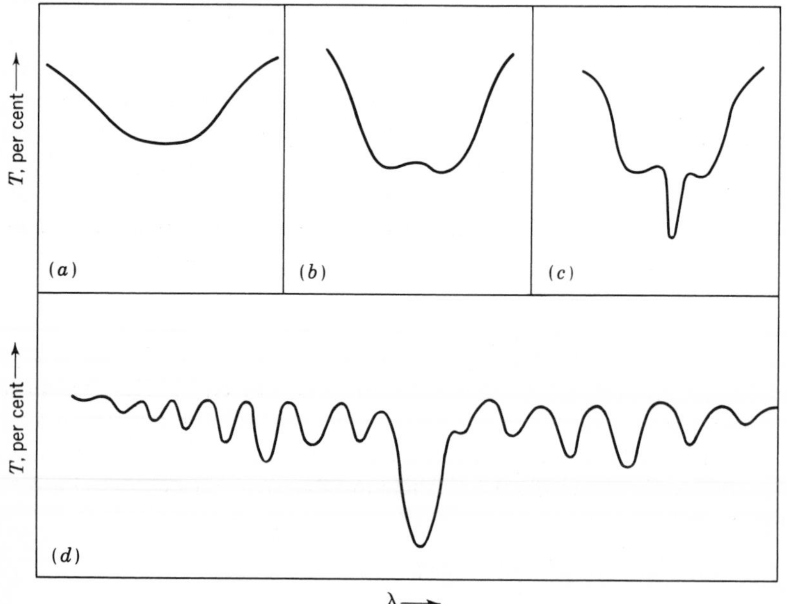

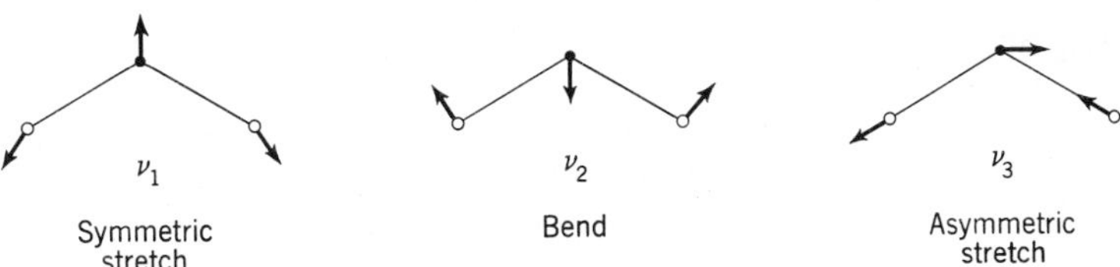

FIG. 2. Normal modes of vibration for SO_2. The lengths of the arrows which indicate displacements from the equilibrium configuration have been exaggerated for clarity.

SO_2 all three fundamentals are infrared active; they will correspond to the three most intense bands in the spectrum. The fundamentals (ν_1, ν_2, ν_3) may be assigned by analogy with the spectra of other molecules: the bending frequency ν_2 should be that of the lowest frequency band, and the asymmetric stretch ν_3 should be that of the highest frequency band.

The structure of SO_2 is confirmed by the presence of all three fundamentals in the infrared spectrum. When this is true, the molecule cannot have a center of symmetry[2] as in O—S—O. Linear unsymmetric structures, such as O—O—S or O——S—O, can be ruled out by the shape of the rotational band envelopes in the infrared spectrum; discussion of this topic is beyond the scope of this book.

In addition to the fundamentals, other much weaker bands may be observed in the spectrum at high pressure. Such weak bands are either overtones ($2\nu_i$, $3\nu_i$, . . .) or combination bands ($\nu_i \pm \nu_j$, $2\nu_i \pm \nu_j$, . . .) which arise from the fact that small anharmonicities tend to couple the normal vibrations. On the basis of intensity, the transitions which involve binary overtones ($2\nu_i$) and binary combinations ($\nu_i \pm \nu_j$) are the most likely to be observed. Thus, any weak bands observed for SO_2 may be assigned as overtones or combinations of the strong fundamentals. Any such assignment should take into account rules which determine whether a given combination will be active in the infrared,[3] but this subject is beyond the scope of this book and will not be discussed.

Valence Force Model. The normal modes of vibration can be expressed in terms of the atomic masses (m_S and m_O), the O—S—O bond angle (2α), and several force constants which define the potential energy of the molecule. These force constants are analogous to the Hooke's law constant for a spring. If a force model is chosen involving fewer force constants than the number of normal modes, the force constants are overdetermined and a check on the validity of the model is then possible. The valence force model assumes that there is a large restoring force along the line of a chemical bond when the distance between the two atoms at the ends of this bond is changed. It also assumes a restoring force for any change in angle between two adjacent bonds. Adopting the notation used by Herzberg,[4] we can write the potential energy of SO_2 as

$$V = \tfrac{1}{2}[k_1(Q_1^2 + Q_2^2) + k_\delta \delta^2]$$

where Q_1 and Q_2 are changes in the S—O distances (whose equilibrium value is denoted by l), and δ is the change in the bond angle 2α. The quantities k_1 and k_δ/l^2 are force constants (usually given in dynes per centimeter) for stretching and bending motions, respectively. Using the classical mechanics of harmonic oscillators, one can obtain[4] for SO_2

$$4\pi^2\nu_3^2 = \left(1 + \frac{2m_O}{m_S}\sin^2\alpha\right)\frac{k_1}{m_O} \tag{1}$$

$$4\pi^2(\nu_1{}^2 + \nu_2{}^2) = \left(1 + \frac{2m_O}{m_S}\cos^2\alpha\right)\frac{k_1}{m_O} + \frac{2}{m_O}\left(1 + \frac{2m_O}{m_S}\sin^2\alpha\right)\frac{k_\delta}{l^2} \tag{2}$$

$$16\pi^4\nu_1{}^2\nu_2{}^2 = 2\left(1 + \frac{2m_O}{m_S}\right)\frac{k_1}{m_O{}^2}\frac{k_\delta}{l^2} \tag{3}$$

If one uses ν in wavenumber units and $m_O = 16$, $m_S = 32$ (atomic weight units), $4\pi^2$ should be replaced by $4\pi^2c^2M_1 = 5.889 \times 10^{-2}$ ($M_1 = \frac{1}{16}$ mass of an O^{16} atom in grams). For SO_2, $2\alpha = 120°$.

Vibrational Partition Function.[5] The thermodynamic quantities for a perfect gas can usually be expressed as a sum of translational, rotational, and vibrational contributions (see Exp. 4). We shall consider here the heat capacity at constant volume. At room temperature and above, the translational and rotational contributions to C_v are constant; for SO_2 (a nonlinear polyatomic molecule),

$$\tilde{C}_v(\text{trans}) = \frac{3R}{2}$$
$$\tilde{C}_v(\text{rot}) = \frac{3R}{2} \tag{4}$$

The vibrational contribution to C_v varies with temperature and can be calculated from the vibrational partition function z_{vib}, which is expressed in terms of the frequencies of the normal modes. $z_{vib} = \prod_i z_i$, where for a harmonic oscillator of frequency ν_i we may write [making use of Eq. (42-1)]

$$z_i \equiv \sum_j e^{-\epsilon_j/kT} = \sum_{v=0}^{\infty} e^{-(v+1/2)h\nu_i/kT} = \frac{e^{-h\nu_i/2kT}}{1 - e^{h\nu_i/kT}} \tag{5}$$

The vibrational contribution to C_v is related to z_{vib} by

$$\tilde{C}_v(\text{vib}) = R\frac{\partial}{\partial T}\left(T^2\frac{\partial \ln z_{vib}}{\partial T}\right) \tag{6}$$

From Eqs. (5) and (6)

$$\tilde{C}_v(\text{vib}) = R\sum_i \frac{u_i{}^2\, e^{-u_i}}{(1 - e^{-u_i})^2} \tag{7}$$

where $u_i = h\nu_i/kT$ and the summation is over all the normal modes.

METHOD[6]

A large variety of infrared spectrometers are in current use. In this section, a brief general description will be given for a simple, single-beam instrument shown schematically in Fig. 3.

The source S provides a continuous spectrum of infrared radiation. Two common sources are the "globar" and the "Nernst glower," which are heated, respectively, to red-orange or white heat by passage of an electrical current. A spherical mirror M_2 focuses an image of the source on the entrance slit S_1 of the monochromator. The absorption cell is usually placed between the source and the monochromator as shown. In the monochromator the radiation from the entrance slit S_1 is dispersed so that a narrow band of almost monochromatic radiation leaves through the exit slit S_2. This dispersion can be accomplished by either

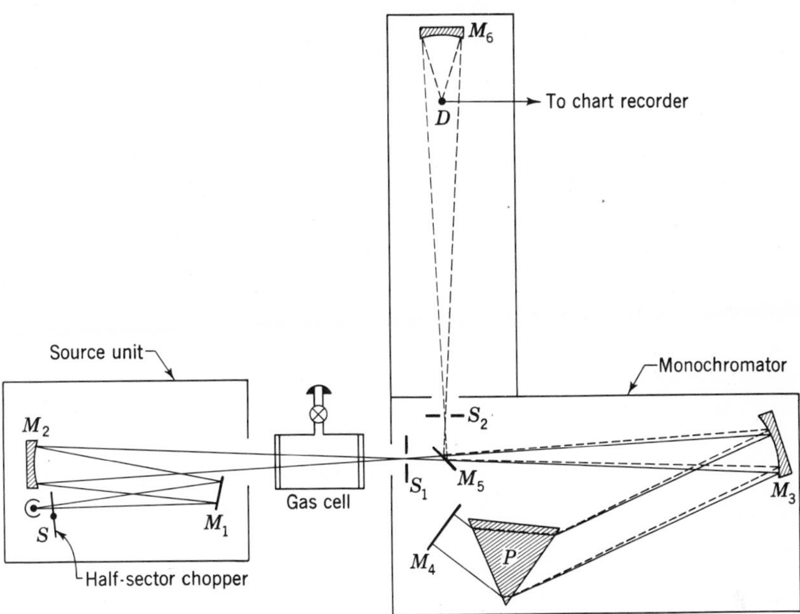

FIG. 3. Schematic drawing of a single-beam infrared spectrometer.

a prism or a diffraction grating. Diffraction gratings give the greater dispersion and thus better resolution but are more difficult to use. In smaller instruments, prisms are commonly used in the region from 400 to 5000 cm^{-1}. Table 1 lists several prism materials and the region in which each has its best resolution. The monochromator shown in Fig. 3 is of a Littrow design; that is, the radiation is passed twice through the prism P to obtain increased dispersion. Thus, radiation which is nearly monochromatic passes through the exit slit S_2. By rotation of the prism, it is possible to scan through a wide spectral range.

The radiation passing through the exit slit is focused by mirror M_6 on the detector D. Infrared detectors are devices which are very sensitive to heat, such as a thermocouple or bolometer. To avoid detecting background "black-body" radiation it is common practice to interrupt, or "chop," the infrared beam either near the source or near the exit slit to create a low-frequency alternating signal at the detector. This signal may be increased by an ac amplifier without amplifying any dc signal due to background.

In addition to infrared absorption by the sample contained in the cell there will be absorption by water vapor and carbon dioxide in the air. With a single-beam instrument it is necessary to sweep the spectrometer with dry nitrogen gas to prevent the occurrence of interfering H_2O and CO_2 bands. Another solution to this problem is to use a double-beam spectrometer where such interfering spectra are canceled out.

TABLE 1

Prism material	Region of best resolution, cm^{-1}
LiF	2000–4000
CaF_2	1200–2400
NaCl	700–1400
KBr	400–800

It is necessary to calibrate the spectrometer to know what frequency corresponds to a given prism setting. Such a calibration is performed with standard samples (H_2O vapor, CO_2, NH_3, polystyrene film, etc.) having sharp bands of known frequency. Calibrations are quite stable, and a check at one frequency may be sufficient to verify a previous calibration.

EXPERIMENTAL

Specific instructions for the operation of the infrared spectrometer to be used will be given in the laboratory. **Use this machine carefully;** if in doubt ask the instructor.

The gas cell is constructed from a short (usually 10 cm) length of large-diameter Pyrex tubing with a vacuum stopcock attached. Infrared-transparent windows are sealed on the ends with clear glyptal resin. If a KBr prism is available for work below 700 cm^{-1}, then KBr windows are needed. If only a NaCl prism is to be used in studying the region from 5000 to 700 cm^{-1}, then NaCl windows will serve. Sodium chloride windows will fog in a moist atmosphere and should be protected when not in use.

Filling the Cell. An arrangement for filling the cell is given in Fig. 4. Attach the cell at *D*. With stopcock *C* open and *B* closed, open stopcock *A* and pump out the system. Make sure that the needle valve of the SO_2 cylinder is closed. Then open *B* and continue pumping.

Close *A* and **slowly** open the valve on the SO_2 cylinder. Fill the system to about 1.2 atm with SO_2. Close the valve on the cylinder and then close *B* and *C*. Remove the cell from the vacuum line and take a spectrum.

Return the cell to the line. With *B* closed and *C* closed, open *A* and pump out the line for a few minutes. Now close *A* and open *C*. Open *A* **very slowly** and carefully to reduce the pressure to about 300 mm Hg. Close *A* and *C*, remove the cell, and record the spectrum. Repeat this process and record the spectrum at pressures of 100, 40, 15, and 5 mm.

Recording of Spectra. Several spectra may be recorded on a single chart, using different colored inks to distinguish them. With NaCl windows on the cell and using an NaCl prism it is not possible to observe ν_2, the lowest frequency fundamental, which lies below 700 cm^{-1}. If this band is not to be studied, a chart recording in the KBr region may be made available for reference or the literature value of ν_2 may be given.

FIG. 4. Gas-handling system for filling infrared cell.

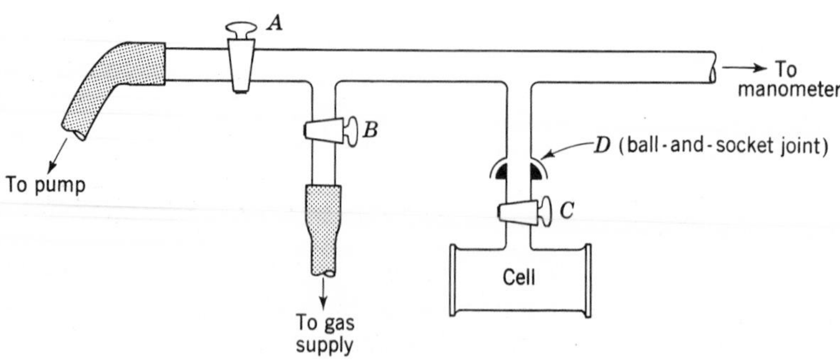

CALCULATIONS AND DISCUSSIONS

Assign the fundamentals of SO_2 gas and report their frequencies. Then assign any other bands observed. Is it possible to infer the ν_2 frequency from a combination band in the NaCl region? Is any indication of rotational structure observed?

Calculate k_1 and k_δ/l^2 from Eqs. (1) and (3) using your values of ν_1, ν_2, and ν_3. Check the valence force model by calculating both sides of Eq. (2) and comparing them.

Using your values of ν_1, ν_2, and ν_3, calculate $\tilde{C}_v$(vib) at 298 and 500°K from Eq. (7). The quantity u_i is equal to $\nu_i/0.6951T$ when ν_i is in cm^{-1} units. Tables of Einstein functions $u^2e^{-u}/(1 - e^{-u})^2$ are available.[7] Compare the spectroscopic $\tilde{C}_v = 3R + \tilde{C}_v$(vib) with the experimental $\tilde{C}_v$ value obtained from directly measured values[8] of $\tilde{C}_p$; $\tilde{C}_v = \tilde{C}_p - R = 7.3$ cal mole^{-1} deg^{-1} at 298°K and 9.0 at 500°K.

APPARATUS

Infrared spectrometer (single-beam instrument such as Perkin-Elmer Model 12 or 112 or double-beam instrument such as Baird Model AB2, Perkin-Elmer Infracord or Model 21, Beckman IR-4); gas cell with NaCl (or KBr) windows; vacuum line for filling cell; cylinder of SO_2 gas with needle valve.

REFERENCES

1. G. Herzberg, "Molecular Spectra and Molecular Structure II. Infrared and Raman Spectra of Polyatomic Molecules," p. 285, Van Nostrand, Princeton, N.J. (1945).
2. *Ibid.,* pp. 251–261.
3. *Ibid.,* pp. 261–269.
4. *Ibid.,* pp. 168–172.
5. W. J. Moore, "Physical Chemistry," 2d ed., pp. 359–360, Prentice-Hall, Englewood Cliffs, N.J. (1955); or M. Dole, "Introduction to Statistical Thermodynamics," chaps. 9 and 10, Prentice-Hall, Englewood Cliffs, N.J. (1954).
6. W. West, Spectroscopy and Spectrophotometry, in A. Weissberger (ed.), "Technique of Organic Chemistry," 2d ed., vol. I, part II, chap. XXI, Interscience, New York (1949).
7. K. S. Pitzer, "Quantum Chemistry," Appendix 13, Prentice-Hall, Englewood Cliffs, N.J. (1953).
8. G. N. Lewis and M. Randall, "Thermodynamics and the Free Energy of Chemical Substances," p. 80, McGraw-Hill, New York (1923).

GENERAL READING

G. Herzberg, *op. cit.,* chaps. II and III.
W. West, *op. cit.*

Experiment 42. Rotation-Vibration Spectrum of HCl

This experiment is concerned with the rotational fine structure of the infrared vibrational spectrum of HCl. From an interpretation of the details of this spectrum it is possible to obtain the moment of inertia of the molecule and thus the internuclear separation. In addition, the pure vibrational frequency determines a force constant which is a measure of the bond strength. By a study of DCl also, the isotope effect can be observed.

THEORY

The simplest model of a vibrating diatomic molecule is a harmonic oscillator, for which the potential energy depends quadratically on the change in internuclear distance. The allowed energy levels of a harmonic oscillator, as calculated from quantum mechanics,[1] are

$$E(v) = h\nu(v + \tfrac{1}{2}) \tag{1}$$

where v is the vibrational quantum number having integral values 0, 1, 2, . . . , ν is the vibrational frequency, and h is Planck's constant.

The simplest model of a rotating diatomic molecule is a rigid rotor or "dumbbell" model in which the two atoms of mass m_1 and m_2 are considered to be joined by a rigid, weightless rod. The allowed energy levels for a rigid rotor may be shown by quantum mechanics[1] to be

$$E(J) = \frac{h^2}{8\pi^2 I} J(J + 1) \tag{2}$$

where the rotational quantum number J may take integral values 0, 1, 2, ... The quantity I is the moment of inertia, which is related to the internuclear distance r and the reduced mass $\mu = m_1 m_2/(m_1 + m_2)$ by

$$I = \mu r^2 \tag{3}$$

Since a real molecule is undergoing both rotation and vibration simultaneously, a first approximation to its energy levels $E(v,J)$ would be the sum of expressions (1) and (2). A more complete expression for the energy levels of a diatomic molecule[2,3] is given below, with the levels expressed as *term values* T in cm^{-1} units rather than as energy values E in ergs:

$$T(v,J) = \frac{E(v,J)}{hc} = \tilde{\nu}_e\left(v + \frac{1}{2}\right) - x_e\tilde{\nu}_e\left(v + \frac{1}{2}\right)^2 + B_e J(J + 1) - D_e J^2(J + 1)^2 - \alpha_e\left(v + \frac{1}{2}\right)J(J + 1) \tag{4}$$

where $\tilde{\nu}_e$ is the frequency in cm^{-1} for the molecule vibrating about its equilibrium internuclear separation r_e and

$$B_e = \frac{h}{8\pi^2 I_e c} \tag{5}$$

The first and third terms on the right-hand side of Eq. (4) are the harmonic-oscillator and rigid-rotor terms with r equal r_e. The second term (involving the constant x_e) takes into account the effect of anharmonicity. Since the real potential $V(r)$ for a molecule differs from a harmonic potential V_{harm} (see Fig. 1), the real vibrational levels are not quite those given by Eq. (1) and a correction term is required. The fourth term (involving the constant D_e) takes into account the effect of centrifugal stretching. Since a chemical bond is not truly rigid but more like a stiff spring, it stretches somewhat when the molecule rotates. Such an effect is

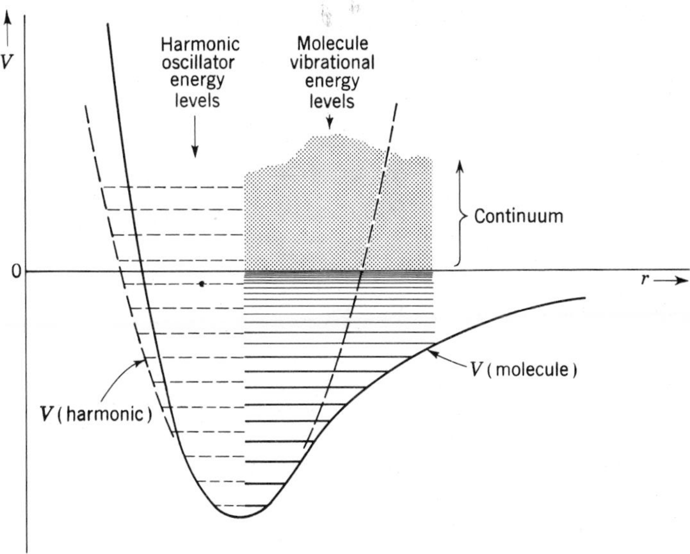

FIG. 1. Schematic diagram showing potential energy V as a function of internuclear separation r for a diatomic molecule. The harmonic potential V_{harm} is indicated by the dashed curve. The vibrational levels are also shown.

important only for high J values, since the constant D_e is very small; we shall neglect this term. The last term in Eq. (4) accounts for interaction between vibration and rotation. During a vibration the internuclear distance r changes; this changes the moment of inertia and affects the rotation of the molecule. The constant α_e is also quite small, but this term should not be neglected.

Selection Rules. The harmonic-oscillator, rigid-rotor selection rules[3] are $\Delta v = \pm 1$ and $\Delta J = \pm 1$; that is, infrared emission or absorption can occur only when these "allowed" transitions take place. For an anharmonic diatomic molecule, the $\Delta J = \pm 1$ selection rule is still valid but transitions corresponding to $\Delta v = \pm 2$, ± 3, etc. (overtones) can now be observed weakly.[3] Since we are interested in the most intense absorption band (the "fundamental"), we are concerned with transitions from various J levels of the vibrational ground state ($v = 0$) to J' levels in the first excited vibrational state ($v' = 1$). From the selection rule we know that the transition must be from J to $J' = J \pm 1$. Since $\Delta E = h\nu = hc\tilde{\nu}$, the frequency $\tilde{\nu}$ (in wavenumbers) for this transition will be just $T(v', J') - T(v, J)$. When $\Delta J = +1$ ($J' = J + 1$) and $\Delta J = -1$ ($J' = J - 1$), we find, respectively, from Eq. (4) that

$$\tilde{\nu}_R = \tilde{\nu}_0 + (2B_e - 3\alpha_e) + (2B_e - 4\alpha_e)J - \alpha_e J^2 \qquad J = 0, 1, 2, \ldots \tag{6}$$

$$\tilde{\nu}_P = \tilde{\nu}_0 - (2B_e - 2\alpha_e)J - \alpha_e J^2 \qquad J = 1, 2, 3, \ldots \tag{7}$$

where $\tilde{\nu}_0$, the frequency of the *forbidden* transition from $v = 0$, $J = 0$ to $v' = 1$, $J = 0$, is

$$\tilde{\nu}_0 = \tilde{\nu}_e - 2\tilde{\nu}_e x_e \tag{8}$$

The two series of lines given in Eqs. (6) and (7) are called R and P branches, respectively. These allowed transitions are indicated in the energy-level diagram Fig. 2. If α_e were negligible, Eqs. (6) and (7) would predict a series of equally spaced lines with separation $2B_e$ except for a missing line at $\tilde{\nu}_0$. The effect of interaction

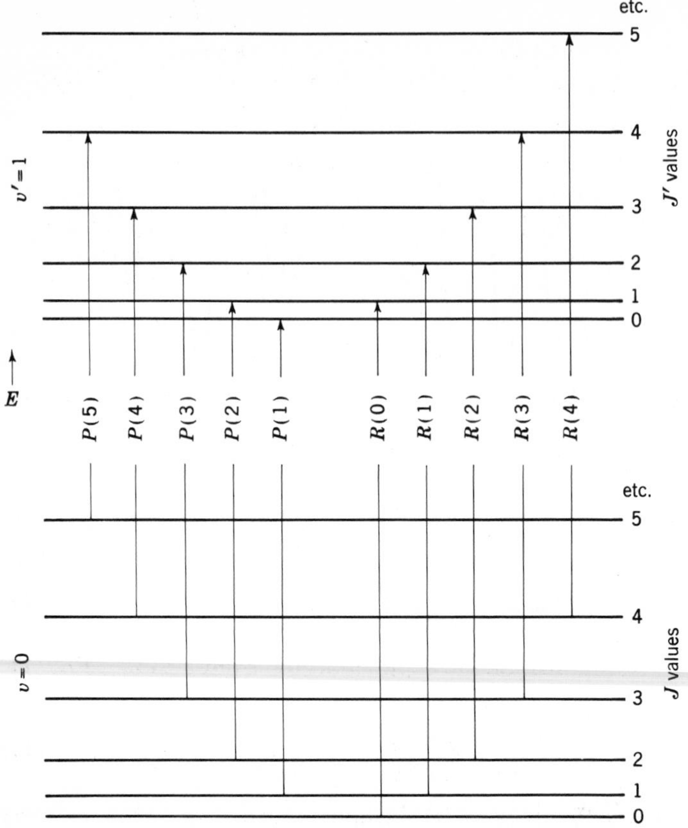

FIG. 2. Rotational energy levels for the ground vibrational state ($v = 0$) and the first excited vibrational state ($v' = 1$) in a diatomic molecule. The vertical arrows indicate allowed transitions in the R and P branches; numbers in parentheses index the value J of the lower state. Transitions in the Q branch ($\Delta J = 0$) are not shown since they are not infrared active.

between rotation and vibration (nonzero α_e) is to draw the lines in the R branch closer together and spread the lines in the P branch farther apart as shown for a typical spectrum in Fig. 3. For convenience let us introduce a new quantity m, where $m = J + 1$ for the R branch and $m = -J$ for the P branch as shown in Fig. 3. It is now possible to replace Eqs. (6) and (7) by a single equation

$$\tilde{\nu} = \tilde{\nu}_0 + (2B_e - 2\alpha_e)m - \alpha_e m^2 \tag{9}$$

where m takes all integral values except zero. The separation between adjacent lines $\Delta\tilde{\nu}(m)$ will be

$$\Delta\tilde{\nu}(m) = \tilde{\nu}(m + 1) - \tilde{\nu}(m) = (2B_e - 3\alpha_e) - 2\alpha_e m \tag{10}$$

Thus a plot of $\Delta\tilde{\nu}(m)$ vs. m can be used to determine both B_e and α_e. With these known, $\tilde{\nu}_0$ can be obtained from any of the lines by using Eq. (9).

Isotope Effect. When an isotopic substitution is made in a diatomic molecule, the equilibrium bond length r_e and the force constant k are unchanged, since they depend only on the behavior of the bonding electrons. However, the reduced mass μ does change, and this will affect the vibration and rotation of the molecule. For a harmonic oscillator model, the frequency ν_{harm} is given by[1]

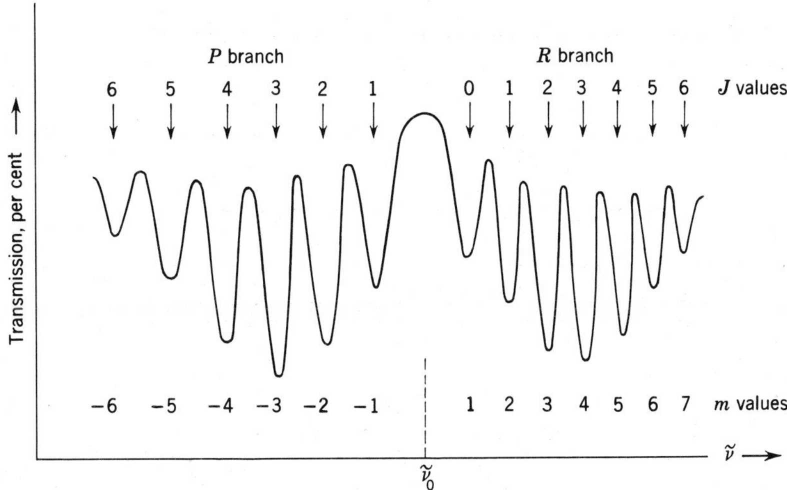

FIG. 3. Schematic rotation-vibration infrared spectrum for a diatomic molecule.

$$\nu_{harm} = \frac{1}{2\pi}\left(\frac{k}{\mu}\right)^{1/2} \tag{11}$$

If an asterisk is used to distinguish one isotopic molecule from another, Eq. (11) leads to the relation

$$\frac{\nu^*_{harm}}{\nu_{harm}} = \left(\frac{\mu}{\mu^*}\right)^{1/2} \tag{12}$$

For a real molecule the anharmonicity should be taken into account,[3] but since this is complicated and would require information from overtone vibrations ($\Delta v > 1$), we shall take Eq. (12) as an approximation and state that $\tilde{\nu}_0^*/\tilde{\nu}_0$ should be close to $(\mu/\mu^*)^{1/2}$. In the case of rotation, the isotope effect can be easily stated. From the definitions of B_e and I, we see that

$$\frac{B_e^*}{B_e} = \frac{\mu}{\mu^*} \tag{13}$$

Since HCl gas is a mixture of HCl^{35} and HCl^{37} molecules, an isotope effect should be present. However, HCl is predominantly HCl^{35} and the ratio of the reduced masses is only 1.0015; therefore only quite high resolution work would detect this effect. For this experiment, we shall assume that the HCl bands obtained are those of HCl^{35}.

If deuterium is substituted for hydrogen, the ratio of the reduced masses, $\mu(DCl^{35})/\mu(HCl^{35})$, is 1.395. Thus there should be a very large isotope effect.

EXPERIMENTAL

A general description of infrared experimental techniques is given in Exp. 41. For this experiment high resolution is required; an LiF (or CaF_2) prism or a grating must be used. In addition, a careful calibration is required; CO and CH_4 are suitable gases for checking the calibration if this is necessary. Detailed instructions for operating the spectrometer will be given in the laboratory. **Use this instrument carefully.**

The cell design and procedure for filling the cell are identical with those described in Exp. 41. Hydrogen chloride gas is available commercially in small cylinders. Make several rapid scans of the HCl spectrum at various pressures to determine what pressure gives the best spectrum, and then record the spectrum at a very slow chart speed. Narrow slit widths are necessary to obtain the desired sharp bands.

Preparation of DCl. If DCl gas is not available in a commercial cylinder or bulb, it must be prepared in the laboratory. Deuterium chloride gas can be synthesized readily by the reaction between benzoyl chloride and heavy water:

$$\begin{aligned} C_6H_5COCl + D_2O &\rightarrow C_6H_5COOD + DCl(g) \\ C_6H_5COOD + C_6H_5COCl &\rightarrow (C_6H_5CO)_2O + DCl(g) \end{aligned} \tag{14}$$

An arrangement for carrying out this reaction is shown in Fig. 4. Approximately 5 ml (0.3 mole) of D_2O in the separatory funnel *S* is added slowly to 140 g (1 mole) of benzoyl chloride in flask *F*. With a water-cooled reflux condenser *C* attached and either ice or Dry Ice and acetone in trap T_1, the flask is gently heated. Stopcocks *A* and *B* are left open, and the system is swept out by allowing some DCl gas to escape through the mercury bubbler into a hood. Stopcock *B* is then closed, and trap T_2 is cooled with liquid nitrogen. After 20 min remove the heat from flask *F*. Wait a few minutes, then close stopcock *A* and disconnect the ball-and-socket joint *J*. Keep trap T_2 in liquid nitrogen, and attach it to the system used to fill the cell (at stopcock *B* shown in Fig. 41-4). After the line is pumped out, the cell can be filled by allowing the DCl in the trap to warm up slowly until the desired pressure is achieved. (If a bulb of DCl gas is available, use the procedure given in Exp. 41.)

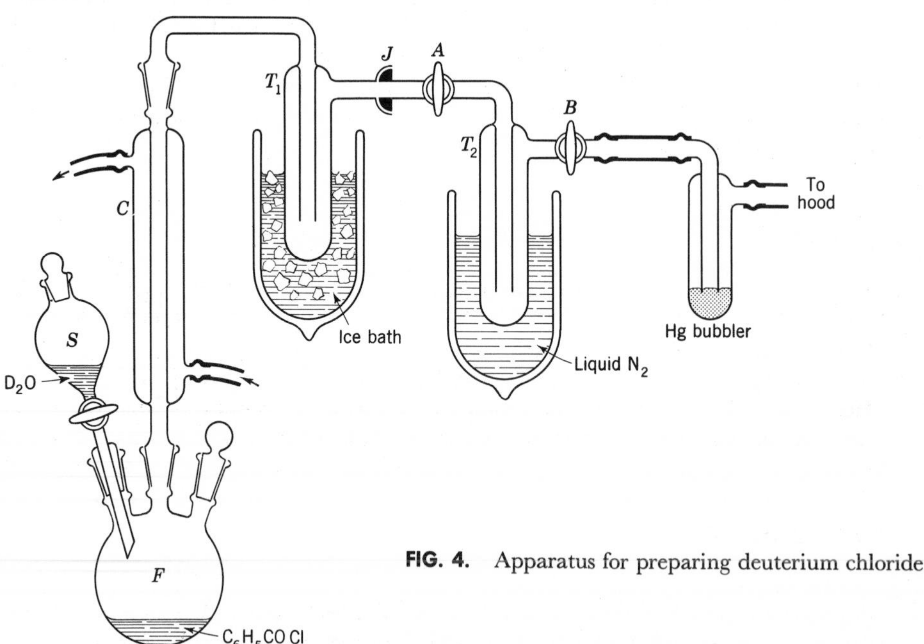

FIG. 4. Apparatus for preparing deuterium chloride.

CALCULATIONS

Select your best HCl and your best DCl spectrum, and index the lines with the appropriate m values (see Fig. 3). Make a table of these m values and the corresponding frequencies $\tilde{\nu}(m)$. Express the frequencies in cm^{-1} units to tenths of a cm^{-1} (if possible). Then list the differences between adjacent lines $\Delta\tilde{\nu}(m)$, which will be roughly $2B_e$ but should vary with m. Plot $\Delta\tilde{\nu}(m)$ against m and draw the best straight line through the points. Compute B_e and α_e from the intercept $(2B_e - 3\alpha_e)$ at $m = 0$ and the slope $(-2\alpha_e)$. Using these B_e and α_e values and Eq. (9), calculate $\tilde{\nu}_0$ from several of the lines with low m values. For both HCl and DCl, present a table of $\tilde{\nu}_0$, B_e, and α_e values all in cm^{-1} units.

Calculate I_e, the moment of inertia, and r_e, the internuclear distance, for both HCl and DCl.

DISCUSSION

Compute the ratios $\tilde{\nu}_0^*/\tilde{\nu}_0$ and B_e^*/B_e and compare them with the predicted values given by Eqs. (12) and (13). Do your spectra show any indications of a Cl^{35}-Cl^{37} isotope effect? Calculate the splitting expected for this effect in HCl and in DCl. Explain the observed band intensities in terms of the Boltzmann population of the ground-state levels.

APPARATUS

High-resolution infrared spectrometer; gas cell with NaCl windows; vacuum line for filling cell; cylinder of HCl gas with needle valve; three-neck round-bottom flask; reflux condenser; glass-stoppered dropping funnel; two traps, one with a stopcock on each arm; mercury bubbler; exhaust hood; bunsen burner or heating mantle; CO and CH_4 gas for calibration check (optional).

Heavy water (5 ml of at least 70 per cent D_2O); benzoyl chloride (140 g); ice or Dry Ice and acetone; liquid nitrogen; or a 5-liter flask of DCl gas (available from Stohler Isotope Chemicals, 92 Beckwith Place, Rutherford, N.J.).

REFERENCES

1. W. J. Moore, "Physical Chemistry," 2d ed., pp. 331–336, Prentice-Hall, Englewood Cliffs, N.J. (1955); or L. Pauling and E. B. Wilson, "Introduction to Quantum Mechanics," McGraw-Hill, New York (1935).
2. K. S. Pitzer, "Quantum Chemistry," Prentice-Hall, Englewood Cliffs, N.J. (1953).
3. G. Herzberg, "Molecular Spectra and Molecular Structure I. Spectra of Diatomic Molecules," 2d ed., chap III, Van Nostrand, Princeton, N.J. (1950).

GENERAL READING

G. Herzberg, *loc. cit.*

W. West, Spectroscopy and Spectrophotometry, in A. Weissberger (ed.), "Technique of Organic Chemistry," 2d ed., vol. I, part II, chap. XXI, Interscience, New York (1949).

Experiment 43. Spectrum of the Hydrogen Atom

Since the hydrogen atom has only one orbital electron surrounding a nucleus consisting of a single proton, it has a particularly simple spectrum. In this experiment, part of this spectrum will be determined. The observed frequencies of the lines can then be compared with the values predicted by quantum mechanics.

THEORY

When a high-voltage discharge takes place in H_2 gas at low pressures, many molecules are dissociated into atoms by electron impact. These atoms are in excited electronic states. Such H atoms in excited electronic states spontaneously undergo transitions to lower energy electronic states with the emission of radiation. Quantum mechanics gives an expression[1, 2] for the allowed electronic energy levels of a H atom in terms of a single quantum number† n;

$$E_n = -\frac{2\pi^2\mu e^4}{h^2}\frac{1}{n^2} \qquad n = 1, 2, 3, \ldots \tag{1}$$

where e is the charge on the electron and h is Planck's constant. The reduced mass μ is given in terms of the mass of the electron m and the mass of the proton M by

$$\mu = \frac{mM}{m + M} \tag{2}$$

There is no selection rule for n; that is, transitions may occur between any of the levels given by Eq. (1). An energy-level diagram for the H atom is given in Fig. 1. Transitions from upper energy levels to lower levels are shown by the vertical lines. These transitions form several series of lines depending on the quantum number of the lower state. Note that the energy levels converge toward a limit as $n \to \infty$. The shaded area above $n = \infty$ indicates a continuum of energy states corresponding to complete separation of the proton and the electron.

We shall be concerned with the Balmer series, the lines of which fall in the visible region of the spectrum. From Eq. (1), it is possible to predict the frequency of a transition from any upper state with quantum number n_1 to any lower state with quantum number n_2, since

$$\Delta E = E_{n_1} - E_{n_2} = h\nu = hc\tilde{\nu} \tag{3}$$

where c is the speed of light and $\tilde{\nu}$ is the frequency in units of cm^{-1} (equal to the reciprocal of the wavelength λ in centimeters). Thus,

$$\tilde{\nu} = \frac{2\pi^2\mu e^4}{h^3c}\left(\frac{1}{{n_2}^2} - \frac{1}{{n_1}^2}\right) = \mathfrak{R}\left(\frac{1}{{n_2}^2} - \frac{1}{{n_1}^2}\right) \tag{4}$$

The quantity $\mathfrak{R}$ is called the *Rydberg constant* and has the calculated value 109,700 cm^{-1}. For the Balmer series, $n_2 = 2$ and $n_1 = 3, 4, 5, \ldots$. Equation (4) predicts a series of lines which converge to a high-frequency limit at $\mathfrak{R}/{n_2}^2$.

† Owing to spin-orbit and quantum electrodynamical effects, the energy levels have a small dependence on another quantum number l, where l can assume any integral value less than n. This energy splitting is very small and can be neglected here.

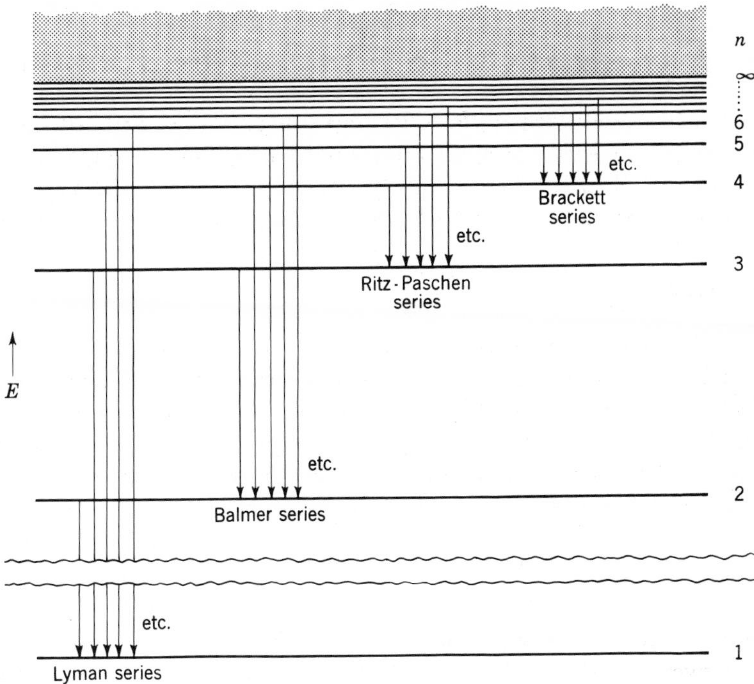

FIG. 1. Electronic energy-level diagram for the hydrogen atom.

METHOD

The frequency (or wavelength) of these Balmer lines can be determined experimentally by comparing the hydrogen spectrum with a reference spectrum for which the wavelengths are known. The iron or mercury spectra are common choices for reference spectra. (Such reference spectral lines must, of course, have been measured absolutely, as by an interferometric technique.) In this experiment, an Hg lamp will be used because the lines of the Hg spectrum can be identified quite easily. In other work the Fe arc is preferable, since there are many more lines (see Exp. 44).

A variety of spectrographs are in current use for work of this kind; although differing in details they are basically similar. Figure 2 shows a schematic diagram

FIG. 2. Spectrograph and source optics, viewed from above. (NOTE: the mirror M is just below the light path from the hydrogen discharge tube.)

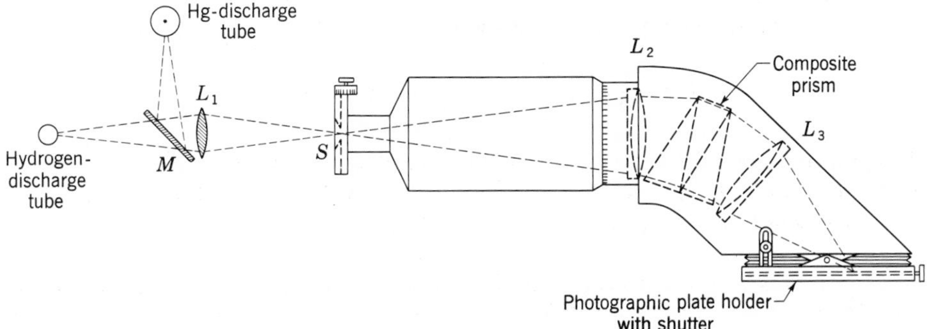

of a typical spectrograph. The sources are mounted in such a way that the hydrogen discharge tube will illuminate half of the entrance slit S and the mercury reference lamp will illuminate the other half. The Hg lamp is off the optical axis of the spectrograph, and a front surfaced mirror M (or a 90° prism) is set at 45° to permit an image of this source to be focused on the slit by lens L_1. The lens L_2 renders the light from the slit parallel before it passes through the dispersing prism P. A camera lens L_3 focuses an image of the slit on the photographic plate.†

The two common prism materials for use in the visible and near-ultraviolet regions are glass and quartz. Glass is preferable in the visible, since it gives a higher dispersion (and therefore better resolution). For wavelengths shorter than about 3000 to 3500 A, most glasses absorb light strongly but quartz prisms may be used. Quartz also begins to absorb light below about 1900 A. Other prism materials (such as fluorite) may be used below 1900 A, but diffraction gratings are generally used in the far ultraviolet. Since the Balmer lines are more and more closely spaced and have decreasing intensity as the short-wavelength limit is approached, both high resolution and long exposures are needed to observe lines with high n_1 values.

Sources. The best Hg source is a low-pressure mercury lamp (General Electric G4T4/1, 4W germicidal lamp) which operates from a small ballast transformer (G.E. 89G435, 0.16 amp, 4-6-8 watts). **There is intense ultraviolet radiation from such a lamp which is dangerous to the eye.** Therefore a Pyrex glass jacket should be placed over the Hg arc to filter out this ultraviolet radiation.

Many designs for hydrogen discharge tubes are available.[3] A convenient commercial hydrogen source is a Geissler tube made by the Tube Light Engineering Co., New York. In this tube the pressure has been adjusted to give strong Balmer lines (0.1 to 0.5 mm). In addition, there is always a weak *band* spectrum due to molecular hydrogen; hydrogen atoms, formed by the electrode discharge, may recombine on the walls to give H_2 molecules in excited electronic states which will emit radiation. Such a band spectrum should be so weak that it will not interfere with determining the Balmer lines. The Geissler discharge tube operates from a neon-sign transformer at about 5000 v and 15 ma; it should glow steadily with a bright red color.

Hg *Reference Spectrum.* A print of the low-pressure Hg arc spectrum is shown in Fig. 3. The upper half of the spectrum was strongly exposed in order to bring out the weak lines, and the lower half was exposed only a short time in order to show the strong lines clearly. The wavelengths of these lines[4] [in air; see Eq. (5)] are given below the spectrum. The spectrum presented in Fig. 3 was made using Kodak 103a-O spectrographic plates; one can also use type 103a-F plates, which are much more sensitive in the long-wavelength end of the visible range.

EXPERIMENTAL

Instructions for the operation of the spectrograph to be used will be given in the laboratory. The placement of the sources and the focus and slit width settings of the spectrograph will be made in advance by the instructor. The sources should

† To align the sources properly, one may open the slit wide and look in at the camera end of the spectrograph. Adjust the source so that it appears in the center of the slit opening. Then close the slit to a narrow opening, and focus the instrument, using the Hg source until the yellow Hg line is well resolved into a doublet sharply focused in the plane of the photographic plate. A ground-glass plate may be placed in the film position and viewed with a small magnifier.

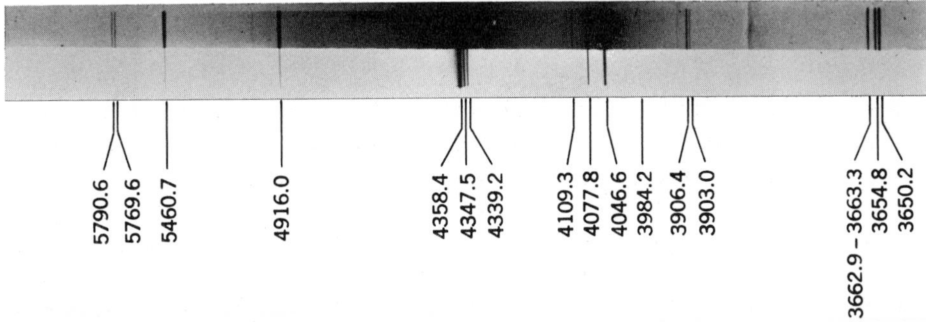

FIG. 3. Mercury-arc reference spectrum. The upper half of this print has been strongly exposed to show the weak lines clearly. The wavelengths (in angstroms) of the Hg lines are given.

be arranged so that one half of the slit is illuminated by the Hg lamp and the other half by the hydrogen discharge tube. A shutter over the slit permits exposures to be made of each source independently without moving the photographic plate. This is important when wavelengths are to be determined by comparison. The photographic plate is placed in a holder which can be raised or lowered to permit several such pairs of spectra to be taken.

The photographic plates are extremely light sensitive. The plate holder must be loaded and unloaded (and developing must be done) in total darkness. The plate should be placed in the holder in such a way that the emulsion side faces the shutter. The emulsion side can be detected in the dark by moistening a finger and touching the plate lightly near an edge. The emulsion side will feel sticky. Having loaded the holder, turn on the lights and place the holder in position on the spectrograph. Set the plate-holder position close to one end of its traverse. Check to see that the slit is properly illuminated by each source. Instructions for operating the sources will be given. The hydrogen discharge tube operates on **high voltage which is possibly lethal;** be very careful. Close the shutter over the slit.

Darken the room and open the shutter on the plate holder. Take an exposure with the hydrogen discharge tube and then with the Hg lamp. Each source should be turned off when not in use. Close the shutter over the slit, move the plate holder, and take another pair of exposures with exposure times different from the first set. Repeat this process several times.

After the final pair of exposures, *close the shutter on the plate holder* and remove the holder from the spectrograph. Turn on the room lights. Set up three developing trays: one with developer, one with water, one with fixer. Set a timer for 3 min. Darken the room and place the plate in developer, *emulsion side up;* start the timer. Agitate gently and remove after 3 min. Drain over the developer tray, rinse briefly in water, and place in the fixer. Allow to remain in the fixer at least 10 min. Lights may be turned on after about 5 min.

Examine the plate. If for some reason the plate is not usable, start over again but omit any long exposures if time does not permit them. If the plate is satisfactory, rinse it under running water for 20 min and then allow it to drain and dry several hours (preferably overnight).

Measurement of Spectral Lines. If a comparator is available, mount the plate on the stage, focus on a suitable pair of exposures, and align the plate so that the spectral lines at both ends of the plate are parallel with the cross hair of the microscope. Starting at one end of the plate, move the stage or microscope until a line is under the cross hair and record the position. Continue this process for all lines, both Hg and H atom (disregard the H_2 molecular band spectrum). Always approach a line from the same direction to avoid errors due to backlash in the screw.

If a comparator is not available, a good enlarger may be used instead. Mount the plate in the enlarger, and project the spectra onto a large sheet of white paper mounted on a drafting board. Choose a suitable pair of exposures and mark the positions of all Hg lines and all H atom lines (disregard H_2 molecular band spectrum) with a sharp pencil. Avoid working near the edge of the image, where there may be distortion. Using a centimeter scale, measure the positions of all lines relative to some arbitrary zero position. Indicate which lines are Hg and which H.

Compare your Hg spectrum with that shown in Fig. 3, and assign wavelengths to all Hg lines. On a large piece of graph paper, plot a calibration curve of Hg wavelengths vs. position in centimeters. Read the wavelengths λ of the hydrogen lines from this curve.

CALCULATIONS

Obtain the frequencies of the Balmer lines $\tilde{\nu}$ (in cm^{-1}) from the wavelength values λ (in A). Present a table of both $\tilde{\nu}$ and λ values together with the value of n_1 for each line observed.

Plot $\tilde{\nu}$ against $1/n_1{}^2$ on a large sheet of graph paper. If the points fall on a straight line, this is a partial confirmation of Eq. (4). From the slope of this line, determine an experimental value of $\mathfrak{R}$. In all this work, wavelengths in air have been used; these are related to vacuum wavelengths by

$$\lambda_{\text{air}} = \frac{\lambda_{\text{vac}}}{n_{\text{air}}} \tag{5}$$

where n_{air} is the index of refraction of air which equals 1.00027 at these wavelengths. To obtain a value of $\mathfrak{R}$ referred to vacuum, one must divide the experimental value by n_{air}. Compare your vacuum value of $\mathfrak{R}$ with the theoretical value.†

DISCUSSION

Show that a typical line in the Lyman series ($n_2 = 1$) lies in the ultraviolet and that a typical line in the Ritz-Paschen series ($n_2 = 3$) lies in the infrared.

Why do the Balmer lines become weaker toward shorter wavelengths? (The first Balmer line at about 6500 A may appear weak owing to poor film sensitivity in the red; it is actually the most intense of all the lines.) What are some experimental factors which influence the line width?

APPARATUS

Spectrograph; low-pressure mercury lamp; hydrogen discharge tube; mounts and power supplies for both sources; front surface mirror; lens; spectroscopic plates (Kodak 103a-F); three developing trays; developer (Kodak D19); acid fixer; flashlight; timer; darkroom.

Comparator microscope; *or* enlarger, drawing board, T square and triangle, good centimeter scale.

† The experimental value[2] of $\mathfrak{R}$ (109,677.581 cm^{-1}) using vacuum wavelengths is known with greater precision than the theoretical value, which is affected by uncertainties in e, h, c, and μ.

REFERENCES

1. W. J. Moore, "Physical Chemistry," 2d ed., p. 262, Prentice-Hall, Englewood Cliffs, N.J. (1955).
2. G. Herzberg, "Atomic Spectra and Atomic Structure," 2d ed., pp. 11–38, Dover, New York (1944).
3. G. R. Harrison, R. C. Lord, and J. R. Loofbourow, "Practical Spectroscopy," pp. 188–192, Prentice-Hall, Englewood Cliffs, N.J. (1948).
4. K. W. F. Kohlrausch, "Ramanspektren," p. 34, Becker and Erler, Leipzig (1943).

GENERAL READING

H. E. White, "Introduction to Atomic Spectra," McGraw-Hill, New York (1934).

Experiment 44. Band Spectrum of Nitrogen

Spectra which are observed in the visible and ultraviolet regions arise from transitions between electronic states. For atomic gases, such electronic spectra consist of individual sharp lines, as shown by the mercury spectrum in Fig. 43-3. For molecular gases, the transitions take place between different rotational-vibrational levels of the upper and lower electronic states and a very large number of lines occur. Under low resolution, groups of lines very close together have the appearance of broad bands in the spectrum. Therefore, such molecular spectra are referred to as *band spectra.*

In this experiment, part of the emission spectrum of nitrogen is to be determined and its vibrational structure analyzed. Homonuclear diatomic molecules, such as N_2, have no infrared spectrum[1] and are experimentally difficult to study by Raman spectroscopy. Thus electronic band spectra provide the most convenient source of vibrational and rotational constants. Since upper vibrational levels are involved, the effect of anharmonicity is easily detected.

THEORY

For a visible emission spectrum, transitions occur from excited electronic states to lower energy electronic states. There are many electronic states for N_2, and the energy-level diagram is quite complex[2] in contrast to the simple diagram for the hydrogen atom shown in Fig. 43-1. We shall discuss only the bands of the "second positive group," which are those to be observed in the present experiment. These bands arise from transitions from the $^3\Pi_u$ electronic state (denoted by C) to the $^3\Pi_g$ state (denoted by B), both of which are excited states. However, the theory presented here is typical of most electronic transitions for diatomic molecules.

Associated with each electronic state there is a characteristic potential curve which represents the potential energy of the nuclei as a function of their internuclear separation r. The potential curves for states B and C of N_2 are given schematically in Fig. 1; allowed vibrational levels are shown by the horizontal lines, while rotational levels have been omitted for clarity. In general, there is different bonding involved in two different electronic states. As a result the two curves do not have their minima at the same value of r and do not have exactly the same shape.

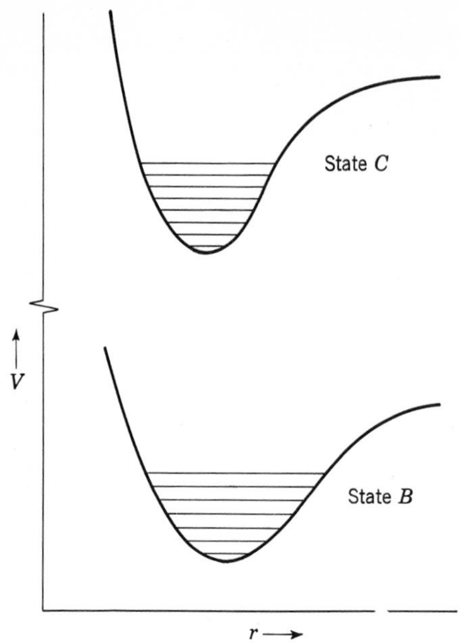

FIG. 1. Schematic potential energy curves for two excited electronic states of N_2. (B is the $^3\Pi_g$ state; C is the $^3\Pi_u$ state.) A few vibrational levels are shown.

The total energy of a diatomic molecule may be separated into translational energy and internal energy. We are concerned here with the internal energy which can be expressed to a good approximation by

$$E = E_{el} + E_v + E_r \tag{1}$$

where E_r is the rotational energy, E_v is the vibrational energy, and E_{el} is the electronic energy. This electronic energy E_{el} refers to the minimum value of the potential curve for a given electronic state. The zero of energy is arbitrarily taken as the minimum in the potential curve for the lowest electronic state (ground state). It is convenient to divide Eq. (1) by the quantity hc to get the so-called "term value" T which has units of cm^{-1}. Thus

$$T = T_{el} + T_v + T_r \tag{2}$$

The advantage in this change is that the frequency $\tilde{\nu}$ (expressed in cm^{-1}) for a transition between two electronic states can be simply expressed by

$$\tilde{\nu} \equiv T' - T'' = (T'_{el} - T''_{el}) + (T'_v - T''_v) + (T'_r - T''_r) \tag{3}$$

where the *single prime* refers to the *upper state* and the *double prime* refers to the *lower state.* Now let us denote $(T'_{el} - T''_{el})$ by $\tilde{\nu}_{el}$. For a given band system involving transitions from the same upper electronic state to the same lower electronic state, $\tilde{\nu}_{el}$ is a constant; in the case of the second positive group of N_2, $hc\tilde{\nu}_{el}$ corresponds to the energy separation between the minima of curves C and B in Fig. 1.

Vibrational Structure. Since rotational energies are usually small compared with vibrational energies, it will be possible to neglect $(T'_r - T''_r)$ in Eq. (3) in order to discuss the vibrational structure of a band spectrum. In essence, this amounts to considering transitions among states without rotational energy. Corresponding to each spectral *line* expected on this basis, there is observed experimentally a *band* of very closely spaced lines resulting from the rotational structure which we are neglecting. From quantum mechanics,[3] one obtains for an anharmonic oscillator the approximate expression

$$T_v = \tilde{\nu}_e(v + \tfrac{1}{2}) - \tilde{\nu}_e x_e (v + \tfrac{1}{2})^2 + \cdots \tag{4}$$

where the vibrational quantum number v has integral values 0, 1, 2, 3, ... (Note that $\tilde{\nu}_e$ is not to be confused with $\tilde{\nu}_{el}$ introduced earlier.) The term in $\tilde{\nu}_e x_e$ takes into account the effect of anharmonicity; in general there are cubic and higher terms in $(v + \tfrac{1}{2})$, but these are much smaller than the quadratic term, and we shall neglect them in Eq. (4). We can now write Eq. (3) as

$$\tilde{\nu} = \tilde{\nu}_{el} + (T'_v - T''_v) \tag{5a}$$

$$= \tilde{\nu}_{el} + \tilde{\nu}'_e(v' + \tfrac{1}{2}) - \tilde{\nu}'_e x'_e (v' + \tfrac{1}{2})^2 - [\tilde{\nu}''_e(v'' + \tfrac{1}{2}) - \tilde{\nu}''_e x''_e (v'' + \tfrac{1}{2})^2] \tag{5b}$$

By writing

$$\tilde{\nu}_{00} = \tilde{\nu}_{el} + \tfrac{1}{2}(\tilde{\nu}'_e - \tilde{\nu}''_e) - \tfrac{1}{4}(\tilde{\nu}'_e x'_e - \tilde{\nu}''_e x''_e) \tag{6a}$$

$$\tilde{\nu}_0 = \tilde{\nu}_e - \tilde{\nu}_e x_e \qquad \tilde{\nu}_0 x_0 = \tilde{\nu}_e x_e \tag{6b}$$

Eq. (5) can be simplified to

$$\tilde{\nu} = \tilde{\nu}_{00} + \tilde{\nu}'_0 v' - \tilde{\nu}'_0 x'_0 v'^2 - (\tilde{\nu}''_0 v'' - \tilde{\nu}''_0 x''_0 v''^2) \tag{7}$$

Obviously, $\tilde{\nu}_{00}$ is the frequency of the transition from $v' = 0$ (in the upper state) to $v'' = 0$ (in the lower state) which is called the 0-0 band. Since there is no selection rule for the quantum number v, any v' value can be combined with any v'' value in Eq. (7) and we should expect a large number of "lines" (bands).

When the separation between vibrational levels in the upper electronic state and in the lower electronic state is not greatly different (that is, $\tilde{\nu}'_0$ close to $\tilde{\nu}''_0$), the vibrational transitions form groups in the spectrum called sequences. For each sequence, $\Delta v (= v' - v'')$ is a constant. Such behavior occurs for N_2 and simplifies the analysis of the bands in the second positive group as seen from Fig. 2.

Once the vibrational transitions in the spectrum have been assigned and the frequencies measured, it is convenient to organize the values of $\tilde{\nu}_{v' \to v''}$ into a *Deslandres table*. As an example, a portion of such a table for PN vapor[4] is presented in Table 1. Note that the frequencies along diagonals (which correspond to bands with the same Δv) lie close together as shown by the schematic spectrum in Fig. 2. Now consider the first two rows in the table. Since the frequencies are for transitions from two adjacent upper vibrational states ($v' = 0$ and $v' = 1$) to common lower vibrational states ($v'' = 0$, 1, 2, or 3), there should be a constant separation between the rows—a separation corresponding to the upper state vibrational sepa-

TABLE 1. Deslandres Table of PN Bands[4]

(Band-head frequencies in cm^{-1}. Differences between the entries in rows 0 and 1, 1 and 2 are in italics.)

v' \ v''	0	1	2	3	Average differences
0	39,698.8	38,376.5	37,068.7	. . . .	
	1,087.4	*1,090.7*	*1,086.8*		*1088*
1	40,786.2	39,467.2	38,155.5	36,861.3	
	1,072.9	*1,069.0*		*1,071.6*	*1071*
2	41,859.1	40,536.2	. . . .	37,932.9	
3	. . . .	41,597.4	40,288.3		

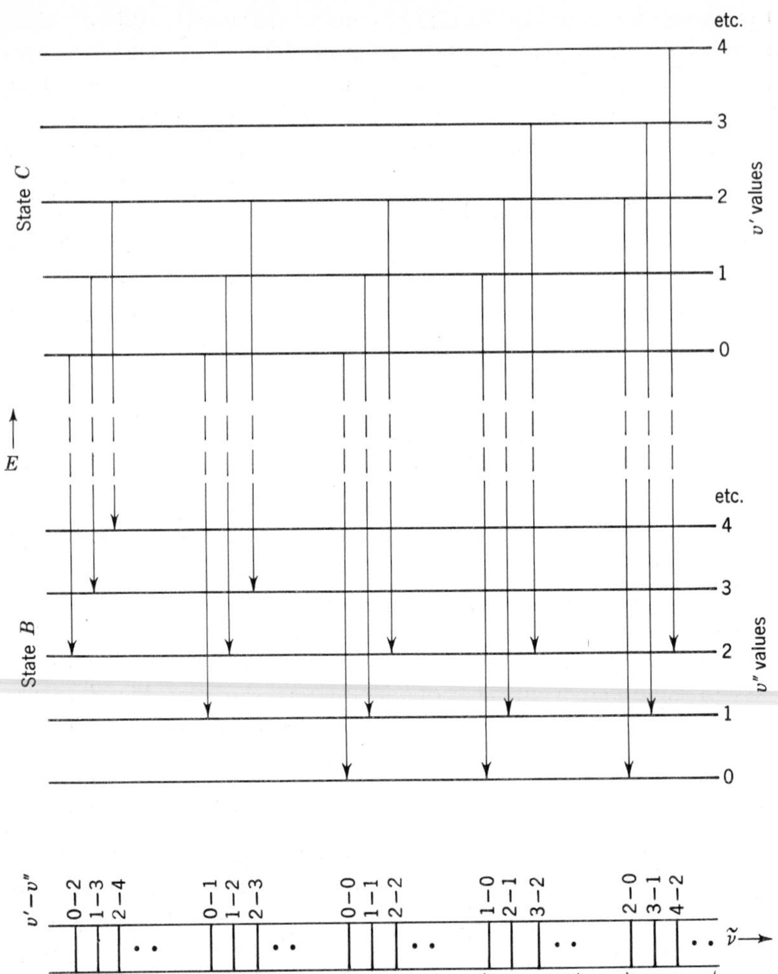

FIG. 2. Vibrational energy levels for states B and C of N_2. The vertical arrows indicate transitions; transitions with the same Δv are grouped together to form sequences. The resulting vibrational-electronic "line" spectrum is shown at the bottom (for clarity only the first three lines in each sequence are shown).

ration ($T'_{v=1} - T'_{v=0}$), as seen from Eq. (5a). The separation between the rows $v' = 1$ and $v' = 2$ will give ($T'_{v=2} - T'_{v=1}$), and so forth. The separation between successive rows should decrease as v' increases owing to the effect of anharmonicity; see Eq. (4). In exactly the same way, the separation between adjacent columns will give information about the vibrational levels of the lower electronic state. Agreement among the separations between corresponding frequencies of two rows (or two columns) is a definite check on the correctness of the entries in the Deslandres table. Inspection of the differences given in Table 1 shows a slight variation which is, however, greater than the experimental error. This is caused by the use of band-head frequencies as discussed below.

Rotational Structure. There are two deficiencies with the theory as presented so far: Eq. (7) predicts a spectrum of lines rather than the observed bands, and the differences in the Deslandres table are not quite constant as they should be. Both of these failures are due to the neglect of rotational transitions. For each electronic-vibrational transition discussed above, there are many rotational transitions which give rise to a large number of closely spaced lines in the vicinity of each $\tilde{\nu}$ as given by Eq. (7). The theory of this rotational fine structure is too complex for presentation here, especially since it involves an interaction between rotational and electronic motions in the molecule. In addition very high resolution is required to observe this fine structure experimentally. Under low resolution, the rotational lines will create the appearance of a band usually having at one end an abrupt change in intensity, called the *band head,* while the intensity falls off slowly at the other end.

This experiment will deal with these easily observed band heads in spite of the fact that Eq. (7) is valid only for the band origins $\tilde{\nu}_0$. (The origin is the position in the band that corresponds to a transition between vibrational states without rotational energy.) Fortunately, the difference $\tilde{\nu}_{\text{head}} - \tilde{\nu}_0$ is small for N_2, varying from about -5 to -10 cm^{-1}. The use of band-head frequencies rather than band origins in Table 1 accounts for the slight lack of constancy in the separations, since $\tilde{\nu}_{\text{head}} - \tilde{\nu}_0$ varies somewhat.

Assignment of Bands. Herzberg[5] discusses the vibrational assignment of a band system when clear sequences are observed on both sides of the 0-0 band. For this experiment, one may take one or two band heads as known from the literature and then assign the others from the sequence pattern shown in Fig. 2. Constancy of the differences in the Deslandres table will confirm the assignment.

EXPERIMENTAL

The method for determining the band spectrum of nitrogen is the same as that described in Exp. 43 for the study of the Balmer lines of hydrogen. It differs only in replacing the hydrogen discharge tube by a nitrogen discharge tube and using an iron arc for the reference spectrum instead of a mercury arc. For this experiment, the richer spectrum of lines from the iron arc is an advantage in obtaining accurate values of the wavelengths of the band heads for N_2.

Sources. A simple design for an iron arc[6] is shown in Fig. 3. An iron oxide bead is used to stabilize the arc, which may be started by shorting the gap with a carbon rod. Excellent reproductions of the Fe arc spectrum together with the wavelengths of all the lines can be found in the literature.[7] The nitrogen source is a Geissler discharge tube (commercially available from Tube Light Engineering Co., New York) in which N_2 molecules are excited by an electrode discharge into upper electronic states. Such excited molecules will spontaneously undergo transitions to lower electronic states and in the process emit radiation. The discharge tube operates from a neon-sign transformer at about 5000 v and 15 ma; it should glow steadily with a pale greenish-blue color.

Procedure. Follow the procedure given in the experimental section of Exp. 43 to obtain several pairs of N_2 and Fe spectra. It may be convenient at the end to include one pair of exposures consisting of an Fe spectrum and a Hg spectrum. This will facilitate identification of the iron lines.

The lines should be measured using a microscope comparator as described in Exp. 43. Since the iron reference spectrum contains many closely spaced lines, it is not necessary to plot a calibration curve. Record the position of every N_2 band

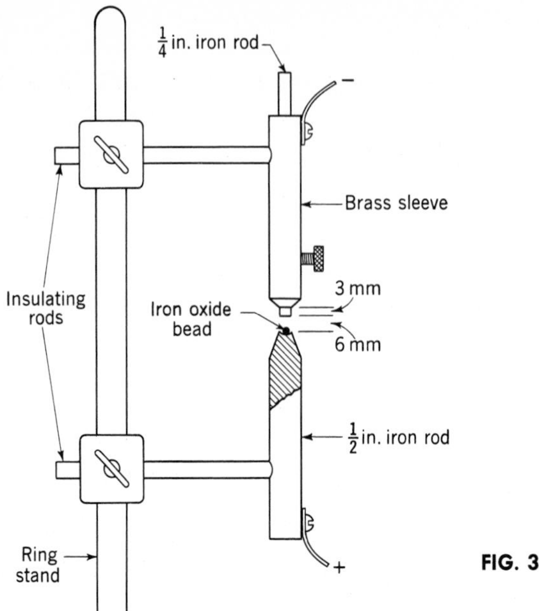

FIG. 3. Iron arc.

head together with the position of one Fe line on each side of the band head. Choose Fe lines which are as close to the band head position as possible. Determine the wavelength of the band head by linear interpolation between these iron lines. A proper identification of the iron lines is crucial; checking them against a Hg spectrum may help. Make a list of the wavelengths (in angstroms) and the frequencies (in cm^{-1}) of all band heads measured.

CALCULATIONS

Several band-head wavelengths for the second positive group of N_2 can be obtained from Fig. 8*a* in Herzberg[8] as an aid to assignment. Assign the v' and v'' values for all band heads observed, and construct a Deslandres table of the frequencies. Indicate in this table the differences, and check their constancy to verify the assignment. Along the bottom and right-hand side of the table, record the average values of the differences between v' and v'' levels, respectively.

Draw a vibrational energy-level diagram for both electronic states like that shown in Fig. 2, and indicate on it the separation in cm^{-1} units between those levels for which the differences $T'_{v+1} - T'_v$ or $T''_{v+1} - T''_v$ are given in the Deslandres table. Use the average values of the differences as recorded in the table.

From Eq. (4) we see that

$$T_{v+1} - T_v = \tilde{\nu}_e - 2\tilde{\nu}_e x_e(v + 1) \tag{8}$$

Using this equation and the separations in the energy-level diagram, determine the best values of the vibrational constants $\tilde{\nu}''_e$ and $\tilde{\nu}''_e x''_e$ for the lower electronic state *B* and the best values of $\tilde{\nu}'_e$ and $\tilde{\nu}'_e x'_e$ for the upper state *C*. From Eqs. (6*b*) and Eq. (7), calculate a value of $\tilde{\nu}_{00}$ using several frequencies from the Deslandres table. Make a table of your values of $\tilde{\nu}''_e$, $\tilde{\nu}''_e x''_e$, $\tilde{\nu}'_e$, $\tilde{\nu}'_e x'_e$, and $\tilde{\nu}_{00}$ and compare them with the literature values given by Herzberg.[9]

DISCUSSION

Is the rotational fine structure resolved in any of the bands studied? If so, compare it qualitatively with the high-resolution spectrum of the 0-2 band given in Herzberg[10] and indicate whether you feel rotational analysis would be possible from your spectrum.

With the data obtained, it is possible to assign the energies of all vibrational levels in both electronic states with respect to the zero of energy taken as the minimum in the potential curve of the ground state if the literature value of the separation between the ground state and state B is known. Such a tabulation on the energy-level diagram may be made if desired.

APPARATUS

Medium-resolution spectrograph; nitrogen discharge tube; iron arc; low-pressure mercury lamp (optional); mounts and power supplies for all sources; front-surface mirror; lens; spectroscopic plates (Kodak 103a-F); three developing trays; developer (Kodak D19); acid fixer; flashlight; timer; darkroom.

Comparator microscope; reproduction of the iron arc spectrum.[7]

REFERENCES

1. G. Herzberg, "Molecular Spectra and Molecular Structure I. Spectra of Diatomic Molecules," 2d ed., pp. 80, 131, Van Nostrand, Princeton, N.J. (1950).
2. *Ibid.,* p. 449.
3. *Ibid.,* p. 151.
4. *Ibid.,* pp. 40–42.
5. *Ibid.,* p. 161.
6. J. Strong, "Procedures in Experimental Physics," p. 351, Prentice-Hall, Englewood Cliffs, N.J. (1939).
7. W. R. Brode, "Chemical Spectroscopy," 2d ed., pp. 619–654, Wiley, New York (1943).
8. G. Herzberg, *op. cit.,* p. 32.
9. *Ibid.,* Table 39, p. 552.
10. *Ibid.,* p. 46.

GENERAL READING

G. Herzberg, *op. cit.,* chap. IV.

XIV

SOLIDS

EXPERIMENTS

Experiment 45. Determination of Crystal Structure by X-ray Diffraction

The object of this experiment is to determine the crystal structure of a solid substance from X-ray powder diffraction patterns. This involves determination of the symmetry classification (cubic, hexagonal, etc.), the type of crystal lattice (simple, body-centered, or face-centered), the dimensions of the unit cell, the number of atoms or ions of each kind in the unit cell, and the position of every atom or ion in the unit cell. Owing to inherent limitations of the powder method only substances in the cubic system should be chosen for study.

Knowledge of the crystal structure permits determination of the coordination number (the number of nearest neighbors) for each kind of atom or ion, calculation of interatomic distances, and elucidation of other structural features related to the nature of chemical binding and the understanding of physical properties in the solid state.

THEORY

A perfect crystal constitutes the repetition of a single very small unit of structure, called the *unit cell,* in a regular way so as to fill the volume occupied by the crystal (see Fig. 1).

A crystal may for some purposes be described in terms of a set of three *crystal axes* **a**, **b**, and **c**, which may or may not be of equal length and/or at right angles, depending on the symmetry of the crystal. These axes form the basis for a coordinate system with which the crystal may be described. An important property of crystals, known at least a century before the discovery of X rays, is that for any crystal the crystal axes can be so chosen that all crystal faces can be described by equations of the form

$$hx + ky + lz = \text{positive constant} \tag{1}$$

where x, y, and z are the coordinates of any point on a given crystal face, in a coordinate system with axes parallel to the assigned crystal axes and with units equal to the assigned axial lengths a, b, c; and where h, k, and l are *small integers,* positive, negative, or zero. This is known as the law of rational indices. The integers h, k, and l are known as the *Miller indices,* and when used to designate a crystal face are ordinarily taken relatively prime (i.e., with no common integral factor). Each crystal face may then be designated by three Miller indices hkl, as shown in Fig. 1. The law of rational indices historically formed the strongest part of the evidence supporting the conjecture that crystals are built up by repetition of a single unit of structure, as shown in Fig. 1.

The crystal axes for a given crystal may be chosen in many different ways; however, they are conventionally chosen to yield a coordinate system of the highest possible symmetry. It has been found that crystals can be divided into six possible systems on the basis of the highest possible symmetry the coordinate system may possess as a result of the symmetry of the crystal. This symmetry is best described in terms of symmetry restrictions governing the values of the axial lengths a, b, and c and the interaxial angles α, β, and γ. The crystal systems are as follows:

Triclinic System. No restrictions.

Monoclinic System. No restrictions on lengths a, b, c; however, $\alpha = \gamma = 90°$; $\beta \neq 90°$.

Orthorhombic System. No restrictions on a, b, c; however, $\alpha = \beta = \gamma = 90°$.

Tetragonal System. $a = b \neq c$; $\alpha = \beta = \gamma = 90°$.

Hexagonal System. Hexagonal division: $a = b = b' \neq c$; $\alpha = \beta = 90°$, $\gamma = \gamma' = 120°$ (there being three axes **a**, **b**, and **b**′ in the basal plane, at 120° angular spacing; the **b**′ axis is redundant).

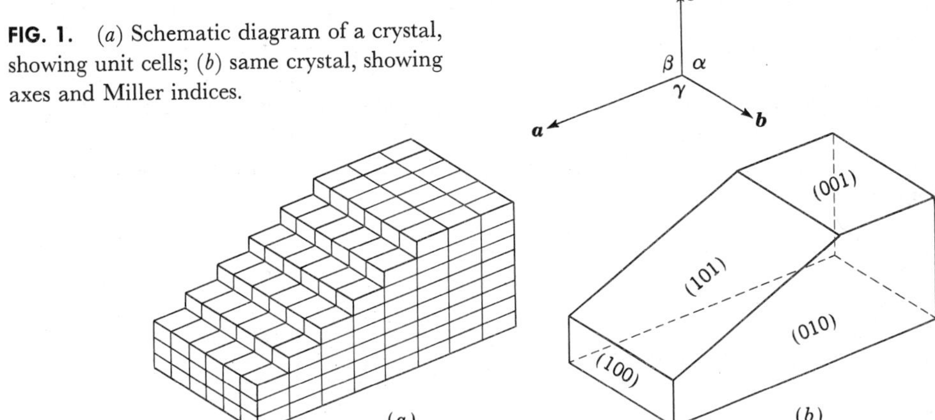

FIG. 1. (*a*) Schematic diagram of a crystal, showing unit cells; (*b*) same crystal, showing axes and Miller indices.

Rhombohedral Division: $a = b = c$; $\alpha = \beta = \gamma \neq 90°$. (Although the coordinate systems in these two divisions are of different symmetry, hexagonal axes may be used in the description of rhombohedral crystals and vice versa.)

Cubic System. $a = b = c$; $\alpha = \beta = \gamma = 90°$ (cartesian coordinates).

The symmetry of a crystal is not completely specified, however, by naming the crystal system to which it belongs. Each crystal system is further subdivided into *symmetry classes,* of which there are 32. On the basis of the detailed symmetry of the atomic structure of crystals, further subdivision is possible. Symmetry will not, however, be discussed in detail here.

Since a crystal structure constitutes a regular repetition of a unit of structure, the unit cell, we may say that a crystal structure is periodic in three dimensions. The periodicity of a crystal structure may be represented by a *point lattice* in three dimensions. This is an array of points that is invariant to all the same translations as leave the crystal structure invariant and to no others. We shall find the lattice useful in deriving the conditions for X-ray diffraction.

To define a crystal lattice in another way, consider the crystal structure to be divided into unit cells (parallelepipeds in shape) in such a way as to obtain the smallest unit cells possible. These unit cells are then called *primitive.* Starting with a set of crystal axes which are parallel to three edges of a unit cell and equal to them in length, a point lattice may be defined as the infinite array of points the coordinates xyz of which assume all possible combinations mnp of integral values (positive, negative, and zero), and *only* integral values. There is then one lattice point per unit cell.

It is frequently found that it is not possible to find a primitive unit cell with edges parallel to crystal axes chosen on the basis of symmetry. In such a case the crystal axes, chosen on the basis of symmetry, are proportional to the edges of a unit of structure that is larger than a primitive unit cell. Such a unit is called a *nonprimitive* unit cell, and there is more than one lattice point per nonprimitive unit cell. If the nonprimitive unit cell is chosen as small as possible consistent with the symmetry desired, it is found that the extra lattice points (those other than the corner points) lie in the center of the unit cell or at the centers of some or all of the faces of the unit cell. The coordinates of the lattice points, in such a case, are therefore either integers or half-integers.

Within a given crystal system there are in some cases several different types of crystal lattice, depending upon the type of minimum-size unit cell that corresponds to a choice of axes appropriate to the given crystal system. This unit cell may be *primitive P* or in certain cases *body-centered I, face-centered F,* or *end-centered A, B,* or *C,* depending on which pair of end faces of the unit cell is centered. The lattices are designated as primitive, body-centered, face-centered, or end-centered depending on whether the smallest possible unit cell that corresponds to the appropriate type of axes is primitive, body-centered, face-centered, or end-centered. There are in all 14 types of lattice.[2] In the cubic system there are three: primitive, body-centered, and face-centered; these are shown in Fig. 2.

Bragg Reflections. Let us now determine the geometrical conditions under which diffraction of X rays by a crystal structure would take place. These are (except for intensity considerations) the same as the conditions for diffraction from the crystal lattice, if a "point scattering center" is placed at each point of the lattice. We shall accordingly examine the geometry of diffraction by such a crystal lattice.

The principle by which X rays would be diffracted by such a lattice is essen-

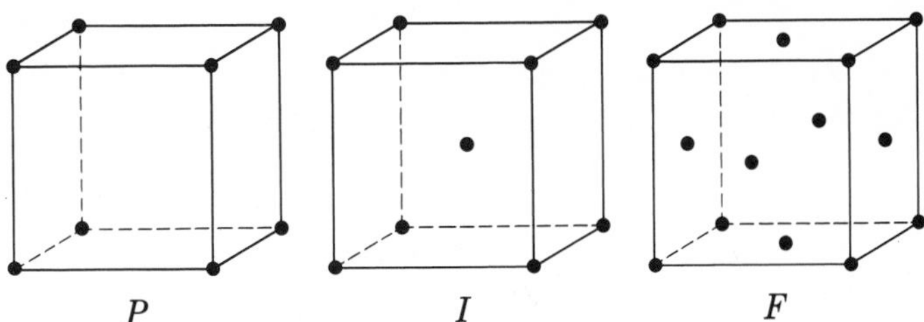

FIG. 2. Cubic unit cells: *P*, primitive; *I*, body-centered; *F*, face-centered.

tially the same as that by which light is diffracted by a ruled grating. When a plane wave impinges on a point scattering center, the scattering center radiates a spherical wave. If there are two or more such scattering centers, the spherical waves will in certain regions tend to reinforce one another and in certain other regions tend to cancel one another out, that is, interfere.

If there are many scattering centers, it is possible for them to be so arranged that the individual spherical waves combine in a certain region a large distance away to form a "reflected" plane wave with an amplitude which represents the sum of the amplitudes of the individual spherical waves at that distance. Such an arrangement is obtained when the scattering centers are confined to a plane surface, in which case the "reflected" plane wave is similar to that which would be obtained if the arrangement of scattering centers were replaced by a plane mirror at the same place. This is the situation represented in Fig. 3 by reflection of rays $\overline{AB}$ and $\overline{DE}$ from the plane Q. It is due to the fact that the path length, along a reflected *ray* of radiation, from a wave front of the incident radiation to a wave front of the reflected radiation is the same for every ray (e.g., $\overline{AB} + \overline{BC} = \overline{DE} + \overline{EF}$) when the angle of incidence is equal to the angle of reflection.

It is not necessary, however, as a condition for maximum reinforcement, that all the path lengths be equal, provided that those which are not equal (e.g., $\overline{AB} + \overline{BC}$ and $\overline{GH} + \overline{HJ}$ in Fig. 3) differ by a wavelength λ or by an integral number of wavelengths $n\lambda$. It can be seen from Fig. 3 that the condition for complete reinforcement is

$$n\lambda = 2D \sin \theta \tag{2}$$

FIG. 3. Condition for Bragg reflection from scattering centers confined to a set of equidistant, parallel planes. (Planes are perpendicular to the page; their traces are indicated by the horizontal lines.)

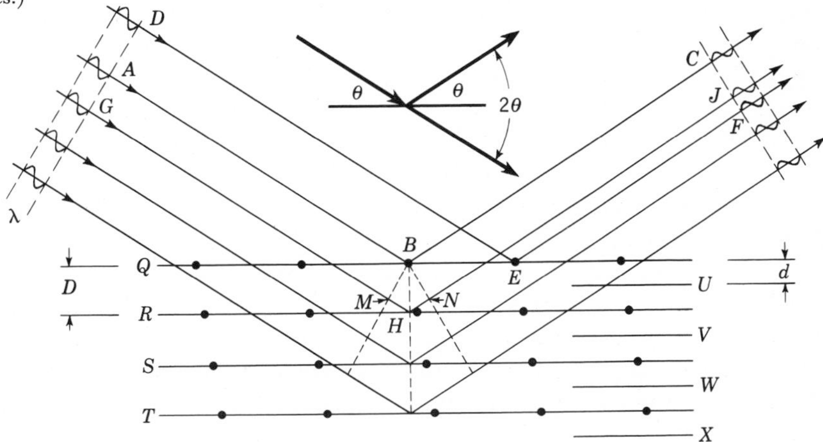

(since $\overline{MH} = \overline{HN} = D \sin \theta$ and the path difference $\overline{MH} + \overline{HN}$ must be equal to $n\lambda$), where n is an integer, often called the order of the diffraction; D is the interplanar spacing; and θ is the angle which the incident ray and the reflected ray make with the reflecting planes. Equation (2) is called the *Bragg equation,* and θ is often called the *Bragg angle.* The angle through which the X rays are deflected from their original direction by reflection from the planes is twice the Bragg angle, or 2θ.

If the spacing angle θ deviates only slightly from that which satisfied the Bragg equation, reinforcement remains almost complete only if there is only a small number of reflecting planes. If, however, there is a very large (or "infinite") number of reflecting planes, the reflection from any given plane is canceled by that from another plane a considerable distance away. Reflection should be observed, therefore, only for values of θ extremely close to those that satisfy the Bragg equation, and this is experimentally found to be the case.

We shall now modify the treatment slightly by taking note of the fact that a second-order reflection ($n = 2$) from the planes $Q, R, S, T, \ldots$ corresponds to a hypothetical first-order reflection from the planes $Q, U, R, V, S, W, T, X, \ldots$ only half of which contain lattice points. By inserting the required number of additional equidistant parallel planes containing no lattice points, we can dispense with the order n and write the Bragg equation in the following form, which is the form that will be used henceforth in this discussion:

$$\lambda = 2d \sin \theta \tag{3}$$

where d is now the interplanar spacing of the new set of planes. We shall now say that Eq. (3) is the necessary condition for reflection of X rays of wavelength λ from a set of crystallographic planes with interplanar spacing d. A set of crystallographic planes is defined as an infinite array of equidistant and finitely spaced parallel planes so constructed that every point of the given crystal lattice lies on some plane of the set (though it is not necessarily true that all planes in the set contain lattice points). It is evident that sets of crystallographic planes may be constructed for a given crystal lattice in many ways (indeed, an infinite number of ways). The equations for such a set of planes are

$$\begin{array}{r}
\cdot \\
\cdot \\
\cdot \\
hx + ky + lz = -2 \\
hx + ky + lz = -1 \\
hx + ky + lz = 0 \\
hx + ky + lz = 1 \\
hx + ky + lz = 2 \\
\cdot \\
\cdot \\
hx + ky + lz = N \\
\cdot \\
\cdot \\
\cdot
\end{array} \tag{4}$$

where x, y, and z are coordinates as previously defined and where, when the coordinate system corresponds to a primitive unit cell, the coefficients h, k, and l may take on any integral values, positive, negative, or zero. They may be called the Miller indices of the set of crystallographic planes and are related to Miller indices as applied to crystal faces. (However, they need not be taken relatively prime.) The different integral values of N, ranging from $-\infty$ to ∞, define different planes in the set. That any given lattice point must lie on one of the planes, in the case of a coordinate system corresponding to a primitive unit cell, is easily seen from the fact that its coordinates xyz must be integers mnp; since the Miller indices are integers, the quantity $hx + ky + lz$ must be an integer, and one of the equations in the set of Eqs. (4) is satisfied.

If the coordinate system is not chosen in correspondence to a primitive unit cell, not all the lattice points have coordinates that are integers and all lattice points will lie on planes in the set only if certain restrictions are placed on the combinations of values which the Miller indices hkl may assume.

For a body-centered lattice I, some of the lattice points have coordinates that are expressible as integers mnp and some have coordinates that must be expressed as half-integers $m + \frac{1}{2}$, $n + \frac{1}{2}$, $p + \frac{1}{2}$. For the latter,

$$hx + ky + lz = hm + kn + lp + \tfrac{1}{2}(h + k + l)$$

and for this quantity to be an integer it is necessary that $h + k + l$ be even.

For a face-centered lattice F, some of the lattice points are at $xyz = mnp$; some at $m, n + \frac{1}{2}, p + \frac{1}{2}$; some at $m + \frac{1}{2}, n, p + \frac{1}{2}$; and some at $m + \frac{1}{2}, n + \frac{1}{2}, p$, where m, n, and p are in each case any three integers. In order that $hx + ky + lz$ be an integer, it is evidently necessary that $k + l$, $h + l$, and $h + k$ simultaneously be even. An equivalent restriction is easily seen to be that h, k, and l must be either all even or all odd.

When these restrictions are not obeyed, no reflections can be obtained from the set of crystallographic planes under consideration, for there will be lattice points lying between the planes and scattering out of phase with those in the planes, resulting in complete cancellation or interference. By observing experimentally what sets of planes reflect X rays one can deduce what the restrictions are and thereby deduce the lattice type.

The interplanar distance d is determined by the Miller indices hkl. For the cubic system it is easy to show by analytic geometry that

$$d = \frac{a_0}{\sqrt{h^2 + k^2 + l^2}} = \frac{a_0}{M} \tag{5}$$

where a_0 is the length of the edge of the unit cube and

$$M^2 \equiv h^2 + k^2 + l^2 \tag{6}$$

Lattice Type. From the angles at which X rays are diffracted by a crystal it is possible to deduce the interplanar distances d, with Eq. (3). To determine the lattice type and compute the unit-cell dimensions, it is necessary to deduce the Miller indices of the planes that show these distances. In the case of a powder specimen (where all information concerning orientations of crystal axes has been lost) the only available information regarding Miller indices is that obtainable by application of Eqs. (5) and (6).

To find which of the three types of cubic lattice is the correct one, we make use of some interesting properties of integers. From Eq. (5) we see that

$$\left(\frac{1}{d}\right)^2 = \left(\frac{1}{a_0}\right)^2 M^2 = \left(\frac{1}{a_0}\right)^2 (h^2 + k^2 + l^2) \tag{7}$$

so that, if we square our reciprocal spacings, we should find it possible to find a numerical factor which will convert them into a sequence of integers, which we shall find convenient to make *relatively prime.* We shall see that the type of lattice is determined by the character of the integer sequence obtained.

For a simple cubic (primitive) lattice, all integral values are independently possible for the Miller indices h, k, and l. Now it is possible to express most, but not all, integers as the sum of the squares of three integers. In Table 1 the various possible values of M^2 are listed in the column under P, and it is seen that there are gaps where the integers 7, 15, 23, 28, 31, 39, 47, and 55 are absent. (Other gaps occur at higher values of M^2.) For those values of M^2 that are possible, the first column of the table gives the Miller indices the sum of whose squares yield the M^2 values. In some cases it is seen that there is more than one possible choice.

For a simple (primitive) cubic lattice P there are no restrictions on the Miller indices and therefore none on M^2 except as noted above. In the case of a body-centered cubic lattice, only those values of M^2 can be allowed which arise from Miller indices the sum of which is even. This has the effect of requiring M^2 to be even, as seen in the first of the two columns under I. We can then divide them by 2 and thereby reduce them to a *relatively prime* sequence, shown in the second column under I, for comparison with the sequence obtained from the $(1/d)^2$ values. We note immediately that the relatively prime sequence obtained differs from that for a primitive cubic lattice in having gaps at different places. By use of this fact it is almost always possible to distinguish between a primitive cubic lattice and a body-centered cubic lattice on the basis of a powder photograph. For the face-centered cubic lattice, application of the restriction that the indices must be all even or all odd produces the characteristic sequence 3, 4, 8, 11, 12, 16, . . . given in the column under F. If most or all of the numbers in this sequence are present, and if none of the excluded numbers is present, the lattice is evidently face-centered cubic.

If no relatively prime sequence of integers can be found to within the experimental uncertainty of the measurements, the crystalline substance presumably does not belong to the cubic system.

When the cubic lattice type has been deduced, the unit-cell dimension a_0 can be calculated. From the unit-cell volume, the measured crystal density, and the formula weight, the number of formulas in one unit cell can be calculated.

Deduction of the Structure. The arrangement of the atoms or ions in the unit cell is at least partly determined by symmetry considerations, but in most cases it is necessary to take account of the *intensities* of the Bragg reflections. The way that this is done in present crystallographic practice is far too complicated to describe here.[3] We shall here only illustrate by a simple example how it is possible to use qualitative arguments based on intensity.

If the substance is a binary compound AB, and if its unit cell is simple cubic P with one formula (one atom of A and one of B) per cubic cell, the relative positions of the two atoms are fixed by symmetry. This is true of the salt cesium chloride, CsCl, the structure of which is shown in Fig. 4. One of the ions, Cs^+ say, may without loss of generality be placed at the origin. The other ion, Cl^-, must be at the center of the unit cell; if it is in any other position, the structure will lack the threefold rotational axes of symmetry which are always present along all four body diagonals of the unit cell in the cubic system.

In many cases, including even some with one formula of a binary compound

TABLE 1. Possible Values of M^2 for Cubic Lattices

hkl	M	P, M^2	I		F, M^2
			M^2	$M^2/2$	
100	1.0000	1			
110	1.4142	2	2	1	
111	1.7321	3			3
200	2.0000	4	4	2	4
210	2.2361	5			
211	2.4495	6	6	3	
		—			
220	2.8284	8	8	4	8
300, 221	3.0000	9			
310	3.1623	10	10	5	
311	3.3166	11			11
222	3.4641	12	12	6	12
320	3.6056	13			
321	3.7417	14	14	7	
		—			
400	4.0000	16	16	8	16
410, 322	4.1231	17			
411, 330	4.2426	18	18	9	
331	4.3589	19			19
420	4.4721	20	20	10	20
421	4.5826	21			
332	4.6904	22	22	11	
		—			
422	4.8990	24	24	12	24
500, 430	5.0000	25			
510, 431	5.0990	26	26	13	
511, 333	5.1962	27			27
		—		—	
520, 432	5.3852	29			
521	5.4772	30	30	15	
		—			
440	5.6569	32	32	16	32
522, 441	5.7446	33			
530, 433	5.8310	34	34	17	
531	5.9161	35			35
600, 442	6.0000	36	36	18	36
610	6.0828	37			
611, 532	6.1644	38	38	19	
		—			
620	6.3246	40	40	20	40
621, 540, 443	6.4031	41			
541	6.4807	42	42	21	
533	6.5574	43			43
622	6.6332	44	44	22	44
630, 542	6.7082	45			
631	6.7823	46	46	23	
		—			
444	6.9282	48	48	24	48
700, 632	7.0000	49			
710, 550, 543	7.0711	50	50	25	
711, 551	7.1414	51			51
640	7.2111	52	52	26	52
720, 641	7.2801	53			
721, 633, 552	7.3485	54	54	27	
		—			
642	7.4833	56	56	28	56

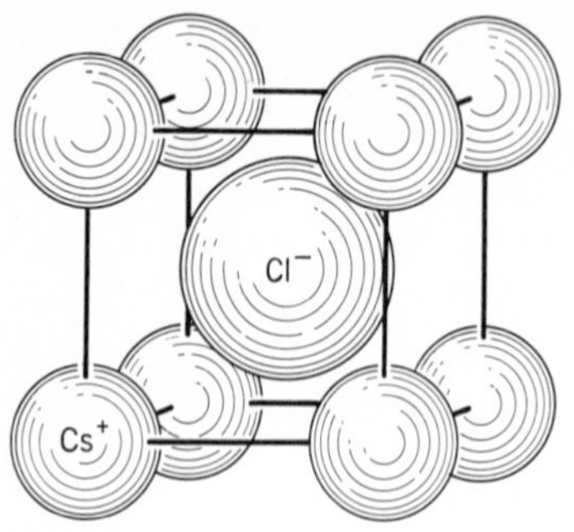

FIG. 4. Unit cell of cesium chloride. Note that this structure is not body-centered cubic but would be if the two ions were identical.

for each lattice point, the positions of the atoms or ions are not necessarily given uniquely by symmetry, though the number of possible choices may not be large. The solution of the structure in some cases may lie in a simple clue from the intensities. Let it be supposed, for example, that a certain class of powder lines are relatively weak and that omitting these lines from the calculation leads to a "pseudo lattice" with a smaller number of atoms per lattice point than in the case of the true lattice. A possible hypothesis might then be that the weak lines owe their weakness to destructive interference between two kinds of atoms or ions and that, if the chemical difference between these two kinds of atoms or ions could somehow be removed, the interference would become complete and the pseudo lattice would become a true lattice. Knowledge of the pseudo lattice (and pseudo cell) may then show where the atoms or ions must be placed (irrespective of kind), and knowledge of the true lattice will then show which atoms are of each kind.

As an example of this kind of clue, let us deduce the relative positions of the ions in cesium chloride, bromide, and iodide (which all have the same structure) from intensity considerations, without appealing to any arguments based on symmetry. Putting the $(1/d)^2$ on a relatively prime basis, we obtain the integers 1, 2, 3, 4, 5, 6, —, 8, 9, 10, 11, 12, 13, 14, —, 16, . . . , which clearly indicates a primitive lattice. From the density we find that there is one formula per lattice point. However, we see that all the odd-numbered lines are somewhat weak in CsCl, much weaker in CsBr, and very faint or absent in CsI. If we neglect them, the sequence of integers obtained (on dividing by 2 to obtain relative primes) indicates a body-centered cubic "pseudo lattice" with one-half formula, or one ion (irrespective of kind), at each pseudo-lattice point. In other words, if we were unable to distinguish between the two kinds of ions, the structure would look like one with a single atom of a single kind at each point of a body-centered cubic lattice. This clearly shows that in the real structure, an ion of one kind is located at (000) and an ion of the other kind is located at (½½½). It may be mentioned that the virtually complete obliteration of the odd lines in CsI is due to the fact that the Cs^+ ion and the I^- ion are *isoelectronic* (that is, have the same number of electrons, namely 54, which is the number in xenon); if any odd lines are observed at all, it is owing to the fact that because of the different nuclear charges of the two ions, the sizes of the electron clouds of the two ions are slightly different.†

When there are more than two atoms per lattice point, the structure determination will be more complicated. One frequently used procedure is that of "trial

† The argument here depends upon the fact that it is the electrons, rather than the nuclei, which scatter X rays.

and error," in which a number of "model" structures are successively proposed and tested by calculation of intensities and comparison with experiment, until a structure is found which yields satisfactory agreement. When the number of possible structures is too large for the practical application of trial-and-error methods, methods must be used that are too advanced for description here. With their use, crystal structures have been found in which there are 500 or more atoms in a unit cell. In such cases and in most ordinary work, however, powder data would be inadequate for determining the structure, and diffraction patterns must be obtained from single crystals.

METHOD

There are several experimental techniques for realizing the diffraction conditions, the most powerful of which depends on having a single crystal of the substance to be studied.[4] Because, however, the single-crystal methods are also rather complicated, we shall concern ourselves here only with the so-called powder method, or Debye-Scherrer method, which makes use not of a single crystal but rather of a powder obtained by grinding up the crystalline or microcrystalline material.[5] This powder contains crystal particles of the order of magnitude of a few microns in size.

In this method, the specimen for diffraction is obtained by sticking some of the powdered material onto a fine (0.1 mm) glass fiber with a trace of vaseline or filling a very thin-walled glass capillary tube (0.2 mm diameter) with the powder. A narrow beam of parallel monochromatic X rays, about 0.5 mm in diameter, impinges on this specimen at right angles to its axis. The source of X rays is usually a Coolidge-type X-ray tube with a copper (or molybdenum) target, equipped with a filter (of nickel foil, in the case of a copper target) to remove all spectral components except the desired $K\alpha$ line. The narrow beam is formed by a *collimator,* which consists basically of a conical tube 5 or 6 cm long with a pinhole or slit at each end. On the opposite side of the specimen is a conical receptacle similar to the collimator but with only an entrance pinhole or slit and no exit; this is the *beam stop,* in which the undiffracted beam is trapped. The diffracted radiation is detected by a strip of photographic film bent into a cylinder and held firmly against the inside wall of a cylindrical camera, coaxial with the specimen. The arrangement of the collimator, specimen, and photographic film is shown schematically in Fig. 5. When the beam impinges on the randomly oriented particles in a stationary powder specimen, most of the particles will not diffract the X rays at all. Only those particles will diffract X rays which happen by chance to be so oriented that Eq. (3) holds for Bragg reflection from some set of crystallographic planes. The direction of the diffracted rays will then deviate from the direction of the incident beam by twice the Bragg angle. Since orientation is completely random with respect to the beam axis, the rays diffracted at a given scattering angle may lie with equal probability anywhere on a right circular cone with apex angle 4θ. In practice, the specimen is usually rotated about its own axis, so that during a single rotation all or nearly all the particles present will have an opportunity to reflect X rays from any given set of crystallographic planes, the resulting diffracted radiation being distributed rather evenly over the cone. Where the cone intersects the photographic film, the latent image of a *powder line* is formed. When the film is removed from the camera and developed, fixed, washed, and dried, it is found to have on it a num-

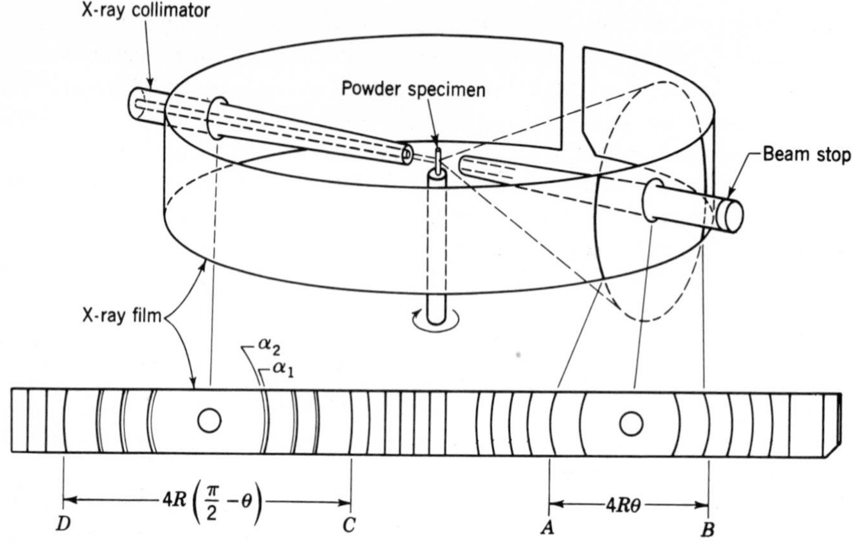

FIG. 5. Schematic diagram illustrating X-ray powder method (Straumanis arrangement[6]). Note splitting of back-reflection lines.

ber of lines, each one of which is due to reflection from one or more sets of crystallographic planes.

The positions of the lines on the film can be measured with a comparator (see Exp. 43) or microphotometer, but adequate measurements can be made with a good millimeter scale. From measurements of the positions of the lines or distances between them, the Bragg angles can be calculated. The determination of these angles is a purely geometric problem. The "effective radius" R of the film in the camera can be obtained by picking two sets of lines, A, B and C, D as in Fig. 5, and measuring the four distances $\overline{AC}$, $\overline{AD}$, $\overline{BC}$, and $\overline{BD}$:

$$4R = \frac{1}{\pi}(\overline{AC} + \overline{AD} + \overline{BC} + \overline{BD}) \tag{8a}$$

If it is desired to calculate angles in degrees rather than in radians, it is convenient to calculate

$$4R^\circ = \frac{\pi}{180}(4R) = \frac{1}{180}(\overline{AC} + \overline{AD} + \overline{BC} + \overline{BD}) \tag{8b}$$

Then

$$\theta\,(\text{rad}) = \frac{\overline{AB}}{4R} \qquad \theta' = \frac{\pi}{2} - \theta\,(\text{rad}) = \frac{\overline{CD}}{4R} \tag{9a}$$

$$\theta\,(\text{deg}) = \frac{\overline{AB}}{4R^\circ} \qquad \theta' = 90 - \theta\,(\text{deg}) = \frac{\overline{CD}}{4R^\circ} \tag{9b}$$

From trigonometric tables, $\sin\theta$ or $\log\sin\theta$ can then be obtained. In processing the back-reflection data, it is unnecessary to convert from $(\pi/2 - \theta)$ to θ; it is sufficient to look up $\cos(\pi/2 - \theta) = \cos\theta'$. We then calculate

$$\frac{1}{d} = \frac{2}{\lambda}\sin\theta = \frac{2}{\lambda}\cos\theta' \tag{10}$$

When the measurements are made and $(1/d)$ is computed, account should be taken of the fact that the $K\alpha$ spectral line generally used as a monochromatic source of X rays is not truly a single line but actually a closely spaced doublet. The doublet is ordinarily not resolved in the forward-reflection part of the film, but in the back-reflection part of the film the lines are usually observably split into two components, known as $K\alpha_1$ and $K\alpha_2$ in order of increasing wavelength (and therefore in order of increasing θ), in the intensity ratio 2:1. When the two components are not resolved, the position taken for the line should be an estimate of the position of the "center of gravity," and the value of the wavelength λ used in the calculation should be the weighted mean wavelength:

$$\lambda_{\text{mean}} = \tfrac{1}{3}(2\lambda_{\alpha 1} + \lambda_{\alpha 2}) \tag{11}$$

When the components are sufficiently well resolved to make possible the measurement of the positions of the two components separately, such measurements should be made and the actual values of the wavelengths should then be used in the calculations. Each component will then yield a separate value of $1/d$; the two values obtained should be in good agreement and may be averaged for the ensuing calculations.

For copper $(K\alpha)$ radiation,

$$\begin{aligned} \lambda_{\alpha_1} &= 1.54050 \text{ A} \\ \lambda_{\alpha_2} &= 1.54434 \text{ A} \\ \lambda_{\text{mean}} &= 1.5418 \text{ A} \end{aligned} \tag{12}$$

In present-day X-ray crystallography, powder photography is only rarely used for complete structure determination. It is, however, frequently used in the precise determination of unit-cell dimensions. Its most common technical use is as an analytical tool; powder patterns of thousands of crystalline substances are known.

EXPERIMENTAL

Preparation of Powder Specimen. A specimen of the material to be studied is finely pulverized in an agate mortar with an agate pestle. The powder is then loaded into a Pyrex or Lindemann glass capillary tube, 0.2 to 0.3 mm o.d., having a very thin wall (0.01 mm or less), so as to obtain a densely filled specimen about 1 cm in length. If the capillary tube is flared out at one end, it is easier to load; even without a flared-out end, however, the powder can be picked up by scraping one end of the capillary against the surface of the mortar and, with this end uppermost, agitating the powder by very gentle rasping with a file. One end of the capillary tube should be sealed off with a flame or with wax before filling, and the other end with wax after filling. The capillary tube is then affixed with wax to the end of a short (⅜ in. or less) length of ⅛-in. brass rod; see Fig. 6.

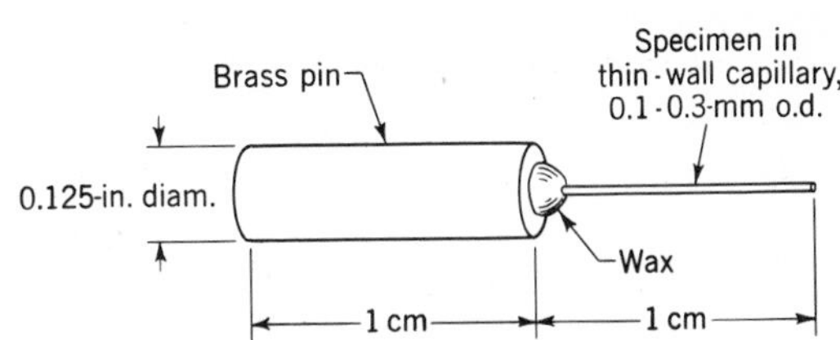

FIG. 6. Mounted powder specimen.

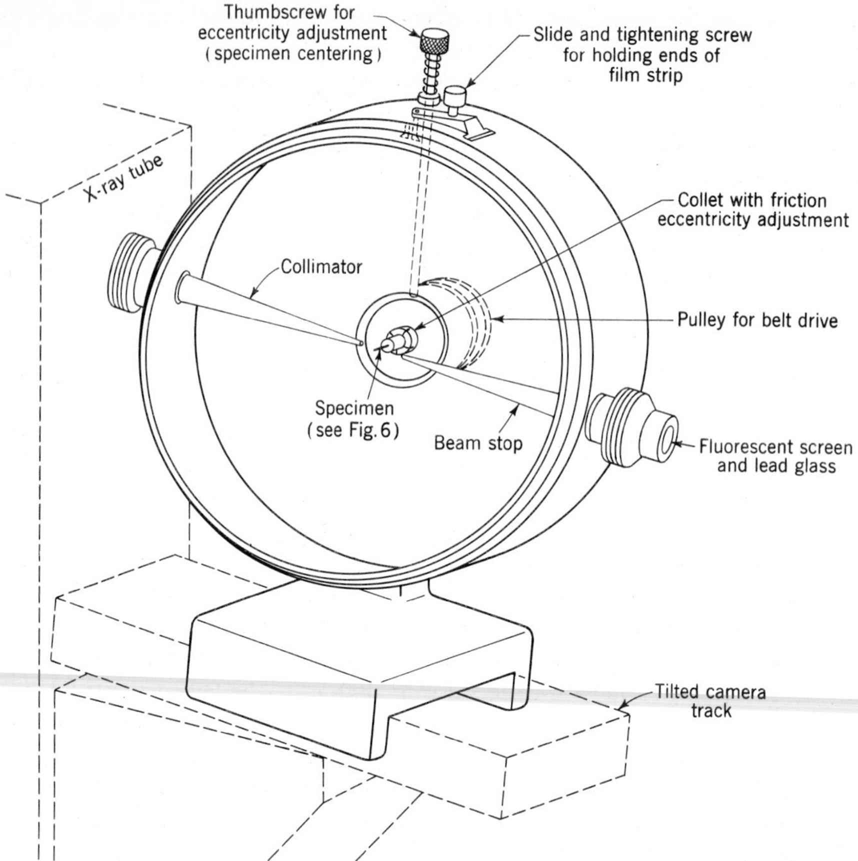

FIG. 7. Philips powder camera (shown with cover not in place).

Installation of the Specimen. A powder camera of the Straumanis design is shown in Fig. 7. It is a valuable instrument and must be handled carefully. The camera should not be used until the procedures for using it have been demonstrated to the student by an experienced user. To install and line up the specimen, proceed as follows:†

Remove the circular cover, and lay it down, inside surface upward, in a *safe place.* Remove the two slits (collimator and beam stop), and lay them down *inside the cover.*

By means of tweezers or long-nose pliers, insert the brass pin supporting the specimen into its receptacle, where it is held by friction. Carefully replace the collimator, being sure not to force it or to drop it.

Place the lens cap over the outside collimator opening, and set the camera down with the beam-stop hole facing a well-lighted surface (beam stop *not* in place). By hand, turn the pulley wheel on the outside of the camera. As it goes around, the silhouette of the specimen should appear to go up and down. Stop it in an "up" position, and by means of the screw on top of the camera push it down to the center of the visual field. Turn the screw back up, and rotate again to see if adjustment

† The procedure given is that applicable to the 114.6-mm camera manufactured by the North American Philips Co.[6]

is needed; if so, use the screw as before. Continue until the specimen appears to undergo no motion as the spindle is rotated.

Remove the lens cap, and replace the beam stop. As in the case of the collimator, do not force it or drop it. Replace the cover.

Loading the Camera with Film. Take the camera into the darkroom. Remove the cover and the collimator and beam stop. Turn off the room light, and under a safelight cut, punch, and insert the film in accordance with specific instructions given. (It is advisable to rehearse the procedure ahead of time with the light on, using a piece of exposed film.) Insert the collimator and beam stop and replace the cover.

Making the X-ray Exposure. This should be done under the constant supervision of a qualified person; detailed instructions cannot be given here. **Be very careful to avoid any X-ray exposure to any part of the body;** make sure that all X-ray ports are covered when the unit is in operation. The optimum exposure time depends on the composition and size of the specimen, the tube current and operating potential, and the dimensions of the collimating system. Typical exposures are 4 to 20 hr. In the absence of a recommended exposure time, make a short trial exposure and a second longer exposure if necessary.

Developing the Film. The camera is taken into the darkroom and the film removed. It should be attached to a clip or other support and developed for 3 to 5 min, depending on the temperature of the developer. Agitate the film, but do not allow its surface to rub against the walls or bottom of the tank or tray. Wash the film for 30 sec and place it in the fixing bath. After the film has cleared, the room light may be turned on. The film should be in the fixing bath for at least twice as long as it takes to clear and should then be washed in running water for at least 30 min. It may then be carefully wiped with clean fingers, rinsed again with distilled water, and hung up to dry.

Measurement of Crystal Density. The density of the substance can be determined with a pycnometer or with a 5-ml (or smaller) volumetric flask used as a pycnometer. The liquid used should be one in which the substance is insoluble; for a water-soluble inorganic salt medium-boiling petroleum ether is convenient. The procedure is described in Chap. I (Sample Report). Make two determinations.

CALCULATIONS

If it is not possible to take the X-ray powder pattern in the laboratory, a contact print of a powder photograph will be furnished and the X-ray equipment will be discussed and shown to the students. The instructions below should be followed with either the negative taken or the print provided.

Measure $\overline{AB}$ or $\overline{CD}$ (see Fig. 5) for as many lines as possible; estimate each distance to ± 0.1 mm. Enter the measurements, together with estimated intensity, into a table. Make a separate measurement for each component of a resolved doublet.

Pick a pair of sharp lines, A, B in the forward-reflection part of the film and another pair C, D in the back-reflection region. Measure the four distances $\overline{AC}$, $\overline{AD}$, $\overline{BC}$, $\overline{BD}$ as accurately as possible. Calculate $4R$ or $4R^\circ$ from Eq. (8).

Calculate θ or θ' for each line or resolved component of a line [Eq. (9)] and look up $\sin \theta$ or $\cos \theta'$. Calculate $1/d$ from Eq. (10), averaging the values obtained for the two components of each resolved doublet. Calculate $(1/d)^2$.

Find a factor that will reduce the $(1/d)^2$ values to relatively prime integers within experimental error. Refer to Table 1 and identify the lattice type. Also, from Table 1, obtain the Miller indices *hkl* for each line.

The most precise values of a_0 are obtained from the lines in the back-reflection part of the film, where θ is close to 90°. This can be seen by combining Eqs. (3) and (5), solving for a_0, and differentiating:

$$da_0 = -\frac{M\lambda}{2\sin^2\theta}\cos\theta\, d\theta$$
$$= -a_0 \cot\theta\, d\theta$$

The experimental uncertainty in measuring θ is proportional to that of measuring the distances between pairs of lines and is approximately constant over the film unless lines in the back-reflection region are unduly faint or broad. However, even if the uncertainty of measurement is a little larger in the back-reflection region, the effect is ordinarily far outweighed by the cot θ factor. In fact, lines very close to the collimator hole should always be used if at all possible, even if they are broad and diffuse. Another good reason for using only lines in the back-reflection region is that they are much more free of shifts due to absorption of X rays by the specimen. From a few well-chosen lines in the back-reflection region, preferably resolved doublets, calculate a_0 from Eq. (5) and average the values obtained.

From the measured density and the a_0 value determined as above, calculate the number of atoms per unit cell and per lattice point. Report the lattice type, the value of a_0, and the number of atoms per unit cell.

DISCUSSION

Determine the crystal structure, if possible, by methods similar to those described for CsCl (see Theory). Draw a diagram of the cubic unit cell showing the positions of all atoms or ions.

APPARATUS

X-ray diffraction apparatus, complete with tube stand, X-ray tube, and power supply; Debye-Scherrer powder camera, preferably Straumanis type (such as North American Philips 114.6-mm camera); film cutter and punch; thin-wall Lindemann glass capillary tubes (may be purchased from Caine Scientific Sales Co., Chicago, Ill.); agate mortar and pestle; small file; X-ray film (Eastman no-screen, 35-mm continuous strip); darkroom, equipped with X-ray developing tank or adequate trays; X-ray developer and fixer solutions; timer; thermometer; good centimeter scale; pycnometer or 5-ml volumetric flask; small pipette or eye dropper.

Small quantity of crystalline material of cubic structure for study (e.g., alkali halides; alkaline earth oxides; cuprous or silver chloride; simple metals such as aluminum or copper, finely powdered with a file); liquid (medium-boiling petroleum ether or CCl_4) for density work.

REFERENCES

1. C. W. Bunn, "Chemical Crystallography," pp. 47–52, Oxford Univ. Press, New York (1946).
2. M. J. Buerger, "Elementary Crystallography," chap. 8, Wiley, New York (1956).
3. H. Lipson and W. Cochran, "The Determination of Crystal Structures," G. Bell, London (1953).

4. M. J. Buerger, "X-ray Crystallography," Wiley, New York (1942).
5. H. P. Klug and L. Alexander, "X-ray Diffraction Procedures for Polycrystalline and Amorphous Materials," chap. 4, Wiley, New York (1954).
6. *Ibid.*, p. 178; M. J. Buerger, *Am. Mineralogist,* **21,** 11 (1936); *J. Appl. Phys.,* **16,** 501 (1945); M. Straumanis and A. Ieviņš, *Z. Physik,* **98,** 461 (1936).

GENERAL READING

W. F. deJong, "General Crystallography: A Brief Compendium," Freeman, San Francisco (1959).
W. L. Bragg, "The Crystalline State I. A General Survey," Macmillan, New York (1934).
R. C. Evans, "Crystal Chemistry," Cambridge Univ. Press, New York (1952).

Experiment 46. Lattice Energy of Solid Argon

From vapor-pressure measurements on solid argon in the range 63 to 77°K, one can obtain the heat of sublimation at 70°K. Combining this with other known thermodynamic data it is possible to obtain a value for the lattice energy of argon. Comparison will be made between the experimental lattice energy and a theoretical value calculated using potential-energy parameters obtained from properties of argon gas.

THEORY

The change in state involved here is simply

$$\text{Ar}(s) = \text{Ar}(g) \qquad (\text{const } p, T) \tag{1}$$

The equilibrium vapor pressure of solid argon as a function of temperature is given by the Clapeyron equation, which has been discussed in Exp. 17. For this experiment it is possible to use the form

$$\frac{d \log p}{d(1/T)} = -\frac{\Delta\tilde{H}}{2.303R} \tag{2}$$

where $\Delta\tilde{H}$ is the molar heat of sublimation. Equation (2) is an approximation based on two assumptions: (1) that the molal volume of solid is negligible compared with that of the gas and (2) that the gas is ideal. For argon at 70°K, $\tilde{V}_s$ is about 0.1 per cent of $\tilde{V}_g$ and deviations from the ideal-gas law are less than 1 per cent. (Correction for gas imperfection could be made if desired; see Exp. 17.) Thus a plot of log p vs. $1/T$ will yield a value of $\Delta\tilde{H}$.

The change in energy for sublimation is related to the enthalpy change by

$$\Delta\tilde{H} = \Delta\tilde{E} + \Delta(p\tilde{V})$$

Using assumptions (1) and (2) above, we have

$$\Delta\tilde{E} = \Delta\tilde{H} - RT \tag{3}$$

Now

$$\Delta\tilde{E} = \tilde{E}_{\text{gas}} - \tilde{E}_{\text{solid}} \tag{4}$$

If we measure the energy content of argon on an arbitrary scale which defines $\tilde{E}_{gas}$ to be zero at 0°K, then $\tilde{E}_{gas}$ at temperature T will be just the translational kinetic energy;[1]

$$\tilde{E}_{gas} = \tfrac{3}{2}RT \tag{5}$$

Thus we find that

$$\tilde{E}_{solid} = \tfrac{3}{2}RT - \Delta\tilde{E} = \tfrac{5}{2}RT - \Delta\tilde{H} \tag{6}$$

There are two contributions to the energy content of solid argon: the *lattice energy*, which is the potential energy of the argon atoms at rest in the lattice relative to a zero of energy for these atoms in the gas at infinite separation, and the vibrational energy, which arises from the motion of the atoms about their equilibrium positions. This vibrational energy is small for the argon lattice at 70°K and can be calculated from the Debye theory of lattice vibrations (see Exp. 47). The appropriate expression[2] is

$$\tilde{E}_s(\text{vib}) = \tfrac{9}{8}R\Theta + 3RTD(\Theta/T) \tag{7}$$

where Θ is a characteristic temperature known as the "Debye temperature." The first term in Eq. (7) is the zero-point vibrational energy, and the second is the thermal vibrational energy, D being the "Debye function." For argon, $\Theta = 85$°K[3]. The quantity $D(\Theta/T)$ can be obtained by interpolation in tables of the Debye function;[4] for argon at 70°K it is 0.617.

Using Eqs. (6) and (7) together with the experimentally determined $\Delta\tilde{H}$ and the known Θ value, one can find the lattice energy from

$$\tilde{E}_s = \tilde{E}_s(\text{lattice}) + \tilde{E}_s(\text{vib}) \tag{8}$$

It is possible to calculate a theoretical value of the lattice energy for a molecular crystal if data are available on the potential energy between atoms as a function of their separation. A commonly used form for the interatomic potential (see Fig. 1) is due to Lennard-Jones;[5]

$$u(r) = 4\epsilon\left[\left(\frac{\sigma}{r}\right)^{12} - \left(\frac{\sigma}{r}\right)^{6}\right] \tag{9}$$

where $u(r)$ is the potential energy for *two* atoms at a distance r. The r^{-12} term is

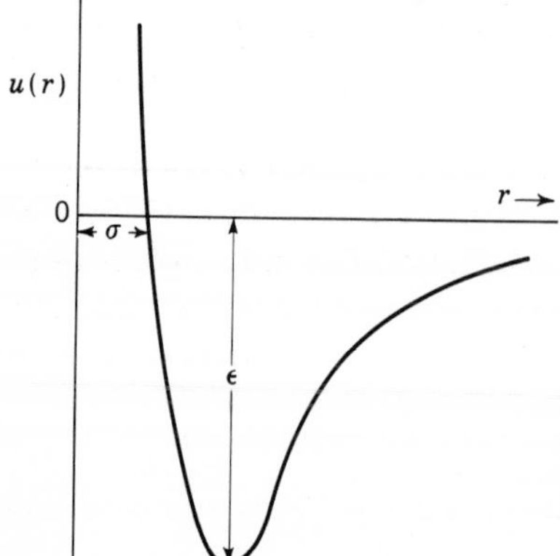

FIG. 1. Lennard-Jones potential $u(r)$ as a function of interatomic distance r. The characteristic parameters ϵ and σ determine this potential curve; see Eq. (9).

an empirical function to describe the repulsion at short distances, and the r^{-6} term represents the r dependence of the potential energy found by London to describe the attraction due to induced dipole-dipole interaction. The Lennard-Jones potential for a given atom is characterized by the two constants ϵ and σ (which are shown in Fig. 1). These parameters can be evaluated from an analysis of gas data (second virial coefficient, Joule-Thomson effect, or gas viscosity); the best values for argon[6] are

$$\frac{\epsilon}{k} = 119°\text{K} \qquad \sigma = 3.41 \text{ A} \tag{10}$$

For the solid it is assumed that the total potential energy (i.e., lattice energy) is the sum of all pair potentials $u_{ij}(r_{ij})$. The result of this summation for a face-centered cubic lattice (such as argon) is[7]

$$\tilde{E}_s\,(\text{lattice}) = 2N_0\epsilon\left[12.132\left(\frac{\sigma}{a}\right)^{12} - 14.454\left(\frac{\sigma}{a}\right)^{6}\right] \tag{11}$$

where a is the distance between nearest neighbors. Note that almost all the repulsion part of the potential comes from nearest-neighbor interactions (nearest neighbors alone would give 12 for both coefficients). Since r^{-6} falls off much more slowly than r^{-12}, the coefficient of the second term in Eq. (11) is considerably greater than 12. A knowledge of the lattice spacing for solid argon and the parameters of Eq. (10) will permit a calculation of the lattice energy for comparison with the experimental value obtained from Eq. (8).

EXPERIMENTAL

Temperatures below 77°K can be achieved with a liquid-nitrogen bath by reducing the pressure over the nitrogen by pumping, thus lowering its boiling point. It is possible to lower the bath temperature to 63°K before liquid nitrogen begins to solidify. Measurement of the temperature can be made by using a gas thermometer (see Exp. 1) or a thermocouple (Chap. XVI) or by measuring the vapor pressure of the nitrogen.

The low-temperature cell, shown in Fig. 2, consists of a copper block containing a small chamber A for solid argon and a larger chamber B for use as a gas thermometer bulb or N_2 vapor-pressure bulb. If a thermocouple is used, it can be brought down the tube into chamber B and stationed near the argon chamber. The cupronickel (or stainless steel) connecting tubes are soldered through a cap with a side arm. This cap fits over the top of a tall glass Dewar flask and is attached to the Dewar with a rubber sleeve.† The side arm is connected by heavy-wall vacuum hose to a high-capacity mechanical vacuum pump.

If the vapor pressure of liquid nitrogen is used for the temperature measurement, one allows N_2 gas to condense in chamber B and the pressures can be read directly on a regular manometer. If a copper-constantan thermocouple is used, the tube to chamber B should be sealed off at the top where the wires come out. Since chamber B is then not used, all further instructions concerning it may be disregarded.‡

† The top of a rubber surgical glove makes an excellent sleeve.

‡ Alternatively, with a slight change in apparatus design, helium-gas thermometry can be used to measure the bath temperature. The procedure is described in Exp. 1.

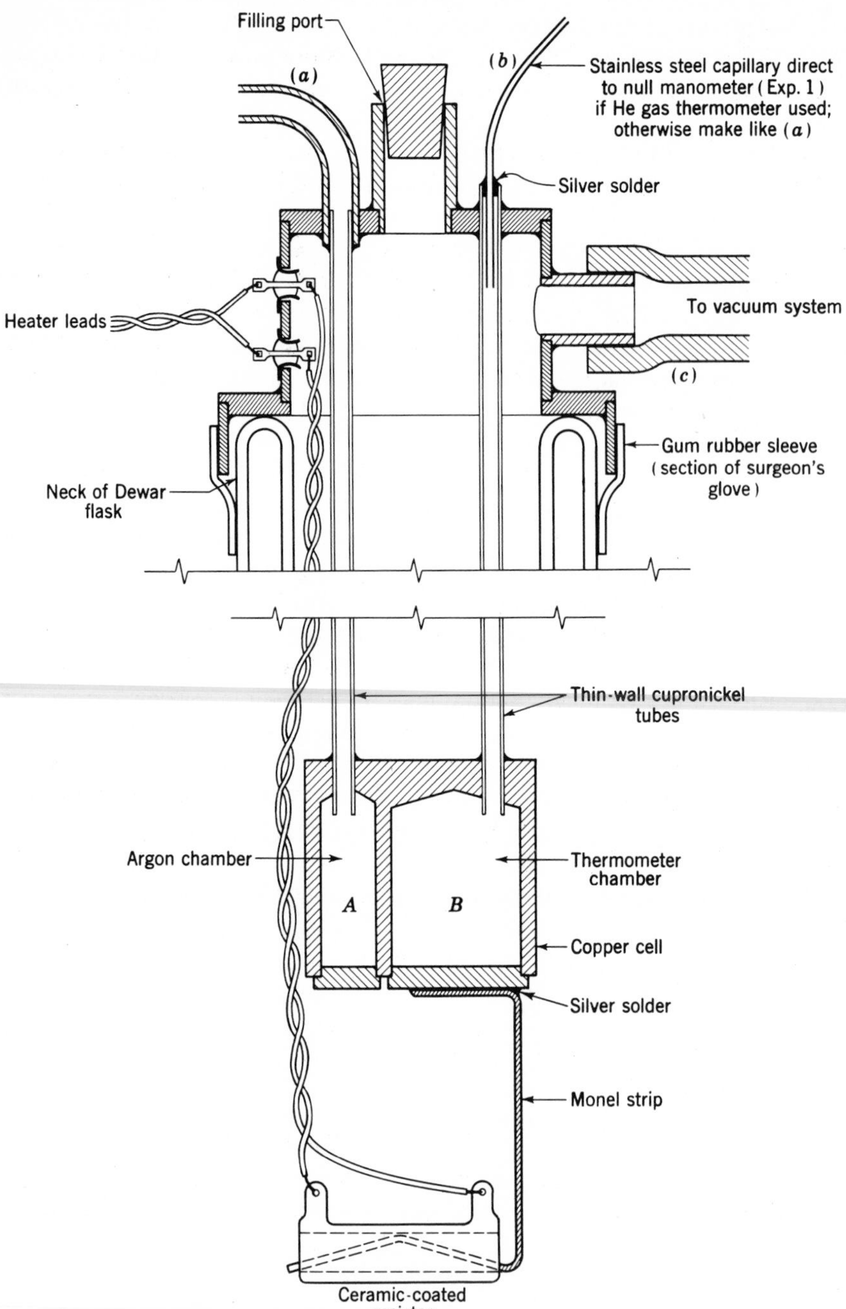

FIG. 2. Low-temperature vapor-pressure apparatus. (Metal parts to be well tinned and soft-soldered, except where otherwise indicated.)

Procedure. The apparatus should be assembled by connecting the necessary manometers, filling lines, and pumping lines; see Fig. 3. Evacuate each chamber by closing clamp or stopcock *C* and stopcocks *A*2 and *B*2 and opening stopcocks

$A1$ and $B1$. Then close stopcocks $A1$ and $B1$ and test for leaks in either chamber by waiting approximately 15 min to see if the manometers indicate any increase in pressure.

Fill chamber A and its manometer with argon at 1 atm and close stopcock $A2$. **Slowly** raise the Dewar filled with liquid nitrogen until the copper cell is almost completely immersed (do *not* immerse the connecting tubes above the cell). The argon pressure should drop to about 200 mm of Hg. **Slowly** allow N_2 gas to enter chamber B until the pressure is constant at about 1 atm, and then close stopcock $B2$. Now raise the Dewar all the way up, and attach the cap to the top of the Dewar. The copper cell should be sufficiently far below the liquid-nitrogen level to ensure that the cell will remain submerged throughout the run. (If necessary, additional liquid nitrogen may be added through the filling port in the cap at this time.) Leave the filling port open.

To ensure the attainment of equilibrium (and to check that no leaks have developed on cooling), take argon pressure readings and temperature readings every 5 min until at least three readings show no significant drift. Also record the atmospheric pressure from a barometer.

Then close the nitrogen filling port with a tightly fitting rubber stopper and begin pumping on the liquid-nitrogen refrigerant by opening clamp or stopcock C. Take argon vapor-pressure readings and temperature readings over the range 63 to 77°K. This can be done by clamping off the pumping line periodically and taking data at intermediate points. Or one can pump as rapidly as possible to achieve the lowest temperature, close off the pumping line, and take data on the warm-up. Since warm-up will be very slow, it is best to have a heater immersed in the liquid nitrogen to provide intermittent heating between readings.

FIG. 3. Vacuum and gas connections for the apparatus shown in Fig. 2.

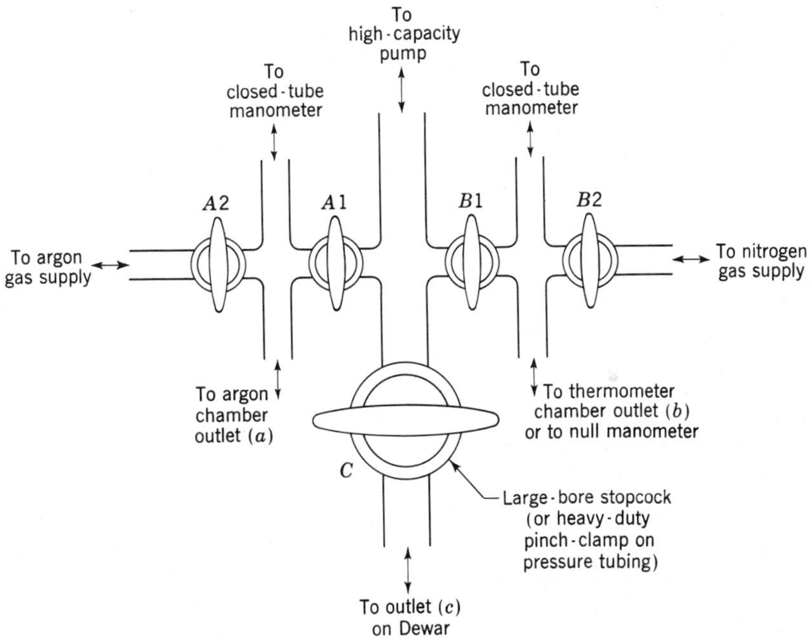

CALCULATIONS

Compute the temperatures and tabulate them along with the corresponding argon vapor pressures. If N_2 vapor pressures were used for thermometry, calculate T from the equation of Henning and Otto[8]

$$\log p(\text{mm}) = 7.781845 - \frac{341.619}{T} - 0.0062649T \qquad (12)$$

The most rapid technique is to calculate p from Eq. (12) at intervals of 1°K, plot p vs. T, and read temperatures from this graph. If a copper-constantan thermocouple was used, convert potential readings to temperatures using Aston's tables.[9] Calculate T_0 (the bath temperature at atmospheric pressure) from Eq. (12), and look up the corresponding emf. Compare it with your observed value. If they disagree, apply a constant additive correction to all emf readings before using the tables.

Plot the argon vapor-pressure data as $\log p$ vs. $1/T$, find the slope at 70°K, and use Eq. (2) to obtain the molar heat of sublimation $\Delta\tilde{H}$.

From Eqs. (6), (7), and (8) calculate the lattice energy of solid argon at 70°K in calories per mole.

X-ray diffraction data[10] give for the cubic cell dimension of solid argon the value 5.43 A. Find the nearest-neighbor distance a, and use Eqs. (10) and (11) to calculate a theoretical value of the lattice energy. Compare the theoretical and experimental values.

APPARATUS

Tall Dewar flask (preferably with vertical unsilvered strip); support for Dewar; copper cell and cap assembly as shown in figure; rubber stopper to fit filling port; rubber sleeve; eight lengths of heavy-wall rubber tubing; high-capacity mechanical vacuum pump; gas-handling assembly with four stopcocks (see figure); heavy-duty hose clamp; two closed-tube manometers; Variac for heater supply. If a copper-constantan thermocouple is to be used, a Dewar flask for ice-water reference junction and a potentiometer circuit are needed.

Supplies of argon and dry nitrogen gas at 1 atm; liquid nitrogen.

REFERENCES

1. W. J. Moore, "Physical Chemistry," 2d ed., pp. 188, 357, Prentice-Hall, Englewood Cliffs, N.J. (1955).
2. L. D. Landau and E. M. Lifshitz, "Statistical Physics," pp. 187–190, Addison-Wesley, Reading, Mass. (1958).
3. "American Institute of Physics Handbook," pp. 4–47, McGraw-Hill, New York (1957).
4. K. S. Pitzer, "Quantum Chemistry," Table A19-2, p. 503, Prentice-Hall, Englewood Cliffs, N.J. (1953).
5. J. A. Beattie and W. H. Stockmayer, The Thermodynamics and Statistical Mechanics of Real Gases, in H. S. Taylor and S. Glasstone (eds.), "A Treatise on Physical Chemistry, vol. II, States of Matter," 3d ed., chap. II, pp. 305–306, Van Nostrand, Princeton, N.J. (1951).
6. *Ibid.,* pp. 323–328.
7. *Ibid.,* p. 309.
8. F. Henning and J. Otto, *Physik. Z.,* **37,** 634 (1936).
9. J. G. Aston, E. Willihnganz, and G. H. Messerly, *J. Am. Chem. Soc.,* **57,** 1642 (1935).
10. "Handbook of Chemistry and Physics," 41st ed., Chemical Rubber Publishing Co., Cleveland (1960).

Experiment 47. Low-temperature Heat Capacity of Solids

The heat capacity of solids has played a lively role in many theoretical developments of the past and continues to present challenging problems even today. As early as 1818 Dulong and Petit stated as an empirical law that the heat capacity of a chemical element in the solid state was approximately 6 cal deg^{-1} g-atom^{-1}. This law played a significant role in the determination of atomic weights from chemical combining weights. Soon after the development of statistical mechanics, this law was given a theoretical foundation based on classical mechanics. However, it was then observed experimentally that heat capacities at low temperatures were much smaller than those at room temperature, in contradiction with the classical Dulong-Petit theory which predicted a constant $\tilde{C}_v$ independent of temperature. Einstein's semiquantitative explanation of the fact that C_v approaches zero as T approaches 0°K was one of the early triumphs of quantum theory.

In the present experiment the heat capacity of aluminum will be determined at several temperatures over the range from 77 to 300°K, and the data will be interpreted in terms of the Debye theory of specific heats.

THEORY

We shall be concerned with developing a theory of the *lattice heat capacity* at constant volume for macrocrystalline solids. Special phenomena such as transition points will not be considered; the contribution of electronic specific heats in the case of metals will be mentioned only briefly. For simplicity the discussion will be limited to monatomic solids with a simple crystal structure (one atom per primitive unit cell), but the results will be applicable at low temperatures to any crystalline solid.

Let us consider a *large* single crystal consisting of N atoms (all of the same kind) which interact with harmonic forces. That is, the atoms are assumed to obey Hooke's law, whereby the restoring force on an atom is directly proportional to the displacement from its equilibrium position. It can be shown that such a crystal is equivalent to a set of $3N$ *independent,* one-dimensional harmonic oscillators.† Therefore, we can write the vibrational energy of the crystal as

$$E = \sum_{i=1}^{3N} (\bar{\epsilon})_i \tag{1}$$

where $(\bar{\epsilon})_i$ is the average energy of the ith oscillator. The classical theory of the equipartition of energy[1] (see Exp. 4) states that the average energy in each vibrational degree of freedom (each normal mode) is kT. Thus, on the basis of classical statistical mechanics

$$E = 3NkT$$

$$\tilde{C}_v = \left(\frac{\partial \tilde{E}}{\partial T}\right)_v = 3R = 5.96 \text{ cal deg}^{-1} \text{ g-atom}^{-1} \tag{2}$$

which confirms the law of Dulong and Petit. As one might expect of a classical

†To be exact there are ($3N$-6) vibrational degrees of freedom and there should be ($3N$-6) oscillators corresponding to the normal modes of vibration (see Exp. 41).

treatment of vibration, Eq. (2) is not adequate at low temperatures. Indeed, this equation is not always valid even at room temperature (see Fig. 1).

The variation of C_v with temperature is a consequence of the existence of discrete, quantized energy levels for each of the one-dimensional oscillators, as required by quantum mechanics. For a harmonic oscillator with vibrational frequency ν, the allowed energy states are

$$\epsilon_n = (n + \tfrac{1}{2})h\nu \qquad n = 0, 1, 2, 3, \ldots \tag{3}$$

In order to find $\bar{\epsilon}$ for this oscillator at a temperature T one must use the Boltzmann distribution law[2] for the population of the various energy states. The probability of finding a harmonic oscillator in the state with energy ϵ_n is

$$P_n = \frac{e^{-\epsilon_n/kT}}{\sum_{n=0}^{\infty} e^{-\epsilon_n/kT}} = \frac{e^{-nh\nu/kT}}{\sum_{n=0}^{\infty} e^{-nh\nu/kT}} \tag{4}$$

The average energy $\bar{\epsilon}$ is obviously

$$\bar{\epsilon} = \sum_{n=0}^{\infty} P_n\epsilon_n = \frac{1}{2}h\nu + h\nu\frac{\sum_n ne^{-nh\nu/kT}}{\sum_n e^{-nh\nu/kT}} \tag{5}$$

Since $\sum_{n=0}^{\infty} x^n = (1-x)^{-1}$ and $\sum_{n=0}^{\infty} nx^n = x(1-x)^{-2}$, we find that†

$$\bar{\epsilon} = \frac{1}{2}h\nu + \frac{h\nu}{e^{h\nu/kT} - 1} \tag{6}$$

Combining Eqs. (1) and (6), we obtain for the entire crystal

$$E - E_0 = \sum_{i=1}^{3N} \frac{h\nu_i}{e^{h\nu_i/kT} - 1} \tag{7}$$

where E_0 is the zero-point energy of the crystal. For the sake of completeness one can include the lattice energy U (see Exp. 46) in E_0 and write

$$E_0 = E_0(\text{vib}) + U = \sum_{i=1}^{3N} \tfrac{1}{2}h\nu_i + U \tag{8}$$

In both Eqs. (7) and (8) ν_i is the frequency of the ith oscillator (ith normal mode of vibration of the lattice). Since E_0 depends only on the volume (both U and all ν_i are functions of the volume per atom) and is independent of temperature, we can obtain immediately a general expression for the lattice heat capacity of any harmonic solid:

$$C_v \equiv \left(\frac{\partial E}{\partial T}\right)_v = k\sum_{i=1}^{3N}\left(\frac{h\nu_i}{kT}\right)^2 \frac{e^{h\nu_i/kT}}{(e^{h\nu_i/kT} - 1)^2} \tag{9}$$

Einstein used Eq. (9) to calculate heat capacities in semiquantitative agreement with experiment by making the simplifying assumption that the atoms oscillate

† This result could also have been obtained directly from $\bar{\epsilon} = kT^2(\partial \ln z/\partial T)$ where z, the vibrational partition function, is given[3] by

$$z \equiv \sum_{n=0}^{\infty} e^{-(n+1/2)h\nu/kT} = \frac{e^{-h\nu/2kT}}{1 - e^{-h\nu/kT}}$$

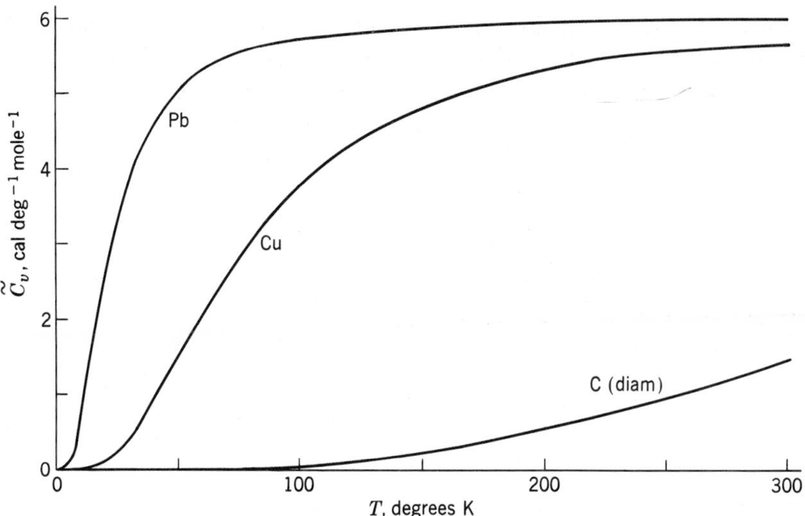

FIG. 1. Low-temperature molar heat capacities of lead, copper, and diamond.

independently and all the oscillators have the same frequency ν_0 (i.e., all $\nu_i = \nu_0$). This model explains in a crude way the great difference in C_v for lead and diamond (see Fig. 1). In a lead crystal the atoms are heavy and the forces between atoms are weak (Pb has a high compressibility); thus ν_0 for lead should be very low and the classical limit will be achieved well below room temperature. In diamond the atoms are light and the forces between atoms are strong (diamond has a low compressibility); thus ν_0 for diamond will be much higher and the classical limit is not achieved even at room temperature. The Einstein model is, however, inadequate at very low temperatures, where it predicts that C_v will approach zero exponentially as T approaches 0°K. The actual dependence of the (lattice only) heat capacity on T at low temperatures has been found experimentally to be T^3.

The failure of the Einstein theory to predict correctly the low-temperature behavior of C_v is due to the crudeness of the simplifying assumption that all $\nu_i = \nu_0$. Actually, of course, atomic motions are strongly coupled through interatomic forces, and the $3N$ normal modes have many different frequencies, as would be expected from our knowledge of molecular vibrations (see Exp. 41). The frequencies of the $3N$ normal modes range from very near zero (sonic vibrations; wavelengths comparable to the dimensions of the crystal) to some highest value (wavelength comparable to the interatomic spacing).

For a large crystal there are about 10^{24} normal modes which are so closely spaced in frequency that it is possible to treat the distribution as continuous and define a *distribution function* $g(\nu)$ such that $g(\nu)\,d\nu$ is the number of normal modes in the interval ν to $\nu + d\nu$. Using this distribution function, Eqs. (7) and (9) can be rewritten as

$$E - E_0 = kT \int_0^{\nu_{\max}} \frac{u}{e^u - 1} g(\nu)\, d\nu \tag{10}$$

$$C_v = k \int_0^{\nu_{\max}} \frac{u^2 e^u}{(e^u - 1)^2} g(\nu)\, d\nu \tag{11}$$

where $u = h\nu/kT$ and ν_{max} is the highest frequency. Thus the problem of the lattice thermodynamic properties of a solid becomes a question of evaluating $g(\nu)$.

Debye Theory. The theory of specific heats was greatly improved by Debye, who assumed that a monatomic solid could be treated as a continuous elastic medium with no dispersion. That is, the mass of the crystal is considered as smeared out uniformly over the entire volume instead of being localized at discrete lattice sites, and the velocity of waves traveling through the solid is taken as independent of their frequency. Such a model provides a reasonable description of the low-frequency modes, since their wavelengths are much longer than the unit cell dimensions of the lattice. Thus the Debye theory should be valid at very low temperatures where only low frequencies contribute significantly to the C_v integral. The brave step taken by Debye was to propose this model for describing a solid over the entire temperature range.

For the Debye model, $g(\nu)$ can be shown[4] to be proportional to ν^2:

$$g(\nu) = \frac{12\pi V}{c^3}\nu^2 \tag{12}$$

where V is the volume of the solid and c is an "average" elastic wave velocity.† For a lattice of N atoms there are $3N$ normal modes and the dynamics of the motion gives a highest frequency ν_{max}, just as in the case of a polyatomic gas molecule. But the Debye theory is based on a continuum model, and one must introduce an artificial cutoff frequency ν_D to restrict the total number of vibrations to $3N$. This cutoff frequency is obtained from

$$3N = \int_0^{\nu_D} g(\nu)\,d\nu = \int_0^{\nu_D} \frac{12\pi V}{c^3}\nu^2\,d\nu = \frac{4\pi V}{c^3}{\nu_D}^3 \tag{13}$$

Therefore, we can rewrite Eq. (12) as

$$\begin{aligned} g(\nu) &= \frac{9N}{{\nu_D}^3}\nu^2 \qquad 0 \leqslant \nu \leqslant \nu_D \\ &= 0 \qquad\qquad \nu > \nu_D \end{aligned} \tag{14}$$

With this Debye distribution function Eqs. (10) and (11) can be written as

$$E - E_0 = \frac{9NkT}{{\nu_D}^3}\int_0^{\nu_D} \frac{u}{e^u - 1}\nu^2\,d\nu = 9NkT\left(\frac{kT}{h\nu_D}\right)^3 \int_0^{h\nu_D/kT} \frac{u^3}{e^u - 1}\,du \tag{15}$$

$$C_v = 9Nk\left(\frac{kT}{h\nu_D}\right)^3 \int_0^{h\nu_D/kT} \frac{u^4 e^u}{(e^u - 1)^2}\,du \tag{16}$$

At this point it is appropriate to introduce a new variable Θ, called the "Debye characteristic temperature" and defined by

$$\Theta = \frac{h\nu_D}{k} \tag{17}$$

† This is defined by

$$\frac{3}{c^3} = \left\langle \frac{1}{{U_l}^3} + \frac{1}{{U_t}^3} + \frac{1}{{U_t'}^3} \right\rangle_{av}$$

In general, the three ultrasonic velocities (one longitudinal and two transverse) depend on the direction of propagation. Many derivations of the Debye theory assume an isotropic medium for which $U_t = U_t'$ and all velocities are independent of direction, but this is not basic to the Debye model.

We can now give expressions for the energy and heat capacity *per gram atom* in terms of this single parameter which characterizes the solid:

$$\frac{\tilde{E} - \tilde{E}_0}{3RT} = 3\left(\frac{T}{\Theta}\right)^3 \int_0^{\Theta/T} \frac{u^3}{e^u - 1}\, du \tag{18}$$

$$\frac{\tilde{C}_v}{3R} = 3\left(\frac{T}{\Theta}\right)^3 \int_0^{\Theta/T} \frac{u^4 e^u}{(e^u - 1)^2}\, du \tag{19}$$

For a "Debye crystal" the zero-point vibrational energy $\tilde{E}_0$(vib) is equal to $\frac{9}{8}R\Theta$; this can be derived from Eq. (8) in a manner exactly parallel to the treatment given above.

The integrals in Eqs. (18) and (19) cannot be evaluated analytically as a function of Θ/T, but numerical values have been tabulated.[5] However, at very low temperatures ($T < \Theta/16$) the values of the integrals are substantially equal to the definite integrals from 0 to ∞ (which are known). Thus, one obtains the famous Debye T^3 law:

$$\frac{\tilde{C}_v}{3R} = \frac{4\pi^4}{5}\left(\frac{T}{\Theta}\right)^3 \tag{20}$$

As a demonstration of the Debye theory we shall replot the data in Fig. 1 as $\tilde{C}_v/3R$ vs. T/Θ; these are shown in Fig. 2 along with the curve predicted by Eq. (19). The Θ values used in Fig. 2 were chosen empirically to give the best possible fit to the theoretical curve, but Θ values could be calculated from experimental low-temperature ultrasonic velocities using the expression

$$\Theta = \frac{h}{k}\left(\frac{3N}{4\pi V}\right)^{1/3} c \tag{21}$$

which is derived from Eqs. (13) and (17). In general the agreement between Debye theory and experiment is quite good but not perfect; in particular, there is often a disagreement between the empirical value of Θ chosen to fit the heat capacity and the ultrasonic value given by Eq. (21). Such difficulties are not surprising,

FIG. 2. A plot of $\tilde{C}_v/3R$ vs. T/Θ for lead, copper, and diamond. The solid line is the theoretical curve given by the Debye theory.

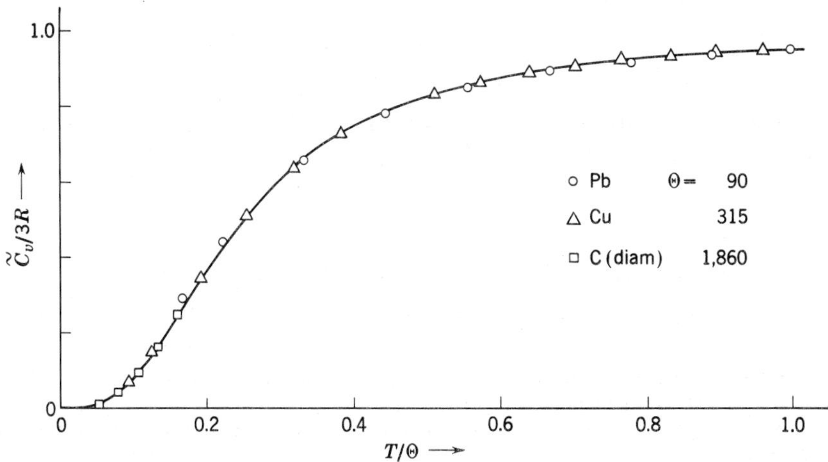

since the Debye theory is based on a quite simplified model for a solid. More recently, considerable progress has been made using the theory of lattice dynamics[4, 6] which is based on a more realistic model but is much more complicated mathematically. It should be emphasized that the Debye theory is still perhaps the best one-parameter theory available and is very useful in many problems because of its simplicity.

$C_p - C_v$ Correction. The theory presented above has been concerned with C_v, the heat capacity at constant volume, but the values measured experimentally for solids are almost always C_p, the heat capacity at constant pressure. The difference between C_p and C_v is given by thermodynamics[7] as

$$C_p - C_v = \frac{9TV\alpha^2}{\beta} \tag{22}$$

where 3α is the volume coefficient of expansion and β is the isothermal volume compressibility. Both 3α and β are functions of temperature, and they are often not known at low temperatures. It is common practice to replace this exact expression by an empirical approximation[7]—the so-called Nernst-Lindemann equation:

$$\tilde{C}_p - \tilde{C}_v \cong AT\tilde{C}_p{}^2 \tag{23}$$

where A is a constant evaluated from the room-temperature properties of the solid.

Electronic Specific Heats. In a metal there are a large number of conduction electrons which are relatively free to move throughout the crystal. The heat capacity of this "free-electron gas" must be considered in addition to the heat capacity due to lattice vibrations discussed previously. Because of the very small mass of the electron, this electron gas does not behave like a classical gas of atoms or molecules, and it is necessary to use quantum statistics to predict its properties. It has been shown[8] that the heat capacity of such a free-electron gas is

$$\tilde{C}_v(\text{el}) = \gamma T \tag{24}$$

where γ is a constant for a given metal and is usually of the order of 10^{-4} cal deg^{-2} g-atom^{-1}. Thus the electronic specific heat at room temperature is only about 3×10^{-2} cal deg^{-1} g-atom^{-1}, and it is almost negligible compared with the lattice heat capacity of about 6 cal deg^{-1} g-atom^{-1}. It becomes important, however, at very low temperatures, since $\tilde{C}_v$ (lattice) goes to zero more rapidly than $\tilde{C}_v$ (el).

METHOD

The method of determining C_p in this experiment is identical in principle with that used in Exp. 10: electrical work is degraded to "Joule heat" by a heating coil, and the resulting temperature rise ΔT is measured. The only difference is that now we wish to use Eq. (V-13*a*)

$$C_p = \frac{-w_{el}}{\Delta T} \tag{25}$$

to obtain C_p for the sample alone *without* any contribution due to the calorimeter itself. To achieve this we must isolate the sample as well as possible from its surroundings (including the walls of the calorimeter) and must reduce stray heat leaks to a minimum (see the discussion in Principles of Calorimetry, Chap. V).

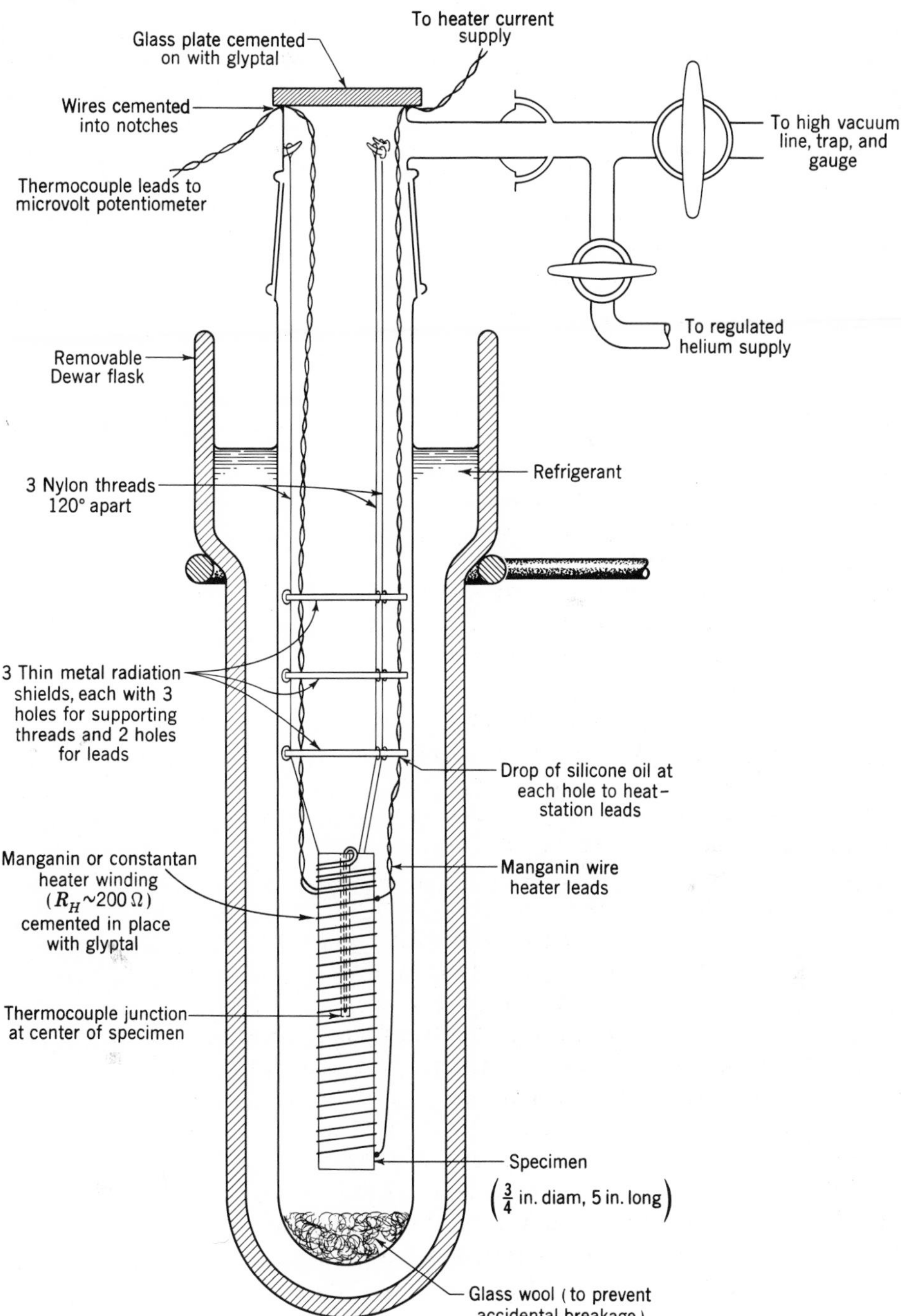

FIG. 3. A simple low-temperature calorimeter.

Calorimeter Design. A simple design for a low-temperature calorimeter is shown in Fig. 3. A large Pyrex tube containing the sample is immersed in a tall Dewar flask filled with the refrigerant. Suitable refrigerants for this experiment are liquid nitrogen and Dry Ice-acetone. The sample (preferably in the form of a cylinder) hangs by three nylon threads from three thin aluminum radiation shields, which are hung from the top of a large, standard-taper joint. Heater and thermocouple leads are sealed tightly in tiny notches in the top edge by attaching a flat glass top plate with glyptal; they are also heat-stationed at the metal shields. Helium gas can be admitted to the system as a heat-transfer gas to bring the sample initially to the bath temperature; then the entire tube can be evacuated to eliminate gas conduction between the sample and the walls of the tube.

Heat leaks due to radiation, residual gas conduction, and conduction along the leads and threads are small but not negligible. This design is satisfactory only if the temperature of the sample is close to that of the bath; the procedure must be planned with this in mind.†

Note that the heat capacity which is measured is that of the sample alone except for a very small contribution due to the "addenda" (heater wire and cement). One may either neglect C_p(addenda) or calculate a value for it and subtract this correction term from the total C_p.

Heating Circuit. The heater should consist of many turns of fine constantan wire wound around the sample cylinder. If a metal sample is used, varnish the surface, and while it is still sticky, coat the sides of the sample with cigarette paper to provide electrical insulation. A convenient heating tape made of constantan wire and silk fibers interwoven (called "Silko ribbon") is available from De Bary and Co. Ltd., Basel, Switzerland. The heater wire must be attached to the sample with an adhesive that provides a reliable thermal contact between the two.

The electrical work in joules is given to a good approximation by

$$-w_{el} = \int \bar{\imath}_H E_H \, dt \cong \bar{\imath}_H \bar{E}_H \, \Delta t \tag{26}$$

where $\bar{\imath}_H$ and $\bar{E}_H$ are the average heater current in amperes and the average potential drop across the heater in volts during a heating period of duration Δt sec. Figure 4 shows an electrical circuit designed to operate a heater of about 200 ohms using a 110-v dc source; this circuit can be easily modified to utilize lower voltage dc sources. Since i_H is about 0.06 to 0.08 amp in this circuit, E_H is approximately 14 v and a potential divider is necessary in order to use a potentiometer for measuring voltages. The potential divider is two high-resistance resistors in parallel with the heater (from a to b in Fig. 4). Use of the dummy heater enables one to achieve a steady current flow through the circuit before switching on the heater; thus i_H and E_H will vary only slightly during a heating period, and only a few values of each are required for each heating.

Combining Eqs. (25) and (26) we obtain for C_p in calories per degree

$$C_p = \frac{\bar{\imath}_H \bar{E}_H \, \Delta t}{4.184 \, \Delta T} = \frac{\bar{\imath}_H (\bar{E} - \bar{\imath}_H R_L) \, \Delta t}{4.184 \, \Delta T} \tag{27}$$

where $\bar{E}$ is the average potential drop across the heater and its leads (from a to b in Fig. 4) and R_L is the resistance of these leads (a to c and b to d in Fig. 4). The value of R_L is measured at room temperature and is assumed to be independent of temperature. The correction term $\bar{\imath}_H R_L$ takes account of the heat dissipated in the

† More complex designs[9] are possible in which the sample is completely surrounded by an adiabatic shield (i.e., a shield isolated from the sample but maintained at the same temperature as the sample at all times). Such designs will reduce heat leaks and permit operation at temperatures considerably above bath temperature, but they require a more complicated procedure and are difficult to construct.

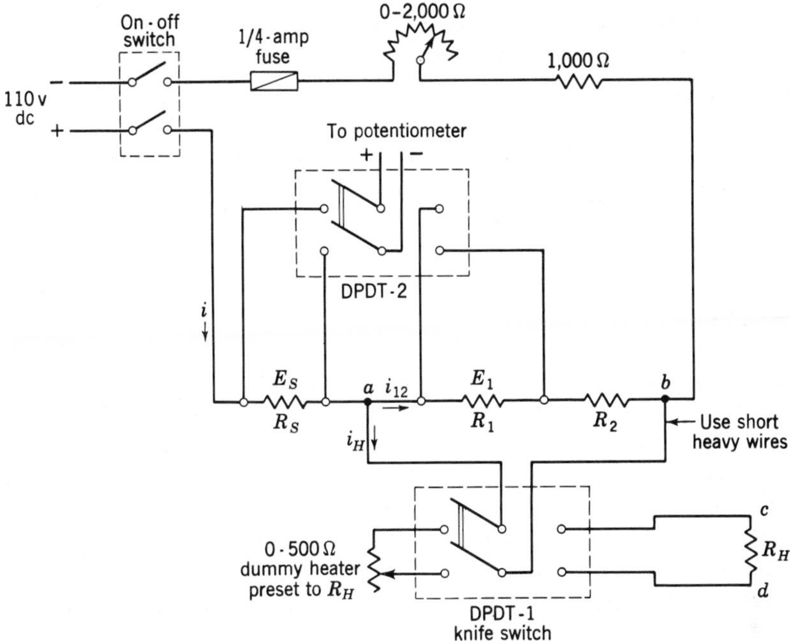

FIG. 4. A heater power-supply circuit designed to operate from a 110-v dc source. Typical values are $R_1 = 1{,}500$ ohms, $R_2 = 25{,}000$ ohms, $R_S = 10$ ohms, $R_H = 200$ ohms, and $R_L \cong 15$ ohms; R_L is the resistance of the leads from *a* to *c* and from *b* to *d*.

leads and is based on the assumption that none of this heat is delivered to the sample. (In the present design most of this heat flows to the radiation shield.) Now the directly measured quantities are E_S, the potential drop across the standard resistor R_S, and E_1, the drop across R_1. From $i_H + i_{12} = i = E_S/R_S$, where i is the total current and i_{12} is the current through the potential divider $(R_1 + R_2)$, and the fact that $i_H(R_H + R_L) = i_{12}(R_1 + R_2)$, one can easily derive an expression for $\bar{\imath}_H$:

$$\bar{\imath}_H = \frac{\bar{E}_S}{R_S[1 + (R_H + R_L)/(R_1 + R_2)]} \tag{28}$$

The term in brackets is very close to unity (1.008 for the values given in Fig. 4) and will be assumed independent of temperature; use the room-temperature value of R_H in calculating it. Also it is clear that $\bar{E}$ is given by

$$\bar{E} = \bar{E}_1 \frac{R_1 + R_2}{R_1} \tag{29}$$

Both E_S and E_1 can be measured with a Student Potentiometer circuit; see Chap. XV for details. Accurate room-temperature values of R_L and R_H must be determined before assembling the calorimeter and should be given. Values of R_1 and R_2 may be determined by the student or given by the instructor.

Temperature. The sample temperature is measured with a thermocouple which should be affixed in a small-diameter hole down the axis of the sample cylinder with an adhesive to ensure good thermal contact. Use either a copper-constantan or a chromel-alumel thermocouple (see Chap. XVI). Since the sensitivity of these thermocouples is ~15 μv deg^{-1} at 80°K and ~40 μv deg^{-1} at

300°K, it is necessary to use a precision potentiometer which will measure potentials in the 1- to 10-mv range to within ± 1 μv. One should also use heating periods which give ΔT between 5 and 10° to reduce the uncertainty in ΔT. Very large ΔT values should be avoided because heat leaks may introduce a serious error (radiation heat loss is especially serious at higher temperatures).

EXPERIMENTAL

It is assumed in the discussion below that an aluminum sample (with heater and calibrated thermocouple attached) has been mounted and that the calorimeter has been assembled. It is also assumed that values of R_1, R_2, R_S, R_L, and R_H as well as the mass of the sample and of the addenda are known.

Make all necessary connections to set up both a Student Potentiometer (for measurement of E_S and E_1) and a high-precision potentiometer (for thermocouple measurements); see Chap. XV. Standardize both potentiometers against a standard cell. At the same time, prepare an ice-water mixture in a 1-qt Dewar flask as the 0°C bath for the reference junction of the thermocouple. Fill the Dewar completely full of crushed ice, rinse the ice with a small amount of cold distilled water, and then add enough cold distilled water to fill the Dewar half full of liquid. Insert the junction well into the liquid.

With the sample at room temperature record the thermocouple emf and check the temperature corresponding to this reading with the reading of a mercury thermometer mounted close to the calorimeter.

With stopcock *C* closed, open stopcocks *A* and *B*. After pumping for 5 min, check the pressure. Continue to pump out the calorimeter until the pressure is less than 10^{-4} mm Hg. During this pumping period, close knife switch DPDT-1 so as to insert the dummy heater into the circuit and turn on the heater power supply. To facilitate later measurements, obtain approximate values of E_S and E_1 with current flowing through the dummy. The knife switch DPDT-2 permits the Student Potentiometer to be connected rapidly to either R_S or R_1. By adjusting the 0- to 2000-ohm variable resistor, obtain a current of between 0.06 and 0.08 amp and record the observed values of E_S and E_1.

When the vacuum is satisfactory, make a heat-capacity measurement at room temperature. Follow the procedure given below.

After this initial measurement is completed, make one or two measurements at liquid-nitrogen temperature. First close stopcock *B* and then open *C* **slowly** to fill the calorimeter with helium gas at about 1 atm. Now close stopcock *A* and slowly raise the Dewar flask, partially filled with liquid nitrogen, up over the calorimeter. Make sure that the top of the Dewar is above the uppermost radiation shield. After the Dewar is clamped in place, fill it to the top with liquid nitrogen. Check the temperature of the sample; it is necessary to reverse the thermocouple leads at the potentiometer in order to measure temperatures below 0°C. It may require about 40 to 50 min for the sample temperature to achieve a steady value. When the rate of drift is zero or very small, pump out the helium as before and check the pressure. After the pressure has dropped to 10^{-4} mm or less, make a C_p measurement as described in the procedure below. If possible, make a second measurement immediately after completing the first one.

Next make measurements at Dry Ice temperature. First remove the Dewar and empty out the liquid nitrogen. Partly fill the Dewar with a Dry Ice-acetone mixture prepared in advance. Fill the calorimeter with helium gas as before, and then slowly raise the Dewar into place and fill it to the top. **Caution:** Dry Ice-acetone baths tend to foam badly; see Chap. XVI for the details of preparing and handling this refrigerant. When the temperature is almost steady but still slowly rising, pump out the helium and carry out one or two C_p measurements in the same manner as at liquid-nitrogen temperature.

At the end of the experiment, leave the calorimeter at room temperature.

Procedure for a Run. We shall assume that the sample temperature is close to bath temperature and that the calorimeter is already evacuated.

Record the thermocouple emf and the clock time every 30 sec for at least 5 min; the rate of change should be small and constant, if not zero. During this time check the standardization of the Student Potentiometer and then set it at the expected value of E_S.

Start a stopwatch and simultaneously turn on the heater by rapidly throwing the knife switch DPDT-1. Record the values of E_S and E_1 during the heating period. First read E_S and then throw switch DPDT-2 and read E_1; alternate the readings until several values of each have been recorded. After a temperature rise of about 7° (the desired thermocouple emf should be determined in advance), turn off the heater and simultaneously stop the stopwatch. Record the elapsed time Δt.

During the heating period it is only necessary to make occasional thermocouple readings in order to decide when to turn off the heater. However, as soon as the heater is turned off, the thermocouple emf must be recorded every 30 sec for 10 min or until the temperature is constant.

If dT/dt (that is, $d\mathcal{E}/dt$) is not too large, another measurement of C_p can be made immediately by using the postheating temperature drift rate as the preheating rate for a second heating period.

CALCULATIONS

For each heating period, calculate the average values $\bar{E}_S$ and $\bar{E}_1$, and use Eqs. (28) and (29) to obtain $\bar{\imath}_H$ and $\bar{E}$. Then determine the initial temperature T_1 and the final temperature T_2. Before electrical heating, the temperature should have changed only *very slowly,* if at all. However, after the heating period, the sample may have slowly cooled toward the bath temperature. If either the pre- or post-heating temperatures show a steady drift, plot the thermocouple emf vs. time for the entire run and extrapolate to the mid-point of the heating period to determine the emf corresponding to T_1 and T_2. Now calculate C_p from Eq. (27); this value is an average over the temperature interval and can be taken as corresponding to a mean temperature $T = (T_1 + T_2)/2$. If the heat capacity of the addenda is known at T, it should be subtracted from the total C_p given by Eq. (27). The molar heat capacity of aluminum is given by

$$\tilde{C}_p(\text{Al}) = \frac{26.97}{W}\,[C_p - C_p(\text{addenda})] \tag{30}$$

where W is the mass of the aluminum sample in grams. The constant-volume heat capacity can now be calculated from Eq. (23); the value of the constant A for aluminum[10] is 2.23×10^{-5} g-atom cal^{-1}. Tabulate the values of T, ΔT, C_p, $\tilde{C}_p$, $\tilde{C}_v$ for each run.

DISCUSSION

The coefficient γ which determines the electronic heat capacity of a metal is 3.5×10^{-4} cal deg^{-2} g-atom^{-1} for aluminum.[11] One can then calculate $\tilde{C}_v$(el) from Eq. (24) and, if necessary, correct $\tilde{C}_v$ to obtain $\tilde{C}_v$(lattice). The Debye characteristic temperature Θ which best fits the lattice heat capacity of aluminum[10] over the range 77 to 300°K is 391°K. Plot your values of $\tilde{C}_v$ vs. T, and for comparison, draw a smooth curve based on the predictions of the Debye theory. Comment on the agreement between your points and the theoretical curve; in particular state whether any deviations can be explained by systematic errors in the method used here.

APPARATUS

Low-temperature calorimeter, assembled containing an aluminum sample with heater attached and thermocouple installed; vacuum line; tall Dewar flask and clamp; 1-qt Dewar for ice; complete potentiometer setup for measuring current and voltage; high-precision potentiometer setup for thermocouple readings; heater power supply; two good-quality knife switches; clock and stopwatch; 0 to 30°C thermometer.

Supply of helium gas; refrigerants (liquid nitrogen and Dry Ice-acetone); distilled-water ice.

REFERENCES

1. C. Kittel, "Introduction to Solid State Physics," 2d ed., p. 120, Wiley, New York (1956).
2. J. C. Slater, "Introduction to Chemical Physics," pp. 52–53, McGraw-Hill, New York (1939).
3. W. J. Moore, "Physical Chemistry," 2d ed., p. 359, Prentice-Hall, Englewood Cliffs, N.J. (1955).
4. J. deLaunay, The Theory of Specific Heats and Lattice Vibrations, in Seitz and Turnbull (eds.), "Solid State Physics," vol. 2, Academic Press, Inc., New York (1956).
5. K. S. Pitzer, "Quantum Chemistry," Appendix 19, pp. 501–503, Prentice-Hall, Englewood Cliffs, N.J. (1953); J. A. Beattie, *J. Math. Phys.*, **6,** 1 (1926).
6. C. W. Garland, *J. Chem. Educ.*, **34,** 597 (1957).
7. Any standard thermodynamics textbook, such as M. W. Zemansky, "Heat and Thermodynamics," 4th ed., chap. 13, McGraw-Hill, New York (1957).
8. C. Kittel, *op. cit.*, pp. 134–136, 257–259.
9. J. M. Sturtevant, Calorimetry, in A. Weissberger (ed.), "Technique of Organic Chemistry," 2d ed., vol. I, part I, chap. XIV, Interscience, New York (1949).
10. W. F. Giauque and P. F. Meads, *J. Am. Chem. Soc.*, **63,** 1897 (1941).
11. "American Institute of Physics Handbook," pp. 4–48, McGraw-Hill, New York (1957).

GENERAL READING

J. deLaunay, *op. cit.*, especially pp. 220–243.
C. Kittel, *op. cit.*, chaps. 5 and 6.
F. Seitz, "The Modern Theory of Solids," chap. 3, McGraw-Hill, New York (1940).

XV
ELECTRICAL MEASUREMENTS

This chapter is concerned with the principles of the design and operation of several important electrical circuits. Major emphasis is given to galvanometers, potentiometers, and Wheatstone bridges, since they are so frequently used in physical chemistry research. Brief mention is also made of standard resistors and potential dividers. At the end of the chapter, capacitance measurements are discussed. A more complete general discussion of electrical circuits can be found in many standard textbooks.[1]

GALVANOMETERS

The D'Arsonval (or moving-coil) galvanometer consists of a rectangular coil of many turns of insulated copper wire mounted in the field of a magnet, usually a horseshoe-shaped permanent magnet. This coil is suspended from a fine wire or very thin metal strip, which serves as an electrical lead and also as a torsion fiber. Attached to the bottom of the coil is a loosely coiled wire, which serves as the other lead. Current flowing through the coil moves perpendicular to the magnetic lines of force and produces a torque on the coil. Therefore, the coil will rotate in the field until the magnetic torque is balanced by an opposite mechanical torque introduced by twisting the suspension. Motion of the coil can be detected in two ways: by the position of an indicating pointer attached to the coil or by the position of a light beam reflected from a small mirror attached to the suspension. The pointer-type galvanometer is cheaper, more rugged, and less sensitive than the reflecting type. For any type of D'Arsonval galvanometer the amount of deflection per unit of current through the coil will depend on certain design parameters (the size of the coil, the number of turns of wire in the coil, the magnetic field intensity, and the stiffness of the suspension).[2]

The three most significant characteristics which should be considered in choosing the proper galvanometer for a given application are sensitivity, period, and external critical damping resistance. Of these, sensitivity is usually the most critical requirement. For each kind of galvanometer there is a definite *current sensitivity,* which is the current in microamperes required to produce a 1-mm scale deflection. (On reflecting-type galvanometers the ground-glass scale on which the light beam is observed is normally mounted 1 m from the mirror attached to the coil.) It is often of more direct interest to know the *voltage sensitivity* in microvolts per millimeter of scale deflection. This is equal to the current sensitivity multiplied by R, the total resistance in ohms of the entire electrical circuit through which the current is passing (i.e., R is the sum of the galvanometer coil resistance and all external resistance in series with the galvanometer). The period of a galvanometer is the time in seconds required for a complete oscillation of the undamped galvanometer. A critically damped galvanometer will almost reach its final deflection within this time, and it is therefore usually convenient to have as short a period as possible. Since most galvanometers are designed to have a period between 2 and 20 sec, this characteristic is seldom of crucial importance in choosing the proper instrument. It is, however, quite important to choose a galvanometer with the best external critical damping resistance (CDRX) to match the resistance of the circuit in which it will be used. If the galvanometer is greatly underdamped (circuit resistance much greater than the CDRX), the coil will oscillate about its final position after a deflection. If greatly overdamped (circuit resistance much less than the CDRX), the coil will move toward its final position very slowly. Either of these conditions can make the instrument difficult to use; a slight underdamping is preferable to any overdamping for most measurements.

The characteristics of several Leeds and Northrup galvanometers[3] are given in Table 1; comparable instruments are also made by Rubicon and several other manufacturers. For student use, pointer galvanometers similar to the L & N models 2310-d and 2310-e are the most suitable and practical types. If the circuit resistance exclusive of the coil resistance is less than about 125 ohms, type 2310-e has the higher voltage sensitivity, but if the circuit resistance exclusive of the coil resistance exceeds about 125 ohms, type 2310-d has the higher voltage sensitivity. Reflecting-type galvanometers are much more sensitive and should be used for high-precision work. The L & N models 2420 and 2430 are box galvanometers with enclosed lamp and scale. The box contains a mirror system which folds the light beam from the moving mirror several times before it falls on the scale; this permits a 1-m light path to be confined in a box about 10 in. long.

Some pointer-type galvanometers have a clamping device to protect the coil suspension from damage while the instrument is not in use; this clamp must be

TABLE 1. Performance Characteristics for Several Galvanometers[a]

L & N Model No.	Type	Current sensitivity, μa mm^{-1}	Voltage sensitivity for CDRX, μv mm^{-1}	Period, sec	Resistance, ohms	
					CDRX	Coil
2310-d	Pointer	0.125	1380	3.5	10,000	1000
2310-e	Pointer	1.0	46	4.5	30	16
2420-c	Reflecting	0.025	400	3.0	15,000	1000
2420-d	Reflecting	0.04	92	3.0	2000	300
2430-c	Reflecting	0.005	2.1	2.5	400	25
2430-d	Reflecting	0.0005	12.8	3.0	25,000	550
2284-d	Reflecting	0.0013	0.1	5.0	50	25
2284-e	Reflecting	0.005	7.5	1.5	1200	300

[a] Data taken from L & N Catalog ED (1956).

released in order to use the galvanometer. At the end of an experiment, be sure to reclamp the suspension. Most reflecting-type galvanometers do not have such a clamping arrangement but may have special spring mountings to minimize the effect of shock. If a reflecting galvanometer is to be moved any appreciable distance, it is wise to attach a short length of wire across the terminals. This will provide considerable overdamping and thus protect the suspension.

POTENTIOMETER CIRCUITS

As the name implies, the potentiometer is a device for measuring electrical potential difference. Basically it is an electrical circuit containing a precision resistor employed as a variable potential divider; indeed, the name "potentiometer" is often used in radio and electronics technology to denote any variable resistor used as a potential divider.

Basic Circuit. The principle of the potentiometer can be described in terms of the simple "slide-wire" potentiometer shown schematically in Fig. 1. With a constant direct current flowing through the *uniform* resistance slide-wire AB, the potential difference between A and C should be accurately proportional to the length AC. Thus the potentiometer is a device for selecting with high precision any desired electromotive force (emf) which is less than a certain maximum value. This maximum value depends on the construction of the slide-wire and the voltage of the battery. The emf across part of the slide-wire (AC) may be compared with another emf by connecting the negative pole of the external emf E with the negative end of the slide-wire (at A) and connecting its positive pole with the positive slide-wire contact C through a galvanometer and a tapping key. When this key is depressed, current will flow through the galvanometer coil and a galvanometer scale deflection will be observed if the emf of E and that between A and C are not equal. The direction of the galvanometer deflection will obviously depend on whether the potential at C is higher or lower than that at the positive pole of E. If the position of the sliding contact is adjusted until no galvanometer deflection is observed on depressing the tapping key, the emf of E must be the same as that between A and C. Indeed, a linear scale marked off directly in volts can be placed alongside the slide-wire, and the emf between A and C can be read directly from this scale, provided that the current through the slide-wire has been properly adjusted by manipulation of the rheostat R.

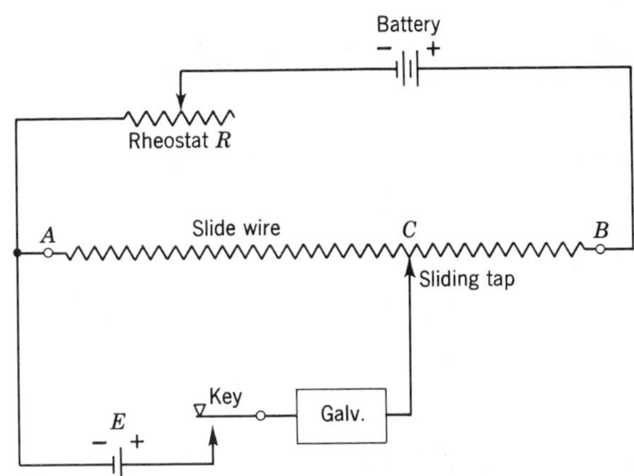

FIG. 1. Schematic diagram of a simple slide-wire potentiometer.

The adjustment of the current through the slide-wire is accomplished by connecting a source of known emf, such as a *standard cell,* in place of the potential E. The slider C is then placed at the setting on the slide-wire scale corresponding to the known potential, and the rheostat R is adjusted until no galvanometer deflection is observed on depressing the tapping key. This "standardization" of the potentiometer against a standard cell should be repeated frequently during the experimental work because the battery voltage usually shows a tendency to drift slightly.

The accuracy of an emf measurement depends most of all on the design and the quality of the potentiometer unit used. For a precision potentiometer, the relative accuracy of measurement (ability to measure very small changes in emf) will depend a great deal on the galvanometer sensitivity while the absolute accuracy will depend more on the accuracy of the standard cell emf value.

Standard Cells. The electrochemical cell used as a standard is the Weston cell:

$$\text{Cd(12.5\% Cd amalgam)} + CdSO_4 \cdot \tfrac{8}{3}H_2O(s),\ CdSO_4(\text{sat}),\ Hg_2SO_4(s) + Hg(l)$$

which has an emf of 1.0184 absolute volts at 25°C and a temperature coefficient of 4×10^{-5} v deg^{-1}. An airtight, H-shaped cell is used with platinum wires sealed through the glass to make contact with the electrodes. The anode arm (negative electrode) consists of a two-phase cadmium amalgam (over-all composition 12.5 per cent Cd by weight) covered with crystals of hydrated cadmium sulfate; the cathode arm (positive electrode) contains a pool of liquid mercury covered by a paste of mercurous sulfate. The rest of the cell is filled with a saturated solution of $CdSO_4$, except for a small air space to allow room for thermal expansion.

In actual practice, it is more common to use a Weston cell containing an *unsaturated* solution of $CdSO_4$ as a standard cell. This cell has the advantage that the temperature coefficient is low (1×10^{-5} v deg^{-1}) and the disadvantage that the emf may vary slowly with time. Such a standard cell has an initial emf between 1.0186 and 1.0196 v, and it should be restandardized every year or two. The best method of checking a "working" standard cell against a very reliable "reference" standard cell is to connect the two cells in opposition and measure the emf difference between them with a precision potentiometer (which is standardized against another working standard cell). In this way the effect of experimental error is almost eliminated, since it affects only a very small difference reading.

In using a standard cell, one must **never** pass more than 10^{-4} amp through the cell. A protective resistance should be in series with the standard cell during the initial stages of standardizing a potentiometer. Take particular care to depress the galvanometer key only briefly, especially when the deflections are large.

Leeds and Northrup Student Potentiometer. The L & N Student Potentiometer, Catalog No. 7651, is a medium-precision unit (accuracy of ±0.5 mv on the 1.6-v scale and ±0.01 mv on the 0.016-v scale) which is widely used for measuring emf's in the range 0.001 to 1.6 v. Indeed, many of the experiments in this book require the use of this instrument (or some other of comparable quality and similar construction). Therefore, we shall discuss its operation in considerable detail. Figure 2 shows a complete potentiometer circuit based on the Student Potentiometer unit; note that several auxiliary components are required in addition to the potentiometer unit.

In the Student Potentiometer the potential difference is selected, not between a fixed end and a variable point, but rather between two variable points, one of which is moved in steps (by means of a step switch) and the other of which is moved

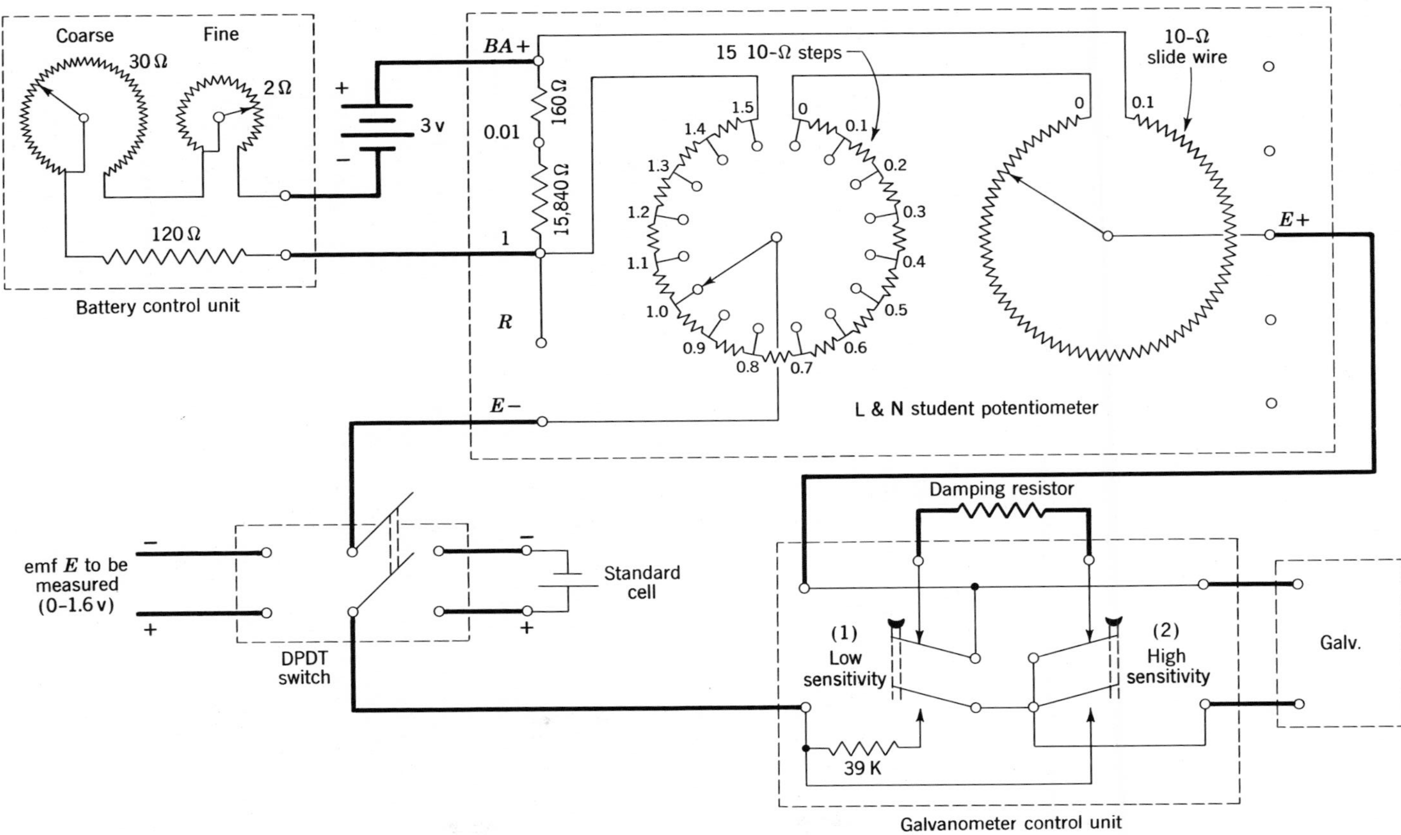

FIG. 2. Complete wiring diagram for a potentiometer circuit based on the L & N Student Potentiometer. The internal-wiring diagram of the potentiometer is somewhat simplified.

continuously (a dial "slide-wire"). The stator of the step switch has 16 contact points, between each adjacent pair of which is a noninductively wound fixed resistor of 10 ohms resistance, all the resistances being precisely equal to one another. The slide-wire is in series with the 15 fixed resistances, and its resistance is precisely equal to the resistance of any one of the fixed resistors. The 16 points of the step switch are numbered in tenths of a volt from 0 to 1.5 v, and the scale of the slide-wire is so graduated (the smallest graduations being 0.0005 v) as to cover the range 0 to 0.1000 v. A potential can be estimated to 0.0001 v from the slide-wire dial reading. The desired potential difference is obtained between binding post E^{-}, which is connected to the rotor of the step switch, and binding post E^{+}, which is connected to the sliding-contact rotor of the dial slide-wire. Thus the desired potential difference or emf is the sum of a step-switch reading and a slide-wire reading. The proper current through the 15 resistances and the slide-wire is obtained from batteries through rheostats, and the current supply is normally connected to the binding posts marked BA^{+} and 1. The potentiometer is standardized against a standard cell in the same way as described previously in the case of the simple slide-wire potentiometer.

If, *after standardization,* the negative lead of the battery circuit is switched from binding post 1 to that marked 0.01, the range of the Student Potentiometer changes from 0–1.6 to 0–0.016 v; that is, all readings must be multiplied by 0.01. This change of scale is accomplished by means of an internal resistive network so designed (see Fig. 2) that the current flowing through the step-switch resistors and the slide-wire is reduced to precisely 1 per cent of the value established during the standardization. The total resistance in the battery circuit is, however, not affected on switching from post 1 to 0.01. This low-scale arrangement permits one to make a more precise measurement of very small emf values, such as thermocouple emf's below 16 mv or the potential drop across a 1-ohm standard resistor when less than 16 ma of direct current are flowing through it (see Exp. 21). Figure 3 shows a convenient way to rewire the DPDT switch so that it is not necessary to move lead wires when using the 0.01 scale.

The battery circuit as shown in Fig. 2 consists of two 1.5-v dry cells connected in series with a battery control unit which permits both coarse and fine adjustment of the current through the potentiometer unit. It is possible to achieve better current stability by using a 2-v low-discharge wet cell. In that case, the 120-ohm fixed resistor in the control unit should be replaced by a 20-ohm resistor so that a current of 10 ma can be obtained.

Also shown in Fig. 2 is a galvanometer control unit, which replaces a simple tapping key. There are two spring-loaded push buttons either of which, when depressed, will close the circuit through the galvanometer. When the low-sensitivity button (1) is depressed, a protective resistance of 39,000 ohms is in the galvanometer circuit. This will limit the current flow through the galvanometer and prevent damage when the potentiometer setting is far from the proper value. When the high-sensitivity button (2) is depressed, this protective resistance is *not* in the circuit. Therefore, button 1 should be used during all preliminary adjustments, and button 2 should be depressed only when the deflections are too small to detect using button 1. Either button should be depressed only briefly and not held down. There is also a position on the control unit for mounting an external damping resistor so that it will be across the galvanometer whenever *neither* button is depressed. This resistor should be chosen to provide approximately critical damping for the galva-

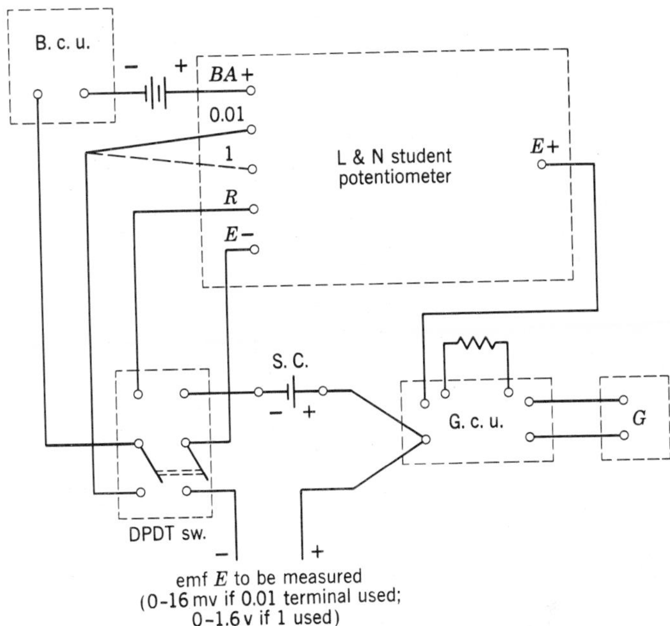

FIG. 3. Alternative method of making connections to the Student Potentiometer. This method is of greatest value when the 0.01 scale is to be used (as shown). For internal wiring of units, see Fig. 2.

nometer used. It is also advantageous to have critical damping when button 2 is depressed; this is more difficult to arrange, as it requires the use of a galvanometer having a critical damping resistance equal to the resistance of the rest of the circuit or else the modification of the circuit to match the critical damping resistance of the galvanometer available.

Finally, a detailed outline is given below of the procedure for using the circuit shown in Fig. 2:

1. Connect the components, taking care that the batteries, standard cell, and unknown emf are connected with the correct polarities. (Until the student has become thoroughly familiar with the potentiometer circuit, it is advisable to omit the connections to the standard cell until the wiring has been checked by an instructor.)

2. Set the step switch and slide-wire dial to the value of the emf of the standard cell. By means of the DPDT switch, place the standard cell in the circuit.

3. Standardize the potentiometer against the standard cell by adjusting the coarse battery control until there is no galvanometer deflection when galvanometer button 1 is depressed. Then adjust the fine battery control until there is no deflection on depressing button 2. Do not hold button 2 down for a prolonged period.

4. Switch from the standard cell to the unknown potential E by reversing the DPDT switch. **Do not disturb the battery current setting.** Vary the potentiometer step switch and slide-wire dial setting until there is no galvanometer deflection on depressing button 1 of the galvanometer control unit; then make any necessary adjustments of the slide-wire until a null point is obtained when button 2 is depressed. NOTE: If it is impossible to achieve balance at any setting of the poten-

tiometer, either the unknown emf E is greater than 1.6 v or E is connected into the circuit with the incorrect polarity.

5. Record the emf value for E, then restandardize and repeat the measurement.

High-precision Research Potentiometers. Several types of potentiometers are available for high-quality research applications; each of them has certain special design features which improve the precision and the convenience of operation. Almost all research potentiometers are designed so that the instrument can be standardized against a standard cell without changing the settings of the step switches or slide-wire. This feature is incorporated in the circuit shown in Fig. 4. By means of a built-in DPDT switch, one pole of the standard cell can be connected through the galvanometer to a fixed contact A on the step switch. The other pole of the standard cell is directly connected to the movable contact on a calibration slide-wire C. Adjustment of the setting on slide-wire C allows one to obtain any potential difference between 1.018 and 1.020 v in order to match the emf of the standard cell used. When the DPDT switch is thrown to the *EMF* position (dashed lines in figure), the E^- terminal is connected through the galvanometer to the movable contact on the step switch. The E^+ terminal is directly connected to the contact on the measuring slide-wire B. Most research potentiometers also have

FIG. 4. Schematic diagram of a potentiometer unit which incorporates some of the special features usually found in high-precision research-quality instruments.

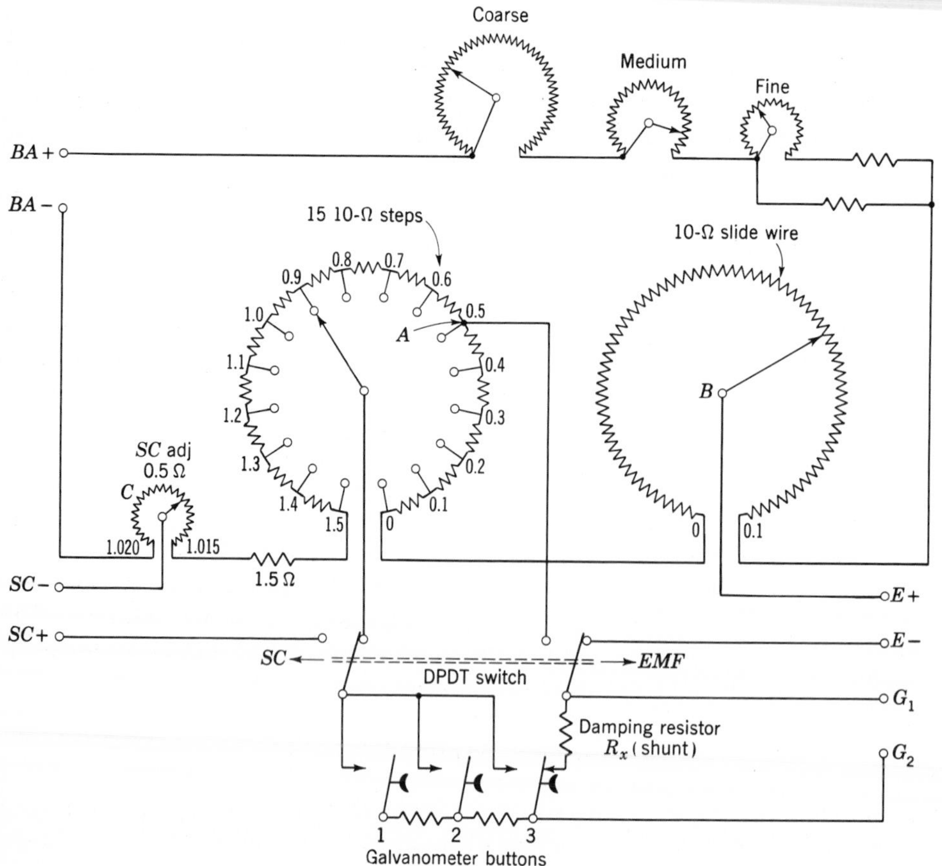

built-in battery control rheostats and galvanometer tapping keys. Figure 4 shows a typical version of both of these features; in each case the design is more elaborate than that discussed for the Student Potentiometer. Note that the galvanometer is always shunted by a resistor R_x except when the highest sensitivity key (key 3) is depressed; the value of R_x should be close to the CDRX of the galvanometer used. Some potentiometers provide several galvanometer binding posts with different R_x values between them to permit easy matching to the CDRX. Other important design features, which have been omitted from Fig. 4 for the sake of clarity, are range switches to provide 1, 0.1, and 0.01 scales in such a way that one can check against the standard cell when the measuring circuit is on any range setting: replacement of a single step switch and slide-wire by as many as five decade step switches; special arrangements to keep the resistance in the galvanometer circuit a constant independent of the settings of the step switches. This last feature is valuable for precise measurements of a thermocouple emf; since the galvanometer sensitivity is constant, deflections can be easily converted into emf values in order to follow small changes. More details on individual potentiometers are given in the manufacturers' catalogues and in the literature.[1, 4]

WHEATSTONE BRIDGE CIRCUITS

Direct-current Wheatstone Bridge. The dc Wheatstone-bridge circuit provides a simple means of accurately determining an unknown resistance. As shown in Fig. 5*a*, an arbitrary dc potential drop is established across the bridge from A to C and a galvanometer with tapping key serves as a detector of current flow from B to D. Since direct current is involved, all arms of the bridge are treated as purely resistive elements. When the bridge is balanced (i.e., no deflection on the galvanometer when the tapping key is closed), the potential at B must be the same as that at D and it follows that

$$\frac{R_1}{R_2} = \frac{R_3}{R_4} \tag{1}$$

A form of this bridge incorporating the slide-wire in an L & N Student Potentiometer is shown in Fig. 5*b*. The slide-wire, which has a scale A reading from 0 to 1000, constitutes two of the four arms of the bridge. When terminals L and H are used, one obtains from Eq. (1) the condition of balance

$$X = \frac{A}{1000 - A} R \tag{2}$$

Often the known resistance R is variable, for example, a decade resistance box. In this case, R can be varied until A is somewhere in the range 450 to 550. A considerably greater sensitivity can then be achieved by shifting the L lead to L' and the H lead to H', obtaining the so-called "long bridge." The two left arms of the bridge now each contain an additional resistance 4.5 times that of the slide-wire itself, and the balance condition then becomes

$$X = \frac{4500 + A}{5500 - A} R \tag{3}$$

In general, use of the long bridge is preferable because of the greater sensitivity provided. In some cases, particularly when X and R are small, use of the long bridge

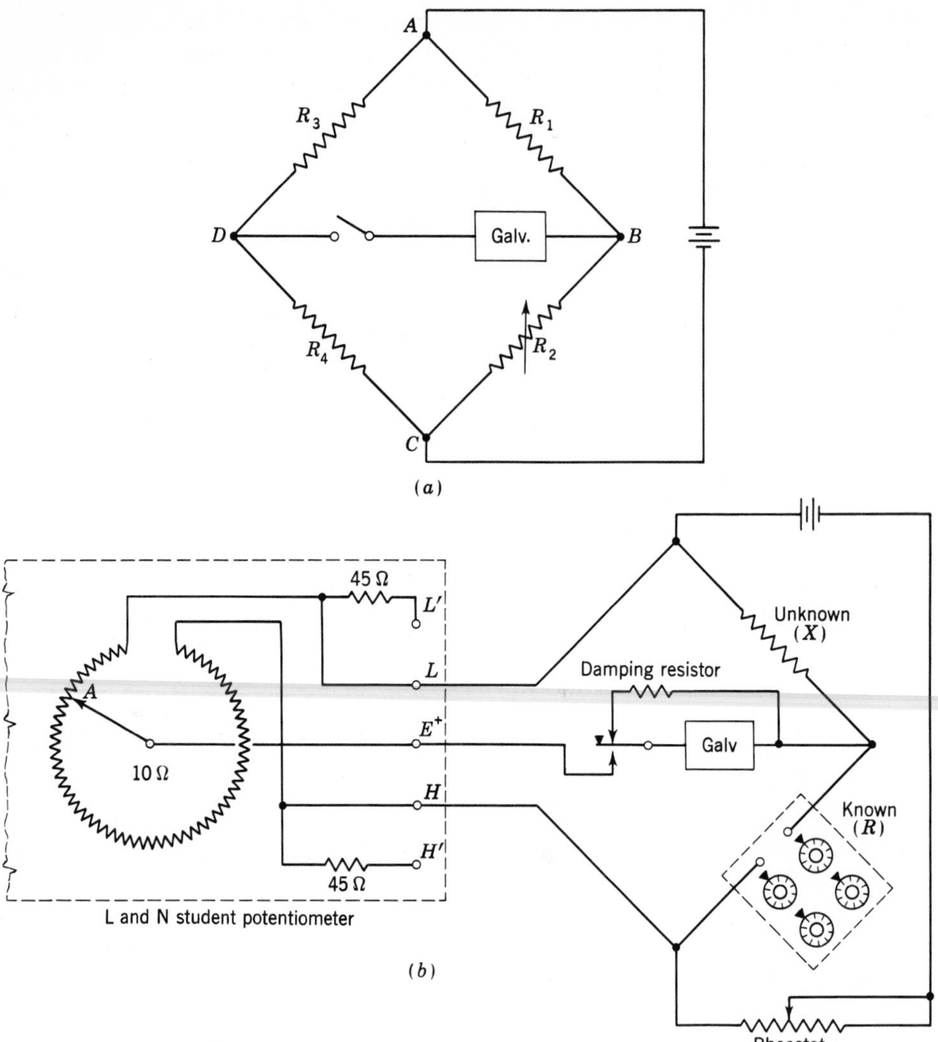

FIG. 5. The dc Wheatstone bridge: (*a*) general schematic diagram of the bridge; (*b*) wiring diagram, based on the use of the slide-wire in an L & N Student Potentiometer. Slide-wire internal circuit slightly idealized.

is not advantageous because the galvanometer sensitivity is the limiting factor and the galvanometer sensitivity is decreased rather than increased by going to the long bridge.

Commercial Wheatstone bridges are available in a form where R_3/R_4 can be set by a step switch to accurate decimal ratios from 10^{-3} to 10^3, and R_2 is a precision four- or five-decade resistance box. Other special features are available for certain applications; the Mueller bridge, used with four-lead platinum resistance thermometers, is shown in Fig. XVI-2.

Alternating-current Wheatstone Bridge. A Wheatstone bridge can be operated with alternating as well as direct current. Indeed, the use of alternating current is necessary to prevent polarization of the electrodes in a conductance cell (see Exp. 22). The basic circuit for an ac bridge is the same as that shown in Fig. 5*a* except that an ac source (such as a tuning-fork oscillator or a vacuum-tube audio oscillator operated at up to 1 or 2 kc) is used and the galvanometer and tapping key are replaced by an audio detector (such as earphones) or an oscilloscope. For an ac bridge the condition of balance is

$$\frac{Z_1}{Z_2} = \frac{Z_3}{Z_4} \tag{4}$$

where Z is the impedance given by $Z = R + iX$, X being the reactance (and i being $\sqrt{-1}$). If Eq. (4) is written in terms of R and X, one can clear fractions and equate the real and imaginary parts to obtain two equations:

$$R_1R_4 - X_1X_4 = R_2R_3 - X_2X_3$$
$$R_1X_4 - R_4X_1 = R_2X_3 - R_3X_2$$

These can be written as

$$R_1R_4\left(1 - \frac{X_1X_4}{R_1R_4}\right) = R_2R_3\left(1 - \frac{X_2X_3}{R_2R_3}\right) \tag{5a}$$

$$R_1R_4\left(\frac{X_1}{R_1} + \frac{X_4}{R_4}\right) = R_2R_3\left(\frac{X_2}{R_2} + \frac{X_3}{R_3}\right) \tag{5b}$$

In order for the resistance balance $R_1/R_2 = R_3/R_4$ (or $R_1R_4 = R_2R_3$) to hold true, the coefficient of R_1R_4 must equal the coefficient of R_2R_3 in both Eqs. (5*a*) and (5*b*). This will occur[5] when

$$\theta_1 = \theta_2 \qquad \text{and} \qquad \theta_3 = \theta_4 \tag{6}$$

where θ_j is the phase angle between the current and voltage in the jth arm of the bridge ($\tan \theta_j = X_j/R_j$).

A more sophisticated ac bridge diagram for conductance measurements is shown in Fig. 6 (see also Fig. 22-1). If the arms R_3 and R_4 are identical noninduc-

FIG. 6. Schematic diagram of an ac Wheatstone bridge (with Wagner earthing device) suitable for conductance measurements; see also Fig. 22-1.

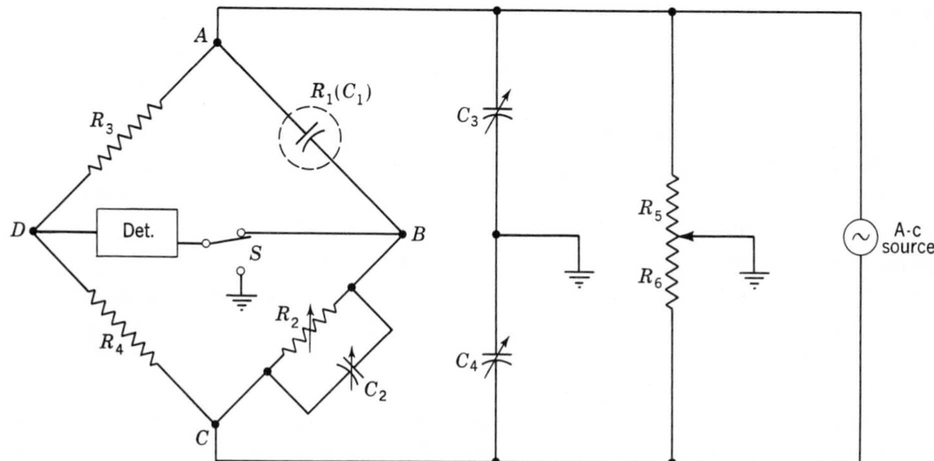

tively wound resistors, θ_3 will equal θ_4. Since the conductance cell has a capacitance C_1 as well as a resistance R_1, there will be a phase shift in that arm of the bridge, but one can still satisfy $\theta_1 = \theta_2$ if a variable condenser C_2 is placed across R_2. Thus, the potential at B and D will be in phase and a balance can be obtained where Eq. (1) will still apply. However, the balance may be a minimum rather than a null point if B and D are not at ground potential, since some current can still flow through the detector to ground via distributed capacity. Detection of the balance point can be improved for very precise work by using a Wagner earthing circuit[5,6] to bring point D (and thus point B) close to ground potential. After an initial bridge balance is achieved, the detector is switched from B to ground and the Wagner earthing circuit (C_3, C_4, R_5, and R_6 in Fig. 6) is adjusted to minimize the signal through the detector. The bridge is then rebalanced, and this process is repeated until the best possible balance point is achieved. The best detector for precise measurements is an oscilloscope, since this can be used in a way which permits separate observation of both the capacitive and the resistive balance[7] (see Chap. XVIII).

STANDARD RESISTORS AND POTENTIAL DIVIDERS

In order to make an accurate measurement of the direct current flowing through a resistive element, a standard resistor is inserted in the circuit in series with the element and the potential drop across this standard resistor is measured with a potentiometer. Obviously, the resistance value of the standard resistor must be chosen so that the potential difference across it will be of the proper magnitude for the potentiometer used. Also, the standard resistor must be designed to have an adequate current rating (wattage), a low temperature-coefficient, and a long-term resistance stability. A small temperature variation of resistance can be achieved if the resistor consists of manganin wire wound on a large insulated spool. Such wire-wound resistors can be obtained commercially from several manufacturers, and one can easily calibrate the resistance value using a precision Wheatstone bridge. Also, resistors certified to be within 0.1 per cent of the nominal value can be obtained from the Shallcross Mfg. Co. For more precise work, Leeds and Northrup offers a NBS-type standard resistor in which the resistance coil is sealed in a container filled with oil. This type of resistor has very heavy leads with two terminals on each lead—one for the current connection and one for the potentiometer connection.

It is sometimes necessary to measure the potential drop across a circuit element when the voltage is higher than the maximum possible setting on the potentiometer. The proper technique in such a case is to use a high-resistance potential divider. A potential divider can be easily constructed from two wire-wound resistors (see Exp. 47 for an application of such a device). Commercial potential dividers, called volt boxes, are available with a design similar to that shown in Fig. 7. By connecting the 0 terminal to one side of the circuit element and the 10, 100, or 200 terminal to the other side it is possible to reduce the voltage accurately by a factor of 10, 100, or 200. Since the resistance in the volt box is high, only a few milliamperes will flow through this shunt provided the voltage is kept below the rated value for each terminal (usually about 5 v per 1000 ohms between the terminals used). It is preferable to have the 0 terminal near ground potential; this prevents possible leakage currents and is safer when high voltages are used.

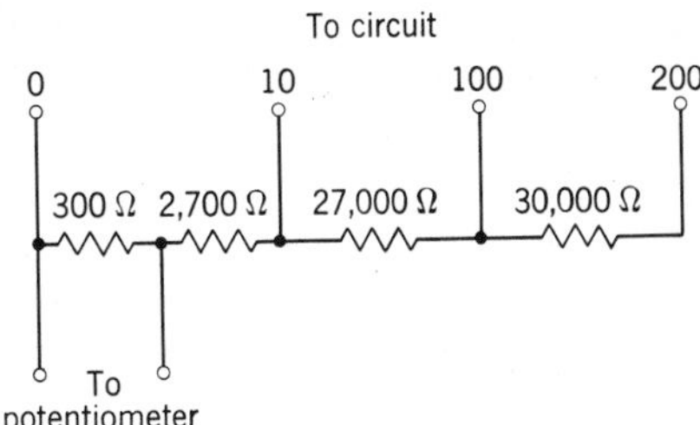

FIG. 7. Basic circuit for a volt box.

CAPACITANCE MEASUREMENTS

The measurement of capacitance is of importance in physical chemistry primarily for the study of dielectric properties. As discussed in Exps. 37 and 38, dipole moments can be determined from the dielectric constants of gases or dilute solutions. There is also considerable interest in the dielectric properties of liquids and solids. When there are strong dipolar interactions between molecules, as in a polar liquid, there is an appreciable relaxation time for dielectric polarization. In that case, *dielectric loss* (dissipation of electrical energy as heat) occurs and the dielectric constant is frequency dependent.[8, 9] In the following discussion we shall be concerned mostly with methods of measuring the capacitance of samples with very low dielectric loss (gases or dilute solutions in nonpolar solvents).[10] For such samples, the resistance of the dielectric cell is very high and its capacitance is independent of frequency.

Heterodyne-beat Method. The heterodyne-beat method is capable of extremely high precision, and it is the method most commonly used for dipole moment measurements. However, this method is limited to the investigation of gases or of solutions and liquids with very low conductance (cell resistance greater than 10^4 ohms). If a substance with appreciable conductance is placed in the dielectric cell, which is part of the LC tank circuit of a high-frequency oscillator tube, too much energy will be dissipated in the tank circuit and there will not be enough feedback to maintain proper oscillation. The heterodyne-beat method is fully described in Exp. 37, and considerable details on the circuitry are available in the literature.[10]

Resonance Method. While the resonance method is not capable of the very high accuracy of the heterodyne-beat method, it is quite satisfactory for many investigations and has the advantages of simple and low-cost circuitry. This method can best be explained in terms of the schematic diagram shown in Fig. 8. The primary circuit consists of an oscillator with the inductance coil L_1 in the plate circuit of the oscillator tube. The secondary circuit is loosely coupled via the inductances to the primary circuit. When the oscillator is in operation, a constant high-frequency alternating current flows through L_1 and a small amount of current also flows in the secondary circuit. The amount of current flowing in the secondary

FIG. 8. Schematic circuit for a resonance apparatus: L_1 and L_2 are fixed inductances; C_T is a coarse tuning capacitor; C_P is a precision air capacitor; C_X is the dielectric cell. A vacuum-tube voltmeter V can be used as the detector (see text).

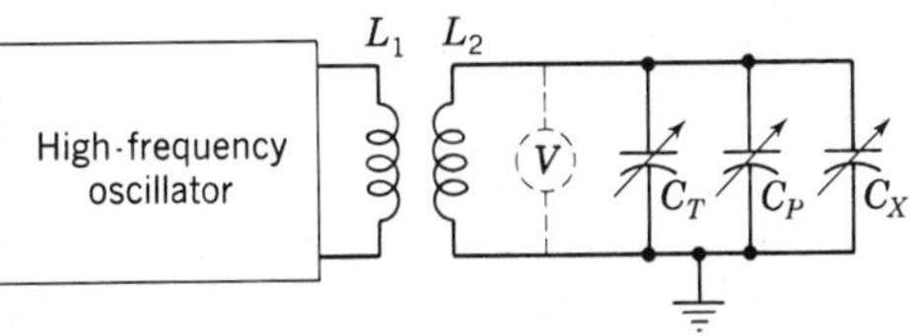

will depend both on the value of L_2 and on the total capacity $C = C_T + C_P + C_X$. By varying C one can achieve the *resonance* condition: $f = 1/2\pi\sqrt{L_2C}$, where f is the frequency of the oscillator. When resonance occurs, the current flow in the secondary will be at its maximum value. This resonance point is detected by observing either a minimum in the dc plate current of the oscillator tube or a maximum in the ac voltage across the secondary. (The latter method requires the use of a vacuum-tube voltmeter.) A variable dielectric cell can be used (as in Exp. 37), or a fixed-plate cell can be used by employing the substitution method (as in Exp. 38). In either case, C_X is obtained from the difference in the settings of C_P necessary to achieve resonance. The coarse tuning condenser is used only to adjust the total capacity C to an initial value near the resonance value and should *not* be disturbed during the actual measurements.

In the above discussion, the secondary circuit was treated as a pure LC network, and that is usually not true in practice. For dielectric-constant measurements this is of no concern, since there is always a unique value of C which will make the secondary circuit resonant. We can also see that the resonance method has one great advantage over the heterodyne-beat method: solutions or liquids with appreciable conductance can be studied. This is due to the fact that the dielectric cell is in the secondary circuit, which is only loosely coupled to the oscillator, and cannot affect the feedback necessary for proper oscillation. Indeed, it is possible to determine dielectric loss with this method, since the sharpness of resonance (Q of the secondary circuit) is related to the loss.[8] The lower the loss in the dielectric, the sharper the resonance and the larger the Q value.

A modified resonance apparatus for routine student use has been described in detail by Bender.[11] In this circuit a 6E5 electron ray ("tuning-eye") tube serves both as an oscillator tube and as the resonance detector. A piezoelectric quartz crystal (1 or 2 mc) in the grid circuit controls the frequency f of oscillation. The LC circuit (shown as the secondary circuit in Fig. 8) is part of the plate circuit and is coupled to the quartz crystal via the internal capacitance of the 6E5 tube. As the capacity in the plate tuning circuit is increased, oscillation begins as $1/2\pi\sqrt{L_2C}$ approaches f and the plate current drops. This continues up to the point of resonance where the plate current is at a minimum and therefore the shadow angle of the tuning eye is also at a minimum. With a further increase of C, oscillation stops, the plate current rises rapidly, and the shadow angle increases abruptly. This point where the eye "opens" is reproducible and can be used as the balance point for capacitance settings.

Bridge Method. An ac impedance bridge used for dielectric measurements is very similar in principle to the ac Wheatstone bridge described previously; however, the reactance X is now large, since the dielectric cell has a large capacitance. Both the theory and the proper experimental techniques of ac bridge measurements are extensively discussed by Hartshorn[12] and by Hague.[13] Only a very brief treatment of the "capacity bridge" will be given here.

The type of bridge often used for dipole moment work is a simple capacity bridge with two resistance arms (the "ratio arms") and two capacitance arms. Figure 9 shows a schematic diagram of a bridge with equal ratio arms of fixed resistance R and with one fixed capacitance arm C. The measuring capacitance arm consists of a parallel combination of a precision air capacitor C_P and the dielectric cell C_X. Large ($\sim 10^4$-ohm), noninductively wound resistors R_1 and R_2 are attached in parallel with the capacitances. These resistors help to balance out any small

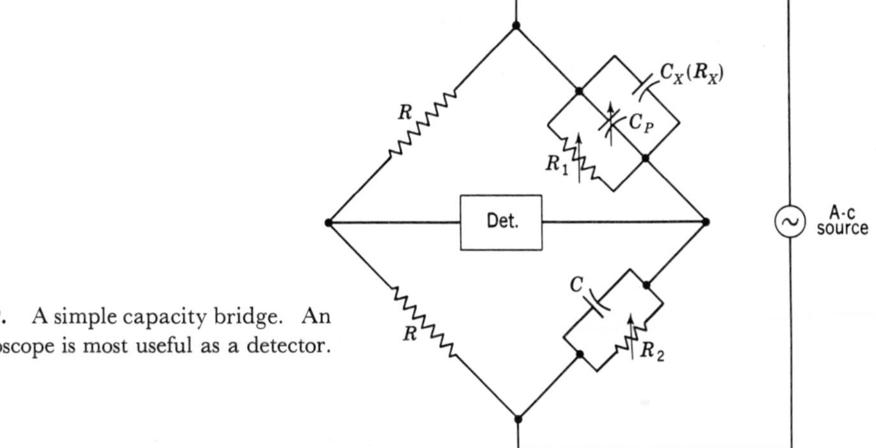

FIG. 9. A simple capacity bridge. An oscilloscope is most useful as a detector.

differences between the resistances of the capacitance arms and are very necessary to achieve balance if the sample has appreciable conductance (i.e., if cell C_X has a finite resistance R_X).[10] Measurements can be made with a fixed-plate dielectric cell by using the substitution method, where a balance is first achieved with C_X in the bridge and then a second balance is achieved with C_X removed. Alternatively, a variable-capacity cell can be used as in Exp. 37; this has the advantage of eliminating any effects due to the capacity or resistance of the leads. If the sample has negligible conductance only an adjustment of the C_P setting is required to achieve balance. For samples having appreciable conductance (finite R_X), it is necessary to adjust both C_P and the resistors R_1 and R_2, alternately, until the balance point is reached. (The cell resistance R_X is then given by $1/R_X = 1/R_2 - 1/R_1$, and the dielectric loss can also be calculated.)[8] In either case, C_X is equal to the difference in the two settings of C_P required to balance the bridge.

For reasonably precise work it is advisable to use a commercial bridge in order to avoid the many difficult problems of design and construction involved. Several suitable types of bridge are manufactured by the General Radio Co., among them a modified Schering bridge (Model 716-C) which is capable of very high precision. In addition to a good bridge, a *stable* oscillator and suitable *high-impedance* detector are required.

REFERENCES

1. W. C. Michels, "Electrical Measurements and Their Applications," Van Nostrand, Princeton, N.J. (1957); A. W. Smith and M. L. Wiedenbeck, "Electrical Measurements," 5th ed., McGraw-Hill, New York (1948).
2. L. Page, "Principles of Electricity," 3d ed., Van Nostrand, Princeton, N.J. (1958).
3. Leeds and Northrup "Catalog ED: Galvanometers" and "Note Book ED2(1): Notes on Moving-coil Galvanometers" are available from Leeds and Northrup Co., 4907 Stanton Ave., Philadelphia 44, Pa.
4. W. P. White, Potentiometers for Thermoelectric Measurements, in "Temperature: Its Measurement and Control in Science and Industry," pp. 265–278, Reinhold, New York (1941).
5. G. Jones and R. C. Josephs, *J. Am. Chem. Soc.,* **50,** 1049 (1928).
6. T. Shedlovsky, *J. Am. Chem. Soc.,* **52,** 1793 (1930).

7. D. Edelson and R. M. Fuoso, *J. Chem. Educ.,* **27,** 610 (1950); G. Jones, K. T. Mysels, and W. Juda, *J. Am. Chem. Soc.,* **62,** 2919 (1940).
8. J. G. Powles and C. P. Smyth, Measurement of Dielectric Constant and Loss, in A. Weissberger (ed.), "Technique of Organic Chemistry," 2d ed., vol. I, part III, chap. XXXV, Interscience, New York (1954).
9. C. P. Smyth, "Dielectric Behavior and Structure," McGraw-Hill, New York (1955).
10. C. P. Smyth, Determination of Dipole Moments, in A. Weissberger (ed.), "Technique of Organic Chemistry," 2d ed., vol. I, part II, chap. XXIV, Interscience, New York (1954).
11. P. Bender, *J. Chem. Educ.,* **23,** 179 (1946); also F. Daniels, J. H. Mathews, J. W. Williams, et al., "Experimental Physical Chemistry," 5th ed., p. 209, McGraw-Hill, New York (1956).
12. L. Hartshorn, "Radio-frequency Measurements by Bridge and Resonance Methods," Wiley, New York (1941).
13. B. Hague, "Alternating-current Bridge Methods," 5th ed., Sir Isaac Pitman & Sons, Ltd., London (1957).

XVI
TEMPERATURE

Temperature is one of the most important variables in thermodynamics and physical chemistry. In this chapter we are concerned with the methods and instruments that are used in measuring and controlling temperature.

TEMPERATURE SCALES

The nature of temperature scales has been briefly discussed in Exp. 1. The *thermodynamic temperature scale,* based on the second law of thermodynamics, embraces the Kelvin (absolute) scale and the Celsius scale, the latter being defined by the equation

$$t_{\text{Celsius}} \equiv T_{\text{Kelvin}} - 273.15 \qquad (1)$$

The size of the Kelvin degree is now (1960)[1,2] determined by the statement that the triple point of pure water is exactly 273.16°K. The practical usefulness of the thermodynamic scale suffers from the lack of convenient instruments with which to measure absolute temperatures routinely to high precision. Absolute temperatures can be measured over a wide range with the helium gas thermometer[3] (appropriate corrections being made for gas imperfections), but the apparatus is much too complex and the procedure much too cumbersome to be practical for routine use.

The *International Practical Temperature Scale* of 1948 (adopted 1960)[1,2] is basically arbitrary in its definition but is intended to approximate closely the thermodynamic temperature scale. It is based on practical thermometers, principally the platinum resistance thermometer. Its formulation over the range −182.97 (the oxygen point) to 630.5°C (the "antimony point") is based on careful comparison of the readings of these thermometers with those of gas thermometers and on the establishment of fixed points and interpolation formulas.

The fixed points of the International Practical Temperature Scale are given in Table 1. The international scale is not defined below the oxygen point. From the oxygen point to 630.5°, the scale is defined in terms of a platinum resistance thermometer. From 0 to 630.5°, the international Celsius temperature t is defined in terms of the resistance of the platinum sensing element by the equation

$$R_t = R_0(1 + \alpha t + \beta t^2) \qquad (2)$$

TABLE 1. Fixed Points of the International Practical Temperature Scale of 1948[a]

Fixed point	Phases in equilibrium[b]	Temperature, °Celsius
Oxygen	Liquid, vapor	−182.97
Water triple point	Solid (ice), liquid, vapor	+0.01
Steam point	Liquid water, water vapor	100
Zinc[c]	Solid, liquid	419.505
Sulfur	Liquid, vapor	444.6
Silver	Solid, liquid	960.8
Gold	Solid, liquid	1063

[a] H. F. Stimson, *Natl. Bur. Standards J. Research,* **65A,** 139 (1961); *Compt. rend. onzième gén. conf. poids et mesures* (1960).

[b] Except for the water triple point, all points are taken at one standard atmosphere: 1,013,250 dyne cm^{-2}, or 760 mm Hg of density 13.5951 g cm^{-3} at standard gravity (980.655 cm sec^{-2}). Where one standard atmosphere cannot be obtained, formulas in terms of pressure are given.[a]

[c] Recommended (1960)[a] to be used in place of the sulfur point.

where the constants R_0, α, and β are determined by calibration at 0.01°, 100°, and 444.6° (or 419.505°). For use from −182.97 to 0° the equation

$$R_t = R_0[1 + \alpha t + \beta t^2 + \gamma(t - 100)t^3] \qquad (3)$$

is used, where R_0, α, and β have been determined by Eq. (2) and γ is determined by a measurement at −182.97°. From 630.5° to the gold point, the international scale is based on the readings of a thermocouple consisting of a platinum wire and a wire consisting of a 10 per cent alloy of rhodium in platinum. Above the gold point an optical pyrometer defines the scale with the Planck radiation law.

In addition to the defining fixed points of the International Temperature Scale (Table 1), a number of secondary reference points have been recommended for use (see Table 2). Below the oxygen point, several temperature scales[4, 5] and fixed points[5] have been proposed.

TABLE 2. Partial List of Secondary Reference Points[a]

Fixed point	Phases in equilibrium[b]	Temperature, °C
Carbon dioxide	Solid, vapor	−78.5
Mercury	Solid, liquid	−38.87
Ice point	Ice, air-saturated liquid	0.000
Sodium sulfate transition	Solid decahydrate, solid monohydrate, saturated aqueous solution	32.38
Indium	Solid, liquid	156.61
Naphthalene	Liquid, vapor	218.0
Tin	Solid, liquid	231.91
Lead	Solid, liquid	327.3
Mercury	Liquid, vapor	356.58
Aluminum	Solid, liquid	660.1
Copper	Solid, liquid	1083
Palladium	Solid, liquid	1552
Platinum	Solid, liquid	1769
Rhodium	Solid, liquid	1960
Tungsten	Melting	3380

[a] H. F. Stimson, *Natl. Bur. Standards J. Research,* **65A,** 139 (1961); *Compt. rend. onzième conf. gén. poids et mesures* (1960).

[b] See footnote *b* to Table 1.

From gas-thermometer measurements the deviations of the International Practical Temperature Scale from the Thermodynamic Temperature Scale have been estimated in certain ranges of temperatures[1,2] and where necessary platinum resistance thermometer readings can be corrected to yield values more closely approximating thermodynamic temperatures. The formula

$$t_{\text{therm}} = t + \frac{t}{100}\left[-0.0060 + \left(\frac{t}{100} - 1\right)(0.04106 - 7.363 \times 10^{-5}t)\right] \qquad (4)$$

where t is the International Practical Celsius Temperature, has been formulated for the range from 0°C to the sulfur point;[1,2] it has been adapted from one given by Beattie[3] for the earlier thermodynamic scale. It gives 99.994°C (therm) for the steam point and 444.70°C (therm) for the sulfur point. The calculated deviations are not much larger than the uncertainties in the gas-thermometer readings on which the above formula was based. For most practical applications, the distinction between the two scales is of little importance.

THERMOMETERS

Mercury Thermometers.[6] By far the most common type of laboratory thermometer is the mercury thermometer, based on the differential volume thermal expansion of liquid mercury (about 1.8×10^{-4} deg^{-1}) and glass (about 0.2×10^{-4} deg^{-1}). In the manufacture of such thermometers, the stem, a capillary of uniform bore, is usually marked at two points (say 0 and 100°C) and then graduated uniformly in between, on the tacit assumption that the volume of a fixed mass of mercury in glass is a linear function of the temperature. The error resulting from this assumption (about +0.12° at 50°C for a 0 to 100° mercury thermometer made with Corning normal thermometer glass) is ordinarily smaller than that due to variations in the bore of the capillary.

When precision of better than about 1 per cent of full scale is required, it is advisable to use a calibration chart which gives corrections to be added to or subtracted from the readings. A calibration can be obtained by submitting the thermometer to the National Bureau of Standards, Washington, D.C. If a laboratory possesses one or two thermometers with Bureau of Standards calibrations, other thermometers can easily be checked against them. The calibrations of thermometers should be checked from time to time, as significant changes may take place in the glass, particularly if the thermometer is used above 150°C.

Laboratory thermometers are commonly available in two types: solid stem and enclosed scale. The former has a stem of solid glass, with a scale engraved on the outside surface; the latter has a slender capillary and a separate engraved scale, both enclosed in an outer glass shell. The enclosed-scale type is preferable for thermometers with extremely fine threads largely because it suffers less from parallax in reading.

Since the mercury in the thread, as well as that in the bulb, is susceptible to thermal expansion, it is important in precise work to take account of the temperature of the thermometer stem. Most thermometer calibrations, especially those for enclosed-stem types, are for *total immersion*—it is assumed that the thread is at the same temperature as the bulb. Other thermometers are meant to be used with partial immersion, often to a ring engraved on the stem, and the remainder of the stem is assumed to be at room temperature (say 25°C). For precise work stem corrections should be made if the stem temperatures differ significantly from those assumed in the calibration. The correction that should be *added* to the thermometer reading is given by the equation

$$\Delta t_{\text{corr}} = -0.00016(\Delta t_{\text{stem}})(\Delta L_{\text{stem}}) \tag{5}$$

where Δt_{stem} is the amount by which the temperature of the stem *exceeds* that for which the calibration applies (or the amount by which it exceeds the thermometer reading itself, if the calibration is for total immersion) and ΔL_{stem} is the length of mercury thread, expressed in degrees Celsius, for which the temperature is different from that assumed in the calibration. To obtain Δt_{stem} a second thermometer may be positioned near the first, with its bulb near the mid-point of ΔL_{stem}.

For most purposes a partial-immersion thermometer need not be stem-corrected because of a few degrees variation in room temperature or few degrees error in the immersion level. On the other hand, it is usually worth while to apply stem corrections to readings of a total-immersion thermometer when used in partial immersion, particularly when reading temperatures well removed from room temperature.

Other important sources of error in mercury thermometers are parallax and sticking of the mercury meniscus. The first can be largely avoided by careful positioning of the eye when reading or use of a properly designed attached magnifier. It can be eliminated entirely by use of a cathetometer (see Chap. XVIII). Sticking of the mercury meniscus is due to the fact that the contact angle of mercury to glass (see Fig. 31-5) varies depending on whether the mercury surface is advancing or receding, and thus the capillarity pressure due to surface tension is variable. This combines with the small but finite compressibility of the mercury and the elasticity of the glass to yield a small variability in meniscus position, especially for very sensitive thermometers. Gentle tapping of the stem before taking readings usually leads to reproducible results. Readings of sensitive mercury thermometers are also slightly pressure dependent; pressure coefficients may be as high as 0.1 deg atm^{-1}.

Special thermometers are made for calorimetric work, where it is desired to measure very accurately (to 0.01 or even 0.001°) a temperature *difference* of the order of a few degrees. For these thermometers the fineness of scale graduation has little to do with the accuracy with which the thermometer measures a single temperature. The scale may be in error by several tenths of a degree, but this error cancels out in taking differences. A typical thermometer for bomb calorimetry has a range of 19 to 35°, with graduations of 0.02°. For measuring freezing-point depressions with water or benzene as solvent, a range of -2 to $+6°$ with graduations of 0.01° is convenient. Such thermometers require careful handling. Not only are they relatively fragile, but they are susceptible to certain malfunctions (separation of the mercury column, bubbles in the bulb) arising principally from the extreme fineness of the thread. Whenever possible keep these thermometers upright; *avoid overly rapid heating or cooling.* If the mercury thread separates (which often happens when thermometers are shipped), cool the bulb in an ice-salt mixture to bring the mercury entirely into the bulb and tap if necessary to bring any bubbles to the top of the bulb. Then allow the thermometer to warm to room temperature in an upright position.

Beckmann Thermometer. The Beckmann thermometer is a *differential* thermometer with a range of 5 or 6° and graduations of 0.01 or 0.02°. It differs from an ordinary thermometer principally in having a provision for changing the position of this 5 or 6° interval on the temperature scale by adjusting the amount of

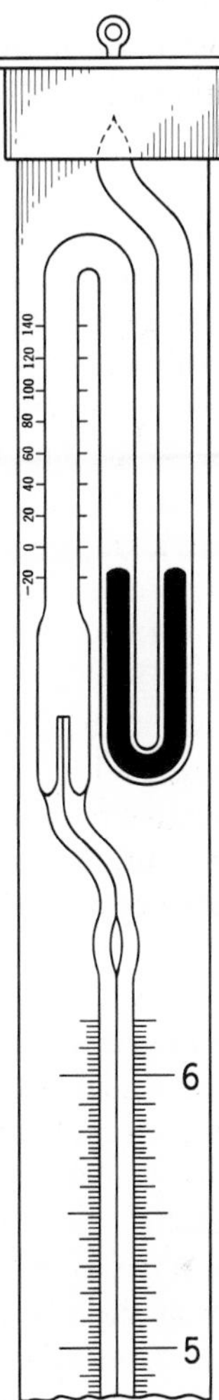

FIG. 1. Upper end of Beckmann thermometer.

mercury in the bulb and thread. For this purpose a special reservoir is provided at the top of the thermometer (see Fig. 1). To raise the setting, the bulb is warmed so as to discharge droplets of excess mercury into this reservoir. To lower the setting the bulb is warmed to bring the mercury thread into the bottom of the reservoir, where it is then united with a column of excess mercury which is brought into position by inverting the thermometer. The bulb is cooled to draw mercury into the thread. At a few degrees above the desired range the excess mercury is broken away from the thread by a sharp tap with the fingers. The thermometer is then brought to an upright position in such a way as to bring the excess mercury to its normal position in the reservoir.

Since the cubical expansion coefficient of mercury is not exactly constant, the magnitude of the true temperature difference represented by a scale division of the Beckmann thermometer varies with the temperature at which the thermometer is set to operate; accordingly, corrections are required in precise work. For a Beckmann thermometer made of Jena 16 glass (which may be taken as representative of German-made Beckmann thermometers), having a calibration which is valid when the mid-point of the scale is at 20°C, a temperature difference measured at temperature t can be corrected by multiplication with the factor $1 + 3 \times 10^{-4}(t - 20) - 10^{-6}(t - 20)^2$.

The Beckmann thermometer is very fragile and often subject to difficulties in use. Its use is best reserved to special purposes not served by available fixed-scale thermometers. Fixed-scale thermometers are ordinarily preferable for calorimetric and cryoscopic work in the usual temperature ranges.

Special Thermometers. For temperatures below the freezing point of mercury (−39°C), pentane thermometers may be used. Mercury thermometers constructed from special glasses may be used far above the normal boiling point of mercury (357°C). However, outside the ordinary mercury range it is usually more convenient, as well as more accurate, to use thermometric devices of other types, especially thermocouples.

Gas Thermometers. Although the attainment of high precision with gas thermometers entails highly complex apparatus and procedures,[3] simple gas thermometers resembling that of Exp. 1 may be used conveniently for moderately precise measurements, especially at low temperatures (see, for example, Exp. 46).

Platinum Resistance Thermometers.[7] The platinum resistance thermometer is capable of extremely high precision, owing to the high purity attainable for platinum and the high reproducibility of its temperature coefficient of resistivity. The resistance element is a coil of pure platinum wire, carefully annealed both before and after winding and enclosed in a tube (usually of glass) containing dry air or helium as a heat-transfer gas. Two leads are ordinarily attached to *each* end of the coil, in order to permit the resistance of the coil to be measured independently of the resistance of the leads. Platinum resistance thermometers in glass housings containing dry air may be used from −183 to 500°C or with a special glass housing to 630.5°C.

The coil resistance is determined by means of a Wheatstone bridge of appropriate design, such as the Mueller type, which is shown schematically in Fig. 2. It will be observed that the thermometric resistance R_t is in the BD arm of the bridge irrespective of the choice of the two positions of the commutator switch. However, the effective position of the junction D with respect to the leads can be switched to either end of the coil (D_e or D_f). For the switch setting shown in Fig. 2

$$R + R_E = R_t + R_F \tag{6}$$

and for the other setting

$$R' + R_F = R_t + R_E \tag{7}$$

where R and R' are the settings of the precision decade resistance at galvanometer balance and R_E and R_F are the resistances of the respective leads. Clearly the thermometric coil resistance is given by

$$R_t = \frac{R + R'}{2} \tag{8}$$

The temperature coefficient of resistivity of platinum is about 0.00392 deg^{-1} at 0°C. A thermometer with a coil of 25.5 ohms will show an increase of about 0.1 ohm deg^{-1} at that temperature. To determine the temperature to within ±0.001°C, it is necessary to measure the resistance R_t to within $\pm 10^{-4}$ ohm. With a bridge current of 2 ma (1 ma per arm) a galvanometer with a coil resistance of about 25 ohms must be sensitive to 0.033 μv, or 0.0013 μa. At a sensitivity of

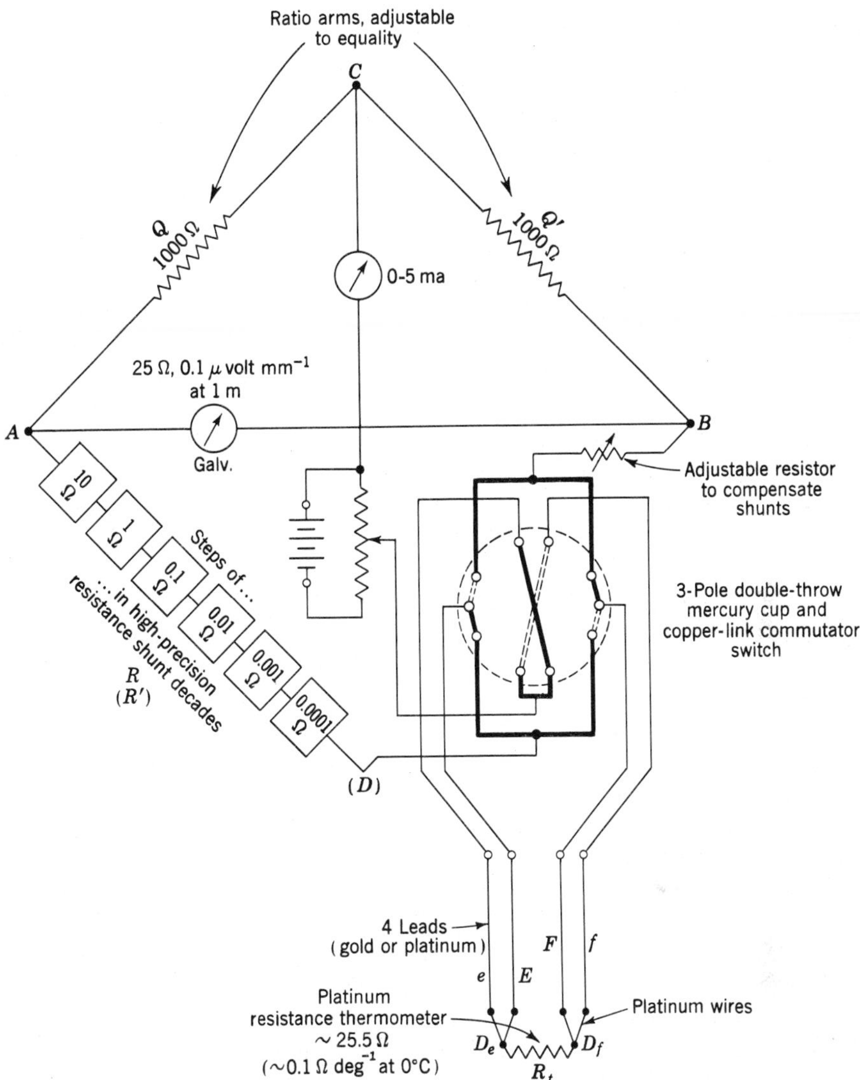

FIG. 2. Simplified schematic diagram of platinum resistance thermometer and Mueller-type bridge. Heavy lines in *BD* arm represent leads of negligible or balanced resistance.

0.1 μv mm^{-1} at 1 m, which is attainable with commercially available galvanometers with this resistance, a deflection of 0.33 mm at 1 m must be observable; this is close to the limit of practical detectability. The deflection can be increased by increasing the bridge current, but there is then the disadvantage of increased ohmic heating of the thermometer coil. Under the conditions cited, about 5 μcal sec^{-1} are dissipated by that coil. Error from this source can be corrected by making measurements at different bridge currents; it is common practice to make measurements at 3 and 5 ma and to extrapolate to zero current.

Although a 25-ohm platinum resistance thermometer with a commercially available Mueller bridge (e.g., the L & N type G-2, Catalogue No. 8069) and galvanometer (e.g., L & N type HS, Catalogue No. 2284-d, 25-ohm coil, 0.1 μv mm^{-1} at 1 m) is capable of measuring temperatures with a reproducibility of 0.001 or

0.002°, its uncertainty in measuring on the International Practical Temperature Scale is usually somewhat larger than that in practice (about 0.01°), being determined largely by the limits within which the calibration temperatures can be established under ordinary laboratory conditions.

Thermistors. Thermistors are thermosensitive resistors made from semiconductors with large (negative) coefficients of resistivity. At room temperature, a typical thermistor changes about 4 per cent in resistance in 1°. Thermistors may be used as resistance thermometers, and they enable high precision to be attained with a less sensitive bridge than is required for a platinum thermometer. However, two of the most valuable characteristics of the platinum thermometer, its high degree of reproducibility and its long-term stability, are not possessed by thermistors.

Thermocouples. Thermocouples provide one of the most convenient means of measuring temperatures over a wide range from very low (−250°C) to very high (1700°C) values. All that is required is a pair of wires made from two suitable metals or alloys, a good potentiometer, and a constant-temperature bath (usually an ice-water bath) for the reference junction.

When two dissimilar metals are placed in contact, a transfer of electrons from one to the other takes place and a double charge layer forms at the junction surface. As in the case of a junction between a metal electrode and an electrolyte solution, the resulting electric potential must be measured in the presence of a reference junction, which in the present instance is a junction of the same two metals at a known temperature. The thermoelectric potential is measured between the ends of two wires of the same metal—one wire leading to the junction at the reference temperature and the other to the junction at the unknown temperature; the two junctions are connected directly by a wire of the second metal completing the circuit. This potential is a measure of the unknown temperature, and in cases where the temperature difference is not large, it is roughly proportional to the difference between the unknown and reference temperatures.

The most useful thermocouple for general work is *copper-constantan,* the latter being an alloy of 60 per cent copper and 40 per cent nickel which is often sold under the trade name Advance. An important advantage of the use of this couple is that one of the metals is copper, which is the metal generally used for the binding posts on galvanometers and potentiometers. Thus, any stray thermoelectric potential caused by temperature differences between the contacts of the thermocouple wires with the binding posts is eliminated. The thermoelectric potential of a copper-constantan couple with the reference junction at 0°C has a temperature coefficient which varies from about 20 μv deg^{-1} at −200°C to 60 at 250°C. At room temperature, it is 48 μv deg^{-1}. This couple cannot be used for long above 500°C.

Another commonly used couple is Chromel P and Alumel, these two being iron-nickel alloys containing chromium and aluminum, respectively. The coefficient is about 40 μv deg^{-1} over a very wide range, and this thermocouple can be used at temperatures as high as 1300°C. *Iron-constantan,* with a somewhat higher coefficient (53 μv deg^{-1} at room temperature), can be used to nearly 1000°C. Platinum together with an alloy of 10 per cent rhodium in platinum has a small coefficient (5.5 μv deg^{-1} at room temperature) but can be used as high as 1700°C.

Although extensive tables are given in various handbooks for converting measured emf's to temperatures, these should be used only as rough guides. Thermocouple wires should be carefully selected, and one or more specimens of each lot should be calibrated at a number of temperatures. For very precise work each thermocouple should be individually calibrated.

Junctions may be joined with soft solder for use at low temperatures; for elevated temperatures they should be hard-soldered or welded. The junctions should be protected from their environment (e.g., aqueous solutions) by suitable jackets. The two wires must be electrically insulated from each other, and some consideration must be given to the temperature characteristics of the insulating materials. In particular, at high temperatures nothing should come into contact with the wires (particularly Chromel P and Alumel) which will form a liquid flux (low-melting eutectic) with the protective oxide film. Pure Alundum tubes or spacers are usually satisfactory.

A satisfactory environment for a 0°C reference junction is provided by a slushy mixture of ice and distilled water in a Dewar flask, with a ring stirrer and a monitoring mercury thermometer.

In very rough work with large-gauge thermocouple wires the thermoelectric emf can be measured directly with a millivoltmeter or galvanometer possessing an internal resistance large in comparison with the thermocouple wires. For ordinary work a Student Potentiometer and an enclosed-scale or pointer-type galvanometer will suffice. (The Student Potentiometer should be set on the 0.01 scale; see Chap. XV.) For very precise work a potentiometer designed for use in the fractional microvolt range is essential. The Wenner potentiometer (L & N Catalogue No. 7559) is such an instrument; it has a low range of 0 to 0.01 v in steps of 0.1 μv and a limit of error of 0.01 per cent plus 0.5 μv. Thus, with a copper-constantan thermocouple (with one measuring and one reference junction) it permits measurement with a limit of error of about 0.01° near room temperature; however, temperature differences can be measured to 0.002°.

An increase in sensitivity can be obtained by the use of a multijunction thermocouple, employing several measuring and reference junctions in alternating sequence (see Fig. 3). This gain is purchased at the price of increased complexity,

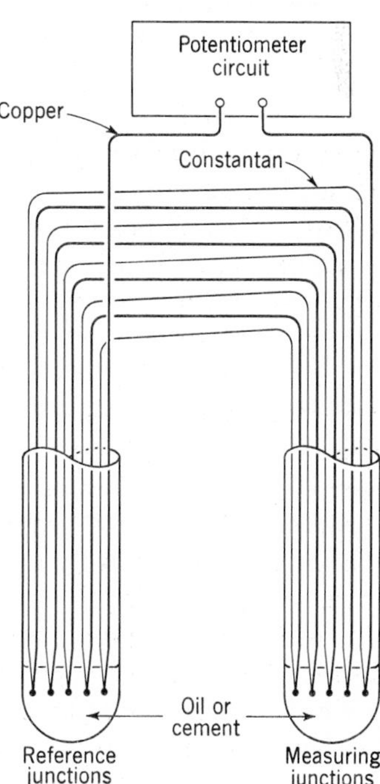

FIG. 3. Schematic diagram of multijunction copper-constantan thermocouple.

particularly in regard to problems of thermal contact and electrical insulation. These problems can be solved fairly easily in the neighborhood of room temperature, and multijunction thermocouples are sometimes employed in calorimetric work.

Optical Pyrometers.[8] The optical pyrometer can be used for the measurement of temperature above 600°C, where black-body radiation in the visible part of the spectrum is of sufficient intensity. The black-body emissivity at a given wavelength in equilibrium with matter at a given temperature is given by the Planck radiation law

$$J_\lambda = \frac{c_1}{\lambda^5} \frac{1}{e^{c_2/\lambda T} - 1} \tag{9}$$

where J_λ is the black-body emissivity per unit wavelength interval and c_1 and c_2 are numerical constants ($c_2 = hc/k = 1.438$ cm deg). The optical pyrometer is essentially a photometer which measures the emissivity of the source in a given wavelength interval. We shall here consider only the most common type of optical pyrometer, the "disappearing-filament" type. The object whose temperature is to be measured is viewed through a telescope containing, at an image plane, a lamp with a carbon or tungsten filament, the temperature of which can be varied by adjustment of the current through it. A red filter in the eyepiece selects a narrow-wavelength range for visual observation. When the current has been adjusted so that the filament becomes invisible against the background, the temperature is obtained by referring the filament current to a calibration curve or chart.

Fixed points for the calibration of the optical pyrometers are the silver and gold points and higher secondary fixed points such as those given in Table 2. Calibration at other temperatures can be accomplished by use of a rotating sector or a filter of accurately known transmission factor between the fixed-point source and the pyrometer, in order to simulate a source of lower temperature in accordance with the Planck equation. Such sectors or filters are used also to permit the optical pyrometer to be used for the measurement of temperatures much above 2000°.

Optical pyrometer measurements are most reliable when the object being examined is the interior of a furnace or cavity of uniform temperature viewed through a small opening. Readings for an exposed surface are somewhat dependent upon the emissivity coefficient of the substance concerned, which for an ideal "black body" is unity and for actual materials is less than unity. The emissivity coefficient in the visible range is near unity for carbon and oxidized metals and considerably less for platinum and other unoxidized metals, especially when polished. Under the best conditions the optical pyrometer is accurate to about 0.2 per cent of the absolute temperature. It is also a convenient instrument for less precise measurements at high temperatures, such as the routine measurement of furnace temperatures, etc.

Other Thermometric Devices. Any physical property that depends sensitively on temperature may, in appropriate circumstances, be used to measure temperature. The vapor pressure of a liquid or a solid is such a property; the use of liquid nitrogen is suggested in Exp. 46. At very low temperatures, the vapor pressures of liquid helium (1 to 4.2°K) and of solid and liquid hydrogen (9 to 20°K) are used as the bases of temperature scales. Between 1 and 20°K, carbon resistance thermometers are widely used.

TEMPERATURE CONTROL

In addition to the measurement of temperature, it is often necessary to maintain a constant temperature. The importance of this type of control in experimental physical chemistry is illustrated by the fact that 27 of the 47 experiments described in this book require temperature control of some kind. Many physical quantities (such as rate constants, equilibrium constants, emf's, osmotic pressures) are sensitive functions of temperature and must be measured at a known temperature which is held constant to within $\pm 0.1°C$ or better. Certain physical techniques are even more demanding; for example, the use of a dilatometer in Exp. 27 requires that the temperature be controlled to within $\pm 0.002°C$.

The simplest method of achieving a constant temperature is to maintain an equilibrium (at constant pressure) between two phases of a pure substance or among three phases in a two-component system. The greatest disadvantage of this method is that one cannot attain a desired *arbitrary* temperature unless a liquid-vapor system is used with a complicated manostat to maintain an arbitrary boiling pressure. In addition, it is often difficult to maintain temperature control for very long periods of time with this method. There are, however, several advantages: economy and simplicity in operation, excellent temperature stability, and potentially high precision in the absolute temperature of the bath. Several commonly used systems of this type are listed below, together with brief comments on their use.

Liquid-nitrogen Bath. Liquid nitrogen at its normal boiling point (77.3°K, $-195.8°C$) provides a very convenient low-temperature bath. Since O_2 dissolved in liquid N_2 will raise the temperature of the bath, the mouth of the Dewar flask should be plugged loosely with glass wool or cotton to retard the slow condensation of atmospheric oxygen. The temperature of a liquid-nitrogen bath can be calculated on the assumption that the nitrogen vapor pressure is equal to the atmospheric pressure. Clearly, temperature stability will depend on the absence of large changes in pressure; fortunately, the boiling point of nitrogen changes only 0.013° per mm Hg change in pressure. This bath is frequently used for freezing out vapors in a trap, especially in high-vacuum applications.

Dry Ice-acetone Bath. Solid carbon dioxide in equilibrium with CO_2 vapor at 1 atm will provide a temperature of $-78.5°C$. Thus, Dry Ice, which is inexpensive and readily available, would seem to be very suitable for a constant-temperature bath at moderately low temperatures. Unfortunately, the use of Dry Ice alone is complicated by two difficulties: the problem of obtaining and maintaining the proper pressure of CO_2 gas and the problem of achieving good thermal contact between the Dry Ice and the object to be cooled. Although these difficulties can be overcome by careful bath design and the use of a heater to cause a constant evolution of CO_2 gas, it is much easier to use a Dry Ice-acetone bath. The acetone (or, indeed, any liquid which does not freeze at Dry Ice temperature) provides good thermal contact throughout the bath and prevents air from diluting the CO_2 gas at the surface of the Dry Ice as it would at an exposed Dry Ice surface. In making up a Dry Ice-acetone bath, it is necessary to minimize the foaming which occurs owing to rapid evolution of gas when Dry Ice is placed in contact with acetone initially at room temperature. The Dry Ice should be pulverized. If a special grinder is not available, one can wrap chunks of Dry Ice in a towel and pound them with a mallet. Be careful in handling pieces of Dry Ice; it can cause painful "burns" if held in the bare hand for more than a few seconds. The use of tongs or insulated gloves is strongly recommended. A Dewar flask is first filled about two-thirds full with acetone, and then small quantities of very finely powdered Dry Ice are added **slowly** with a spatula. This Dry Ice will evaporate almost immediately, and there will be considerable foaming at the surface. Add more Dry Ice only after the foaming has subsided. After a while the acetone will have cooled to the point where the evaporation of Dry Ice is much slower, and some Dry Ice will begin to accumulate on the bottom of the Dewar. At this point, small lumps of Dry Ice can be added without causing serious foaming. Good temperature control with this bath is ensured only if it is well stirred and there is a slow but steady stream of CO_2 bubbles rising from the bottom. **Caution:** Acetone is flammable and care should be taken in the vicinity of any open flames.

Ice Bath. The ice-water equilibrium at 0°C provides an excellent constant-temperature bath. The ice should be washed, and distilled water must be used. To avoid thermal gradients between water at 4°C (maximum density) at the bottom of the Dewar and a 0°C liquid surface in which ice is floating, it is usually necessary to stir this bath. As a bath for the reference junction of a thermocouple, gradients can be eliminated by completely filling the Dewar with ice and adding only a small amount of cold distilled water; the weight of ice above the liquid will force ice down to the very bottom of the Dewar.

Sodium Sulfate Bath. Pure sodium sulfate decahydrate can be decomposed to a mixture of the monohydrate and a saturated aqueous solution by gentle heating in a warm water bath until the temperature (as shown by a mercury thermometer) begins to rise above 32.4°C. Additional decahydrate can then be stirred in, and the container insulated (or the mixture transferred to a Dewar flask). The mixture will maintain a temperature of 32.38°C as long as the two solid phases and one liquid phase are present in equilibrium.

Vapor Baths. Boiling acetone (56.5°C), water (100°C), naphthalene (218.0°C), and possibly sulfur (444.6°C) can be used as vapor baths. In each case, the object to be thermostatted is immersed in the refluxing or condensing vapor. See Exp. 1 for details of a steam bath.

The second important method of achieving temperature control is to use a thermosensing element with a feedback system to control the input of heat (or of refrigeration) to a bath so that the temperature is maintained close to any desired arbitrary value. The thermosensing device may be any thermometric instrument that provides an electrical signal, such as thermocouple or resistance thermometer. Or it may be a mercury thermometer equipped with an auxiliary device for converting its reading into an electrical signal; commonly a wire contact is fixed above the mercury meniscus to provide a simple "off" or "on" electrical signal depending on whether the temperature is below the desired level or above it. The signal is received by a thermoregulating circuit which switches or varies the power to the heating (or refrigerating) element so as to correct the temperature deviation detected by the thermosensing element.

As in any system employing feedback to maintain a steady-state condition, certain design criteria must be met in order to obtain reasonably rapid response to environmental changes while avoiding excessive "hunting" or even uncontrolled oscillations. The performance of the system will depend upon such factors as the sensitivity and speed of response of the thermosensing element, the circulation of heat in the system (stirring, convection), and the fraction of the total energy input (heat input plus stirring work, etc.) that is being controlled by the thermoregulator.

This fraction should be no larger than is required to accommodate the expected variation in heat loss to the surroundings.

To provide damping of oscillations, a "proportionating" circuit is often employed; in the vicinity of the desired temperature the current or power to the heater is made roughly proportional to the difference between the actual temperature and a temperature setting which is slightly above the desired value. Such a circuit usually has an adjustment for providing an optimum range of proportionation, since a proportionating system provides stability at the expense of some precision of temperature control. Many on-off systems provide some accidental proportionation in the form of rapid cycling of the thermosensing element due to mechanical vibration, etc.

For automatic temperature measurement thermocouples are often used with recording potentiometers; to achieve temperature control a proportionating circuit, controlling a variable transformer with a servo system, can be connected directly to the automatic potentiometer. Analogous systems are available for platinum resistance thermometers. For very fine control a Mueller bridge or thermocouple potentiometer can be used, with a proportionating circuit controlled by a photocell in the reflected light beam from the galvanometer.[9] It is also possible to use a resistance thermometer in an ac bridge and to use the magnitude and phase of the unbalance signal to control a relay or Thyratron.[10, 11]

Water Baths. The water bath, equipped with stirrer, thermoregulator, control circuit, and heater, provides the most commonly required means of temperature regulation. A good water bath for student use makes use of a large rectangular tub perhaps 18 by 36 in. in horizontal area and 18 in. deep, with a water capacity of about 170 liters, constructed of welded stainless steel; glass windows in two or more sides are convenient. Thermoregulators and stirrers are best mounted in the middle, leaving the ends free for experimental work. There should be adequate provision for mounting rods and clamps to support flasks, electrochemical cells, etc. Depending on the experiment, two or four pairs of students can work in a single bath of this size. The bath should be provided with the following:

Stirrer: A centrifugal water circulator, driven by a 1/20-hp motor, provides adequate stirring. It should be positioned carefully so that the effluent stream will cause efficient circulation through the entire tank.

Heater: A single-blade type heater of 250 watts' capacity is adequate for temperature regulation up to about 30°. At higher temperatures a second one may be added. It is advisable to position the heater in the effluent stream from the stirrer. If two heaters are employed, one may be intermittent under the control of the thermoregulator and the other under power constantly or both may be intermittent, depending on their power ratings, the temperature to be maintained, and other factors.

Thermosensing element: Thermocouples and platinum resistance thermometers, apart from the required control circuitry, need no further discussion. Most thermosensing devices for laboratory temperature control are of the off-on thermoswitch type. Thermoswitches based on the making and breaking of contacts by bimetallic strips are useful where long-term reliability and regulation to better than about 1° are not required. The most commonly used type of thermosensing element is a thermometer-like device in which an electrical contact is made by a platinum or other wire to a mercury meniscus in a capillary when the temperature has attained the desired value. The liquid in the bulb may be entirely mercury, or it may be in larger part a liquid such as toluene with a higher thermal expansion coefficient,

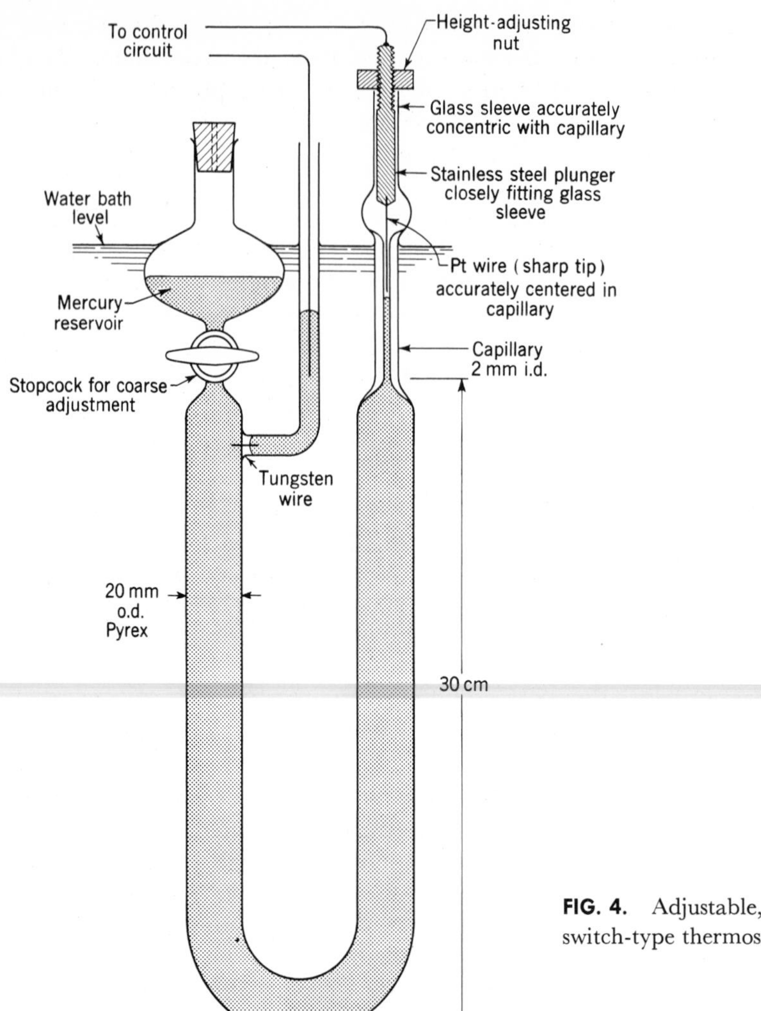

FIG. 4. Adjustable, mercury thermo-switch-type thermosensing device.

and the wire contact may be fixed or adjustable. Completely sealed devices for one or several fixed temperatures or with provision for adjustment of the amount of mercury in the thread are available commercially. Unfortunately they are often unsatisfactory; their bulbs are usually too small to give the required sensitivity, their capillaries are small enough to give trouble because of breaking of the thread, and there is eventual trouble from accumulation of "dirt" at the contact due to sparking. The most reliable devices are probably homemade ones, which can be cleaned and adjusted from time to time. A suitable design is shown in Fig. 4. It contains about 200 ml of mercury in a U-shaped glass tube no larger than 20 cm o.d., with a movable platinum contact accurately centered in a capillary of 2-mm bore. The stopcock and associated storage bulb permit large changes in the temperature setting and facilitate cleaning. To clean the capillary tube and mercury meniscus, mercury is sucked out of the capillary through a long hypodermic needle attached to a suction flask, the capillary is wiped clean with a pipe cleaner, and fresh mercury is admitted from the storage reservoir.

Thermoregulating circuit: We shall consider only the regulation of power to a heater with a signal from an off-on thermoswitch, without proportionation. This can be done by electromechanical or electronic relays. A simple circuit for this purpose is shown in Fig. 5. Other circuits, including ones in which the heating load is controlled by one or more Thyratrons, can be found in the literature.[12, 13]

Water-level control: When a thermostat bath is operated for long periods, it is subject to loss of water by evaporation to a point which will interfere with its normal operation unless the water is replaced. Therefore the tank should have an overflow drain and should be provided with a continuous supply of cold water that can be controlled from a few drops per minute to a small, steady stream. This supply of water also performs an important control function. A 1/20-hp motor delivers constantly about 37 watts of mechanical energy to the bath, and, on days when the room temperature is not far below the desired bath temperature, this amount of energy is itself sufficient to maintain the bath temperature above the desired level. A stream of cold water may compensate largely or entirely for the stirring heat. The adjustment of the water flow is often critical and must be changed frequently. If the thermoregulating relay is one with double throw, the contacts opposite the heater contacts can be used to operate a solenoid valve to turn the water off and on and thereby permit a larger and less critical water flow, possibly at the expense of some fineness of temperature regulation.

Miscellaneous: To reduce rusting of iron hardware in the bath, a zinc or aluminum electrode with an applied anodic potential of a few volts with respect to the tank as ground may be provided. This should be protected from accidental contact by a perforated tube of bakelite or other plastic.

Oil Baths. Above 50°C water baths are subject to severe evaporation. Oil baths employing heavy cylinder oil can be used as high as 300°C (in a closed thermostat, because of fire hazard); with silicone oil higher temperatures may be reached. A eutectic mixture of sodium, potassium, and lithium nitrates (14, 56, and 30 per cent by weight, respectively) is liquid at 120°C and with care can be used as high as 400 or even 450°C.

Air Thermostats. Complex gas-handling systems of large size are often not well accommodated by water or oil baths. A double-walled air thermostat can be constructed with suitable insulation (air, fiberglass, vermiculite, foamed plastic, etc.)

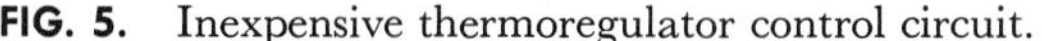
FIG. 5. Inexpensive thermoregulator control circuit.

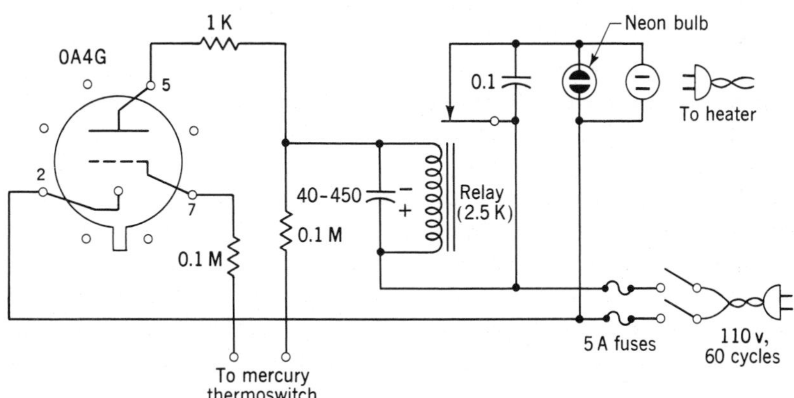

and with double glass windows where needed. Air is circulated by a blower. Thermoregulation is accomplished in much the same way as in a water bath.

Ovens and Furnaces. Commonly available laboratory ovens can be used to temperatures as high as 200 or 300°C. They are usually regulated to 1 or 2° with a bimetallic thermoswitch. Air circulation is by convection, and the temperature is usually nonuniform. For obtaining better temperature uniformity and improved regulation, a lining made of thick sheet aluminum or copper can be installed.

For higher temperatures electric furnaces are used. These are obtainable commercially, but satisfactory ones can be made in the laboratory (see Fig. 28-1). A pregrooved Alundum core is wound with suitable heating wire (Nichrome, Chromel A, Kanthall), 12 to 20 gauge, and covered with a thick coating of Alundum cement. This is surrounded by several inches of powdered magnesia for thermal insulation, in a large metal container. After assembly the furnace is slowly heated to slightly above 1000°C to set the cement. A cover plug may be cut from firebrick. Internal metal radiation shields (platinum is best; molybdenum may be used if a neutral or reducing atmosphere is maintained) are needed if a high degree of temperature uniformity is required. Temperature is controlled with a Variac or similar transformer, operated manually or by a proportionating thermoregulator circuit with a thermocouple potentiometer or resistance thermometer bridge.

For temperatures above 1000 to 1200°C a platinum winding on a silica core or a combustion tube furnace heated by Globar or carbon rods may be used. These and other special high-temperature furnaces, including induction furnaces, vacuum furnaces, and arc furnaces, are beyond the scope of this book.

REFERENCES

1. H. F. Stimson, *Natl. Bur. Standards J. Research,* **65A,** 139 (1961).
2. *Compt. rend. onzième conf. gén. poids et mesures* (1960).
3. J. A. Beattie, in "Temperature, Its Measurement and Control in Science and Industry" (see General Reading below), vol. II, p. 63 (1955).
4. R. B. Scott, *op. cit.,* vol. II, p. 179.
5. H. J. Hoge, *op. cit.,* vol. I, p. 141; H. J. Hoge and F. G. Brickwedde, *Natl. Bur. Standards J. Research,* **22,** 351 (1939).
6. J. Busse, in "Temperature, Its Measurement and Control," vol. I, p. 228 (1941).
7. E. F. Mueller, *op. cit.,* vol. I, p. 162.
8. W. E. Forsyth, *op. cit.,* vol. I, p. 1115.
9. J. A. Beattie, *Proc. Am. Acad. Arts Sci.,* **69,** 395 (1934).
10. C. T. Tomizuka and D. Zimmerman, *Rev. Sci. Instr.,* **30,** 40 (1959).
11. A. A. Brooks, *ibid.,* **27,** 746 (1956); **28,** 297 (1957).
12. J. M. Sturtevant, Temperature Control, in A. Weissberger (ed.), "Technique of Organic Chemistry," 2d ed., vol. I, part I, pp. 41–42, Interscience, New York (1949).
13. C. A. Proctor, *Rev. Sci. Instr.,* **22,** 1023 (1951).

GENERAL READING

"Temperature, Its Measurement and Control in Science and Industry," vol. I (1941), papers presented at a Symposium of the American Institute of Physics, November, 1939; vol. II (1955, H. C. Wolfe, ed.), papers presented at a Symposium under AIP and other auspices, Reinhold, New York (October, 1954).

J. M. Sturtevant, Temperature Measurement and Temperature Control, in A. Weissberger (ed.), "Technique of Organic Chemistry," 2d ed., vol. I, part I, pp. 1–48, Interscience, New York (1949).

XVII
VACUUM TECHNIQUES

This chapter contains a discussion of several topics of importance in the theory, design, and practice of handling gases at low pressures. Major emphasis is given to high-vacuum techniques, since they play a vital role in many physical chemistry research problems. For vacuum applications in this book, see Exps. 8, 28, 33, and 47. Some of the material presented is also pertinent to the problem of pumping on refrigerant baths; for an application of this technique, see Exp. 46. This chapter is not intended as a comprehensive treatment; more detailed information is available in the works cited in the General Reading list.

THEORETICAL BACKGROUND

The basic theory needed here is the kinetic theory of gases, which is discussed in Chap. IV. It will be assumed that gases always obey the perfect-gas law and have an essentially Maxwellian distribution of molecular velocities. The most important properties for our present purpose are the mean free path $\bar{l}$, the coefficient of viscosity η, and the coefficient of thermal conductivity K; in particular, we are concerned with the dependence of these three properties on pressure at constant temperature. According to Eqs. (IV-3), (IV-14), and (IV-18) $\bar{l}$ varies inversely with p while η and K are independent of p. The expression given by Eq. (IV-3) for $\bar{l}$ is correct over the entire pressure range, but Eq. (IV-14) is valid only at pressures high enough so that $\bar{l}$ is small compared with the dimensions of the container. At lower pressures, where $\bar{l}$ becomes comparable to the apparatus dimensions, both η and K decrease with decreasing pressure. When $\bar{l}$ is considerably larger than the apparatus dimensions (i.e., at pressures less than 0.01 mm Hg for most apparatus), η and K will vary linearly with the pressure. This limiting behavior is a consequence of molecular-flow conditions where the mechanism of momentum or kinetic-energy transport depends on collisions between gas molecules and the walls rather than on intermolecular collisions.[1] In this limiting region, the pressure dependence of viscosity or thermal conductivity serves as the basis for the operation of several types of vacuum gauges.

PUMPING SPEED FOR A SYSTEM

Detailed calculations of pumping speed are seldom necessary for designing a system to obtain a static vacuum in a small, closed line. However, certain qualitative principles of vacuum-line design are important. When one must pump out a large volume or pump on a system where there is a continuous evolution of gas inside the system (as when pumping on a refrigerant bath, for example), a careful quantitative design is essential. Over-all pumping speed will depend on the characteristics of the pump (or pumps) used and also on the impedance to gas flow through the connecting tubing.

Conductance of Pumping Lines. First one must define the flux Q, which is the quantity of gas (in pressure-volume units) flowing past a given plane in unit time. The flux is given by

$$Q = pV^* = N^*RT \tag{1}$$

where V^* is the volume of gas at temperature T flowing in unit time past a plane in the system where the steady-state pressure is p and N^* is the number of moles flowing past that plane in unit time. The conductance of a connecting tube is related to Q by

$$Q = C(p_1 - p_2) \tag{2}$$

where p_1 and p_2 are taken as fixed pressures at the inlet and outlet of the tube, respectively. Equation (2) is completely analogous to Ohm's law for an electrical circuit: Q is analogous to the electric current i; $(p_1 - p_2)$ is similar to the potential difference E; C plays the same role as the electrical conductance $1/R$. The net conductance for a combination of several connecting tubes is also given by the same equations that govern the case of electrical conductance:

$$\frac{1}{C} = \sum_{i=1}^{n} \frac{1}{C_i} \tag{3}$$

for a combination of n tubes connected in series, and

$$C = \sum_{i=1}^{n} C_i \tag{4}$$

for a parallel combination of n tubes.

One can now cite the appropriate formulas for calculating C for the simplest kind of pumping tube, a cylinder with circular cross section. In general, turbulence is not involved for the gas flow through a pumping line, and we shall neglect it completely. In the higher pressure range viscous flow is dominant. Combining Eq. (1) with Eq. (5-8) for the laminar flow of a gas (and noting that N^* has the same meaning as ϕ_N) we obtain

$$Q = \frac{\pi d^4}{128\eta L}\,\frac{p_1 + p_2}{2}(p_1 - p_2) \qquad \text{dyne cm sec}^{-1} \tag{5}$$

where d is the diameter of the tube in centimeters, L is its length in centimeters, η is the viscosity expressed in poises, and p_1 and p_2 are in dynes per square centimeter. Comparing Eqs. (2) and (5) we see that

$$C_\eta = \frac{\pi d^4}{128\eta L}\bar{p} \qquad \text{cm}^3\ \text{sec}^{-1} \tag{6}$$

where $\bar{p} = (p_1 + p_2)/2$ is the average pressure in the tube. The subscript η on C_η is a reminder that this expression is valid only for the viscous flow that occurs at high pressures. For air at 298°K, Eq. (6) reduces to

$$C_\eta(\text{air}) = \frac{0.18d^4}{L}\bar{p} \qquad \text{liter sec}^{-1} \tag{7}$$

where $\bar{p}$ is now expressed in microns ($1\mu = 10^{-3}$ mm Hg).

At very low pressures, molecular flow is the predominant mechanism for gas transport; it can then be shown[1] that the appropriate expression for C is no longer Eq. (6) but rather

$$C_m = \frac{d^3}{6L}\left(\frac{2\pi kT}{m}\right)^{1/2} \tag{8}$$

where m is the molecular mass. The subscript m shows that this expression is limited to the region of true molecular flow. Note that in this region the conductance is independent of pressure. For air at 298°K, Eq. (8) can be simplified to give

$$C_m(\text{air}) = \frac{12.2d^3}{L} \qquad \text{liter sec}^{-1} \tag{9}$$

At intermediate pressures where the flow is neither purely viscous nor purely molecular, one can use an empirical expression of Knudsen[2]

$$C = C_\eta + FC_m \tag{10}$$

The factor F is a complicated function of m, T, d, η, and $\bar{p}$; it has values for air which vary between ~0.8 at high pressures and 1.0 at low pressures.

Equations (6) to (10) do not include the effect of the conductance of the inlet aperture where the tube is connected to another region of larger cross section (to a bulb, for example). Unless L is very much larger than d, this aperture conductance C_a will have a significant effect on the total conductance of the tube. From Eqs. (2) and (IV-7) we see that, *for low pressures* where molecular flow occurs,

$$C_a = \frac{d^2}{8}\left(\frac{2\pi kT}{m}\right)^{1/2} \tag{11}$$

(For air at 298°K, $C_a = 9.15d^2$ liter sec^{-1}.) The total conductance at low pressures is therefore given by

$$\frac{1}{C} = \frac{1}{C_m} + \frac{1}{C_a} \tag{12}$$

in accordance with Eq. (3). At higher pressures where viscous flow occurs, the calculation of C_a is very difficult, but fortunately $1/C_a$ is usually negligible compared with $1/C_\eta$.

It will be helpful to make some qualitative generalizations about design parameters on the basis of the equations presented above. In the high-vacuum region ($p < 0.1\mu$) the conductance is effectively that given by Eq. (12) for free molecular flow. Usually, aperture conductance will be an important factor, and it may cause a 10 to 50 per cent loss in over-all conductance. Thus in the design of high-speed vacuum systems it is important to use short, large-diameter tubes with as few constrictions as possible. In the pressure region from 100 to 1000 μ, viscous flow becomes important and the conductance for a given tube becomes considerably larger than for pure molecular flow. Also the volume flow rate required to achieve a given Q is less because of the higher prevailing pressures. Thus, for pumping at higher pressures (as in the line between a diffusion pump and forepump) smaller diameter tubes can be used.

No mention has been made yet of the effect of bends on tube conductance. Except for very short tubes a few smooth bends will not greatly reduce the conductance. Approximate ways of estimating the effect of a right-angle bend are (1) to consider each bend as an additional aperture or (2) to increase the effective length of the tube by 1.33 d for each bend.

Speed of the Pump. The *effective* speed S of a pump operating at a pressure p is defined as the volume of gas measured at a constant temperature T and the given pressure p which is removed from the system per unit time; thus $S = Q/p$. This effective speed is related to the *intrinsic* pump speed S^* by

$$S = S^*\left(1 - \frac{p^*}{p}\right) \tag{13}$$

where p^* is the ultimate pressure attainable by the pump. It is not possible to make an accurate calculation of pump speeds, but there are reliable experimental methods for measuring S^*. Both dynamic and static methods have been used: In the dynamic method, the change in the steady-state pressure is measured when a metered leak is closed; in the static method, the rate of pressure change is measured for the evacuation of a bulb of fixed volume. Details of these methods are given by Dushman.[3] Once S^* is known, Eq. (13) permits one to calculate S, which is the quantity of practical interest.

Over-all Pumping Speed. Consider, for example, a large bulb connected via a tube of conductance C to a pump of effective speed S. We wish to find S_T, the over-all pumping speed for this composite system. The rate of gas removal from the bulb Q equals $S_T p_1$ where p_1 is the pressure in the bulb. Also, Q must equal $C(p_1 - p_2)$ for the flow through the tube where p_2 is the outlet pressure at the pump end of the tube. Finally, Q equals Sp_2 at the pump itself. Since

$$\frac{Q}{C} = p_1 - p_2 = \frac{Q}{S_T} - \frac{Q}{S}$$

we can write

$$\frac{1}{S_T} = \frac{1}{S} + \frac{1}{C} \tag{14}$$

Although the speed of a pump differs from the conductance of a tube in being defined in terms of a single pressure rather than a pressure difference, Eq. (14) shows that, for the kind of system being considered, S can be treated in the same way as C in calculations involving series or parallel combinations of pumps and pumping lines.

Up to this point, pumping speeds have been discussed for the case of fixed pressures for which Q is given by $-p\,dV/dt$. In general, Q is defined as $-d(pV)/dt$; for the case of evacuation of a *fixed volume* V, Q becomes $-V\,dp/dt$. Thus we have for this case

$$S_T = \frac{Q}{p} = -\frac{V}{p}\frac{dp}{dt} \tag{15}$$

The calculation of the time required to evacuate a volume of V liters is complicated by the fact that S_T varies with the pressure.[3] For the simple case where S_T is constant over the range from an initial pressure p_i to a given final pressure p_f, one can integrate Eq. (15) to obtain

$$\Delta t = \frac{V}{S_T} \ln \frac{p_i}{p_f} \tag{16}$$

where Δt is the time required in seconds.

PUMPS

Four types of pumps will be discussed in this section. The very simple Toepler pump is much too slow for practical use in evacuating a large system, but it is quite useful for the quantitative transfer of small amounts of gas from one part of a system to another. Rotary oil pumps are used for pumping on refrigerant baths and as the forepump for "backing" low-pressure pumps. For most high-vacuum work, diffusion pumps are used to achieve pressures of about 10^{-6} mm; however, ion pumps can now be used to achieve ultra-high vacuums of 10^{-9} mm or less.

Toepler Pump.[3] The Toepler pump permits one to transfer gas from a bulb A into another bulb B without loss or contamination. This is accomplished by alternately lowering and raising the mercury level in a reservoir connected with both bulbs. When the mercury level is lowered, gas expands from A into the reservoir; when it is raised, this gas is forced into B. Many cycles of operation are necessary to effect an almost complete transfer of the gas. Obviously, this transfer could be accomplished much more easily for a condensable gas by merely cooling bulb B with liquid nitrogen. The Toepler pump is most useful in handling those few substances (such as He, H_2, CO, N_2, Ar, CH_4) which either condense below 77°K or have an appreciable vapor pressure at that temperature. One of the most common applications of this device is to remove gas from a reaction bulb for quantitative analysis at the end of a kinetics run; for example, in Exp. 28, a Toepler pump would be necessary to remove quantitatively the hydrogen gas from the furnace.

Rotary Oil Pumps. The basic design of a mechanical oil pump is illustrated by Fig. 1. An eccentric cam is rotated against the cylindrical walls of the stator by means of a motor-driven pulley (not shown). For all positions of the rotor a sliding vane is pressed firmly against the top of the rotor by a spring-loaded rocker arm. Gas which expands into region A through the intake is isolated when the contact point C passes the intake opening. This gas is then compressed (in region B) by the motion of the rotor. When the cam reaches the point in its rotation corresponding to maximum compression, this gas is expelled through the exhaust valve. The surfaces of the rotor, stator, and vane and also the seat of the exhaust valve are precision ground to minimize leakage. In addition, the entire pump is immersed in a low-vapor-pressure oil. Small amounts of oil on the inside of the pump act as an additional seal as well as a lubricant; the oil-check valve on the exhaust prevents appreciable flow of oil into the pump.

There are considerable variations on this basic design. Many commercial types are compound pumps in which two single stages are mounted on the same shaft and are connected in series as a means of increasing the pumping speed and improving the ultimate vacuum. The pumping speed at high pressures depends

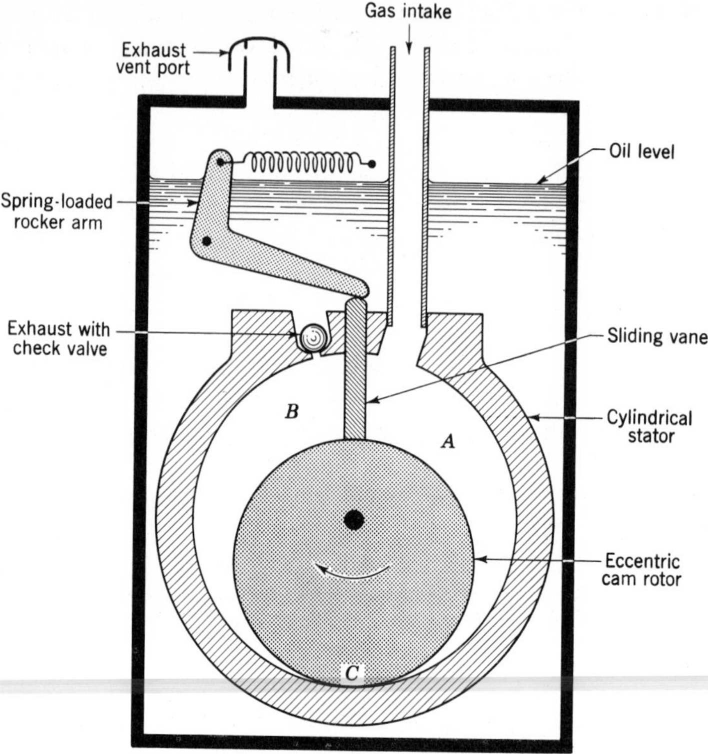

FIG. 1. Typical design of a mechanical rotary oil pump.

on both the size and design of the pump; it varies from about 0.1 to more than 20 liter sec^{-1} for small laboratory-type pumps. The pump speed decreases slowly as the pressure decreases and then drops sharply for pressures in the micron region. The ultimate vacuum is usually in the range from 0.1 to 5 μ. Welch Duo-Seal pumps are excellent as forepumps in high-vacuum work, while Kinney pumps or Cenco Hypervac pumps are available for applications which require very high pumping speed.

The proper operation of an oil pump requires a certain amount of care. Dirt (which will eventually cause serious wear on the machined surfaces) and condensable vapors (which will limit the ultimate vacuum) should never be allowed to contaminate the pump oil. Occasional cleaning and refilling of the pump is advisable. Proper tension in the driving belt is important, and adjustment should be made periodically. Also the motor should be lubricated and kept in good working condition. Certain types of oil pumps have the disadvantage that the oil may rise into the system if the pump stops while the intake is under vacuum. In normal operation, it is good technique to vent an oil pump before turning it off. Insertion of a bulb or trap between the system and the pump will eliminate any serious damage caused by an accidental power failure. See Fig. 2 for details of the connection between a forepump and diffusion pump.

Diffusion Pumps. The essential features of an all-glass mercury diffusion pump are also shown in Fig. 2. The mercury in the boiler is vaporized by a heater, and this mercury vapor emerges as a high-velocity stream from the pump nozzle.

Gas molecules from the system diffuse into the jet stream and undergo collisions with the mercury atoms. Such collisions impart a downward velocity component to the gas molecules. Thus the gas is forced downstream and is compressed into the discharge section of the pump from which it is removed by a rotary oil pump, acting as a *forepump*. The cooling jacket keeps the walls cold enough to condense mercury vapor efficiently, and the condensed liquid mercury is returned to the boiler via a U tube. Most of the details of design are not critical for proper operation, but it is important that the nozzle extend well below the level of the cooling water in the condenser.

Such mercury diffusion pumps have quite high pumping speeds at pressures below a few microns and can achieve an ultimate pressure of about 10^{-6} mm Hg. However, they cannot operate unless the forepump maintains the discharge pressure below a certain critical value. This critical value depends on the pump design and on the heater input. One disadvantage of mercury as the boiler fluid is its high vapor pressure at room temperature ($\sim 1\mu$). A cold trap between the pump and the vacuum manifold is necessary to prevent diffusion of mercury vapor into the system. This problem can be eliminated by using, instead of mercury, high-molecular-weight organic liquids which have very low vapor pressures at room temperature. When organic oils (such as Octoil and Octoil S) are used, precautions must be taken to avoid air oxidation or thermal decomposition of the hot oil.

FIG. 2. Typical all-glass mercury diffusion pump, shown with appropriate connections to the vacuum manifold and to the mechanical forepump.

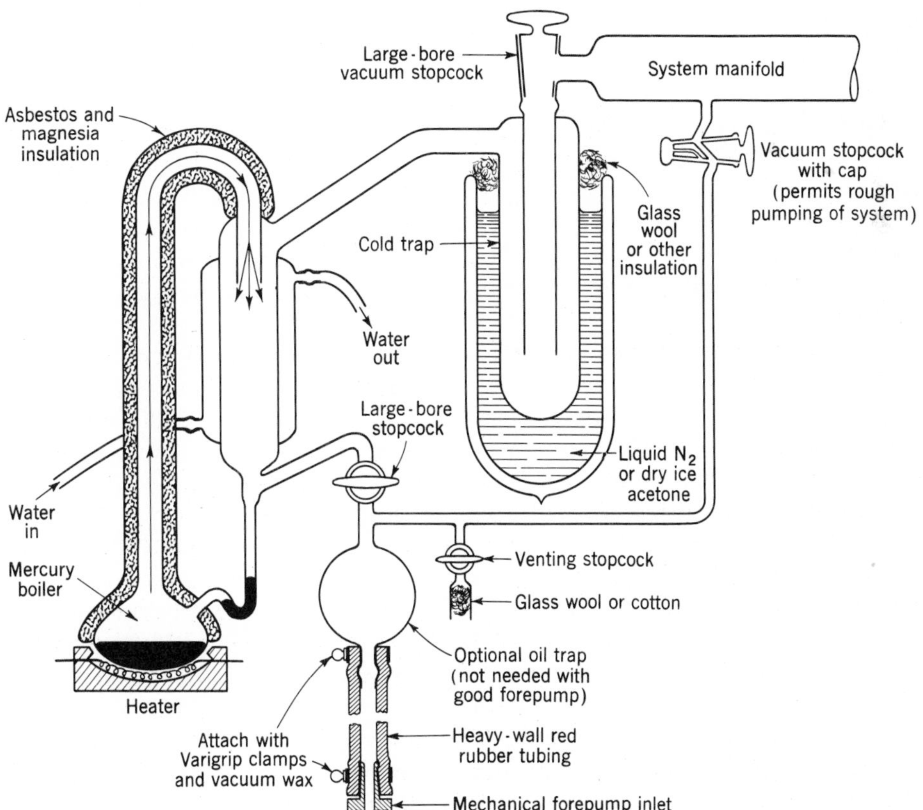

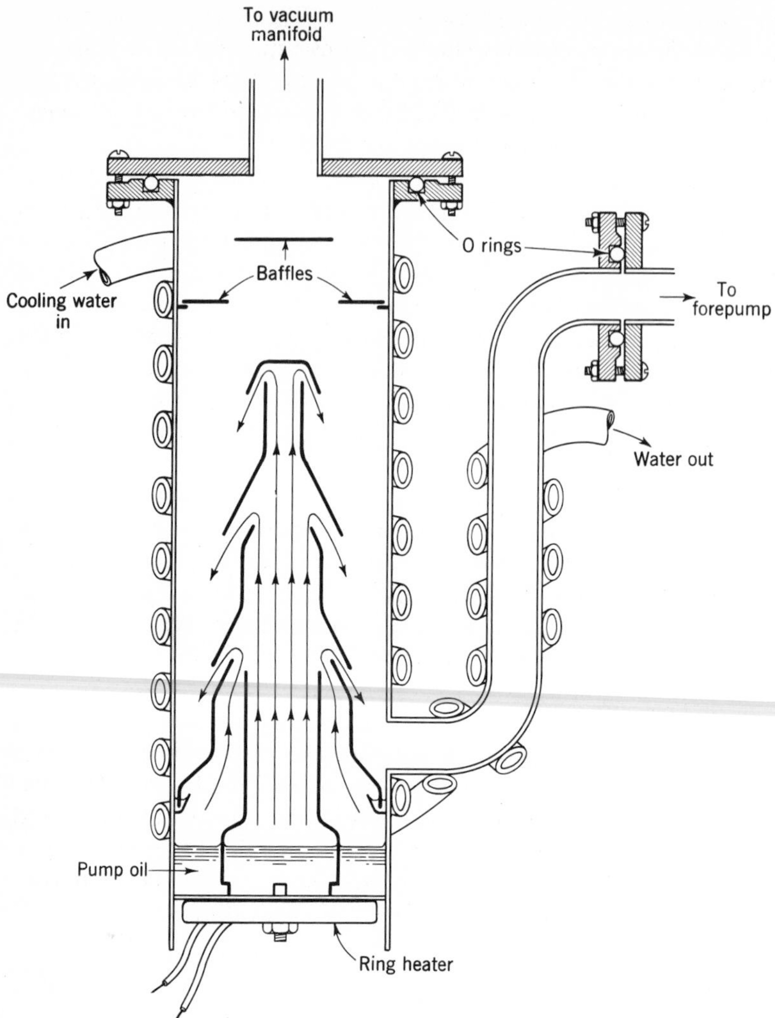

FIG. 3. Schematic drawing of a multistage, all-metal oil diffusion pump. The arrows indicate the flow of oil vapor.

In recent years, the development of silicone oils as pumping fluids has greatly reduced these problems.

All-metal oil diffusion pumps (see Fig. 3) are commonly used for applications which require high pumping speed and a low ultimate pressure. For such pumps, a cold trap is often replaced by a baffle which prevents both the back-diffusion of oil and the creep of an oil film along the walls. The limiting forepressure at which a single jet diffusion pump will operate increases with decreasing annular spacing between the exit rim of the nozzle and the pump wall. Therefore, high-speed diffusion pumps usually have two or more stages of jet nozzles and are referred to as multiple-stage pumps. By the proper design of the size and spacing of these jets, the pump acts like several separate diffusion pumps connected in series. The smallest, fastest stage is positioned nearest to the system, and the largest, slowest stage (which operates on the highest forepressure) is nearest to the forepump, as shown in Fig. 3. Oil diffusion pumps have higher intrinsic speeds than corresponding mercury pumps, since the oils have molecular weights between 300 and 500 compared with 200 for mercury. Thus an oil jet has a greater downward momentum component and will provide more efficient pumping.

Ion Pumps. An ion pump is based on the production of ions from gas molecules by high-velocity electron impact. These ions are collected on an electrode plate and covered by a film of titanium, which is continuously sputtered from a pure titanium cathode. The titanium film also chemisorbs active gases in addition to burying the ions. Ultimate pressures of 1×10^{-10} mm Hg are obtainable with this type of pump. Although a forepump is needed to reduce the pressure initially to below 10^{-3} mm, it is not needed for continuous operation at lower pressures. Another attractive feature of this pump is that it also serves as a vacuum gauge.

VACUUM GAUGES

A large variety of gauges is available for the measurement of low pressures, and the range of useful operation depends a great deal on the type used (see Table 1). This section contains a discussion of the principles of operation for the most commonly used vacuum gauges. More specific details of construction and operation are given in the references listed under General Reading and in the appropriate manufacturers' pamphlets.

Manometers. A U-tube manometer filled with mercury is simple to construct, requires no calibration, and operates over a wide pressure range. With each arm connected to a separate region, the manometer can be used to obtain differential pressures or can be used as a null device. Most commonly, one arm is evacuated and the manometer directly indicates the total pressure. To obtain the *absolute* pressure, a temperature correction is necessary. This correction allows one to convert the observed p to p_0, the pressure in millimeters of Hg at 0°C:

$$(p - p_0) = p\frac{3\alpha t - \beta(t - t_s)}{1 + 3\alpha t} \approx 3\alpha t p \qquad (17)$$

where 3α is the volume coefficient of expansion for mercury (average value of 3α between 0 and 40°C is 18.2×10^{-5} deg^{-1}), β is the linear expansion coefficient of the scale, t is the centigrade temperature of the manometer, and t_s is the temperature at which the scale was graduated. Equation (17) does not contain any correction for the small effect due to the difference between local and standard values of gravity. For precise work, large-bore tubing (~25 mm o.d.) is used to avoid

TABLE 1. Operational Range of Various Vacuum Gauges
(given in mm of Hg)

Gauge	Range
Mercury manometer	1–1000
Oil manometer	0.03–10
McLeod gauge	10^{-6}–1
Pirani gauge	10^{-4}–0.3
Thermocouple gauge	10^{-3}–0.1
Philips gauge	10^{-5}–10^{-2}
Knudsen gauge	10^{-5}–10^{-3}
Ionization gauge	10^{-9}–10^{-3}

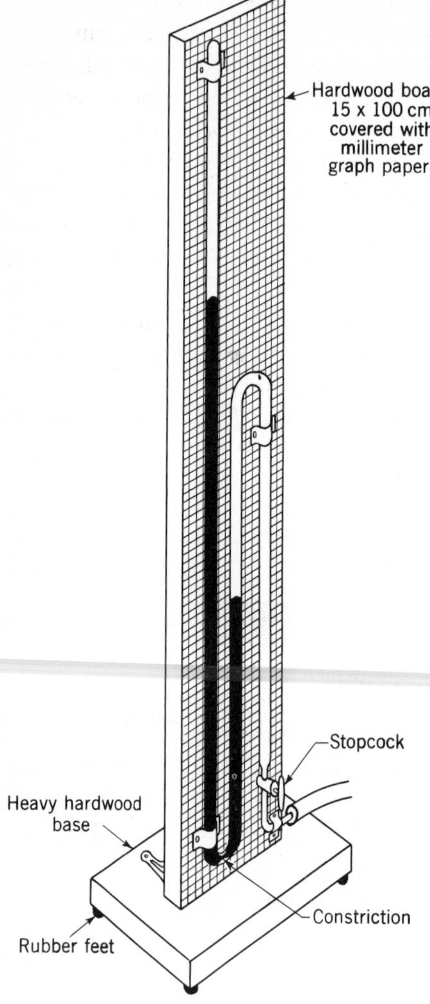

FIG. 4. Design for a closed-tube laboratory manometer.

distortion of the meniscus, and the mercury levels are measured with a cathetometer (see Chap. XVIII). A suitable manometer design for medium-precision work is shown in Fig. 4. In this design the scale is constructed by carefully covering a smooth hardwood board with good-quality millimeter paper and the U tube is rigidly attached to this board. The thermal expansion β for a paper scale can be neglected in Eq. (17).

For pressures between 0.03 and about 10 mm Hg, oil manometers are more accurate than mercury manometers, since oil has a much lower density. For example, dibutyl phthalate, which is often used, has a density of 1.046 g ml^{-1} at 20°C. The absolute pressure is given by

$$p_0(\text{in mm Hg}) = \frac{13.59}{\rho_{\text{oil}}} h \tag{18}$$

where h is the reading of the oil manometer in millimeters. However, oil-filled manometers have two drawbacks. Most gases are quite soluble in oil, and this may cause frothing or erratic behavior when the pressure changes suddenly. Also, the wetting of the walls of the manometer by a viscous oil causes sluggish response.

McLeod Gauge. This gauge is very widely used because of its simplicity of operation and its wide pressure range. In addition, the readings depend only on the geometry of the gauge and not on the properties of the gas whose pressure is being measured. Its operation involves the compression of a known large volume V of gas at an unknown pressure p into a known small volume v where the final pressure p' can be measured. Both p' and p are quite low, and the perfect-gas law can be used in the form $pV = p'v$, since the compression is carried out at constant temperature.

A typical McLeod gauge design is given in Fig. 5. A closed capillary (0.5 to 2 mm i.d., length 12 to 20 mm) of uniform cross section is sealed to the top of a large bulb (volume 200 to 700 ml). A reference capillary of the same bore is mounted parallel to the closed capillary to minimize the effects of capillary depres-

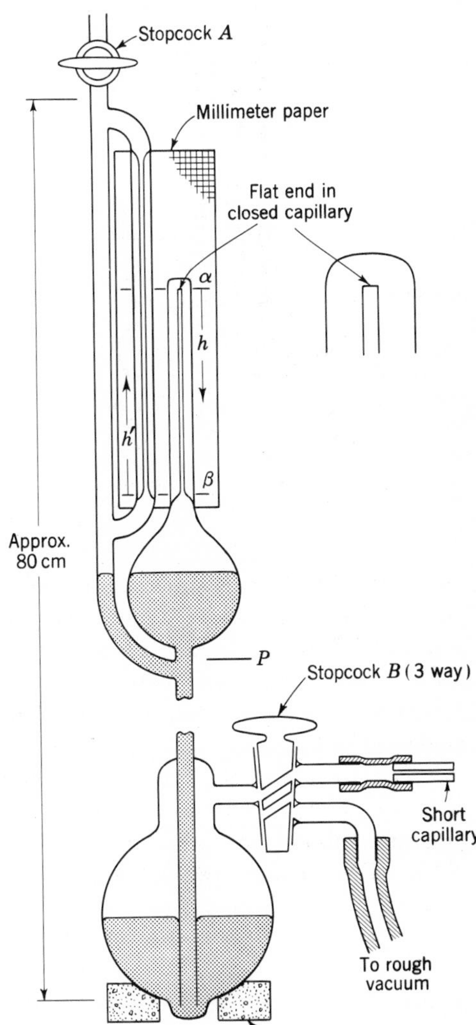

FIG. 5. A typical McLeod gauge.

sion on the readings of the differences in mercury level. The cross-sectional area A of the closed capillary is determined before the gauge is assembled by measuring the length and weight of a slug of mercury placed in the capillary. The volume V is measured from the cutoff plane P and includes the volume of the bulb and that of the capillary tubing. This is determined by measuring the weight of water required to fill the gauge prior to sealing off the closed capillary but after the side arm is attached.

To make a reading with the McLeod gauge, open stopcock A *slowly* and, if necessary, reduce the pressure on the mercury reservoir to prevent mercury from rising above the cutoff plane P. After waiting about a minute for pressure equilibrium, *carefully* open stopcock B to the atmosphere to allow the mercury level to rise slowly in the gauge. As the mercury rises above the plane P, the gas contained in the bulb is compressed into the closed capillary where its pressure can be measured.

There are two methods of reading a McLeod gauge. For low-pressure measurements the mercury is raised until the level in the reference capillary is at point α (even with the top of the closed capillary) and the level in the closed capillary h is then read. Applying the perfect-gas law we find that $pV = (h + p)(Ah)$; neglecting p in comparison with h, one obtains

$$p = \frac{A}{V}h^2 = kh^2 \tag{19}$$

where the apparatus constant k is completely determined by the calibration data. For measurements at higher pressures the mercury is raised until the level in the closed capillary is at a fixed point β (near the bottom of the capillary) and the level in the reference capillary h' is then read. Again, by using the gas law and neglecting p in comparison with h', we obtain

$$p = \frac{v}{V}h' \tag{20}$$

where v, the volume between α and β, equals $A(\alpha - \beta)$. The range of the gauge when used in this way can be extended to higher pressures by having a small bulb just above β so that v is larger.

There are several disadvantages to the McLeod gauge which somewhat offset its attractive features. Since it contains mercury, a cold trap (containing Dry Ice or liquid nitrogen) may be necessary between the gauge and the system to avoid unwanted mercury vapor. It is slow in operation, which is a handicap when used for leak detection. Finally, it cannot measure the pressure of a vapor which will condense when compressed into the capillary. Such condensation will occur as soon as h (or h') exceeds the room-temperature vapor pressure of the substance.

Pirani Gauge. The operation of this gauge depends on the pressure variation of the thermal conductivity of a gas at low pressures. A fine wire or ribbon filament, often in the form of a coil for greater sensitivity, is sealed into a glass envelope which is connected to the vacuum system. The filament is made of a metal with a high-temperature coefficient of resistance (such as platinum, nickel, or tungsten) and is heated electrically. For a fixed energy input the temperature of the filament, and therefore its resistance, will depend on the gas pressure (the resistance will decrease as the pressure increases). The filament resistance can be measured by making the gauge one arm of a Wheatstone bridge. Since the performance of the gauge depends on its geometry and design and on the nature of the gas, it is necessary to calibrate a Pirani gauge against a McLeod gauge. This can be done by maintaining a constant filament current and determining the resistance as a function of pressure or by determining the current necessary to maintain a constant resistance at each pressure. Ambient-temperature fluctuations can cause erratic readings, since thermal conduction depends on the temperature of the walls of the envelope as well as that of the filament. For accurate measurements, one can thermostat the gauge or use a compensating dummy gauge in an opposite arm of the Wheatstone bridge. This dummy gauge is made as nearly like the measuring gauge as possible except that it is evacuated and sealed off.

Thermocouple Gauge. This type of gauge, which also depends on the pressure variation of gaseous thermal conductivity, is almost identical with the Pirani gauge. It differs from the Pirani gauge in that the temperature of the filament (rather than the resistance) is measured by a very fine wire thermocouple which is welded to the mid-point of the filament. The thermocouple output is usually measured with a low-resistance microammeter (~70 ohms) connected in series with the thermocouple. The thermocouple gauge must also be calibrated against a McLeod gauge; as with the Pirani gauge there are two ways to perform this calibration. However, the standard method of calibration and operation is to maintain constant filament current and obtain the thermocouple emf as a function of pressure. The thermocouple gauge is a rugged, inexpensive instrument which is well suited for leak detection, since it is direct reading and has a rapid response to pressure changes.

Ionization Gauge. The most common type of ionization gauge is the *thermionic gauge.* It contains a filament which is heated to cause electron emission, a grid toward which the electrons are accelerated by a positive potential, and a plate (held at a negative potential) which collects the positive ions produced by collision of the electrons with gas molecules. The magnitude of the ionization current (plate-filament current) will depend on the nature of the gas being measured; for a given gas, this current will increase with increasing pressure. For pressures up to about 1 μ, the positive-ion current varies linearly with pressure if the electron current from filament to grid is maintained at a constant value (usually 5 to 10 ma).

For low-pressure measurements the positive-ion current is small and is usually amplified before being measured. It is important to degas the walls of the gauge by gentle heating with a cool flame and to degas the grid by heating it electrically to a dull red for several minutes prior to making measurements in the low end of the range. Do not leave the filament operating at full current over long periods, and **never** operate the gauge unless the pressure is known to be below 10^{-3} mm, since there is a danger of burning out the filament.

Philips Gauge. This gauge is a special type of ionization gauge which does not use a heated filament but rather depends on maintaining a high-voltage discharge in a low-pressure gas. A loop anode is placed midway between and parallel to two large flat cathodes. A potential difference of several thousand volts is maintained between the anode and cathodes, and an external magnetic field causes the emitted electrons to spiral in the region between the electrodes before they are eventually discharged at the anode. Since this gauge uses a high-voltage, cold-cathode discharge, it is free from filament burnout. However, it cannot be operated at as low a pressure as the thermionic gauge.

Special Gauges. There are many other types of pressure gauge suitable for work at low pressures which cannot be described here in detail. The Alphatron ionization gauge depends on the ionization of a gas by alpha particles emitted from a small amount of radioactive material. Since it does not use a heated filament, this gauge can be used at high pressures; indeed its range of linearity extends from about 10^{-8} to 10 mm Hg! In a Knudsen gauge, a lightweight vane is placed between two surfaces of difference constant temperature. When the mean free path is longer than the apparatus spacings, a pressure-dependent deflection of the vane is observed. Various viscosity gauges have been designed; these all depend on the pressure dependence of viscosity at low pressures. In diaphragm gauges, the deflection of a thin, silvered glass membrane can be detected optically and used as a measure of pressure. Finally, one can build quartz spiral manometers in which the pressure produces a torsional force in a thin-walled, coiled quartz tube. These and other special-purpose gauges are described in detail in some of the references listed under General Reading.

DESIGN OF VACUUM LINES

Most vacuum problems encountered in physical chemistry require small "static" vacuum lines (i.e., systems of low pumping speed) capable of achieving ultimate pressures of 10^{-6} mm Hg or below. For such purposes an all-glass system is generally used. It has the advantage of ease of construction, even for complex designs, without the use of couplings or gaskets; it can be easily degassed after assembly; and the detection and repair of leaks are usually straightforward.

In order to build and repair a glass vacuum system one must be familiar with certain techniques of glass blowing. An adequate description of the method for making even simple seals is beyond the scope of this chapter; the student should refer to one of the several detailed books on this subject.[4] Indeed, it is our opinion that even extensive reading about the proper techniques is not sufficient for the beginning glass blower. The advice and demonstration of a skilled worker and considerable personal practice are required to achieve the proper manual dexterity. Certain general principles can, however, be mentioned briefly. Fortunately, glass has a quite high mechanical strength for compression; to take advantage of this, vacuum lines are usually constructed with cylindrical or spherical sections. In addition to strength, a low coefficient of thermal expansion is needed to avoid cracking on sudden or local temperature change while blowing the glass. Although fused silica is excellent in this regard ($\alpha = 6 \times 10^{-7}$ deg^{-1}), it is impractical for general use owing to very high cost and a very high softening point of $\sim$1200°C. (However, silica bulbs are used for high-temperature applications.) Pyrex glass is the proper type to use for general-purpose vacuum work. It has a linear thermal expansion coefficient of 3×10^{-6} deg^{-1}, which is about one-third that of soda-lime glass ("soft" glass).

Since the annealing temperature† for Pyrex is 560°C and the proper working temperature (point where glass is fluid enough to flow readily) is about 800°C, an oxygen-gas torch is required to blow this glass. In general, it is easiest to work with tubing between 8 and 15 mm in diameter. The danger with small tubing is that the walls will collapse and form a solid plug; the difficulty with large tubing is that uneven heating over the surface will cause strains and subsequent cracking. Standard practice involves slowly heating a large area of the glass with a large, gas-rich

† At the annealing temperature, strains in the glass will disappear in a few minutes and an evacuated bulb will collapse.

flame until it begins to soften. Then a smaller, hotter flame is used to work the glass. An inexperienced glass blower may have better success by working with the hot flame on only part of the joint at a time, but it is vital to avoid appreciable cooling anywhere until the joint has been completed and annealed. After the seal is completed, the entire area must be heated enough to relieve any internal strains and then cooled slowly through the annealing temperature range. This is commonly done by lowering the temperature of the flame until a deposit of carbon soot appears on the glass surface.

Mercury diffusion pumps made of glass are inexpensive and convenient for a general-purpose vacuum system. The diffusion pump is connected to the forepump by a short length of *heavy-wall,* large-diameter, red-rubber tubing. It is often wise to place a ballast bulb or oil trap in this section to avoid contamination if oil accidentally backs up from the forepump. Provision for isolating the diffusion pump and for rough pumping on the system is also advantageous (see Fig. 2). The Hg diffusion pump is connected to the manifold via a cold trap and large stopcock. This manifold is a length of large-diameter ($\sim$35 mm) tubing mounted horizontally at a height of at least 1 m from the base of the vacuum bench. A vacuum gauge (McLeod gauge or thermocouple and ionization gauge) and the desired experimental apparatus are attached directly to this manifold via stopcocks. Special vacuum stopcocks (preferably with an evacuatable cap on one end of the barrel, as shown in Fig. 2) must be used, since it is vital that the plug and barrel mate properly. Commercial vacuum stopcocks are made from Pyrex by Corning Glass Co.; the less-expensive types are marked with a *V* (for "vacuum"), while the best grades are numbered on both the plug handle and on the barrel. In some cases it is necessary to make part of the apparatus demountable from the vacuum line. The use of long standard-taper joints is best for this purpose. Ball-and-socket joints can be used if a certain amount of flexibility is needed, but they do not make so reliable a vacuum seal as do the tapered joints. The entire vacuum line should be clamped securely to ½-in. rods which are mounted on a sturdy vacuum bench. The base of this bench should be at least a foot off the floor in order to provide space for locating the forepump.

The presence of stopcocks† necessitates the use of a good-quality vacuum grease. Such greases have a high viscosity and a very low vapor pressure ($\sim 10^{-6}$ mm). Recommended commercial vacuum greases are Apiezon (type L or N), Dow Corning Silicone High-Vacuum grease, and Fisher Cello-Seal.

It is important to choose a grease of the proper viscosity for the ambient temperature of the line. If the grease is too firm, the stopcock will be difficult to turn and striations may appear in the grease after several rotations; if too soft, the grease may flow out of the stopcock and leave too thin a film to make a vacuum seal. The proper method of greasing a stopcock is as follows. Remove old grease (if any) from plug and barrel surfaces, including bore and stopcock leads, with a solvent such as acetone or benzene. A pipe cleaner is useful. Make four longitudinal streaks of stopcock grease 90° apart on the plug. The streaks should be 2 to 3 mm wide and about ¼ mm thick and should be as free of bubbles as possible. Insert the plug into the barrel in the open position. Press the two parts together so that the grease spreads; if necessary wiggle the plug back and forth through a small angle. When the grease has spread over the entire surface, rotate the plug a few times. Look

† Good high-vacuum practice calls for use of the minimum necessary number of stopcocks.

for striations resulting from air bubbles and for excess grease accumulation in the stopcock bore or leads, either of which may make it necessary to dismantle, clean, and regrease the stopcock.

In order to obtain a high vacuum of 10^{-6} mm or less, it is necessary to eliminate "virtual leaks" due to the desorption of gases and vapors from the glass walls and the slow evolution of dissolved gas from the stopcock grease. These can be reduced by thorough cleaning of the glass prior to assembling the line and by the use of scrupulously clean grease. However, the main cause of these virtual leaks is adsorbed water vapor on the glass. This water can be driven off by degassing (heating the walls to about 200°C under vacuum). After the vacuum line is completely assembled and pumped down, the walls are carefully heated with a soft flame from a hand torch while pumping is continued. Do not heat the stopcocks or any greased joints; instead, slowly rotate each of these several times to speed up the removal of dissolved gas. It will normally require protracted pumping to achieve a good vacuum on a new line. After this initial degassing, avoid venting the line to the atmosphere if possible.

For "kinetic" vacuum lines where there is a steady influx of gas from some unavoidable source or when pumping on refrigerant baths, high pumping speed is needed. This requires large oil diffusion pumps and large-diameter tubing; therefore, all-metal systems are normally used. The construction of such lines requires considerable knowledge of "vacuum plumbing" and of special equipment such as bellows devices, Wilson seals, and vacuum gaskets. Only one important feature of such systems will be mentioned here—the use of O-ring gaskets between bolted flanges. Both synthetic and natural rubber gaskets, in the form of a ring with circular cross section (O ring), are available commercially[5] in a wide variety of sizes which are manufactured to very close tolerances. These rings should be seated in a smooth retaining groove cut in one side of the flange. The dimensions of this groove should be such that there is only a moderate compression of the gasket (say 15 per cent) when the two flanges are bolted together in metal-to-metal contact. Excellent suggestions for the proper design of gasket grooves are given by the manufacturers and should be followed in detail.

Finally, a comment should be made about high-vacuum connections between glass and metal parts. The use of waxes and rubber-hose connections should be avoided in favor of special glass-to-metal seals whenever possible. It is possible to obtain commercially a wide variety of Kovar-to-Pyrex seals.[6] Large tubular seals are available for joining major sections of a system, and many special types can be obtained for introducing electrical leads or small tubes into the walls of a vacuum system. Small vacuumtight leads (tungsten and platinum) can be sealed into glass walls; a bead of special (e.g., uranium) glass is often required.

LEAK DETECTION

One of the major problems of vacuum work is the detection and repair of leaks. Leak trouble can be best avoided by very careful work in building the system; extra effort in constructing the line will be more than repaid in a saving of time in leak hunting. The most important general rule is to keep the system as simple as possible—every extra stopcock, joint, or appendage is a potential source of trouble. The entire design should be carefully thought out before any construction is started. Wherever possible use permanent joints and avoid wax joints, hose connections, and flanges. It is best to build the system in sections and vacuum-test each section on an auxiliary line before attaching it to the manifold.

Sufficiently large leaks can be detected by filling the section with air at a pressure slightly over 1 atm and locating the sound of escaping gas. (This large a leak is very rare in all-glass systems but may occur in a solder joint on a metal line.) Smaller leaks can be located by using a few pounds overpressure of air or some other gas, applying a dilute soap solution to the suspected areas, and watching for bubbles produced by the escaping gas.

In a glass system, very small pinholes (usually at a seal) can be detected by a spark discharge if the internal pressure is reduced to below about 0.1 mm. Leak detectors utilizing a Tesla coil are available commercially; it is convenient to solder a short length of copper wire to the electrode tip of these leak testers in order to obtain a small and flexible probe. When this probe is passed slowly over the surface of the glass, a wide, low-intensity discharge occurs until the probe is close to a pinhole leak. Near the pinhole a concentrated, intense spark will take place through the hole. (Near any area where the glass is thin, the discharge may puncture the wall if too high a potential is used.) Obviously, this method cannot be used near a metal electrode or clamp; a leak in such a region can often be detected by applying acetone and watching for a change in the color of the discharge produced by a Tesla coil at some point between this region and the pump.

When a McLeod gauge is used to hunt for leaks in an assembled system, the best procedure is to pump down the entire system, then close off as many sections as possible (including the manifold), and let the system stand for several hours. The pressure is then measured in the gauge itself, gauge plus manifold, and so on, until a section with a high pressure is located. This section can then be carefully rechecked with a Tesla coil, and the stopcocks in it can be regreased. Direct-reading gauges, such as the thermocouple or ionization gauge, are more suitable for leak hunting, since they can be read continuously. They also show a rapid response to pressure changes and a selective response to certain gases or vapors. One standard technique is to swab or flood the suspected area with liquid acetone or methyl alcohol. When a small leak is covered with the liquid, there is a rapid decrease in the leak rate probably caused by the increase in viscosity. Thus, a gauge will indicate an abrupt drop in pressure. Another technique involves covering the suspected area with a plastic bag and filling this bag with hydrogen or helium gas. Since both the thermal conductivity and the ionizability of H_2 and He differ greatly from those of air, a change in gauge reading should occur if the covered area contains a leak. Once a leak is definitely established, a small jet of gas can be used as a probe to locate the exact position.

In order to find those very small and frustrating leaks which defy all other methods, one can use mass-spectrometer leak detectors. In this method the system is pumped out through the detector which contains a simple mass-spectrometer tube permanently adjusted to detect only helium. The search technique is the same as that described above for use of gases with direct-reading gauges. Although helium leak detectors are complex and expensive instruments, they have the great advantages of speed in operation, extreme sensitivity, and an unambiguous response. They are of special value for metal systems.

When leaks are found, they should be repaired in a permanent way. For glass systems, this involves venting the line and reblowing the glass at the site of the leak. If necessary, emergency repairs can be made by warming the glass with a cool flame and covering the leak with de Khotinsky wax, but such repairs should always be considered as temporary.

SOURCES OF VACUUM EQUIPMENT

Given below is a short list of some of the most important sources of vacuum equipment. The principal types of equipment which are available from each manufacturer are indicated by the following symbols: FP, rotary oil forepump; DP, diffusion pump; IP, ion pump; MV, metal valves; TG, thermocouple gauge; IG, ionization gauge; and LD, helium leak detector.

Central Scientific Co., Chicago, Ill.: FP, DP
Consolidated Vacuum Engineering Corp., Palo Alto, Calif.: DP, MV, IG, LD, IP
Edwards High Vacuum Ltd., Manor Royal, Crawley, Sussex, England (also P.O. Box 515, Burlington, Ontario, Canada): FP, DP, IG
Granville-Phillips Co., Boulder, Colo.: MV
Hoke Inc., Cresskill, N.J.: MV
Kinney Manufacturing Co., Boston, Mass.: FP
National Research Corp., Newton Highlands, Mass.: DP, TG, IG
Varian Associates, Palo Alto, Calif.: IP
Veeco Vacuum Corp., New Hyde Park, N.Y.: DP, MV, IG, LD
W. M. Welch Scientific Co., Chicago, Ill.: FP, DP

REFERENCES

1. E. H. Kennard, "Kinetic Theory of Gases," chap. VIII (especially pp. 302, 305, 318), McGraw-Hill, New York (1938).
2. M. Knudsen, *Ann. Physik,* **28,** 75 (1909).
3. S. Dushman, "Scientific Foundations of Vacuum Technique," 2d ed. (J. M. Lafferty, ed.), chap. 3, Wiley, New York (1962).
4. "Laboratory Glass Blowing with Pyrex Brand Glasses," Corning Glass Works, Corning, N.Y. (1957); J. D. Heldman, "Techniques of Glass Manipulation in Scientific Research," Prentice-Hall, Englewood Cliffs, N.J. (1946); E. L. Wheeler, "Scientific Glassblowing," Interscience, New York (1958).
5. Goshen Rubber and Mfg. Co., Goshen, Ind.; Linear, Inc., Philadelphia, Pa.; Plastic and Rubber Products Co., Los Angeles, Calif., and Chicago, Ill.
6. Available from the Carborundum Co., Refractories Division (formerly the Stupakoff Ceramic and Manufacturing Co.), Latrobe, Pa.

GENERAL READING

S. Dushman, "Scientific Foundations of Vacuum Technique," 2d ed. (J. M. Lafferty, ed.), Wiley, New York (1962).
A. Guthrie and R. K. Wakerling, "Vacuum Equipment and Techniques," McGraw-Hill, New York (1949).
Swami Jnanananda, "High Vacua," Van Nostrand, Princeton, N.J. (1947).
G. W. C. Kaye, "High Vacua," Longmans, London (1927).
L. H. Martin and R. D. Hill, "A Manual of Vacuum Practice," Melbourne University Press, Australia (1947).
J. D. Strong, "Procedures in Experimental Physics," chap. III, Prentice-Hall, Englewood Cliffs, N.J. (1938).
J. Yarwood, "High Vacuum Technique," 2d ed., Wiley, New York (1945).

XVIII
INSTRUMENTS

This chapter consists of brief descriptions and discussions of certain devices and instruments which are commonly used in experimental physical chemistry. Considerably greater detail can be found in the references cited.

BALANCES

It is common practice to use the terms *mass* and *weight* as interchangeable, but of course they have quite different meanings. Whereas the mass m of an object in grams is a measure of the amount of matter in that object, the weight w represents the gravitational force exerted on the object by the earth and should properly be expressed in dynes. Since $w = mg$ and g varies with geographical location, the weight of an object of a given mass will depend on where it is measured. The usage of such expressions as "a 10-gram weight" to mean a mass whose weight equals that of a 10-g mass arises naturally from the common method of comparison weighing. Unless otherwise specified (as in Exp. 39), the term weight as used in this book actually means the mass in grams; this should be clear from the context and from dimensional analysis.

We shall assume that the reader has some prior experience with the use of an equal-arm analytical balance, with which an object is weighed by determining the weights which must be added to the right-hand side of the beam in order to make the rest point of the loaded balance the same as the zero point (rest point of unloaded balance). The design, construction, and operation of an undamped balance using a milligram rider are described in detail by most standard textbooks on quantitative chemical analysis.[1–4] Given below are brief descriptions of two other types of analytical balance which are especially rapid and convenient to operate.

"Chainomatic" Balance. The essential features of a magnetically damped chain balance with a notched beam are shown in Fig. 1. The use of a heavy rider on the notched beam eliminates the need for small fractional-gram weights on the pan and permits more rapid operation. Note that the zero position of the rider is *not* at the center of the beam, and therefore the rider must always be on the beam during a weighing. Adjustments of less than a tenth of a gram are made with a link chain suspended between the right-hand side of the beam and a movable support mounted on a vertical graduated scale. The position of this support can be

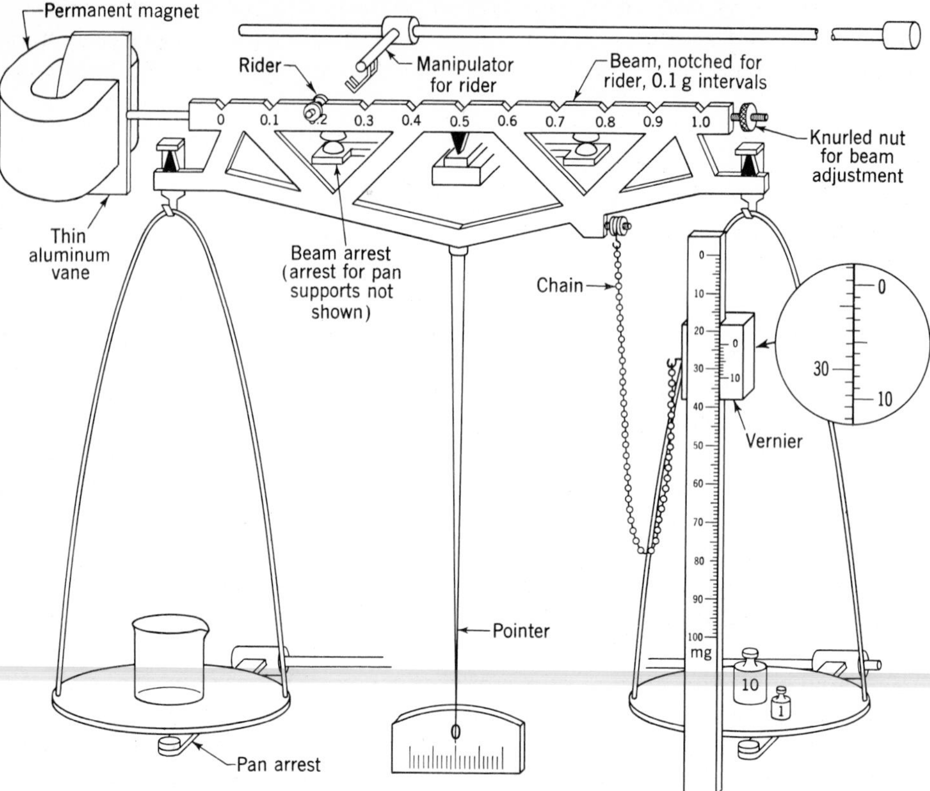

FIG. 1. Essential features of a notched-beam, magnetically damped chain balance. Weight shown is 11.2234 g.

controlled by a large knob projecting from the right side of the balance case. As the support is lowered, a greater length of chain, and therefore a greater weight, hangs from the beam. By using a vernier scale, one can easily record the chain setting to tenths of a milligram. The use of a chain balance is especially convenient if there is provision for magnetic damping, since a damped balance will reach its rest point rapidly and the method of swings is not necessary. Damping is achieved by attaching to one end of the balance beam a thin aluminum plate in a position between the poles of a small horseshoe magnet; eddy currents in this plate caused by its motion in the field result in a force opposing the motion of the beam.

"Automatic" Balance. The single-pan, constant-load analytical balance is capable of being used even more rapidly than a damped Chainomatic balance. A set of weights and the pan are suspended from the front end of a concealed beam, while the back end of the beam consists of a fixed weight which counterbalances them. When an object is placed on the pan to be weighed, one *removes* some of the suspended weights in order to restore balance. Thus the beam is under a constant load (usually 200 g) and the balance sensitivity (change in rest point per milligram) is constant. This permits one to determine weight differences of less than 100 mg from the equilibrium beam deflection, which is indicated optically on an illuminated scale, and eliminates the need for a chain. Weights greater than 0.1 g are manipulated by means of control knobs on the front of the balance.

Operation of Balances. Any type of precision analytical balance should be mounted level on a sturdy bench, free from vibrations, in a room with a fairly stable temperature (no drafts or direct sunlight near the balance). Detailed instructions for the operation of the particular type to be used should be made available by the instructor. Indeed, if the student is not already familiar with the use of that particular design, demonstration by an experienced user and a practice weighing are strongly recommended. The most important general principle is the need for a sense of personal responsibility. Analytical balances are delicate instruments which are capable of excellent precision if they are used with respect and care. It is especially important to use the beam and pan arrest controls properly, since they protect the components of the balance (especially the knife-edges) from damage. If any difficulties arise, consult an instructor; **do not attempt repairs or adjustments.** After use, leave the balance clean and restored to the zero settings as a courtesy to other users.

Errors and Corrections. Unequal beam arms can obviously cause an unknown weighing error. However, the length of the arms on a good analytical balance should be the same within 0.002 per cent and the small uncertainty from this source is usually neglected. This source of error cannot be completely eliminated by the use of a calibration factor, since the ratio of the arm lengths may vary slightly with temperature and might also change abruptly owing to displacement of the knife-edge position caused by an accidental jarring of the balance. For very high precision weighings, the effect of unequal arms can be eliminated by the method of substitution or the method of double weighing.[1, 3]

Buoyancy will also affect the results of a weighing, since air will exert a buoyant effect both on the object and on the weights; in general, these two effects will not cancel. The weight in vacuo W_v of an object can be obtained from the weight in air W_a by adding the weight of air displaced by the object and subtracting the weight of air displaced by the weights. Thus,

$$W_v = W_a + V\rho - v\rho \tag{1}$$

where V is the volume of the object, v is the volume of the weights, and ρ is the density of air. Since analytical weights are almost always made of brass (lacquered or plated with gold, nickel, or chromium), we can replace v by $W_a/8.4$, where 8.4 g cm^{-3} is the density of brass, to obtain

$$W_v = W_a\left(1 - \frac{\rho}{8.4}\right) + V\rho \tag{2}$$

Equation (2) is useful if V is known, but often it is not. However, if d_0 (the density of the object) is known, V can be replaced by W_v/d_0 to give

$$W_v = W_a \frac{1 - (\rho/8.4)}{1 - (\rho/d_0)} \cong W_a\left[1 + \left(\frac{1}{d_0} - \frac{1}{8.4}\right)\rho\right] \tag{3}$$

where the final approximation is excellent as long as $\rho/d_0 \ll 1$. Although the density of air varies with temperature, pressure, and moisture content, ρ can be taken to be approximately 0.0012 at any relative humidity over the range 15 to 30°C and 730 to 780 mm Hg.[1] Buoyancy corrections are often neglected in the weighing of solids, but they are essential in weighing gases and are quite important in weighing large volumes of liquids (as when calibrating volumetric apparatus). For example, W_v for water is 0.1 per cent higher than W_a, and the buoyancy correction for 100 g of water would be about 100 mg (much greater than any other source of weighing error).

The most common source of error in weighings is due to inaccurate weights. Even in a good set, the weights are often in error by as much as 1 mg. It is recommended that a given set of weights be used only with a single balance and that these weights be calibrated on that balance against a good secondary-standard set certified by the National Bureau of Standards. The calibration procedure is given in detail elsewhere.[2, 3, 5] Corrections for each weight and each rider position should be posted on the balance and should always be used. For Chainomatic balances, it is necessary to calibrate about ten chain positions, since a linked chain is not perfectly homogeneous (i.e., the weight per unit length is not quite constant) and the corrections may vary rather erratically over the range.

Finally, there are several other weighing errors which may occur as a result of poor technique but which can usually be avoided. Volatile, hygroscopic, or efflorescent samples and samples which adsorb gases (e.g., CO_2 or O_2) should be kept in closed weighing bottles. An object should never be weighed while warm, since convective air currents will occur, causing the weighing to be in error. Weighings may also be in error because of the condensation of moisture on dry glass walls or the force produced by static charge caused by vigorous wiping of a glass surface.

BAROMETER

The Fortin barometer is simply a single-arm, closed-tube mercury manometer equipped with a precise metal scale (usually brass). The bottom of the measuring arm of the barometer dips into a mercury reservoir which is in contact with the atmosphere. The mercury level in this reservoir can be adjusted by means of a knurled screw which presses against a movable plate (see Fig. 2). When the meniscus in the reservoir just touches the tip of a pointed indicator, the zero level is properly established and the pressure can be determined from the position of the meniscus in the measuring arm. Both the front and back reference levels on a sliding vernier are simultaneously lined up with the top of this meniscus in order to eliminate parallax error, and the height of the arm can be read to the nearest tenth of a millimeter using the vernier scale. A thermometer should be mounted on or near the barometer, since the temperature must be known in order to make a correction for thermal expansion. This correction is discussed in Chap. XVII, and the appropriate formula is given by Eq. (XVII-17). The metal scale on most barometers is made of brass (linear coefficient of thermal expansion 1.84×10^{-5} deg^{-1}) and is usually graduated so as to read correctly at 0°C. A table of barometer corrections over the range 16 to 30°C and 720 to 800 mm is given in Appendix B. High-precision work also requires corrections for the effect of gravity, residual gas pressure in the closed arm, and errors in the zero position of the scale.[6, 7] Since these usually amount to only a few tenths of a millimeter, they will not be discussed here.

CATHETOMETER

A cathetometer is used for the accurate measurement of vertical distances, such as the height of the menisci in a wide-bore manometer. It consists of a heavy steel bar (or rod) mounted on a sturdy tripod stand. This steel bar is graduated in

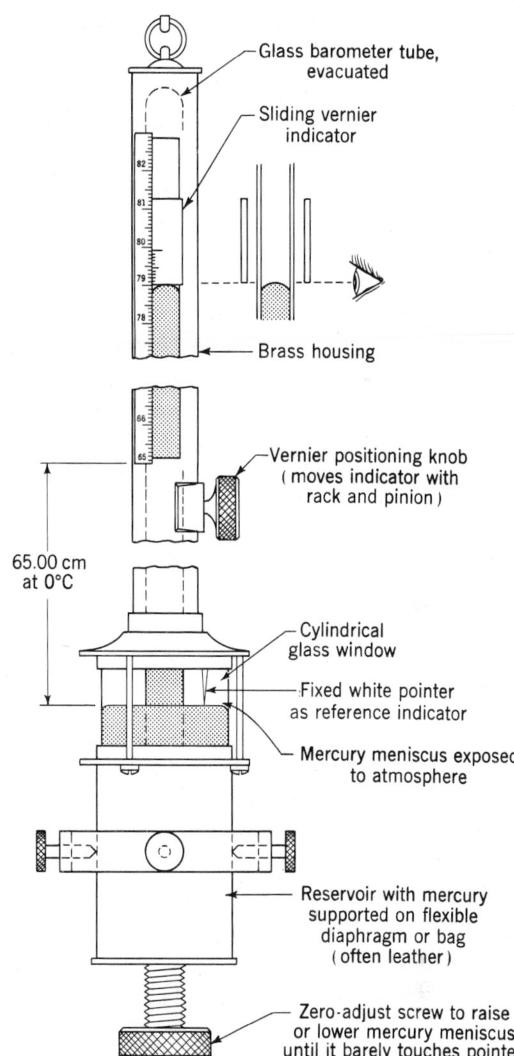

FIG. 2. Detailed sketch of a Fortin barometer. Uncorrected reading shown is 79.02 mm.

millimeters and supports a traveling telescope, which can be moved vertically through about 100 cm and can also be rotated in a horizontal plane. Leveling screws in the base of the stand are used to obtain an accurate vertical alignment of this steel scale, and the telescope mounting is equipped with a fine-adjustment screw and a spirit level to ensure accurate horizontal positioning of the telescope. The meniscus to be measured is brought into focus and aligned with respect to a cross hair in the eyepiece; the position of the telescope on the scale is then read to the nearest 0.1 or 0.05 mm with a vernier scale. A cathetometer is especially convenient for reading levels on an apparatus which must be immersed in a constant-temperature bath (e.g., an osmometer).

OSCILLOSCOPE[8]

In a cathode-ray tube, electrons are emitted from a cathode and are then accelerated and focused by a series of special anodes to form a beam which impinges on the face of the tube. This face is coated with fluorescent material, and the beam produces a sharp visible spot. Displacement of this spot from the center of the screen can be achieved by passing the electron beam through the electrostatic field between a pair of charged plates. There are two independent sets of these deflection plates which control, respectively, the vertical and the horizontal position of the spot. Since high voltages are required across these plates to produce a suitable displacement of the beam, oscilloscopes have wide-band amplifiers to provide voltage amplification for the input signals.

The primary use of an oscilloscope is to display the shape of a voltage waveform (i.e., to plot out voltage vertically against a horizontal time scale). To accomplish this, there must be a sweep voltage applied to the horizontal deflection plates which will cause the beam to move from left to right at a uniform rate and then return very rapidly to the starting point. Almost all oscilloscopes have an internal sawtooth generator to produce this linear time base sweep.

In order to achieve a stationary trace on the screen, the period of the sweep must be exactly equal to the period of the test voltage applied to the vertical input or some integral multiple thereof. One or more complete cycles of the test voltage are then observed on the screen. Most oscilloscopes have a sweep-frequency range switch, a fine frequency control, and a synchronization control. When an oscilloscope is used, the synchronization control is first turned to zero and the sweep frequency is adjusted to give as stable a pattern as possible. If there is still a slow drift of the pattern across the screen, it can be eliminated by turning up the synchronization control. Since the persistence of human vision is about 0.05 sec, any synchronized sweep with a frequency greater than about 20 cps will appear as a steady pattern without flicker. This phenomenon is enhanced by the fact that most screens have an afterglow (phosphorescence) of appreciable duration.

If the vertical deflection sensitivity of the cathode-ray tube can be accurately calibrated (many oscilloscopes provide an internal calibration signal), the oscilloscope is an excellent device for measuring ac voltages. Two advantages are the very high input impedance (several megohms) and the wide frequency range (from about 20 to at least 50,000 cps). Perhaps the greatest advantage over a conventional ac voltmeter is the ability to measure peak-to-peak voltages regardless of the shape of the waveform.

An oscilloscope can also be used as a very sensitive device for comparing the frequencies of two different sinusoidal waveforms. One signal is applied across the usual vertical input terminals, and the other signal is applied to a special "external horizontal input" (i.e., the internal sweep is replaced by this external sine-wave voltage). When the ratio of the two frequencies is a rational fraction, a symmetric closed pattern (called a Lissajous figure) will appear on the screen. The frequency ratio can be obtained from the form of the pattern by using the formula

$$\frac{f_H}{f_V} = \frac{n_V}{n_H} \tag{4}$$

where f_H and f_V are the frequencies applied at the horizontal and at the vertical inputs, n_H is the number of points at which the figure is tangent to a horizontal line, and n_V is the number points of tangency between the figure and a vertical line. Several simple types of Lissajous figures are shown in Fig. 3*a*.

Shown in Fig. 3*b* is the Lissajous figure for several different values of the phase

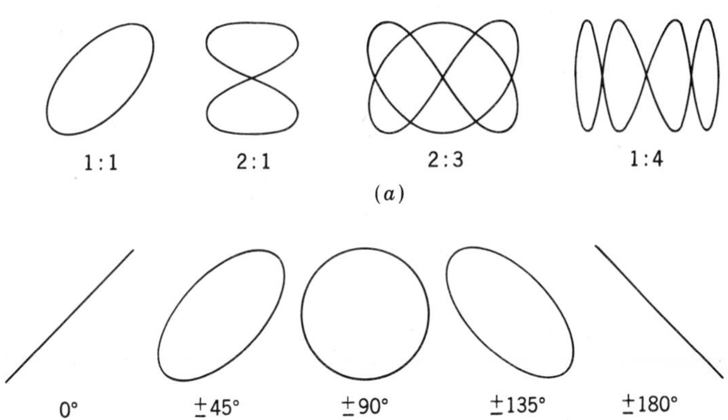

FIG. 3. Lissajous figures: (*a*) several simple figures, with the ratios $f_H:f_V$ indicated; (*b*) the 1:1 figure for various values of the phase angle between signals of equal amplitude.

angle between two signals of the same frequency and amplitude; note that the pattern is a circle when the two sine waves are 90° out of phase and is a straight line tilted at 45° when the phase angle is 0 or 180°. This fact provides a convenient means of determining the phase shift in a circuit. For balancing an ac Wheatstone bridge, a signal from the ac power source is applied to the horizontal input, and the unbalance signal across the bridge is applied to the vertical input. The bridge is first balanced capacitively by obtaining a straight-line pattern. After this is done, the resistive balance is indicated by obtaining a horizontal line (zero vertical amplitude).

pH METER

A pH meter is a special type of millivolt potentiometer designed to measure the emf of a cell in which the electrolyte contains hydrogen ions. A "glass electrode" is employed as the measuring electrode, and a calomel electrode is used as the reference electrode.

Calomel Electrode. In addition to pH measurements there are many other emf cell measurements for which it is convenient to use the calomel electrode as a reference electrode against which a measuring electrode is compared. Actually, this "electrode" is really a half-cell which is connected via a KCl salt bridge to another half-cell containing the solution of interest. (A discussion of cells with a KCl salt bridge is given in Exp. 25.) The *saturated* calomel electrode can be written as

$$Hg(l) + Hg_2Cl_2(s),\ K^+Cl^-(aq, \text{sat.}),\ \text{aq. electrolyte} \tag{5}$$

There are two other common versions of this half-cell: the *normal* and *tenth normal* calomel electrodes, in which the KCl concentration is either 1.0 or 0.1 *N*. The saturated electrode is the easiest to prepare and the most convenient to use but has the largest temperature coefficient. The half-cell potential for each of the calomel electrodes has a different value relative to the standard hydrogen electrode; these emf values are given in Table 1. Calomel electrodes can be easily prepared in the

TABLE 1. Half-cell Potentials of Calomel Reference Electrodes[a]

KCl conc.	Potential at 25°C, v
0.1*N*	−0.3338
1.0*N*	−0.2800
Saturated	−0.2415

[a] W. J. Hamer, *Trans. Electrochem. Soc.*, **72,** 45 (1937).

laboratory and are also available commercially. Two typical calomel cell designs are shown in Fig. 4.

Glass Electrode.[10] This electrode is usually a silver-silver chloride electrode, surrounded by a thin membrane of a special glass which is permeable to hydrogen ions. The glass membrane is essentially a special type of salt bridge—one in which the anions are immobile (have zero transference number), since they are part of the porous glass framework through which the H^+ cations can move. The glass electrode may be formulated as

$$\mathrm{Ag}(s) + \mathrm{AgCl}(s),\ \mathrm{H^+Cl^-}(aq,\ a_0),\ \mathrm{H^+(glass)^-},\ \text{aq. electrolyte containing } \mathrm{H^+} \text{ at activity } a_{\mathrm{H^+}} \tag{6}$$

The change in state per faraday for this half-cell is thus

$$\mathrm{Ag}(s) + \mathrm{Cl^-}(a_0) + \mathrm{H^+}(a_0) = \mathrm{AgCl}(s) + \mathrm{H^+}(a_{\mathrm{H^+}}) + e^- \tag{7}$$

FIG. 4. Two typical calomel cell designs: (*a*) laboratory type, shown unsaturated; (*b*) commercial type, shown saturated.

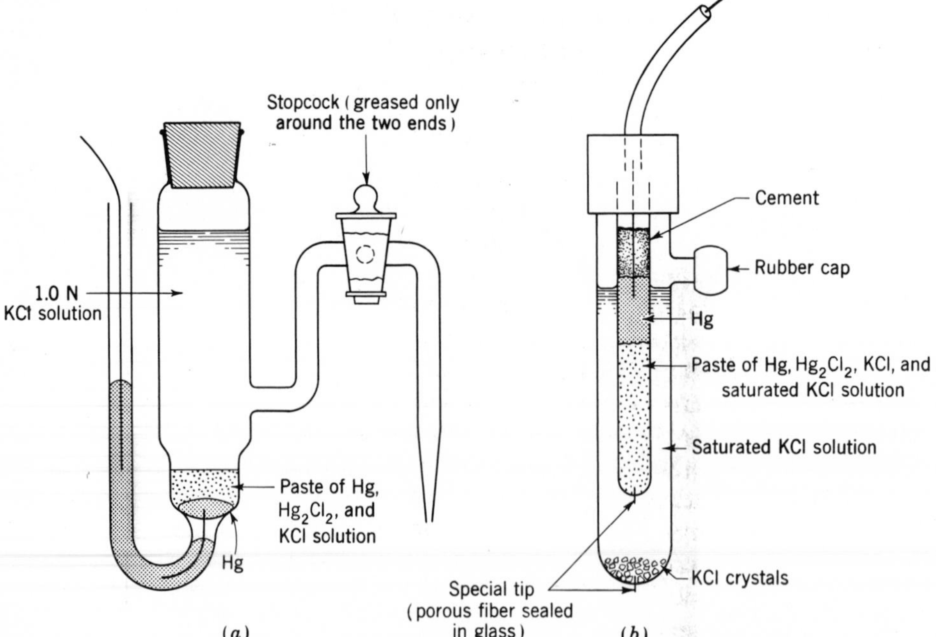

The activity a_0 has a definite constant value, usually obtained by using 0.1 M HCl as the solution inside the membrane. An important advantage of the glass electrode is that it can be used under many conditions for which the hydrogen electrode is subject to serious error.[11]

pH Measurement.[11] The over-all emf for a cell with a calomel and glass electrode dipping into an aqueous electrolyte solution is

$$\mathcal{E} = \mathcal{E}' - \frac{RT}{\mathcal{F}} \ln a_{H^+} = \mathcal{E}' + \frac{2.303RT}{\mathcal{F}}(\text{pH}) \tag{8}$$

where $\text{pH} \equiv -\log a_{H^+}$ and $\mathcal{E}'$ is the difference between the half-cell potential of the calomel reference electrode and the "standard potential" of the glass electrode. Obviously, $\mathcal{E}'$ will depend on the type of calomel electrode used and on the activity a_0 of hydrogen chloride in the inner solution of the glass electrode. Since these factors are kept constant, changes in emf are a direct indication of variations in pH.

Because of the high resistance of the glass membrane (10 to 100 meg) it is not practical to measure the emf directly. Instead pH meters either use a direct-reading electronic voltmeter or amplify electronically the small current which flows through the cell and detect potentiometrically the voltage drop across a standard resistor. Both battery-operated and ac line-operated pH meters are available commercially from such firms as Leeds and Northrup Co., Beckman Instruments, Inc., Coleman Instruments, Inc., and Central Scientific Co. Such pH meters are calibrated to read directly in pH units, have internal compensation for the temperature coefficient of emf, and have provision for scale adjustments.

Since the operation of a pH meter is very simple but slightly different for each model, no detailed operational procedure will be given here. However, a few general remarks are necessary. If a glass electrode and a silver-silver chloride electrode were placed in an HCl solution for which a_{H^+} equals a_0, the emf of this cell should ideally be zero (i.e., there should be no potential difference across the glass membrane). However, there is always some small emf (1 or 2 mv) across the membrane under these conditions. This so-called *asymmetry potential* is presumably due to strains in the membrane and may change slowly with time or be temporarily changed by exposure of the electrode to very strong acid or base. Therefore, it is necessary to compensate for this asymmetry potential by calibrating the pH meter frequently against a buffer solution of known pH. Also, pH readings on solutions of pH greater than 10 are usually in error owing to a significant contribution from sodium-ion transference in the glass at these low hydrogen-ion concentrations. This difficulty can be avoided by the use of special lithium glass membranes.

POLARIMETER

The polarimeter (Fig. 5) is an instrument for measuring the optical rotation produced by a liquid or solution.[12] The *specific rotation* $[\alpha]_\lambda{}^t$ of a solute in solution at a given wavelength λ and Celsius temperature t is given by

$$[\alpha]_\lambda{}^t = \frac{100\alpha}{Lc} = \frac{100\alpha}{Lp\rho} \tag{9}$$

where α is the angle in degrees through which the electric vector is rotated, L is the path length in *decimeters,* c is the concentration of solute in grams per 100 ml of

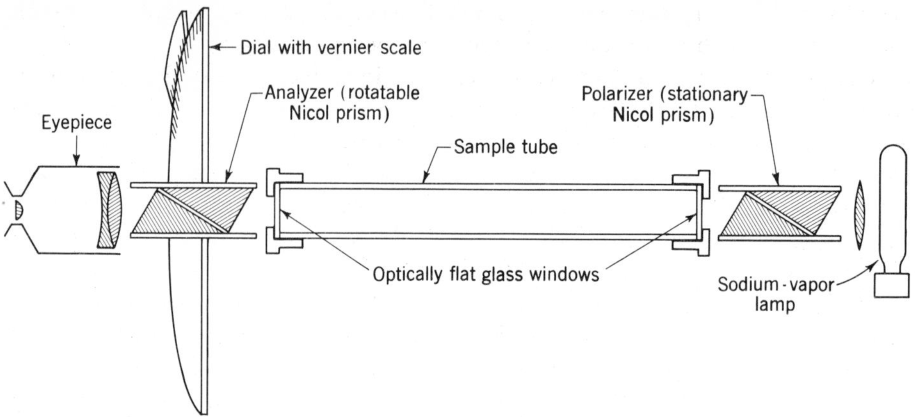

FIG. 5. Schematic drawing of a polarimeter.

solution, p is the weight per cent of solute in the solution, and ρ is the density of the solution. The angle α is considered positive if the rotation of the electric vector as the light proceeds through the solution is in the sense of a left-hand screw or negative if in the sense of a right-hand screw. The optical rotatory power of a compound is also expressed as a *mole rotation,* which is the specific rotation multiplied by the molecular weight. (In the older literature this product was divided by 100.)

Usually the optical rotation is measured with the sodium D yellow line (a doublet, 5890–5896 A). For more precise work the 5461 A green mercury line may be used.

Light from the source (a sodium-vapor arc lamp or a type H-4 mercury-vapor lamp with appropriate filter) is polarized by a nicol prism, termed the polarizer, which consists of two prisms of calcite cemented together with Canada balsam so that one of the two rays produced in double refraction (the "ordinary ray") is totally reflected at the interface and lost while the other (the "extraordinary ray") is transmitted. The polarized light passes through the solution and then through a second nicol prism, termed the analyzer, which can be rotated around the instrument axis. The normal position (zero rotation) is one in which the two nicol prisms are at 90° to each other, and no light passes through. When an optically rotating medium is introduced between the two nicol prisms, light is transmitted; the observed rotation α is the angle in degrees through which the dial must be turned (clockwise with respect to the observer if α is positive, counterclockwise if negative) in order to restore the field to complete darkness.

As the dial is turned, the intensity of emergent light is proportional to $\sin^2 (\alpha - \alpha_d)$, where α_d is the setting for complete darkness. Since this behaves approximately quadratically near the dark position, the setting is of limited sensitivity if only a single polarizer and a single analyzer are used. In many instruments the field of view is divided into two equal parts with polarization angles differing by a few degrees. This is done either by use of a composite polarizer (two nicol prisms cemented together side by side with their planes of polarization at a small angle) or by use of an added nicol prism covering half of the field of the polarizer. In use, the analyzer is adjusted so that the two fields appear equally bright.

Although laboratory polarimeters generally use nicol prisms as polarizers and analyzers, dichroic crystals (such as tourmaline) or dichroic sheet polarizers such as Polaroid may be used in the construction of special apparatus.†

The polarimeter is commonly used in organic and analytical chemistry as an aid in identification of optically active compounds (especially natural products) and in estimation of their purity and freedom from contamination by their optical antipodes. The polarimeter has occasional application to chemical kinetics as a means of following the course of a chemical reaction in which optically active species are involved. Since the rotation α is a linear function of concentration, the polarimeter can be used (in the same way that a dilatometer might be used) in studying the acid-catalyzed hydrolysis of an optically active ester, acetal, glycocide, etc.

In modern organic chemistry optical rotatory dispersion,[13] or the variation of optical rotatory power (and certain related properties) with wavelength, is used in molecular-structure investigation as a means of identifying and characterizing chromophore groups. Automatic polarimetric spectrophotometers of high complexity have been developed for this purpose.

RADIATION DETECTORS

Many devices have been developed for detecting and measuring radiant energy. We shall be concerned here only with direct-reading devices. We shall give no discussion of photography, as most of the techniques required for routine work are well known or described adequately in instructions supplied with commercial photographic materials. The principles of the photographic method are adequately described elsewhere.[14]

Thermal Detectors.[15] In infrared spectrophotometers the radiation is generally detected as thermal energy: The radiation detector is basically an approximation to an isolated black-body absorber of small heat capacity combined with a sensitive device for detecting change in temperature.

The *bolometer* is essentially a resistance thermometer, usually with a platinum element, although a thermistor may also be used. In the platinum bolometer two arms of the bridge are thin ($\sim 1\mu$), narrow (0.5 mm) strips; one of these, which serves as the receiver of the radiation, is blackened with an evaporated metal. The strips are usually mounted in an evacuated chamber. Under optimum conditions the bolometer is capable of detecting as little as 10^{-3} μw.

More often used is the *thermopile* (a multijunction thermocouple). The receiver is usually a thin metal foil, blackened with a metal black customarily deposited onto the metal surface by evaporation. The thermocouple leads are narrow strips cut from thin foils of copper and constantan or bismuth and silver; the junctions are soldered with pure tin and cemented to the receiver. The reference junctions are cemented to a similar "compensation" foil, which is not exposed to the radiation. The thermopile is protected from air currents by means of an enclosure and is frequently operated in vacuum to prevent heat loss by gas conduction.

† In the phenomenon known as dichroism, the optical absorption depends strongly on the orientation of the plane of polarization with respect to the crystallographic axes (or axis of preferred orientation). Commercial sheet polarizers are made from acicular dichroic crystals, herapathite (iodoquinine) in the case of Polaroid, suspended in a viscous or plastic medium and aligned by extrusion or stretching. Dichroic polarizers and analyzers are inferior to nicol prisms for use in polarimeters because the transmission is considerably less than unity when the planes of polarization are parallel and the absorption is not quite complete when they are perpendicular.

An alternative method of construction is to deposit the receiver foil and the thermocouple metals by successive vacuum evaporation, through masks, onto a very thin plastic film such as Formvar. The thermocouple metals are in this case usually antimony and bismuth.

In infrared spectrophotometry the radiation is chopped to create a square-wave output from the thermopile. This output is ac amplified and detected, and the resulting signal is displayed directly on a chart recorder. For certain applications a thermopile may be connected directly across the terminals of a sensitive galvanometer; the resistance of the thermopile should be that required for critically damping the galvanometer. The reading of the galvanometer, after subtraction of the zero reading and allowance for drift if any, is proportional to the energy per unit time (i.e., power) absorbed by the receiver. This is for most practical purposes the same as the total energy per unit time incident upon the receiver, essentially independent of wavelength over the entire infrared, visible, and ultraviolet spectrum.

The thermopile may be calibrated by use of a special carbon-filament lamp obtainable from the NBS.

A thermal detector which is sometimes used is the *Golay cell.* This consists of a small chamber filled with gas and having a flexible wall or diaphragm. Radiation impinging on the blackened outer surface of this chamber causes thermal expansion of the gas, and the resulting distention of the wall causes the deflection of light by an attached mirror. This deflection is usually detected by a photocell. The Golay cell is very sensitive and has a very fast response. It is particularly useful in the far infrared.

Photoelectric Cells.[16] Photoelectric cells, commonly called photocells, are much more sensitive than thermopiles to visible light but are almost completely insensitive in the infrared. Moreover, their response is usually very dependent on wavelength. Photocells are of three main types: the photoconductive cell, exemplified by the selenium cell; the photovoltaic cell, exemplified by the copper-cuprous oxide cell; and the photoemission cell, exemplified by the sodium or cesium phototubes.

The selenium cell consists of a thin film of selenium on a grid of electrodes. The operation depends on the fact that selenium is a semiconductor with a narrow energy gap. Incident light quanta of sufficient energy will generate free carriers, and this results in an increased electrical conductivity during the illumination. A cell of this kind will respond to daylight or direct illumination by an incandescent lamp; it is not useful at low illumination levels, owing to a residual conductivity which results in a "dark current." Powered by a few volts from a battery the cell will operate a milliammeter or a sensitive electromechanical relay. These cells are useful mainly in the visible range, but selenium-tellurium cells can be used down to 1.5 μ in the near infrared.

The photovoltaic cell or barrier-layer cell, as exemplified by the copper-cuprous oxide cell, is used widely in exposure meters for photography. It is made by carefully oxidizing a clean copper surface to obtain a thin film of cuprous oxide, to which electrical contact is made by means of an exceedingly thin, optically transparent film of silver metal or other conducting material. Its operation depends upon photoexcitation and migration of electrons in the semiconducting oxide and the resulting formation of a charge double layer at the copper-cuprous oxide interface. This cell requires no battery and with sufficient illumination will operate a millivoltmeter. In principle it could be used at low illumination with a sensitive galvanometer, but ordinary vacuum-tube photocells are more satisfactory.

The photoemission cell, or phototube, depends on the photoemission of electrons from a surface having an electronic "work function" no greater than the energy of the photons which are to be detected. The simplest such cells are evacuated tubes containing a plate (or part of the tube wall) coated with an alkali metal, and a collector anode consisting of a wire, plate, or grid. This anode is operated at a few volts positive potential in order to collect the photoelectrons efficiently. The range of the sodium cell extends from about 6000 A in the visible to as far in the ultraviolet as the glass or fused silica envelope will transmit (3000 or 2000 A, respectively). The visible range is completely covered by the cesium cell, with moderately uniform sensitivity. Special cells with oxidized cesium-silver photocathodes have ranges extending to 1.2 μ in the near infrared. The photocurrent at a given wavelength is proportional to the incident radiation intensity (with a quantum efficiency less than unity) and is relatively insensitive to applied voltage over a wide range. The photocurrent resulting from moderately strong illumination is sufficient to operate a sensitive electromechanical relay, but nearly all photocells of this kind are used with electronic amplification.

At very low light intensities, the photoemission cell is ineffective owing to small leakage or "dark" currents which limit the sensitivity, and a modification known as a *photomultiplier tube* is used. In this tube the photoelectric current is amplified by a cascade process: The photoelectrons strike the first of several successive anodes, producing secondary electrons which are accelerated to the next anode to produce more secondary electrons, and so on. By this means the photocurrent is greatly amplified while the leakage current is unaffected. The sensitivity of the photomultiplier tube is ultimately limited by thermal emission of electrons from the photocathode. This can be reduced by operating the tube at low temperatures (i.e., with liquid-nitrogen refrigeration). For highest sensitivity the photomultiplier requires a high-gain preamplifier with high input impedance.

The range of 2000 A to the order of 100 or 200 A is called the "vacuum ultraviolet" because the transmission of all window materials, including glass and quartz, is very small. A photoelectric cell may be used provided it is made an integral part of the vacuum system so that the radiation does not have to pass through a solid window.

Radiation Counters.[17] Electromagnetic radiations with wavelengths below about 10 A are called X rays or gamma rays. These have a penetrating power which increases strongly as the wavelength decreases and is dependent on the atomic numbers of the atoms present rather than their state of chemical combination.

A 1-A photon has about 8000 ev of energy, while ultraviolet radiation has only 3 or 4. This much energy, absorbed in matter, may result in the virtually simultaneous production of many ions—enough so that under optimum conditions the absorption of a single X-ray or gamma-ray photon can be detected with an efficiency approaching 100 per cent. The measurement of X-ray and gamma-ray intensities thus amounts to a *counting* of discrete events whereby individual photons are detected.

The best known detector is the *Geiger-Müller counter.* This usually consists of a cylindrical container (the cathode) filled with an absorbing gas such as argon or krypton, with an insulated central wire (the anode) to serve as a collector for electrons. When an X-ray photon is absorbed, producing ions and electrons, acceleration of the ions and electrons to the electrodes results in collisions resulting in more ionization; thus a cascade process develops which results in a general gas discharge. This continues until the fall of potential between the electrodes is sufficient to quench the discharge and allow the potential to be restored. The Geiger-Müller counter with its associated circuitry is relatively simple but for many radiation-counting purposes suffers from a long "dead time" (0.1 to 1 msec) resulting from the complete discharge and required recharge. This dead time results in coincident counts and nonlinear response at counting rates higher than about 100 counts per second. Another limitation of the Geiger-Müller counter is that the size of the pulse generated is independent of the energy of the incoming particle.

To overcome these limitations the self-quenching *proportional counter* has been developed. This counter is very much like the Geiger counter in construction. The electrons and positive ions from the primary ionizing event go to their respective electrodes, but the production of additional electrons through positive-ion bombardment of the wall is prevented by molecules of some organic compound (i.e., ethanol) which are present as a "quench gas." Thus the tube does not discharge completely. The pulse is of very short duration, of the order of 1 μsec. Therefore, counting rates of up to 10,000 counts per second are essentially linear with intensity. Since the pulse is very small, the proportional counter requires an exceedingly sensitive (high-gain) preamplifier, well shielded from electrical disturbances. Most important for many purposes is the fact that the pulse height depends upon the energy of the incident photon or other particle. The output of the preamplifier may be fed to an electronic pulse-height discriminator circuit, connected to two or more scaling and counting circuits, among which the pulses are distributed according to the height ranges in which they fall. The self-quenching proportional counter does not last indefinitely; after about 10^{11} counts the quench gas is entirely consumed, and the tube thereafter behaves like a Geiger-Müller counter.

Another commonly used detector is the *scintillation detector*. This makes use of a crystal which produces a scintillation (pulse of visible light) on absorption of an X-ray photon. The visible light is detected by a photomultiplier tube and associated amplifier circuit, which is sensitive enough to detect nearly every scintillation. The scintillating crystal is usually sodium iodide doped with an activator such as thallous iodide.

The counters described above are widely used in counting nuclear radiations: gamma rays (electromagnetic radiations, usually of higher energy than X rays), alpha rays (helium nuclei), beta rays (electrons and positrons), neutrons, etc. For beta rays and especially for alpha rays the counter windows must be very thin. For thermal-neutron counting (e.g., in neutron diffraction) $B^{10}F_3$ is added to the counter gas.

In most counting applications the counting rate is too high to permit the direct use of a mechanical register. An electronic scaling circuit with a binary scale going to 32 or 64 is sufficient for use with a mechanical register if the counting rate is within the linear range of a Geiger-Müller counter. Much higher scaling ranges are required in order to make best use of a proportional or scintillation counter; these usually operate on a scale of 10 and comprise several decades, completely obviating the use of a mechanical register. For many purposes (such as X-ray powder spectrogoniometry) the counting rate, which is proportional to the "intensity," is obtained from the rapid stream of pulses by an electrical circuit and recorded directly on a strip-chart recorder.

REFRACTOMETERS[18]

The term *refractometer* is principally applied to instruments for determining the index of refraction of a liquid, although instruments also exist for determining the indices of refraction of a solid. The index of refraction n for a liquid or an isotropic solid is the ratio of the phase velocity of light in a vacuum to that in the medium. It can be defined relative to a plane surface of the medium exposed to vacuum as shown in Fig. 6*a*; it is the ratio of the sine of the angle ϕ_v which a ray of light makes with a normal to the surface in vacuum to the sine of the corresponding angle ϕ_m in the medium:

$$n = \frac{c_v}{c_m} = \frac{\sin \phi_v}{\sin \phi_m} \tag{10}$$

It is common practice to refer the index of refraction to air (at 1 atm) rather than to vacuum, for reasons of convenience; the index referred to vacuum can be obtained from that referred to air by multiplying the latter by the index of refraction of air referred to vacuum, which is 1.00027.

The index of refraction is a function of both wavelength and temperature. Usually the temperature is specified to be 20 or 25°C. The former is more in accord with past practice, but the latter is somewhat the easier to maintain with a constant-temperature bath under ordinary laboratory conditions. The wavelength is usually specified to be that of the yellow sodium D line (a doublet, 5890–5896 A), and the index is given the symbol n_D.

Most refractometers operate on the concept of the *critical angle* ϕ_{crit}; this is the angle ϕ_m for which ϕ_v (or ϕ_{air}) is exactly 90° (see Fig. 6*b*). A ray in the medium with any greater angle ϕ_{m_1} will be totally reflected at an equal angle ϕ_{m_2} as shown in Fig. 6*c*. The index of refraction is given in terms of the critical angle by

$$n = \frac{c_v}{c_l} = \frac{1}{\sin \phi_{crit}} \tag{11}$$

In a refractometer the critical angle to be measured is that inside a glass prism in contact with the liquid, since the index of refraction of the glass is higher than that of the liquid. Therefore

$$\frac{c_l}{c_g} = \frac{c_l}{c_v}\frac{c_v}{c_g} = \frac{n_g}{n} = \frac{1}{\sin \phi_g}$$

FIG. 6. Reflection and refraction at an interface: (*a*) $\phi_m < \phi_{crit}$, (*b*) $\phi_m = \phi_{crit}$, (*c*) $\phi_{m_1} > \phi_{crit}$.

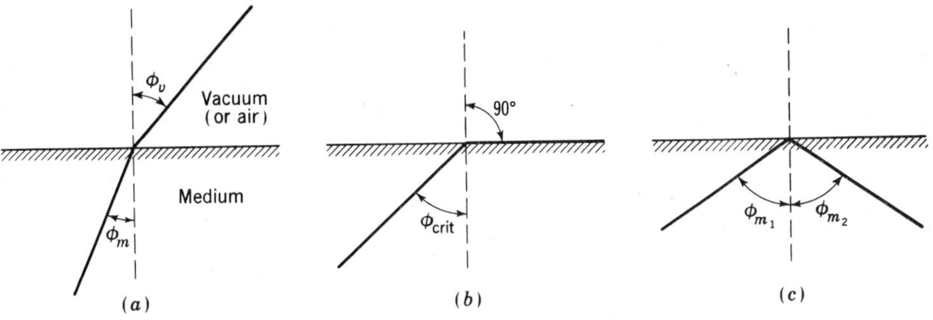

where n_g is the index of refraction of the prism glass and ϕ_g is the critical angle in the glass. By trigonometry it can be shown that the index of refraction of the liquid is given by

$$n = \sin\delta\cos\gamma + \sin\gamma\sqrt{n_g^2 - \sin^2\delta} \tag{12}$$

where γ is the prism angle (angle between the two transmitting faces) and δ is the angle of the critical ray in air with respect to the normal to the glass-air prism face (see Fig. 7).

The most precise type of refractometer is the *immersion refractometer*. It contains a prism fixed at the end of an optical tube containing an objective lens, an engraved scale reticule, and an eyepiece. It also contains an Amici compensating prism (see below). In use, the instrument is dipped into a beaker of the liquid clamped in a water bath for temperature control. A mirror in the bath or below it reflects light into the bottom of the beaker at the requisite angle and with some angular divergence. The field of view is divided into an illuminated area and a dark area, as shown in Fig. 7; the scale reading which corresponds to the boundary-line (critical-ray) position is read and referred to a table to obtain the refractive index. This instrument is capable of measuring the refractive index to ±0.00003. Its scale normally covers only a small range; a set containing several refractometers or detachable prisms is required to cover the ordinary range of refractive indices for liquids (1.3 to 1.8).

The most commonly used form of refractometer is the *Abbe refractometer*, shown schematically in Fig. 8. This differs from the immersion refractometer in two important respects. First, instead of dipping into the liquid, the refractometer contains only a few drops of the liquid held by capillary action in a thin space between the refracting prism and an illuminating prism. Second, instead of reading the

FIG. 7. Essential features of an immersion refractometer. The behavior of the critical ray is shown in detail, since this represents the basic principle of almost all refractometers.

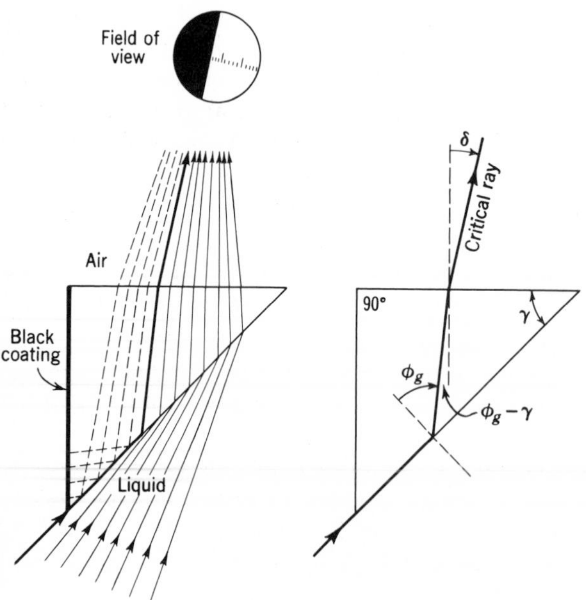

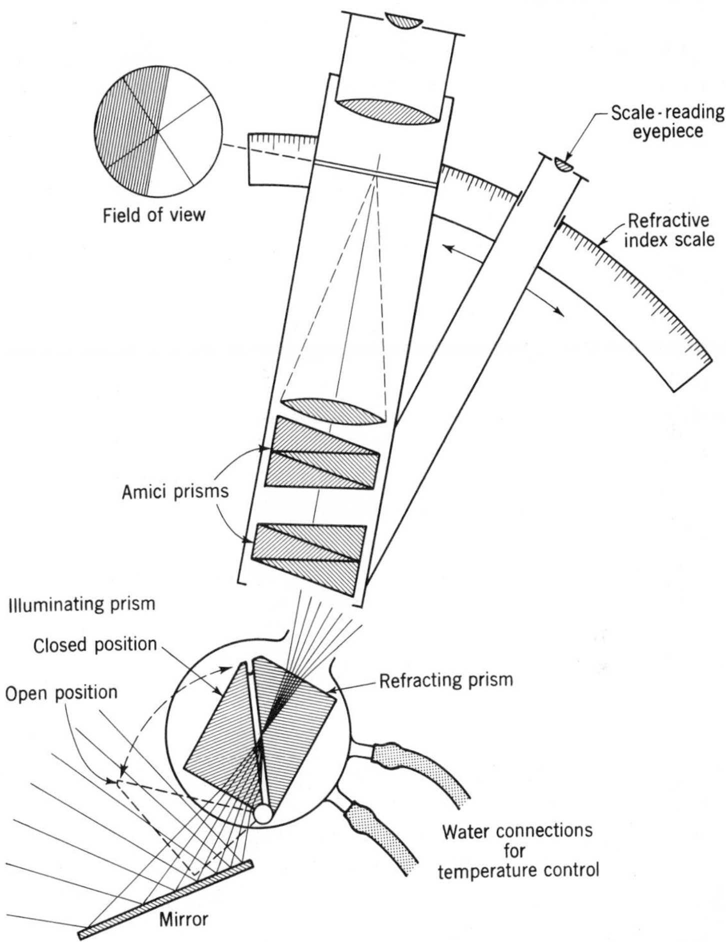

FIG. 8. Schematic diagram of an Abbe refractometer.

position of the critical-ray boundary on a scale, one adjusts this boundary so that it is at the intersection of a pair of cross hairs by rotating the refracting prism until the telescope axis makes the required angle δ with the normal to the air interface of the prism. The index of refraction is then read directly from a scale associated with the prism rotation.

The Abbe refractometer commonly contains two Amici compensating prisms, geared so as to rotate in opposite directions. An Amici prism is a composite prism of two different kinds of glass, designed to produce a considerable amount of dispersion but to produce no angular deviation of light corresponding to the sodium D line. By use of two counterrotating Amici prisms the net dispersion can be varied from zero to some maximum value in either direction. The purpose of incorporating the Amici prisms is to compensate for the dispersion of the sample so as to produce the same result that would be obtained if a sodium arc were used for illumination. This is achieved by rotating the prisms until the colored fringe disappears from the field of view and the boundary between light and dark fields becomes sharp. It should be borne in mind that the dispersion of a sample is not always exactly compensated, for dispersion is not exactly defined by a single parameter for all substances. The most precise results are obtained with illumination from a sodium arc, the Amici prisms being set at zero dispersion.

The Abbe refractometer is less precise (± 0.0001) than the immersion refractometer and requires somewhat less exact temperature control ($\pm 0.2°C$). For this purpose water from a thermostat bath is circulated through the prism housings by means of a circulating pump. Alternatively, tap water is brought to the temperature of a thermostat bath by flow through a long coil of copper tubing immersed in the bath, and is then passed once through the refractometer and down the drain.

The procedure for the use of the Abbe refractometer is as follows:

1. If a sodium arc is being used, check to see that it is operating properly. The sodium arc should be treated carefully and should be turned on and off as infrequently as possible. It should be turned on at least ½ hr before use.
2. Check to see that the temperature is at the required value by reading the thermometer attached to the prism housing.
3. Open the prism (rotate the illuminating prism downward and away from you). Wipe both prism surfaces *gently* with a *fresh* swab of cotton-wool dampened with acetone or benzene. When the prism surfaces are clean and dry, bring them to the closed position.
4. Introduce the sample (a few drops to about 2 ml) with an eye dropper or pipette into the entrance hole.
5. Rotate the prism until the boundary between light and dark fields appears in the field of view. If necessary, adjust the light source or the mirror to obtain the best illumination.
6. If necessary, rotate the Amici prisms to eliminate the color fringe and sharpen the boundary.
7. Make any necessary fine adjustment to bring the boundary between light and dark fields into coincidence with the intersection of the cross hairs.
8. Turn on the lamp (if any) that illuminates the scale, and read off the value of the refractive index.
9. Open the prism and wipe it *gently* with a clean swab of cotton-wool, dampened with acetone or benzene. When dry, close the prism.

If the sample is very volatile, it may evaporate before the procedure is completed. In this case or in the event of drift, add more sample.

One of the worst enemies of the refractometer is *dust.* A gritty particle may scratch the prisms badly enough to require their replacement. The cotton-wool used for wiping the prisms should be kept in a covered jar. Each swab of cotton-wool should be used only once and then discarded. *Do not rub* the prisms with cotton-wool, and do not attempt to wipe them dry; if streaks are left when the acetone or benzene evaporates, wipe again with a fresh swab dampened with fresh solvent. Do not use lens tissue on the prism surfaces. Finally, the instrument should be protected with its dust cover when not in use, and the table on which the instrument is used should be kept scrupulously clean.

For adjustment of the scale a small "test piece" (rectangular block of glass of accurately known index of refraction) is usually provided with the refractometer. The illuminating prism is swung out and the surface of both the refracting prism and the test piece are carefully cleaned. They are then carefully brushed with a clean camel's-hair brush (which is normally kept in a stoppered container) and inspected at grazing incidence to detect particles of dust or grit. A very small drop (ca. 1 mm^3) of a liquid (such as 1-bromonaphthalene or methylene iodide) which has a higher refractive index than the refracting prism is placed on the test piece, and the latter is then carefully pressed against the refracting prism and carefully moved around to spread the liquid. The reading of refractive index is made in the usual way. If it is not in agreement with the true value of the test piece, an adjustment of the instrument scale is made or a correction is calculated.

The procedure for determining the index of refraction of an isotropic solid sample is similar; like the test piece it must have at least one highly polished plane face.

The refractometer is essentially an analytical instrument, used to determine the composition of binary mixtures (as in Exp. 18) or to check the purity of compounds. Its most common industrial application is in the food and confectionary industries, where it is used in "saccharimetry"—the determination of the concentration of sugar in sirup. Many commercially available refractometers have two scales: one calibrated directly in refractive index, the other in per cent sucrose at 20°C.

The refractive index of a compound is a property of some significance in regard to molecular constitution. The *mole refraction,* defined by Eq. (37-13), is a constitutive and additive property; for a given compound it may be approximated by the sum of contributions of individual atoms, double bonds, aromatic rings, and other structural features.[18]

TIMING DEVICES

For measuring long time intervals (10 min or longer), a sweep-second-hand watch or electric clock is often adequate. The accuracy of a good mechanical watch is usually between ±0.05 and 0.2 per cent, depending on the quality of the watch and the precision of its adjustment. However, this adjustment will change with time and cannot be relied on over a period of months. An electric clock operating on the 60-cycle ac power line has the advantage of excellent long-term stability. The time accuracy of an electric clock depends directly on the frequency stability of the power source, and the *average* line frequency over a 24-hr period is maintained very close to 60 cycles. However, the line frequency may differ from 60 cycles by as much as ±0.1 per cent over a period as long as several hours.

For timing short intervals (less than 10 min), there is an appreciable problem in accurately reading a moving sweep-second hand. The uncertainty in a time interval caused by this difficulty can easily be as large as ±1 sec. This error can be greatly reduced by using a stopwatch or electric interval timer. Although the reading error per se is then eliminated, one must recognize the error due to the reaction time of the experimenter who is manually operating the start-and-stop mechanism. Reaction times vary greatly from one individual to another, but a reasonable estimate of the error in a time interval from this source would be ±0.2 sec.

A considerable improvement in timing accuracy can be achieved by the use of a precision electric timer[19] driven by a synchronous motor which is operated from a constant-frequency ac power supply. Power supplies controlled by a tuning-fork oscillator are subject to frequency variations of less than 0.01 per cent if the input voltage and ambient temperature are reasonably stable. Such precision timers have an electrically activated mechanical clutch which allows the motor to run continuously but which permits the timer hands to move only while this clutch is engaged. The clutch action will introduce an uncertainty of about ± 0.01 sec for an ac-operated clutch or about ± 0.005 sec for a dc clutch. The error due to human reaction time is still present unless the timer is operated automatically.† The performance of an interval timer can be checked against a secondary time standard (such as a frequency counter) or against the time signals broadcast by the NBS over radio station WWV. Such a calibration will considerably reduce the systematic error due to an operating frequency which differs from the nominal value (often by about 0.1 per cent).

For the most precise timing, a high-speed electronic frequency counter can be used to count the oscillations of an ultrastable crystal-controlled oscillator. Hewlitt-Packard Co., Palo Alto, Calif., offers several instruments capable of making time measurements accurate to within a few parts per million.

WESTPHAL BALANCE

The Westphal balance[20] is an instrument for measuring the density or specific gravity of a liquid by application of the principle of Archimedes. Although it is not usually capable of the very high accuracy obtainable with a pycnometer (Exp. 12), it is easier and more rapid to use. It is far more accurate than a hydrometer.

The Westphal balance (Fig. 9) measures gravimetrically the buoyancy exerted on a glass-enclosed body of definite volume immersed in the liquid. This body is an elongated glass bulb weighted with mercury and containing a thermometer. It is suspended by means of a slender platinum wire from one arm of a balance. The volume of the test body is carefully adjusted to some definite value, say 5 ml, by grinding the glass at the bottom. A weight, at the upper end of the platinum wire, enables the beam to be balanced when the test body is hung in air.

The beam is notched in nine places to divide the space between the two knife-edges into 10 equally spaced intervals. Ω-shaped riders are provided in 5-, 0.5-, 0.05-, and 0.005-g sizes. These correspond, respectively, to the first, second, third, and fourth places after the decimal point in the specific gravity. Two of the 5-g riders are provided in order to permit measurement of specific gravities that are equal to or greater than unity. For 1.0, one 5-g rider is hung from the same hook that supports the test body or two 5-g riders are hung at the 5 division or at the 4 and 6 divisions, etc. When two or more riders are to be hung at the same division, one is placed on the beam at the notch and the others are hung from the hooks on the side of the first. The specific gravity indicated by the rider positions shown in Fig. 9 is 0.9447.

In use, the Westphal balance is set up on a flat surface, and the test body is suspended from the hook. The beam is raised high enough to permit a small graduated cylinder containing the liquid to be brought underneath without disturbing it. The "leveling screw" is adjusted to bring the beam pointer level with the stationary pointer. The cylinder is then raised until the level of liquid is at the designated point on the wire, and a supporting block or stand is placed underneath it. Riders are then placed on the beam to restore the pointer to the desired posi-

† For example, the heating period in a calorimetry experiment can be timed automatically by using a fast double-pole switch to control both the timer and heater circuit simultaneously.

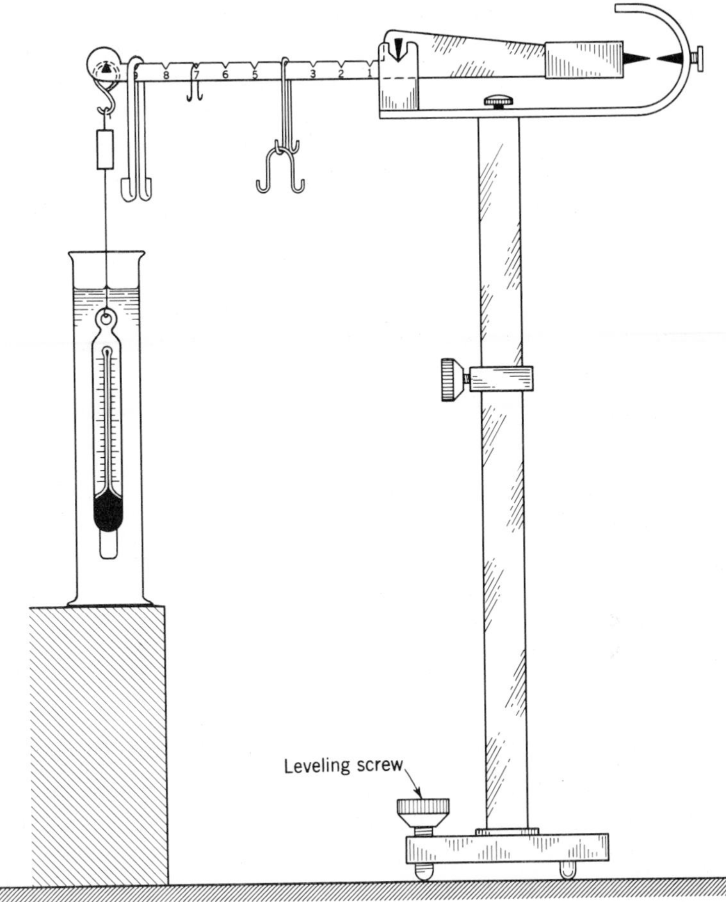

FIG. 9. A typical Westphal balance. As shown here, the specific gravity of the test liquid is 0.9447 (see text).

tion, and the specific gravity is read. The temperature should be ascertained by reading the thermometer contained in the test body.

For precise work a measurement is made first on water, with the weights set to the specific gravity for water at the measured temperature (consult a handbook). If the pointer is not at the desired position, make a fine adjustment with the leveling screw. Remove the water, dry the bulb, and place the unknown liquid in position. No air-buoyancy corrections are ordinarily needed, as the weights are usually adjusted so as to take air buoyancy into account (at 1 atm). In work of high precision a small correction may be made for surface tension acting on the wire.

The specific gravity of a liquid is the ratio of its density to that of water at 4°C, the temperature of maximum density; this is 0.999973 g cm^{-3} in vacuum. Thus, for nearly all practical purposes, the specific gravity may be taken as equivalent to the density in grams per cubic centimeter.

Other Westphal balances have different construction. In some cases a triple beam, for three riders, is provided. A chain is provided in some balances for interpolating between rider positions.

REFERENCES

1. H. A. Fales and F. Kenny, "Inorganic Quantitative Analysis," chap. IV, Appleton-Century-Crofts, New York (1939).
2. L. F. Hamilton and S. G. Simpson, "Quantitative Chemical Analysis," 10th ed., chap. IV, Macmillan, New York (1952).
3. I. M. Kolthoff and E. B. Sandell, "Textbook of Quantitative Inorganic Analysis," 3d ed., chap. XIII, Macmillan, New York (1952).
4. W. C. Pierce, E. L. Haenisch, and D. T. Sawyer, "Quantitative Analysis," 4th ed., chap. 3, Wiley, New York (1948).
5. Design and Test of Standards of Mass, *Natl. Bur. Standards Circ.* 3, 3d ed., Washington (1918).
6. G. W. Thomson, Determination of Vapor Pressure, in A. Weissberger (ed.), "Technique of Organic Chemistry," 2d ed., vol. I, part I, chap. V, Interscience, New York (1949).
7. W. G. Brombacher, D. P. Johnson, and J. L. Cross, "Mercury Barometers and Manometers," National Bureau of Standards Monograph 8, Washington (1960).
8. T. Soller, M. A. Starr, and G. E. Valley, Jr., "Cathode-ray Tube Displays," vol. 22 of MIT Radiation Laboratory Series, McGraw-Hill, New York (1948).
9. W. J. Hamer, *Trans. Electrochem. Soc.*, **72,** 45 (1937).
10. M. Dole, "The Glass Electrode," Wiley, New York (1941).
11. H. H. Willard, L. L. Merritt, Jr., and J. A. Dean, "Instrumental Methods of Analysis," 3d ed., pp. 448–460, Van Nostrand, Princeton, N.J. (1958).
12. T. R. P. Gibb, "Optical Methods of Chemical Analysis," chap. VIII, McGraw-Hill, New York (1942).
13. C. Djerassi, "Optical Rotatory Dispersion," McGraw-Hill, New York (1960).
14. C. E. K. Mees, "The Theory of the Photographic Process," Macmillan, New York (1952).
15. G. R. Harrison, R. C. Lord, and J. R. Loofbourow, "Practical Spectroscopy," chap. 12, Prentice-Hall, Englewood Cliffs, N.J. (1948).
16. K. S. Lion, "Instrumentation for Scientific Research," chap. 5, McGraw-Hill, New York (1959).
17. S. A. Korff, "Electron and Nuclear Counters," 2d ed., Van Nostrand, Princeton, N.J. (1955).
18. T. R. P. Gibb, *op. cit.,* chap. VII.
19. See, for example, "Precision Timers," Publication 198-A of the Standard Electric Time Co., Springfield 2, Mass.
20. N. Bauer, Determination of Density, in A. Weissberger (ed.), "Technique of Organic Chemistry," 2d ed., vol. I, part I, chap. VI, p. 278, Interscience, New York (1949).

XIX

MISCELLANEOUS PROCEDURES

Physical chemistry laboratory work involves many manual arts, techniques, and procedures in addition to those described in earlier chapters. In this last chapter we shall deal with some of the more important of these.

VOLUMETRIC PROCEDURES

Several experiments in this book require either titration of solutions to determine concentrations of a given chemical species or successive dilutions of a solution to obtain a series of solutions with known concentration ratios. A complete description of the necessary volumetric techniques will not be given here, since many students will be well acquainted with them from a previous course in quantitative analysis. For the benefit of those without such previous experience, we shall present a brief summary of the more important aspects of those volumetric methods that are commonly encountered in physical chemistry laboratory work. Considerably greater detail is available in many standard textbooks of quantitative chemical analysis.[1]

Volumetric Apparatus. Volumetric glassware (Fig. 1) of importance to us is of three principal kinds: (1) volumetric flasks, (2) volumetric pipettes, and (3) burettes. The *volumetric flask* has a ring engraved around its neck; when the bottom of the liquid meniscus is level with this ring, at the designated temperature, the volume of liquid contained is that indicated by the engraved label. Frequently the letters "TC," meaning "to contain," are present on the label. When such a flask is used "to deliver," it should be allowed to drain for at least 1 or 2 min; even so, its accuracy is not so high when used to deliver as when used to contain.

The *pipette* has a single ring engraved on its upper stem, and its label frequently contains the letters "TD," meaning "to deliver." The pipette is filled by drawing liquid above the ring (use a rubber bulb if there is any possibility that the liquid is toxic!), and the top of the upper stem is closed with a finger tip. By careful manipulation of the finger tip the meniscus is allowed to fall to the ring. On delivering the contents into a vessel, the pipette is held at an angle of about 35°

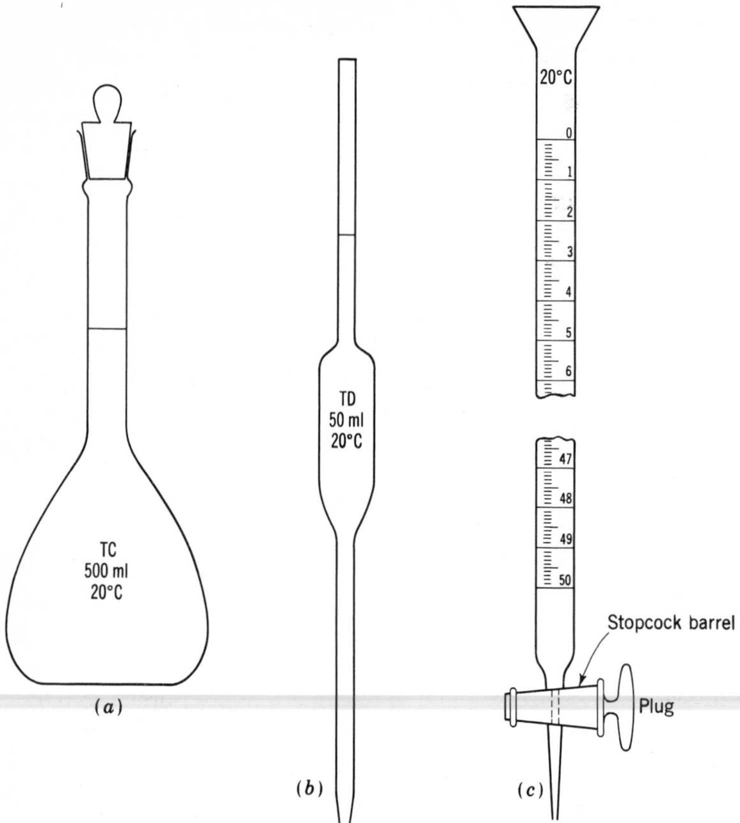

FIG. 1. Typical volumetric glassware: (*a*) volumetric flask, (*b*) volumetric pipette, (*c*) burette.

from the vertical and the tip is held against the wall of the vessel to prevent spattering. When the meniscus stops falling, the pipette should be held for about 30 sec to allow drainage and then withdrawn after again touching the tip to the wall of the receiving vessel but *without* blowing out the liquid held in the tip by capillary action.

The *burette* is a cylindrical tube of uniform cross section which is graduated in volume units along its length. A stopcock and drawn-out tip are attached at the bottom. A burette with bad chips in the tip should be replaced or repaired. If the stopcock does not turn smoothly or shows streaks or grease plugs, it should be cleaned (see below) and regreased. Small particles of stopcock grease which clog the burette tip may be removed with a fine wire.

In use, the burette should be mounted vertically and firmly by means of a clamp that allows the entire burette scale to be visible from the front. With the burette graduations facing the operator, the stopcock handle is generally at his right. A right-handed individual should learn to operate the stopcock with his left hand in order to leave his right hand free for swirling, manipulating a wash bottle, etc. The crook between the thumb and forefinger fits around the burette at the top of the barrel, and the handle is grasped with the thumb and first two fingers. With practice very fine control can be obtained in this way, and a fraction of a drop can be delivered if necessary.

In reading the burette, avoid parallax error. The line of sight should be accurately perpendicular to the burette axis; the rings engraved all the way around the burette will help. Read the *bottom* of the meniscus to about a tenth of the smallest division. Some help in seeing the meniscus can be obtained from a white card containing a heavy horizontal black line, held behind the burette so that the line is reflected in the meniscus. Move the card upward until the top edge of the line and the bottom edge of its reflection become tangent in your field of view; read the position of the point of tangency.

The burette is filled with the required solution (after two or three rinsings with portions of the same solution; see below) to a point above the zero graduation. Solution is run out into a beaker until the meniscus has dropped to zero or some position on scale. Be sure that no air bubbles are present, especially in the tip, and that no drop is hanging when the initial reading is made. The burette is now ready to deliver solution. After running out any significant volume, allow at least 30 sec for drainage from the burette walls before reading. Also, before reading, remove any hanging drop by touching the tip against the wall of the receiving vessel. The volume delivered is the difference between initial and final readings, subject to calibration corrections and temperature corrections if needed.

Calibration. The NBS has established specifications[2] for volumetric glassware which specify that the error shall be no larger than 0.03 to about 0.3 per cent, depending on the type and size. A 200-ml volumetric flask (TC) should be accurate to 0.1 ml; a 25-ml volumetric pipette (TD) to 0.03 ml; a 50-ml burette to 0.05 ml. The tolerances of most commercially available glassware are less precise by approximately a factor of 2 or 3; thus a 50-ml burette is ordinarily reliable only to about 0.1 ml.

Where more reliable volumetric measurements are required, the glassware should be calibrated, preferably at 20°C. Volumetric flasks (TC) are best calibrated by weighing them empty and then filled with water. Pipettes are calibrated by filling with water, delivering their contents into a weighed glass-stoppered weighing bottle, and then reweighing. A burette is filled with water, and 10 to 20 per cent at a time is run out into a weighed glass-stoppered weighing bottle or flask, which is stoppered and weighed after each addition (without being emptied in between); a calibration curve (required correction plotted against burette reading) is then prepared, analogous to a thermometer calibration curve. In each case the correct density of water at that temperature (0.99823 g ml^{-1} at 20°C) is used in the calculations, and air-buoyancy corrections (see Chap. XVIII) are applied.

Thermal Expansion. The NBS has specified 20°C as the *normal temperature* for volumetric work. The cubical coefficient of expansion of Pyrex is about 0.9×10^{-5} deg^{-1}; that of water at 20°C is about 2.1×10^{-4} deg^{-1}. The expansion of glass will be of importance only in very precise work; that of water, however, will affect molar concentrations and will be of significance if the actual temperature is more than about 5° removed from 20°C.

Cleaning of Glassware. Volumetric work of any quality depends upon glassware with a surface clean enough to be wet uniformly by water and aqueous solutions; if the meniscus pulls away from areas of the glass leaving dry spots, the glass requires cleaning. If cleaning with an ordinary laboratory detergent (such as trisodium phosphate or an organic sulfonate) is not sufficient, a chromic acid cleaning solution may be needed. About 10 g of $Na_2Cr_2O_7$ is dissolved in the minimum quantity of hot water, and after cooling, about 200 ml of concentrated sulfuric acid is slowly added with stirring. The cleaning solution must be kept in a glass-stoppered bottle. If after much use it appears greenish, it should be replaced. Contact with any organic material (e.g., wood, cloth) or with the skin must be carefully avoided. Glassware to be cleaned is ordinarily filled with this solution, which may be moderately warm but should not be hot. Stopcocks should be dismantled and degreased with solvent beforehand; glassware should be reasonably dry to avoid dilution of the solution with water. The solution will attack most fillers and pigments used to fill graduations of burettes and other volumetric glassware; confine the solution to the inside surfaces as much as possible. After 15- to 30-min contact with this solution the glassware should be emptied and thoroughly rinsed with distilled water. The stopcock of a burette should be dried and properly greased (see Chap. XVII for a satisfactory technique). The clean glassware usually is allowed to drain if it is not to be used immediately; burettes, however, are often filled with distilled water and covered by an inverted beaker pending use.

Rinsing. Volumetric glassware need not be dry before filling with the appropriate aqueous solution if the vessel is first rinsed two or three times with the solution. Several *small* portions are more effective than the same total volume of solution in a single portion.

Titration. In titration the amount of a solution required to react quantitatively with a reactant in a vessel is measured by a burette. The "end point" is shown by a color change in a chemical indicator present in small concentration or is indicated electrometrically. The technique of titration is principally concerned with approaching the end point with reasonable speed without "running over"; it is better learned by practice than by reading a description, but a few words here may help.

The burette is mounted on a stand with a white glass or porcelain base to facilitate observation of indicator color changes. The titration vessel is typically a 125-ml erlenmeyer flask. Into it the reactant to be titrated is introduced, by pipette (typically 20 or 25 ml) if it is in solution or from a weighing bottle if it is a solid. In the latter case, the transfer is made quantitative by washing the weighing bottle with a stream of distilled water from a wash bottle (a polyethylene squeeze-type bottle is recommended). Other reagents are added as required; the indicator may be added at this point or in certain cases (e.g., starch solution in iodimetry) at a later time.

Initially the solution is allowed to run out of the burette into the titration vessel at full speed, the vessel being held so that the stream runs against a wall to avoid spattering. The flask is continuously swirled to mix the reagents, so that only a portion of the mixture shows the indicator color change. As the color change becomes more general, the stream is slowed down, and when the color change almost pervades the entire mixture, the stream is stopped. The walls of the flask are then rinsed down with distilled water from the wash bottle, and the flask is swirled until the color change disappears. Allow the solution to run from the burette at the rate of a drop every few seconds with continuous swirling, until a significant change in behavior after successive drops is observed. Thereafter add only one drop or a fraction of a drop at a time; in each case touch the tip to the wall, rinse down, and swirl. When the desired color change persists on swirling, the end point has been reached.

If you "overrun" the end point, you may "back-titrate" with another burette containing an additional quantity of the same solution originally pipetted into the flask. With the accumulation of some experience the necessity for back-titration will become a rare occurrence.

For acid-base titrations, 0.1 *M* NaOH and HCl standard solutions are useful. A NaOH solution made up to approximately this concentration from carbonate-free NaOH (prepared as described later) is standardized by titrating, with phenolphthalein as indicator, a weighed quantity of potassium acid phthalate, $KH(C_8H_4O_4)$. This salt should be kept dry in a desiccator pending use. The NaOH solution can then be used in the standardization of an HCl solution. When a strong base is used to titrate a weak acid, phenolphthalien is the preferred indicator; for titrating a weak base with a strong acid, methyl red or methyl orange should be used. Any of these indicators or certain others (e.g., brom-thymol blue) can be used in titrating a strong acid with a strong base.

Redox, or oxidation-reduction, titrations are well exemplified by the titration of iodine with thiosulfate in Exp. 20. Commonly used standard solutions for redox titrimetry include iodine (in excess potassium iodide) and potassium permanganate as oxidizing reagents and sodium thiosulfate as reducing agent. Sodium thiosulfate solutions can be standardized by titration of the iodine liberated when a precisely weighed quantity of potassium iodate is dissolved in water and potassium iodide and sulfuric acid are added in excess.

When iodine is titrated with sodium thiosulfate, the most commonly used indicator is starch. A satisfactory starch indicator solution is obtained by grinding about 0.1 g of starch in a small amount of water to form a smooth paste and adding this to about 50 ml of boiling water. About 0.2 to 0.5 mg of mercuric iodide may be ground with the starch to serve as a preservative.

Preparation and Storage of Solutions in Large Quantities. In a physical chemistry laboratory experiment that is performed by many students, many liters of each solution are normally required. For the preparation and storage of such solutions, 18-liter carboys (such as those used for commercial handling of acids) are convenient. Reagents are weighed out on a triple-beam balance or measured out with a graduated cylinder and introduced into the carboy, water is added to fill the carboy, the contents are well mixed, and samples are withdrawn by pipette for standardization by titration. The carboy is clearly labeled and placed in the laboratory for student use. A convenient arrangement is shown in Fig. 2.

FIG. 2. Method of using a carboy for dispensing large quantities of solution.

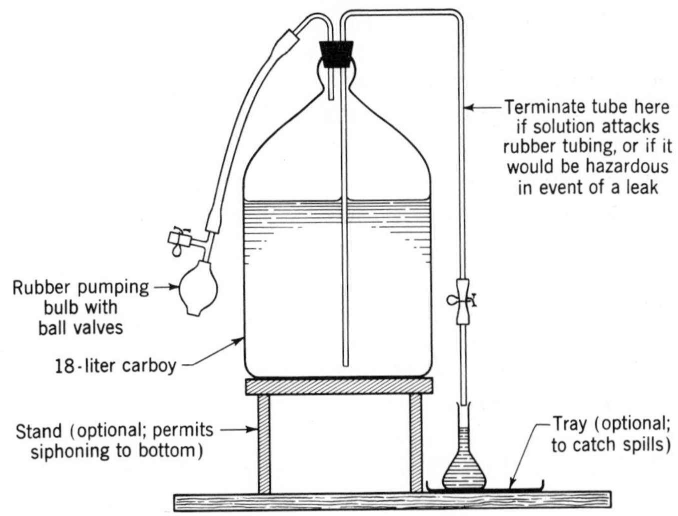

If the solution must be made up to a precisely specified concentration, a 2000-ml volumetric flask can be used one or more times. If a very large quantity is required, the concentration of the solution in a carboy can be adjusted by two or three progressively smaller additions of reagent or of water each followed by a titration.

A special word should be said about *mixing,* particularly in the case of large volumes. It will not suffice merely to swirl the carboy for a few minutes. When the carboy is filled, enough air space (1 or 2 liters) should be left to permit effective mixing. Most convenient for thorough mixing is an electric stirrer, comprising a motor with a long shaft and a swivel-mounted propeller which will go through the mouth of the carboy. This will produce adequate mixing in 15 to 20 min. If such a device is not available, the carboy should be tightly stoppered and turned onto its side on a table covered with a towel. It should then be *vigorously shaken* by a rapid back-and-forth rolling motion sufficient to distribute air bubbles throughout the volume. This should be continued for at least 1 or 2 min. After the carboy has been allowed to stand upright for a few minutes, samples should be withdrawn both from the bottom and from the top for titration.

PURIFICATION METHODS

Mercury. Reagent or triple-distilled mercury is available commercially and can be used without further treatment for virtually all purposes in a physical chemistry laboratory. Through ordinary use mercury becomes dirty and should be either returned in exchange for new reagent mercury or else cleaned in the laboratory. If the contamination is merely a surface accumulation of dust and oxides, sufficient cleaning can be accomplished by "filtering" the mercury through a piece of filter paper in which a small pinhole has been punched; the small quantity of mercury which does not flow through the pinhole will support all the scum and can be poured off into a flask for further purification at a later time.

When mercury is contaminated with dissolved metals, more rigorous purification methods are required. A thin stream of mercury can be allowed to fall through a tall column containing a dilute solution of nitric acid and mercurous nitrate; several repetitions of this procedure may be required before all metal contamination has been removed. Alternatively, the solution is placed in a flask with the mercury, and clean air is bubbled through the mercury so as to agitate it and put it into good contact with the solution. Wet mercury may be first dried over filter paper and then "filtered" through a small hole in a dry filter paper as described above in order to remove the last droplets of water.

For highest purity, mercury (especially when contaminated with noble metals, copper, and lead) should be redistilled repeatedly until a satisfactory spectrographic analysis is obtained. It is now seldom necessary for a laboratory to maintain its own mercury still unless mercury with purity higher than that of commercially obtainable mercury is required for special purposes.

Mercury vapor is toxic. Mercury spills should be meticulously cleaned up. Where inaccessible, mercury droplets may be covered with a fine dusting of sulfur to retard evaporation.

Water. Ordinary distilled water is pure enough for most purposes. For some purposes dissolved air is objectionable and can be removed by boiling for a short period. For conductance work, ions other than those resulting from the ionization of water itself must be reduced to the minimum possible concentrations.

Neutral organic substances are usually not objectionable in trace amounts;

therefore deionized water, obtainable from columns containing ion exchange resins, is suitable for almost all purposes. The best conductivity water is triple-distilled water (ordinary once-distilled water is distilled a second time from dilute acidified permanganate to oxidize organic impurities, and a third time with a block-tin condenser from dilute barium hydroxide to remove volatile acids and CO_2). Conductivity water can be stored in polyethylene bottles or in glass bottles that have been washed for long periods or otherwise treated to remove the more soluble constituents from the glass surface. Exposure to air should be minimized to prevent contamination by carbon dioxide.

Organic Liquids. The principal contaminant of *benzene* is thiophene, C_4H_4S, which cannot be removed from benzene by distillation but can be removed by treatment with concentrated sulfuric acid. Water can be removed by fractional distillation, a binary azeotrope coming over first. *Ethanol* cannot be freed of water by a simple fractionation, since an azeotrope with 5 per cent of water forms. Benzene can be added, permitting the water to be removed in a ternary azeotrope by fractionation. Alternatively, the 95 per cent ethanol can be digested with calcium oxide to remove water and then distilled. For highest purity, this should be preceded by treatment with silver oxide to remove aldehydes. Absolute alcohol should be protected from exposure to air in order to prevent water contamination. *Ether* should be dried over sodium or lithium wire and then distilled to remove peroxide; since these peroxides are explosive, the distillation must not be continued to dryness. *Hydrocarbons* can be purified by extensive fractionation combined with treatments with molecular sieves.

Sodium Hydroxide. For use as a reagent in acidimetric titration, sodium hydroxide must be freed from contamination by sodium carbonate, which rapidly forms on exposure to air. Commercially obtainable reagent sodium hydroxide needs no further purification if available in stick form, since any carbonate that forms on exposure to air can be quickly washed off with distilled water before dissolving the sticks in CO_2-free water (distilled water, reboiled if necessary) to make up the desired solution. This probably cannot be done effectively with the usual pellets. However, sodium carbonate is virtually insoluble in a saturated solution (15 to 18 M) of sodium hydroxide. Such a solution can be made up by stirring the solid hydroxide with cracked ice and allowing the resulting hot solution to cool. This sirupy liquid can be stored in a polyethylene bottle. When the insoluble carbonate has settled, the clear hydroxide solution can be drawn off as needed by pipette or siphon and diluted with CO_2-free water to the desired concentration. Sodium hydroxide solutions should not be stored for long in untreated glass flasks or bottles. Polyethylene bottles, or glass bottles coated inside with paraffin, are satisfactory.

Other Procedures. It is seldom necessary in physical chemistry laboratory work to purify chemical compounds beyond the purity attainable commercially. For special purposes such techniques as crystallization, fractional distillation, chromatographic separation, and zone refining may be used.

GAS-HANDLING PROCEDURES

Many of the experiments in this book involve the use of one or more gases such as oxygen, nitrogen, hydrogen, helium, argon, and carbon dioxide. We shall be concerned here with procedures for handling these gases.

Cylinders, Reducing Valves, Regulators. Although some gases (e.g., hydrogen) can be prepared in chemical generators, it is far more convenient to obtain

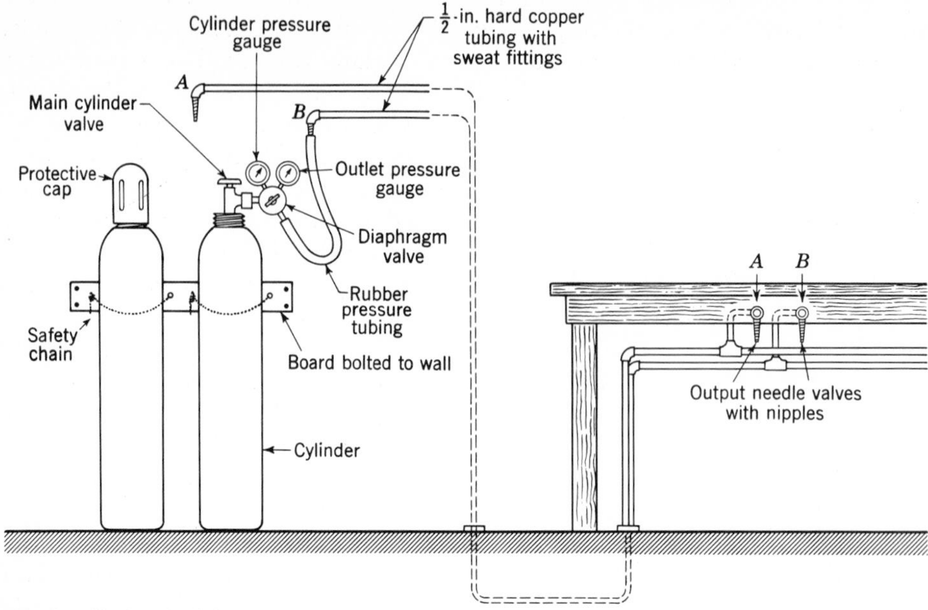

FIG. 3. Design for laboratory gas lines.

gases commercially in steel cylinders. These cylinders are available in several types and sizes. The large size ordinarily used in the laboratory is illustrated in Fig. 3. A typical cylinder is 51 in. in height and 9 in. in diameter; at 2200 psi and 70°F it contains 244 ft^3 of gas (1 atm). In addition, smaller cylinders and very small "lecture bottles" are useful for supplying occasionally needed gases such as hydrogen chloride, ethylene, etc.

Each cylinder is delivered with a protective cap which should be removed only when the cylinder has been chained against a laboratory table or a wall. *Cylinders should always be chained* to prevent upset, which has been known to cause violent release of the gas or even bursting of the cylinder, with serious consequences.

At the top of the cylinder are a needle valve and a threaded outlet. To clear the outlet of dust the needle valve should be barely opened for an instant and reclosed. In most laboratory work a *regulator* is attached to the cylinder, as shown in Fig. 3. This usually comprises a Bourdon gauge to indicate the cylinder pressure (up to 4000 psi), another gauge to indicate outlet pressure (ordinarily up to 60 psi), and an adjustable diaphragm valve to regulate the outlet pressure. The diaphragm valve is a simple form of manostat (see below) in which the needle of a needle valve is attached to a flexible diaphragm separating the low-pressure gas from the room air. When the outlet pressure exceeds the desired value (controlled by a spring between the diaphragm and an adjusting screw), the motion of the diaphragm is such as to close the needle valve, shutting off the flow of gas from the high-pressure side; when the outlet pressure is too low, the diaphragm opens the needle valve.

The fittings and threads on the cylinder outlet are of several types, depending on the kind of gas, in order to prevent the wrong regulator or other fitting from being used with a given cylinder.

The regulator fastens to the cylinder with a metal-to-metal contact, no gasket ordinarily being required except in the case of CO_2 cylinders. The connection is made tight with a large wrench. To verify that the seal is gastight, the cylinder valve is opened and then closed and the pressure gauge is watched for a few minutes.

When it is desired to use the gas, the cylinder valve is opened *all the way*. It is good practice to close this valve when gas is no longer needed (e.g., at the end of a laboratory period). Do not allow a cylinder to be emptied down to 1 atm; there should be some pressure left when the cylinder is returned. Unneeded cylinders should be returned to the supplier to avoid needless demurrage charges.

A simple *reducing valve,* consisting of a needle valve with fittings to match the cylinder and a nipple for the low-pressure connection, can be used in place of a regulator for some purposes where gas flow through an open system is desired. This device is less expensive than a regulator, but its use requires more care because if the system should accidentally be closed, the pressure will build up to whatever is required to burst it at its weakest point if less than the full cylinder pressure. It is advisable to connect the system to the reducing valve with a lightweight rubber tube that will easily blow off the nipple if the pressure becomes too high or provide some other safety valve near the inlet end of the system.

Most gases undergo a Joule-Thomson cooling when they expand in a regulator or reducing valve. In the case of CO_2 the cooling at high flow rates is often large enough to be troublesome, causing frosting of apparatus or even clogging of the regulator or the reducing valve with solid. In addition to this effect, there may be a compressional heating of the gas if a significant pressure is built up quickly in some part of the system. If a gas must be maintained at a constant temperature, it should be passed through a long coil of copper tubing immersed in a constant-temperature bath. One hundred feet of ¼-in. copper tubing is adequate for flow rates up to about 5 liter min^{-1}.

Needle Valves. For control of gas flow at ordinary pressures, needle valves give much better control than stopcocks. The hard-steel tapered needle, at the end of a screw-threaded shaft, seats in a cylindrical hole so that the area of open space for gas flow is gradually increased or decreased on rotating the shaft. Persons whose acquaintance with valves is limited to water faucets often damage needle valves by needlessly overtightening them when shutting off the flow. This results in a decrease in the sensitivity of control of the gas flow. It is important not to exert any more force than necessary.

Gas-distribution Lines. For an individual experiment, the cylinder may be chained at the laboratory table and the gas carried from the regulator to the experimental apparatus by a length of rubber tubing. If the same gas is needed simultaneously in several experiments, a gas-distribution line (see Fig. 3) is a great convenience. The cylinders are chained against a wall, and the gas is conducted through ½-in. copper tubes to the laboratory tables, where they service as many outlets as are needed. Each outlet consists of a needle valve with a convenient knob and a nipple to which a length of rubber tubing may be attached. If two or more gas lines are available, they should be clearly distinguished by color coding. When a line is changed from one gas to another, it should be well flushed out before use.

Hoses. Gases for open systems may be carried by ordinary ¼- or 5⁄16-in. gum-rubber tubing. Closed systems may require rubber or plastic pressure tubing, which can safely be used with pressures up to several atmospheres. **Warning:** Do not subject glass apparatus containing bulbs more than 2 or 3 in. in diameter to internal pressures of more than 1 atm above the outside pressure.

Gas Purification. Although in many cases the gas from the cylinder is sufficiently pure for direct use, for certain purposes it should be subjected to one or more purification procedures. Hydrogen is frequently contaminated with small amounts of oxygen, which should be removed if the gas is to be used in a hydrogen electrode. The most convenient procedure is to use a catalytic purifier such as Deoxo, which contains palladium; the oxygen combines with hydrogen to form water, which is subsequently removed with a drying tube if objectionable. Oxygen can also be removed by bubbling the gas through an alkaline solution of pyrogallol.

Another frequent contaminant is water vapor. This can be removed by passing the gas through a U tube filled with a suitable drying agent. A tube of this type is shown in Fig. 5-4. Gas flow should not be too fast, or the drying will be incomplete. Use of two or more drying tubes in series may provide better drying. Suitable adsorbents are anhydrous magnesium perchlorate (sold commercially as Anhydrone), anhydrous calcium sulfate (Drierite, often colored blue with added cobalt chloride which turns pink when hydrated), and activated molecular sieves (such as Linde type 4A). Phosphorus pentoxide and calcium chloride are effective drying agents but eventually liquefy after absorbing sufficient water. Drierite and molecular sieves can be reactivated by heating in a laboratory oven at 250°C in the presence of air. **Caution:** Cloth and other organic materials impregnated with magnesium perchlorate can be dangerously flammable.

Soda-lime is commonly used for removing carbon dioxide; alternatively, sodium hydroxide-impregnated asbestos (Ascarite) followed by a drying agent such as magnesium perchlorate can be used.

Water Saturation. Gases to be used in systems containing water or aqueous solutions should be saturated with water before they are admitted. For this purpose a bubbler containing a fritted disk which disperses the gas in the form of very small bubbles is far superior to the ordinary laboratory bubbler. The temperature of the bubbler should be the same as that of the system, and the connection to the system should be as short as possible to avoid condensation of water from the gas before it enters the system.

Flowmeters. Figure 4 shows a simple flow manometer[3] which can be easily constructed in the laboratory. In this device a pressure difference, caused by viscous flow in a capillary tube (see Exp. 5), is measured by a simple manometer containing mercury or a colored organic liquid (such as dibutyl phthalate with added eosin). The response of this flowmeter is very nearly linear over the range in which the gas flow in the capillary is laminar and may be roughly linear over a useful range even when the flow is turbulent. By variation of the capillary length and diameter and of the liquid density a wide range of flow rates can be measured.

A steady gas flow for calibrating a flowmeter of this kind can be obtained from a needle valve attached to a regulator set to 5–10 psi or more (to avoid perturbations due to small variations in outlet pressure). At small flow rates the volume of gas flow over an interval of time measured with a stopwatch can be determined with a gas burette such as that used in Exp. 2; a three-way stopcock can be used to switch the gas burette in and out of the system. For larger flow rates a water-filled inverted graduated cylinder or volumetric flask, its mouth held under the surface of a water bath, can be used to collect gas from a rubber tube held underneath it for a time interval measured with a stopwatch. For precise work a correction should be made for the partial pressure of water vapor in the gas collected.

Another type of flowmeter is the Rotameter, manufactured by the Brooks

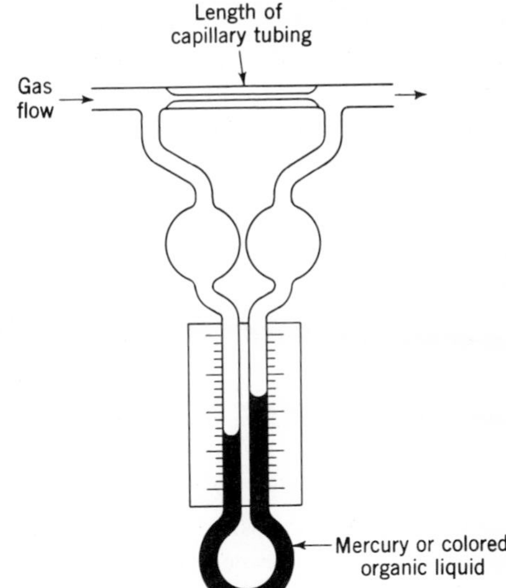

FIG. 4. A typical flow manometer.

Rotameter Co., Lansdale, Pa. A small "float," contained in a vertical glass tube with an inside taper, is supported by the flowing gas and has a steady-state position which depends upon the rate of gas flow. This device can be made closely linear and is available in a wide variety of ranges of flow rate.

Pressure Gauges. The Bourdon gauge is a dial gauge which can be used for measuring high pressures approximately. It makes use of a curved metal tube of oval or flattened cross section; high pressure tends to straighten out this tube slightly, producing a motion that is converted to a rotation of the indicating needle by a rack and pinion. A direct-reading gauge for lower pressures makes use of a flexible metal diaphragm, usually corrugated, with appropriate mechanical linkages.

For precise work other devices may be used. The most accurate is the manometer (see Chap. XVII). For very high precision a closed-tube mercury manometer is used, and the meniscus positions are determined with the aid of a cathetometer (see Chap. XVIII). Clearly the mercury manometer is convenient only for pressures that do not exceed a few atmospheres. For higher pressures a *deadweight gauge* may be used.[4] This gauge measures the force exerted by the gas on a highly polished piston with a close sliding fit in a highly polished vertical cylinder, the mean diameter being known accurately. The effect of friction is largely eliminated by the presence of a lubricant and by a reciprocating mechanism that rotates the piston or the cylinder back and forth a few degrees around the vertical axis. The force due to gas pressure is balanced by weights placed on a pan supported by the floating piston. Pressures up to thousands of atmospheres can be measured with high precision.

Manostats. A manostat is a device for maintaining the pressure in a system at a constant value. A regulator like that described above, operating in conjunction with an outlet leak, constitutes a simple manostat. More precise manostats, also operating on the feedback principle, make use of mercury or oil manometers. An electrical contact, made or broken when a mercury meniscus reaches a certain level, can be made to cause the opening or closing of a solenoid-operated valve. Somewhat better control, which may include a proportionating feature, can be obtained by using a light source and photocell to sense the position of the manometer meniscus. Manostats of this kind are analogous to thermoregulating systems (see Chap. XVI).

A simple device, obtainable commercially from the Emil Greiner Co., makes use of the "cartesian diver" principle to control gas flow into a manostat system.[5] A variety of devices which can easily be made in the laboratory depend for their operation on the fact that gas can flow through fritted glass disks while mercury at ordinary pressures cannot because of its high surface tension. Such a disk, constituting the system outlet, can be built into a mercury manometer so that it is covered by mercury until the pressure equals or exceeds the desired value.

Precautions. In addition to several precautions suggested above for gas handling, certain particular precautions should be followed in handling hydrogen and oxygen.

Hydrogen is very flammable and also forms explosive mixtures with air over a wide range of compositions. If used in any quantity the effluent hydrogen should be vented out of doors by a tube through a window. This is not essential for the slow rates of flow necessary with a hydrogen electrode, but good ventilation is important; there should be no open flames, and no smoking permitted.

Oxygen is hazardous when in contact with flammable substances, particularly oil. *No oil or other organic substance should be allowed to come into contact with oxygen under pressure.* Oxygen lines, valves, and regulators must be kept scrupulously free of oil. Organic packing materials should not be used in needle valves employed with oxygen; graphite-impregnated asbestos is satisfactory to moderately high pressures.

ELECTRODES FOR ELECTROCHEMICAL CELLS

We shall describe below the electrodeposition procedures required in the preparation of the platinum and silver-silver chloride electrodes used in the electrochemical experiments described in this book. We shall not attempt to give a general treatment of electroplating or of electrode preparation.

Platinum Electrodes. These are used in conductivity cells and in hydrogen electrodes. For these purposes they are usually covered with a deposit of platinum black to increase the surface area. For certain other purposes, such as use in redox electrodes, this is usually not necessary.

Platinum can be used in the form of thin sheet or screen. Platinum wire can be welded to a small square of sheet or screen by placing it in position on a metal surface, heating to red heat with a torch, and striking lightly with a small ball-peen hammer. The platinum wire can then be sealed into the end of a piece of soda-glass tubing, and electrical contact can be made through mercury placed in this tube.

Platinum can be plated onto other metals by use of a solution containing 1 g platinum diammino nitrate, 1 g sodium nitrate, 10 g ammonium nitrate, and 5 cm^3 concentrated ammonium hydroxide in enough water to make 100 ml of solution. The cleaned metal is made the cathode, and a strip of platinum metal the anode; three dry cells (4.5 v), a rheostat, and a milliammeter are connected between the electrodes, and the plating is carried out at a current density of 50 to 100 ma per square centimeter of cathode surface.

For depositing platinum black a solution of 3 g platinic chloride and 0.2 g lead acetate in 100 ml of distilled water is prepared. This can be kept in a glass-stoppered bottle and used repeatedly. The platinum electrode should be treated with warm aqua regia (one part concentrated HNO_3 to three parts concentrated HCl) to clean the surface and, if necessary, to remove old platinum black. It is then rinsed thoroughly with distilled water. While still wet the electrode is immersed in (or the cell filled with) the platinizing solution. If there is only one electrode to be treated, platinum wire will serve as the anode. Two dry cells and a rheostat in series are connected between the electrodes, the electrode to be platinized being the cathode (negative). The rheostat is adjusted so that gas is produced only slowly. If both electrodes are to be platinized, the polarity is reversed every 30 sec. The electrolysis should be stopped as soon as the electrodes are sooty black; an excessive deposit should be avoided. The platinic chloride solution is then returned to its stock bottle; the electrodes are rinsed thoroughly in distilled water, and electrolysis is continued with a very dilute solution of sulfuric acid in order to remove traces of chlorine. After a final washing with distilled water the electrodes are ready for use. Pending use they should be stored in contact with water; they should never be allowed to dry out.

Silver-Silver Chloride Electrodes. These electrodes may be made from thin sheet silver of high purity, but it is probably better to plate silver onto a clean square of platinum sheet or screen. This is made the cathode and a strip of very pure sheet silver (at least 99.95 per cent pure) the anode in a plating bath containing 41 g silver cyanide, 40 g potassium cyanide, 11 g potassium hydroxide, and 62 g potassium carbonate per liter. Use three dry cells connected in series with a rheostat and milliammeter. Set the rheostat to about 1000 ohms and make electrical connections to the electrodes *before* immersion; then adjust the rheostat so as to obtain a current density of about 5 ma cm^{-2}. Plate for a few hours. Remove the electrodes, and wash very thoroughly with distilled water to remove all trace of cyanides.

The silver-plated electrode is "aged" in an acidified solution of silver nitrate and is then made the anode (and a platinum wire the cathode) in a 1 *M* HCl solution at a current density of 5 to 10 ma cm^{-2}. In a few minutes a brownish coat of silver chloride will appear and the electrolysis can be stopped. The electrode should be aged for a few days in distilled water before use and should never be allowed to dry out. After long periods the potential of the electrode changes, probably owing to crystal growth. The old silver chloride coating can be removed with ammonia or cyanide, and after washing, a fresh coating can be prepared.

In use, care should be taken to avoid exposure of a silver-silver chloride electrode to bromides. Best results are obtained when oxygen is removed from the solution by a stream of nitrogen.

MATERIALS FOR CONSTRUCTION

In this section we shall comment on a wide variety of materials that can be used in the construction and repair of laboratory apparatus.

Glass. Glasses[6] and glass blowing are discussed briefly in Chap. XVII in connection with vacuum systems. The transparency, low thermal and electrical conductivity, and chemical inertness of glass make it a valuable material for constructing many pieces of apparatus. Because of its low thermal expansion coefficient, Pyrex glass can be blown into many complex shapes without too great a danger of cracking due to internal strains. Pyrex is also preferable to soft glass, since it can be used at temperatures up to 500°C without undergoing plastic deformation.

The thermal-expansion coefficient of Pyrex is lower than that of most metals;

platinum will not make a satisfactory glass-to-metal seal in Pyrex. Tungsten can be sealed in Pyrex if cleaned with sodium nitrite in a flame beforehand. For vacuum-tight glass-to-metal seals commercially available Kovar seals are recommended.

Soft glass (soda-lime glass) has a lower softening point and a higher expansion coefficient than Pyrex and is much more subject to thermal stress. It is mainly useful in the laboratory as a glass that will produce a vacuum-tight seal with platinum. It will not seal directly to Pyrex, but "graded seals" (tubes of Pyrex and soft glass joined together with several intermediate glasses in between) are commercially available.

Fused silica or "fused quartz" has high tensile strength and very low mechanical hysteresis; these properties make quartz fibers useful for certain instrument suspensions. Fused silica is very useful for apparatus that must be used above 500°C. Vycor glass, which contains a few per cent of other oxides and has a working temperature intermediate between fused silica and Pyrex, can also be used. Vycor-Pyrex graded seals are available.

Metals. Hot-rolled steel is the least expensive metal for construction purposes and in sheet, strip, rod, girder, and angle form is useful in the laboratory for constructing stands and frameworks. To prevent rusting, it should be galvanized (zinc dipped), cadmium plated, or at least painted. Aluminum paint is the most effective paint for retardation of rusting; it can be covered with additional coats of ordinary paint if desired. Cold-rolled (low-carbon) steel is also used for heavy-duty structural purposes, but owing to its excellent machining properties it also has many uses in apparatus construction. It can be galvanized or plated with cadmium, copper, nickel, chromium, or any of several other metals. Copper should be plated on steel before nickel and both before chromium. Steel parts can be joined by welding, silver soldering, soft soldering, or copper brazing (if previously copper- or nickel-plated). High-carbon steels, such as tool steels (e.g., drill rod), are less easily machinable but have the advantage that they can be hardened by heat-treatment.

Stainless steels are in a special class, differing from other steels in being nonmagnetic and essentially free from rusting and corrosion. So-called "18-8" stainless steel contains 18 per cent chromium and 8 per cent nickel. The chemical resistance of stainless steel makes it very attractive for many purposes, but its high cost and the difficulty of machining it limit its use somewhat. It can be silver-soldered or welded; soft soldering is difficult.

Aluminum and its alloys are excellent structural metals, with good machinability, fair corrosion resistance, good electrical and thermal conductivity. It is readily sand-cast or die-cast. Aluminum is seldom plated; it can be anodized (to produce a thick oxide layer) and then dyed or painted. Aluminum is difficult to weld owing to its flammability. Soldering is also difficult but can be aided by tinning with indium metal. The low melting point of aluminum (660°C) somewhat restricts its application. Aluminum should not be allowed to come into contact with mercury.

Aluminum and its alloys are often used in the laboratory in the form of sheet for making electrical chasses and panels and in the form of rods for constructing frames for apparatus support. Aluminum foil is useful for heat-reflecting shields in low-temperature work. A common structural alloy is Duralumin (Dural), which contains about 4 per cent of copper and traces of manganese and magnesium. Duralumin that is heated to 530°C and quenched in water is ductile for ½ hr or more and can be readily cold-worked; thereafter the alloy hardens and attains considerable strength. The hardening can be delayed for long periods (for rivets, etc.) by storage at Dry Ice temperatures.

Copper is used where its high electrical and thermal conductivity, its malleability and ductility, and its ease of soft soldering confer advantages. OFHC (oxygen-free, high-conductivity) copper should be used where highest conductivity is required or when employed in a vacuum system, particularly when soldering or welding is to be done in a hydrogen atmosphere. Copper can be made very soft by heating and is useful for making vacuum gaskets; the oxide which forms on heating can be removed with ammonia solution. Soft copper becomes hard on cold-working; accordingly, a soft copper gasket should be used only once or else reannealed before each reuse. Soft copper is exceedingly difficult to machine. It is subject to oxidation and should not be heated above 100 to 200°C for any length of time except in a reducing atmosphere or unless adequately plated. Copper can be joined by brazing, silver-soldering, or soft-soldering. Copper amalgamates readily with mercury.

Brass is basically a copper-zinc alloy; bronze a copper-tin alloy. In practice both often contain many other metals. Their high machinability, resistance to corrosion, and ease of soft-soldering make them very useful in apparatus construction. Owing to the volatility of zinc, brass should not be used in high-vacuum components that must be baked out or operated hot. Certain bronzes such as phosphor bronze are useful for springs and diaphragms; beryllium copper is also useful in these applications.

Monel and Inconel are basically Ni-Cu-Co alloys containing small amounts of iron and manganese. These alloys have fair machinability and high corrosion resistance even at elevated temperatures; some are magnetic, others not. They can be brazed, silver-soldered, and soft-soldered. Monel and cupronickel are very useful in the construction of apparatus for low-temperature work owing to their low thermal conductivities. Inconel can be used for heating elements; Nichrome (Ni-Cr or Ni-Cr-Fe-Mn) and Chromel (Ni-Cr-Fe) are also useful for this purpose.

Invar (64 per cent iron, 36 per cent nickel) has a very low coefficient of thermal expansion (1×10^{-6} deg^{-1}). It is magnetic and only moderately corrosion resistant. Kovar (53.7 per cent iron, 29 per cent nickel, 17 per cent cobalt, 0.3 per cent manganese) has been mentioned in Chap. XVII as a glass-sealing metal.

Silver is an excellent conductor of heat and electricity and a good reflector of light. It is relatively immune to oxidation but becomes tarnished by exposure to sulfur compounds in exceedingly small concentrations. It is an excellent electroplating metal and can also be deposited in thin films by evaporation. In Dewar flasks and other vacuum glassware it is deposited from an aqueous medium by the Brashear process.[7] Silver is an excellent brazing material and an important constituent of "silver solder." The term "silver" is often applied to alloys of silver with copper; "Sterling" contains 7.5 per cent copper, "U.S. Coin" contains 10 per cent. "Fine" silver is 99.9+ per cent silver.

Platinum and palladium are useful because of their chemical inertness, electrical conductivity, high reflectivity, and high melting point; their high cost restricts their use to applications in which only small amounts are employed: electrical contacts, suspension wires, heating elements, radiation shields, etc. They absorb hydrogen; palladium is very permeable to it and may be mechanically damaged by exposure to it. These metals easily spot-weld to themselves and to each other.

Gold is also very useful because of its inertness. It is an excellent plating material and can be deposited by vacuum evaporation or chemical deposition.

Tungsten has the highest melting point of any known metal (3380°C) and is useful for heating elements and various vacuum-cell components. It is difficult to work and is usually handled in the form of wire or ribbon. Tungsten wires tend to have a fibrous structure; lead-through tungsten-Pyrex seals may not be vacuum-tight unless one end of the wire is welded over with nickel. Tungsten spot-welds to itself and to nickel and tantalum. Tungsten wires will oxidize if heated in air. Molybdenum and tantalum are much more easily machinable and workable, are chemically resistant, and also have high melting points; they are much used in vacuum tubes.

High-polymeric Materials. There now exists a vast array of high-polymeric materials, both natural and synthetic. We shall concern ourselves here only with a few which are of particular usefulness in laboratory apparatus construction.

Rubber is the most commonly encountered of such materials. In its vulcanized form it is used in rubber tubing and rubber stoppers. The sulfur coating which appears on the surface of stoppers in the course of time can be removed by boiling them for a short time in sodium hydroxide solution. For tubing (other than pressure tubing) pure gum rubber is preferable, although it must be replaced more frequently.

Neoprene (du Pont) is a rubberlike material which is a polymer of 2-chlorobutadiene-1, 3. Somewhat less flexible than natural rubber, it has much greater resistance to oils, greases, and chemicals. Neoprene is useful in vacuum work in the form of gaskets, O rings, and tubing.

A convenient substitute for rubber tubing in the laboratory is transparent vinyl-plastic tubing such as Tygon B44-3, a compounding of polyvinyl chloride with certain liquid plasticizers. This tubing is tough and flexible and makes a very good seal with glass fittings. It tends to become yellow with age, and after long exposure to water it may become somewhat milky. It is attacked by many organic solvents but has fairly good resistance to most other ordinary chemicals.

Cellulose is a material of construction which is used in the laboratory in the natural forms represented by cork, wood, and cotton and in the reconstituted forms represented by rayon fiber and cellophane film. These have been supplanted for most uses by synthetic fibers and films. However, unlacquered cellophane (available as sheet and as sausage casing) is useful for semipermeable membranes to be used in dialysis and osmotic pressure work.

Bakelite, a phenolic resin, is often used by itself or in combination with paper, textiles, or natural fibers to provide inexpensive, readily machinable, electrically insulating materials for panels and various small parts. Vulcanite (hard rubber) is also useful for this purpose.

Lucite and Plexiglas (polymethylmethacrylate as marketed by du Pont and by Rohm and Haas, respectively) and polystyrene are transparent thermoplastic materials. Their machinability is fairly good, but somewhat limited by their thermoplasticity. They are strongly attacked by solvents such as acetone. They can be cemented with solvents alone or with such cements as Duco. Over long periods cracks may develop at points of strain, and discoloration may result from prolonged exposure to strong light.

Nylon (du Pont polyhexamethylenediamine adipic polyamide) is available in solid form as well as fiber and sheet. It has high strength and mechanical stability, excellent machinability, and low surface friction; it is excellent for bearings, small gears and cams, etc., where it can be used with minimal lubrication or none at all. Nylon fibers and threads are useful in apparatus construction.

Teflon (du Pont polytetrafluoroethylene) is a somewhat more flexible solid which is virtually unsurpassed in chemical inertness, electrical insulating properties, and self-lubricating qualities. It is available in the form of rod, tube, tape, and sheet and is readily machinable. It is useful for gaskets and bushings, unlubricated vacuum seals for rotating shafts, etc. It can be used in dynamic high-vacuum systems if these are not baked out much above 150°C. **Caution:** When Teflon is heated to decomposition, it reportedly gives off fumes which are extremely toxic. After machining it, clean up all chips and scraps at once.

Saran (Dow vinylidene dichloride) is a tough, horny, chemically resistant plastic available in a variety of forms useful in the laboratory. Saran pipe or tubing can easily be welded to itself or sealed to glass and is useful for handling corrosive solutions. Thin Saran film, available as a packaging material, is useful for windows, support films, etc. Mylar and other polyester films are also useful for these purposes and for electrical insulation, dielectrics in capacitors, etc. Much thinner than these are films that can be made in the laboratory by allowing a dilute ethylene dichloride solution of Formvar (polyvinyl acetal) to spread on a water surface and dry. Such films are commonly used in electron microscopy for specimen supports but have many other potential uses in research.

Polyethylene and polypropylene are somewhat similar to Teflon but are inferior in chemical resistance and many other respects. They are useful in the form of bottles, flasks, and beakers for containing such reagents as hydrofluoric acid, strong bases, etc., which attack glass. Polyethylene tubing is much less flexible than rubber or Tygon but more flexible than Saran; it can be used for handling caustics, corrosive gases, etc. Polyethylene film has better chemical resistance than Saran and Mylar but lower strength and poorer optical properties.

Miscellaneous Construction Materials. Transite, a product of the Johns Manville Co., consists of asbestos and portland cement; it is available in various forms, including sheets and tubes. It is useful in the construction of heat- and flame-resistant table tops, oven exteriors, etc. It will not withstand very high temperatures, since the portland cement contained in it will dehydrate.

Mica (muscovite or phlogopite) is useful for electrical insulation, thin windows, etc. It can be cleaved to very thin sheets by scraping an edge and inserting a razor blade between the laminae.

Lava is the trade name of various natural stone materials (talc, soapstone) marketed by the American Lava Corporation; they can be machined with ordinary machine tools operated very carefully at low speeds. On firing at a temperature of about 1050°C, Lava No. 1137 loses its natural water, undergoes a slight shrinkage (2 per cent), and assumes the character of a hard ceramic. The firing should be done gradually; the rate of heating should be only 150°C hr^{-1}, and the final temperature should be held for 45 min. The furnace is then shut off and allowed to cool before opening. These materials are useful in fabricating structural elements and insulators in vacuum cells.

Thermal Insulating Materials. Vermiculite (expanded mica) is useful for insulating ovens and furnaces where the temperature is not too high. At high temperatures (~1000°C) powdered magnesia, diatomaceous earth, or firebrick can be used.

At room temperature and below, foamed plastics are very effective. Polystyrene foam is easily cut into any shape desired. Certain commercially available urethane foams can be "foamed in place" to fill awkwardly shaped insulating spaces.

Cements and Adhesives. Little need be said here regarding general-purpose cements, such as household glue and Duco, which dry by evaporation of solvent. We shall mention several special-purpose cements, adhesives, and sealing agents with which the student is less likely to be familiar.

For making semipermanent seals in vacuum systems, *de Khotinsky cement* (shellac compounded with wood tar), *picein,* and *Apiezon W* (black waxes of petroleum origin) are useful. These soften or melt on warming to 50–150°C, flow readily on warm surfaces, and stick well to clean glass or metal surfaces. They have fairly low vapor pressures, but their exposed surfaces in vacuum systems should be kept to a minimum.

For a wide variety of vacuum-sealing applications, *Glyptal* (General Electric glycol phthalate), a lacquer with or without added pigment and with a solvent such as xylene, is useful. It adheres well to clean glass or metal and has a relatively low vapor pressure after baking. It should not be heated above 150°C. Glyptal hardens very slowly because it forms a surface film which retards evaporation of solvent from beneath the surface. It should be allowed to dry for several days at room temperature or for 12 hr under an infrared lamp.

Temporary seals in vacuum systems can be made with a mixture of *beeswax* and *rosin,* melted together in equal parts; this mixture is particularly useful in sealing around bell jars. It is applied smoking hot and smoothed with a heated soldering iron. It is not very strong and can easily be cut loose with a knife. *Apiezon Q*, a compounding of petroleum residues and graphite, has a low vapor pressure and a puttylike constituency; it can be used for sealing bell jars, temporary sealing of leaks, etc.

For miscellaneous mounting and positioning jobs, such as seating the mercury supply bulb for a McLeod gauge, *plaster of paris* (dehydrated calcium sulfate) may be useful. This is mixed with water to form a thick paste, which gradually hardens. A mortar of *portland cement* and sand can be used for the same purpose.

An irreversible cement useful for many purposes is *litharge-glycerin.* Pulverized litharge (PbO) is first heated to 400°C and after cooling is mixed with glycerin to form a thick paste. It sets to form a tough, adherent solid, which will withstand temperatures as high as 250°C. It is useful in plumbing but should not be used in vacuum work.

An irreversible ceramic cement which is not vacuum-tight but which can be used for anchoring structures in vacuum systems is *sauereisen cement* (Central Scientific Co.). This is made by suspending ceramic powders in sodium silicate solution (water glass). The cement sets very hard and withstands temperatures up to 590°C. *Zinc oxychloride* (dental cement), made by mixing calcined zinc oxide powder with concentrated zinc chloride solution, can also be used at high temperatures.

An increasing number of cementing problems are now being solved with cements based on *epoxy resins* and related substances. Among these are Araldite (Ciba Co.), A-6 (Armstrong Products Co.), F-88 (American Consolidated Dental Co.), and Tygoweld (U.S. Stoneware Co.). Each consists of a resin liquid plus an activator which is mixed in before applying. These cements set irreversibly to form tough, adherent solids which bond well to metals (usually including aluminum) and most other materials. They are relatively inert to chemicals and solvents. It used to be said (rather dogmatically) that no materials of this kind could be permitted in a vacuum system; however, under the pressure of necessity it has been found that vacuums of 10^{-5} to 10^{-6} mm can be obtained in vessels with interiors *coated* with epoxy resins, even in the presence of intense ionizing radiations. This requires high pumping speeds and involves various considerations that cannot be discussed here. Epoxy resin cements available in stationery stores often contain fillers and are not necessarily as good for laboratory purposes as those mentioned above. **Caution:** Epoxy resins are considered to be toxic until thoroughly set; skin contact should be avoided.

A special-purpose adhesive which forms an exceedingly strong bond to metals and most other materials is Eastman 910 Adhesive (Eastman Kodak Co.). It is expensive, but only small amounts are needed.

SHOPWORK

Experimental work in physical chemistry is not limited to the assembly of standard pieces of laboratory apparatus and the making of measurements with them. New or modified apparatus is frequently needed. This must be designed and often constructed by the experimenter himself. Therefore he must be acquainted not only with the appropriate materials for constructing various apparatus but also with many of the techniques of machine work, soldering, wiring, etc. We shall here limit ourselves to a very brief comment on machine tools and a short discussion of various soldering and welding techniques.

The most important machine tools are the drill press, the band saw, the grinding wheel, the lathe, and the milling machine. The first three of these are very simple basic tools that every experimentalist should learn how to use. The lathe and the milling machine are more complex and more expensive tools of great value in constructing special apparatus; if possible, anyone interested in physical chemistry research work should learn how to operate these tools also. At the very least, it is necessary to understand the principles of their operation and to appreciate what they can and cannot do. Indeed, a familiarity with machine tools is a vital part of the ability to design complex apparatus properly. No attempt will be made here to describe the operation of any machine tools. Written descriptions are available elsewhere,[8] but it is of greatest importance to obtain basic instruction in the use of these tools from a qualified machinist in order to avoid risk of personal injury to the operator and damage to the machines.

Soldering is the technique of joining two metals with a fused metal of lower melting point which wets both surfaces.[8] *Soft solder* is a low-melting alloy of lead, tin, and sometimes other metals (e.g., bismuth or antimony). It is commonly used in making electrical connections, making connections between copper or brass tubes or fixtures by means of "sweat fittings" (such as sleeves, elbows, tees, etc.), assembling small parts of an apparatus, and occasionally assembling large parts when reliance is not placed on it for much mechanical strength. It can be used for ordinary vacuum work but is not satisfactory for high-vacuum work, since its low melting point ($\sim$200°C) is lower than most bake-out temperatures.

Silver solder is a common form of *hard solder;* it is an alloy of silver and copper often with tin, zinc, or cadmium added. Silver solder melts at 600 to 700°C and has high mechanical strength. Gold solders are hard solders consisting mainly of gold and copper, melting generally above 800°C.

In electrical wiring, soft solder is commonly used with noncorrosive rosin fluxes and soldering pastes. Soldering of electrical connections with rosin-core solder is easiest when both parts to be joined have been "tinned," i.e., wet with a coating of solder. Hookup wire is often pretinned, as are pigtails of resistors and capacitors, lugs of tube sockets and terminal strips, etc. Copper wire usually requires no tinning but may require scraping to remove Formvar or other lacquer (which is often invisible) or oxide and dirt. Before a connection is soldered, it should first be made in such a manner that the solder is not relied on for mechanical strength. A tinned soldering iron carrying a drop of solder is applied to the connection and held there until the solder spreads over the metal by capillary action; more solder can be applied if necessary, but the minimum required amount should be used.

Soft-soldering of copper, iron, steel, and brass objects of larger size is usually accomplished by the use of a burner or hand torch, with an acid flux—frequently an aqueous solution of zinc chloride which is brushed onto the hot metal concurrently with the addition of solder. The surfaces to be joined should be pre-tinned, if convenient, and excess solder is shaken off or wiped off with a cloth. The two surfaces to be joined are then placed in contact and heated with the torch until the solder begins to flow; more solder is then added as required, and the pieces are allowed to cool undisturbed. The finished work should be washed thoroughly with water to remove the flux.

Hard-soldering, or silver-soldering, requires the use of a hand torch and a soldering paste of borax and boracic acid. The pieces to be joined are placed in contact, and the surfaces brushed with the flux during heating. Solder is applied as soon as the work is hot enough to melt it and encouraged to spread if necessary by further application of flux. Silver solders containing zinc or cadmium should not be used in vacuum systems that must be baked out or operated hot.

The cleanest and most reliable joints in vacuum systems are made by *hydrogen furnace brazing*. The parts to be assembled are clamped together with a thin gasket or sheet of the brazing alloy (silver or gold solder) between them. They are heated in a hydrogen atmosphere until the brazing alloy melts, runs, and wets both metal surfaces. No flux is required.

Welding techniques are many and varied and will not be discussed in detail. The laboratory worker will usually prefer to have any needed welding done by a qualified welder. Thin sheet metals and wires can be spot-welded; this is the most usual means of assembling the internal components of vacuum tubes. Stainless-steel housings of vacuum systems should be heliarc-welded on the *inside* of the joint.

REFERENCES

1. I. M. Kolthoff, V. A. Stenger (vols. I and II), and R. Belcher (vol. III), "Volumetric Analysis," Interscience, New York (vol. I, 2d ed., 1942; vol. II, 2d ed., 1947; vol. III, 1957).
2. E. L. Peffer and G. C. Mulligan, Testing of Glass Volumetric Apparatus, *Nat. Bur. Standards Circ.* 434, Washington, D.C. (1941).
3. A. F. Benton, *Ind. Eng. Chem.,* **11,** 623 (1919).
4. J. A. Beattie and W. L. Edel, *Ann. Physik,* 5F, **11,** 633 (1931).
5. R. Gilmont, *Ind. Eng. Chem., Anal. Ed.,* **18,** 633 (1946).
6. Corning Glass Works, Bulletin B-88 (1951).
7. J. Strong, "Procedures in Experimental Physics," pp. 154–157, Prentice-Hall, Englewood Cliffs, N.J. (1943).
8. *Ibid.,* pp. 569–582.

APPENDIX A

GLOSSARY OF SYMBOLS

Listed below are the most common meanings of those symbols which occur frequently in this book; special usages of these symbols and the meanings of any unlisted symbols are defined in the text wherever they occur.

Symbol	*Meaning*
a	Activity
c	Concentration, speed of light
d	Molecular diameter, density
e	Electronic charge, base of natural logarithms
f	Force
g	Acceleration due to gravity, gas
h	Planck's constant, height
i	Electric current
k	Boltzmann's constant, specific rate constant
l	Liquid, length
$\bar{l}$	Mean free path
m	Mass, mass of molecule, molality
n	Number of molecules, index of refraction
$\bar{n}$	Concentration in molecules per cubic centimeter
p	Pressure
q	Heat absorbed by the system
r	Radius
s	Solid
t	Celsius (centigrade) temperature, time
u	Root-mean-square velocity
v	Velocity, vibrational quantum number
w	Work done by the system
x, y, z	Linear coordinates
z	Valence of an ion, molecular collision frequency, molecular partition function
A	Helmholtz free energy, area, absorbancy
B	Second virial coefficient
C	Heat capacity, capacitance, number of components
C_p	Heat capacity at constant pressure
C_v	Heat capacity at constant volume
D	Diffusion constant
E	Internal energy, potential difference
F	Variance
G	Gibbs free energy
H	Enthalpy (heat content), scalar magnetic-field intensity

Symbol	*Meaning*
I	Intensity of radiation, moment of inertia
J	Rotational quantum number
K	Equilibrium constant, coefficient of thermal conductivity
K_f	Molal freezing constant
L	Specific conductance
M	Molecular weight, molarity
N	Number of moles, number of equivalents, normality
N_0	Avogadro's number
P	Number of phases
P_M	Molar polarization
Q	Electric charge, generalized thermodynamic quantity
R	Gas constant, resistance
S	Entropy
T	Absolute temperature, transference number
U	Potential energy, ionic mobility
V	Volume
W	Weight
X, Y	Mole fraction
Z	Molar collision frequency, atomic number
$\mathbf{E}$	Electric field intensity (vector quantity)
$\mathbf{F}$	Local (internal) electric field intensity (vector quantity)
$\mathbf{H}$	Magnetic field intensity (vector quantity)
$\mathbf{I}$	Magnetization (vector quantity)
$\mathbf{P}$	Polarization (vector quantity)
$\mathcal{E}$	Electromotive force (emf)
$\mathcal{F}$	Faraday constant
$\mathcal{R}$	Rydberg constant
α	Thermal-expansion coefficient, degree of dissociation, polarizability, optical rotation
α_0	Distortion polarizability
β	Coefficient of compressibility
γ	Activity coefficient, surface tension
δ	Deviation
ϵ	Molecular energy, dielectric constant, error, extinction coefficient
η	Coefficient of viscosity
θ	Surface coverage, angle
λ	Wavelength, equivalent ionic conductance, limit of error
μ	Ionic strength, chemical potential, Joule-Thomson coefficient, dipole moment, reduced mass
ν	Frequency
$\tilde{\nu}$	Wavenumber (in cm^{-1})
ρ	Density
σ	Molecular area or dimension, standard error
τ	Relaxation time
ϕ	Apparent molal volume, angle
χ	Magnetic susceptibility
Θ	Debye characteristic temperature
Λ	Equivalent conductance
Π	Osmotic pressure

Symbol	*Meaning*
aq	Aqueous solution
ln	Natural logarithm
log	Logarithm to the base 10
pH	$-\log (a_{H^+})$
°C	Degree Celsius (centigrade)
°K	Degree Kelvin
Q^0	Any thermodynamic property Q of a substance in its standard state
$\tilde{Q}$	Molal quantity Q
$\bar{Q}_A$	Partial molal quantity Q for component A

APPENDIX B

BAROMETER CORRECTIONS

The entries in the table below are calculated from Eq. (XVII-17) on the assumption that the barometer has a *brass* scale graduated to be accurate at 0°C (see Chap. XVIII). These corrections should be **subtracted** from the observed barometer readings. (If the brass scale is accurate at 20°C, the appropriate corrections are approximately 0.3 mm greater than those given.)

t, °C	720 mm	740 mm	760 mm	780 mm	800 mm
16	1.88	1.93	1.98	2.03	2.09
17	1.99	2.05	2.10	2.16	2.22
18	2.11	2.17	2.23	2.29	2.35
19	2.23	2.29	2.35	2.41	2.48
20	2.34	2.41	2.47	2.54	2.60
21	2.46	2.53	2.60	2.67	2.73
22	2.58	2.65	2.72	2.79	2.86
23	2.69	2.77	2.84	2.92	2.99
24	2.81	2.89	2.97	3.05	3.12
25	2.93	3.01	3.09	3.17	3.25
26	3.04	3.13	3.21	3.30	3.38
27	3.16	3.25	3.34	3.42	3.51
28	3.28	3.37	3.46	3.55	3.64
29	3.39	3.49	3.58	3.68	3.77
30	3.51	3.61	3.71	3.80	3.90

APPENDIX C

CONCENTRATION UNITS FOR SOLUTIONS

Name	Symbol	Definition
Weight per cent	%	(Grams of solute/grams of solution) × 100
Mole fraction[a]	X_A	Moles of A/total number of moles
Molarity	M	Moles of solute per liter of solution
Normality	N	Equivalents of solute per liter of solution
Formality[b]	F	Formula weights of solute per liter of solution
Molality	m	Moles of solute per 1000 g of solvent
Weight formality[b]	f	Formula weights of solute per 1000 g of solvent

[a] The symbol Y_A is often used for the mole fraction of A in a gas phase which is in equilibrium with a liquid solution.

[b] These units are infrequently used but are of great convenience in expressing the over-all composition of a solution when the solute is partially associated or dissociated.

APPENDIX D
SAFETY

Electrical Hazards. Several experiments make use of 120-v ac or dc electrical power and employ apparatus in which exposed metal parts are "live." These may include innocent-looking potentiometer connections when a potentiometer is employed to measure potentials or current in such a circuit. If the laboratory table has a metal surface, cover it with an insulating sheet of plywood or other material before assembling an electrical circuit. Remember that metal fixtures of all kinds and pipes or tubes of any kind that carry water are usually grounded. Turn off all electrical apparatus before altering circuits, if possible; if apparatus must be left on, use properly insulated test prods and leads. Be on the lookout for charged condensers, which may not be discharged owing to a broken circuit or a defective bleeder resistor. Naturally, 220 v provides a greater hazard than 110 v. It should be kept in mind that the laboratory is often served with 220 v in a three-wire system, with 110 v each side of ground. If 110-v outlets are supplied with a ground wire and one side of the 220-v line, as much as a 220-v difference can be obtained in accidental contact between circuits plugged into outlets serviced by opposite sides of the 220-v line. Shock, if it does occur, can be a serious matter; medical help should be summoned at once. Keep the victim quiet and comfortable; administer no stimulants of any kind.

Chemical Hazards. These are many and varied. It should be taken for granted that any chemical substance taken by mouth or inhaled is toxic until and unless definite assurance has been given to the contrary. Poisonous solutions (such as cyanides) and doubtful ones should not be pipetted by mouth; use a rubber bulb. Mercury vapor can attain a hazardous concentration in the laboratory atmosphere. Mercury should be kept in covered vessels at all times. Spills should be carefully cleaned up (a capillary tube attached to a suction flask is convenient for this), and inaccessible droplets in floor cracks and hard-to-reach places should be covered with a light dusting of powdered sulfur. Another insidious hazard is that of organic vapors, particularly benzene and chlorinated hydrocarbons (e.g. CCl_4). These should not be used indiscriminately for cleaning purposes, and spills should be avoided. Good ventilation is important.

Chemical Burns. Strong acids (particularly oxidizing acids) and bases may cause severe burns to the skin. If skin contact is made, wash copiously with water. If the exposure is to a strong acid, washing with a very dilute weak base (ammonia) is helpful; for a strong base use a very dilute weak acid (acetic acid). For the eyes, use nothing but water or a dilute solution of boric acid.

Fire and Explosion. Any flammable substance provides a potential fire hazard. In experiments which make use of hydrogen gas or other flammable gases, not only open flames but also cigarettes and sparking electrical contacts provide the possibility of explosion. The distillation of flammable liquids is most safely done in the absence of open flames; use a steam bath or electrical heating mantle. If an experiment involves an irreducible risk of fire or explosion, arrange for an adequate barrier. *Safety glasses* are strongly recommended in all circumstances in which fire or explosion is a possible eventuality; the use of glasses at all times in the laboratory has much to recommend it. In the event of serious burns, do not apply ointments or medications; summon medical help.

Radiation Hazard. Ultraviolet light from a mercury lamp or carbon arc is highly damaging to the eyes. Ordinary glasses give considerable protection, but the experimental arrangement should be well shielded so as to decrease the possibility of accidental exposure to a minimum. Prolonged exposure of the skin to such radiation can produce a severe "sunburn." Exposure to X rays and to the radiation from radioactive materials must be carefully guarded against in experiments dealing with them. Any such experiments should be done under the direct supervision of an experienced research worker who will assume personal responsibility for all required safety measures.

Mechanical and Other Hazards. Most mechanical hazards are too clearly apparent to warrant mention here. Vacuum systems often carry a hazard of collapse or implosion; bulbs more than 1 liter in volume should be surrounded by a metal screen or else wrapped with electrical tape to reduce hazard from flying glass particles in the event of implosion. The bursting of a container due to overpressure is a frequent cause of accident or injury. A compressed-air line (usual pressure: of the order of 50 psi) should never be connected to a closed system containing rubber tubing or glass bulbs. No closed system of any description should be attached to a cylinder of compressed gas (usual maximum pressure: about 3000 psi) unless a suitable reducing valve is attached; even then, a relief valve should be provided to guard against accidental overpressure. Gas cylinders should be chained to prevent their falling over.

Laboratory Safety Equipment. The laboratory should be arranged so as to provide two or more avenues of escape from any experimental setup in case of emergency. At least one shower and a CO_2 fire extinguisher should be provided near one exit. A first-aid kit containing Band-Aids, sterile gauze, adhesive tape, petroleum jelly, a mild antiseptic, sterile cotton swabs, tweezers, a set of sewing needles, a packet of razor blades, an eye cup in a sterile wrapper, a dilute boric acid solution for eyes, and a quick-reference first-aid manual will provide adequately for most emergencies. The location of an inhalator, a stretcher, and other rescue equipment, if not in the laboratory itself, should be known.

Except when absolutely necessary, no person should be allowed to work in the laboratory alone.

Finally, safety depends on habits that must be gained outside the laboratory as well as inside. Thus, on your way to and from the laboratory, look both ways before crossing the street; after finishing the writing of that laboratory report, don't smoke in bed.

INDEX

PHYSICAL CONSTANTS AND CONVERSION FACTORS

1. *Values of Defined Constants*

Standard gravity, 980.665 cm sec^{-2}
Standard atmosphere, 1,013,250 dyne cm^{-2}
Standard mm Hg pressure, 1/760 atm
Thermochemical calorie, 4.184 abs joule
Temperature of the triple point of water $\begin{cases} 273.16° \text{ Kelvin} \\ 0.01° \text{ Celsius} \end{cases}$

2. *Values of Basic and Derived Constants*†

Velocity of light (c), 2.99793×10^{10} cm sec^{-1}
Planck's constant (h), 6.6252×10^{-27} erg-sec
Faraday constant ($\mathcal{F}$), 96,493.5 coulombs $equiv^{-1}$
Avogadro's constant (N_0), 6.02295×10^{23} $mole^{-1}$
Absolute temperature of ice point (T_0), 273.150°K
Gas constant (R), 82.0560 cm^3 atm deg^{-1} $mole^{-1}$
8.31432 joule deg^{-1} $mole^{-1}$
1.98717 cal deg^{-1} $mole^{-1}$
Electronic charge (e), 1.60206×10^{-19} coulomb
Boltzmann constant (k), 1.38045×10^{-16} erg deg^{-1}

3. *Conversion Factors*

1 liter = 1000.028 cm^3
1 bar = 10^6 dyne cm^{-2}
1 joule = 10^7 erg
= 9.8692 cm^3 atm
= 0.23901 cal
1 coulomb = 0.1 emu = 2.9979×10^9 esu
= 0.23901 cal $volt^{-1}$
1 electron volt = 1.60206×10^{-12} erg $molecule^{-1}$
= 23.062 kcal $mole^{-1}$
= 8065.7 cm^{-1}
$\ln x = 2.302585 \log x$

† These values are taken from G. N. Lewis and M. Randall, "Thermodynamics" (revised by K. S. Pitzer and L. Brewer), 2d ed., pp. 41–42, 693–694, McGraw-Hill, New York (1961), except that the values of N_0 and R have been corrected in view of the recent (1961) change in the atomic weight scale [see H. Remy, *Angew. Chem.*, **74,** 69 (1962)].